To Our Wives

PREFACE

The purpose of this text is to present the concepts of digital simulation techniques and to demonstrate their application to the analysis of industrial systems. Like other quantitative techniques, simulation deals with the manipulation of a model of the system under study. Simulation is by no means new. The Monte Carlo technique has been in existence for many years. However, simulation as a discipline is just now emerging and is gaining widespread acceptance as a powerful and versatile tool for the analysis of complex systems.

Basically the book is directed toward those people with an interest in systems analysis who possess at least the following background:

1. Mathematics through basic calculus.
2. Knowledge of elementary statistics.
3. Knowledge of the FORTRAN programming language.

Additional knowledge in the basic concepts of operations research and numerical analysis would be helpful, but not required. Since the text is directed toward students having a background in statistics limited to an introductory course in statistical methods, the authors felt that a review of probability theory would be helpful. This is presented in Chapter 2.

The text can be divided into four sections:

1. Probability Theory and Mathematical Modeling.
2. Simulation Modeling.
3. Model Validation and Analysis of Results.
4. Simulation Languages.

The first section deals entirely with the mathematical development of queueing, inventory, quality control, and reliability models in addition to probability theory. These are included for three reasons. First, the text could be used for an introductory course in operations research. Second, their inclusion provides for the unified treatment of these topics by both the classical methods in this section and by simulation methods in Section Two. Finally, mathematical models are often used as a means to validation of simulation models. In this respect some knowledge of mathematical modeling is helpful in simulation analysis.

Section Two covers in great detail the methodology of constructing a computer simulation model. This includes chapters on the generation of random numbers and the generation of stochastic variates. A good background in probability theory is necessary for complete understanding of Chapter 7, entitled "Process Generators." In Chapter 6 the multiplicative congruential methods for generating uniform random numbers is presented and two generators of this type are shown. This is the only aspect of the discussion which must necessarily be "machine orientated." In Chapter 8, "Simulation of Queueing Systems," the "next event" concept is developed in great detail. The authors feel this to be an extremely important concept and employ it in the development of many major simulation models.

Section Three, "Model Validation and Analysis of Results," presents several useful techniques for validating the simulator and analyzing results. Chapter 11 deals with the analysis of the output of a simulation experiment and includes several examples regarding optimization schemes for simulation experiments. In this chapter simulators developed in previous chapters are used in conjunction with various optimization techniques.

The final section entitled "Simulation Languages" discusses briefly three simulation languages, namely GPSS/360, SIMSCRIPT, and SIMSCRIPT II. It is not intended to provide the reader with the capability to program in these languages, but just to introduce the concepts about which they are structured.

In general, the authors have attempted to refrain from using formal definitions to present concepts. Rather, the approach is to demonstrate the concept through the use of examples. In addition, where practical, each chapter is concluded by a lengthy set of exercises for student assignment. At the end of Chapter 11 several large-term project-type problems have been included for student assignment. The authors feel that this serves as a very important addition to the text.

All computer programs in the text have been written in FORTRAN IV for either the IBM 7040 or the IBM System/360. The choice of FORTRAN as the source language was based upon the universality of the language. Programs presented in the text were written expressly for teaching purposes and are not intended to be particularly efficient in execution. Further, computer simulation models were developed primarily for systems for which mathematical models presently exist. This was done to show the validity of the simulation approach and the characteristics of the search techniques used.

Many individuals contributed significantly toward the completion of the manuscript, and to enumerate them would be an almost impossible task. We would particularly like to thank Mr. C. C. Cook of Wheeling Steel Corporation for his encouragement in the beginning of the project; Dean C. A. Arents of the College of Engineering, West Virginia University, for his assistance throughout the project; and Mr. D. C. Montgomery of Virginia Polytechnic Institute for his assistance and comments regarding the topics of Chapter 11. We would also like to thank Misses Mary K. Spatz, Linda Allison, Donna Guynn, and Kathy Myers for their typing assistance throughout the various stages of the manuscript; and Mr. Ron Franklin for his assistance; and finally Dr. Paul E. Torgersen, Head of the Department of Industrial Engineering at Virginia Polytechnic Institute, for his continued interest, encouragement, and assistance.

December, 1969   J. W. Schmidt
                                             R. E. Taylor

TABLE OF CONTENTS

SECTION ONE
Probability Theory and Mathematical Modeling

SECTION TWO
Simulation Modeling

SECTION THREE
Model Validation and Analysis of Results

SECTION FOUR
Simulation Languages

APPENDIXES

SECTION ONE

Probability Theory and Mathematical Modeling

CHAPTER
1

INTRODUCTION

BASIC CONCEPTS

If you were asked to study the operation of a certain production process for the purpose of increasing the output of that process, what would you do? If you were given the assignment to determine the optimal number of parts to stock of a given item, how would you approach the problem? If you were asked to determine the number of private, semiprivate and ward rooms to construct in a hospital, where would you begin? In what ways are these hypothetical assignments similar? In what ways do they differ? In order to arrive at an answer in all of the above cases you must follow some definite sequence of steps. From the point of view of the investigator these steps are essentially the same for all three assignments. The problems are all similar in that they involve the determination of some operating doctrine or policy. They are also similar in that each is a problem with a definite objective. In the first case the objective is to increase production, thereby presumably increasing profits. To reach that objective, some form of quantitative analysis must be employed to aid in the determination of a rational policy which will accomplish the objective. If the objective is reached, the analysis is said to be "effective." The price paid to reach the objective determines the "efficiency" of the policy employed.

The body of mathematical techniques grouped rather loosely under the heading "Operations Research" provides the means whereby effective policies may be determined as efficiently as possible. Simulation is yet another approach to optimization, *i.e.*, the determination of the best possible policy among several feasible alternatives. It is one of many techniques which could be employed in a given situation. Later we shall attempt to identify those situations in

3

which simulation could most effectively be employed. First, let us define what simulation is.

We shall define simulation to be the action of performing experiments on a model of a given system. In this text a system is defined as a collection of entities which act and interact together toward the accomplishment of some logical end. We shall see that the definition of the system under consideration is dependent upon the experiment being conducted. For instance, our system might be defined as the entire production facility for one experiment. The definition of the system under study might, later, be refined to include only the facilities of one machine center instead of the entire facility.

A model is a representation of the system. In this text we shall employ mathematical and digital computer program models which capture the logical interactions and relations of the entities of the system we are modeling. Computer simulation models often include descriptions of interactions which exist in the real world system but are difficult to express adequately in a pure mathematical model.

This, then, is a textbook about the aspects of performing experiments upon a model of a given system. We shall restrict ourselves to investigations of discrete systems only. We shall further restrict ourselves to digital computer simulation techniques.

We make a distinction between discrete and continuous systems because there exists an entirely separate discipline concerning the study of continuous systems. Continuous systems are found in most process industries, such as chemical plants. The study of these involves analog simulation methods and is concerned with models containing differential equations. Other examples of continuous systems are readily available. The launch trajectory and orbiting of a satellite can be modeled as a continuous system over time. The flow of water in a river past an industrial plant is still another continuous system. This area of study is receiving great attention today.

Discrete systems are commonly found in product industries. Generally the system is such that certain aspects of it can be quantified into discrete units. Rather than dwell with long definitions we shall simply use the practice of defining by examples. Upon the completion of the text, the reader will be aware of the characteristics of a discrete system.

JUSTIFICATION FOR SIMULATION

The importance of quantitative analysis and evaluation of complex systems has been well-established over the past two and one-half decades. The wide application of such tools as Operations Research and Statistics in industry, the military, and all levels of government serves to emphasize the importance of the quantitative approach to systems analysis. In most cases the performance of a system is evaluated through a quantitative model which is a mathematical representation of the system under study. Often this model involves an equation or equations which vary in degree of complexity with the complexity of the system represented by the model.

Generally, in attempting to develop a mathematical model for a given system, we find one of three cases arises:

1. The system is amenable to both description and analysis by a mathematical model.
2. The system is amenable to description by a mathematical model. However, correct analysis of the model is beyond the level of mathematical sophistication of the analyst.
3. The system is so complex that description of the system by a mathematical model is beyond the capabilities of the analyst.

Cases 2 and 3 lend themselves to simulation for solution. With this tool the analyst can prepare a quantitative model of the system while possessing a relatively limited background in mathematics.

If simulation is to stand as a technique for systems analysis, we should attempt to compare its advantages and disadvantages to those of alternative solution methods.

The primary advantages are listed below:

1. The model of a system, once constructed, may be employed as often as desired to analyze different situations.
2. Simulation methods are handy for analyzing proposed systems in which information is sketchy at best.
3. Usually data for further analysis can be obtained from a simulation model much more cheaply than it can from the real world system.
4. As mentioned previously, simulation methods are often easier to apply than pure analytic methods and hence can be employed by many more individuals.

This list is not intended to be either profound or exhaustive. Further advantages will become apparent as the reader progresses in the text material.

There are also disadvantages to consider in using simulation:

1. Simulation models for computers are very costly to construct and to validate. In general, a different program must be constructed for each separate system. Special purpose simulation languages, discussed in Chapter 12, have helped to reduce this factor. However, this is still a formidable disadvantage.

2. The running of the simulation program, once constructed, can involve a great deal of computer time, which is also very costly.

3. Perhaps the largest single disadvantage of simulation is directed more toward people than the technique. This disadvantage is that people tend to use simulation when it is not the best method of analysis. As people become more familiar with the methodology of simulation they attempt to employ it in situations where other analytic techniques are better suited. This is an insidious effect, and it is easy to succumb.

It is not within the scope of this text to dictate the set of rules which could be employed to determine when simulation can best be used. It is doubtful that such a set of rules exists, for each analysis is unique in some manner. However, the authors hope that this text will provide the framework about which an analyst can construct a simulation model of any system.

If possible, it is best to formulate mathematical models and solve them analytically. As we mentioned above, this is not always possible, and in such cases simulation provides an alternative method for solution. It is obvious that in either approach the results are dependent upon the validity and utility of the input information to the model. A poorly constructed mathematical model of a system can do more harm than good. Similarly, a poorly conceived simulation model can lead to false conclusions about the system. The saying in computing circles of "Garbage in—garbage out" applies in both approaches. The objectives must dictate how "rich" the model should be and of what character it should be. These objectives shall be discussed in a later section of this chapter.

THE PROCESS OF SIMULATION

It will be helpful to characterize the general simulation process of analysis before proceeding into the detailed material of the text. In the simulation process we shall attempt to build a model of the system which captures the salient features of that system. What, then, are the basic features of a given system? Figure 1.1 shows a system as a "black box" which has three essential characteristics.

The purpose of any systems analysis is to optimize the measure of effectiveness by describing a policy for the decision variables in the light of the uncontrollable variables. These definitions are discussed further in a later chapter.

For example, most inventory systems take as their measure of effectiveness the total system cost. Optimizing the measure of effectiveness means minimizing that cost. The objective is then to obtain a set of values for the reorder point and the order quantity (decision variables) which minimize that cost in light of demand and other costs (uncontrollable variables).

In formulating a model we wish to associate the measure of effectiveness with both the decision variables and the uncontrollable variables. In order to develop this model we may need to make some simplifying assumptions to be able to optimize the measure of effectiveness by a pure analytic method. When the assumptions are violated, the model may become, at best, a poor representation of the system.

In the construction of any model it is paramount to identify these characteristics before proceeding to any optimization scheme. This is the first step in this simulation process, *i.e.*, to identify the measures of effectiveness, the decision variables, and the uncontrollable variables. The next step is to formulate the logical interactions among these characteristics.

This logical interaction is sometimes referred to as the "effectiveness function." We construct a computer simulation model of the

FIGURE 1.1
Pertinent Characteristics of a System

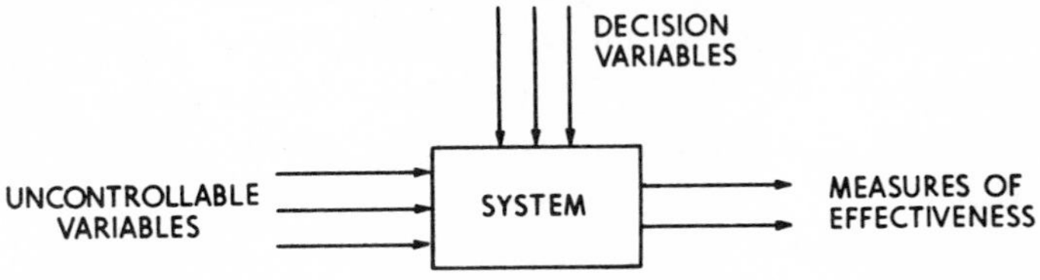

Measures of effectiveness—Those quantities which are accepted as the goal or goals of the system.

Decision variables—Those variables of the system which are under direct control of the decision maker.

Uncontrollable variables—Those variables over which the decision maker has no control whatsoever.

effectiveness function, choose values for the decision variables, and then allow the model to "simulate" the system under this set of conditions. After the simulation is complete, we obtain the value of the measure of effectiveness and perhaps choose a new set of conditions to simulate.

The reader is perhaps perplexed with this rather vague description of the simulation process. However, until the reader actually proceeds into the detailed discussion of the modeling of specific systems, the process shall remain somewhat a mystery. We shall, therefore, forego further general discussions regarding methodology until later chapters, when techniques are discussed in detail.

OBJECTIVES TO BE CONSIDERED

We have stated that simulation is the act of performing experiments on a model of a system. In order to make this an efficient technique of analysis in the determination of effective and rational policies there are different objectives to be considered. These objectives in the simulation process are of three types:

1. Objective of the system being studied—Generally, the objective is to utilize allocated resources in such a manner as to optimize a quantity or quantities which are recognized as the goal of the system. We previously called this the measure of effectiveness.
2. Objective of the simulation model—The objective of the computer simulation model (assuming that it adequately represents the system) is to efficiently generate output statistics. These output statistics are those parameters which must be known in order to apply the model of the application.
3. Objective of the simulation analyst—The objective of the simulation analyst is to allocate the resources of the simulation project budget in such a manner that the expected benefits to be derived (from recommendations made as a result of the project) are maximized. That is, the objective of the simulation analyst is to determine effective policies as efficiently as possible.

There exists a hierarchy among these objectives. The objective of the system being studied must necessarily take precedence over all others. The accomplishment of this objective is paramount to the organization. The second most important is the objective of the simulation analyst. The objective of the simulation model comes last.

This is subservient to the objective of the analyst, which is subservient to the objective of the system. What this really means is that the system does not exist for us to analyze it and we do not exist to necessarily write computer simulation programs.

These objectives are ever present in each simulation analysis. They may be either explicit or implicit, but they must be considered in order to derive maximum benefit from the project.

It is desirable to quantify all of these objectives whenever possible. This is often almost impossible, but it is helpful to attempt to quantify objectives as much as one can. An attempt alone is often enough to provide great insight into the system being studied. Although the authors may not explicitly define these objectives by type in subsequent chapters, it will be most helpful for the reader to consider them as the material is presented.

In the determination of rational policies through the use of simulation we must recognize that the simulation of a given system is not an end in itself. The simulation model is a vehicle from which data for further analysis are collected. This aspect of simulation analysis is discussed in detail in Chapters 10 and 11. Taken in this context the simulation model becomes an intermediate phase of the experimental process. It provides information which may be analyzed in order to draw conclusions about the system under study. In some cases we shall see that the actual simulation model is used in an interactive manner with an optimization technique which dictates various policies to be simulated. The output is then analyzed, and another policy is dictated to be simulated in an attempt to "seek" an optimal policy.

CONCLUSIONS

Digital computer simulation is one method for analyzing systems. We must remember that the simulation model is a means for collecting information about the performance of a system based upon conditions established by the analyst. In this text we shall investigate both the aspects of constructing and validating computer simulation models as well as the aspects of analyzing the output from simulation experiments.

CHAPTER
2

BASIC PROBABILITY THEORY

In examining the basic concepts of probability theory let us consider an experiment in which a die is cast repeatedly. A trial will be considered one toss of the die. At each trial an outcome occurs which we shall define as the number of dots appearing on the face of the die after it comes to rest. Therefore there are six possible outcomes which could occur at any trial of the experiment. The set of all possible outcomes which may occur at any trial of an experiment is called the sample space.

To generalize, let us define m as the number of outcomes comprising the sample space, and let O_i be the ith outcome, $i = 1, 2, \ldots, m$. To estimate the probability that the outcome O_i occurs at any trial, we might conduct N trials of the experiment, recording the number of times each of the possible outcomes occurs. Let n_i be the number of times the ith outcome, O_i, occurs.

$$\sum_{i=1}^{m} n_i = N \tag{2.1}$$

An estimate of the probability that O_i occurs would be given by

$$P(O_i) = \frac{n_i}{N} \tag{2.2}$$

Note that the sum of $P(O_i)$ over i is unity.

$$\sum_{i=1}^{m} P(O_i) = \sum_{i=1}^{m} \frac{n_i}{N}$$

$$= \frac{1}{N} \sum_{i=1}^{m} n_i = 1 \tag{2.3}$$

In general, the probability of any outcome, O_i, must have the

10

following properties:

1. $0 \le P(O_i) \le 1$

2. $\sum_i P(O_i) = 1$

If each of the outcomes comprising the sample space is equally likely, then

$$P(O_i) = \frac{1}{m}, \qquad i = 1, 2, \ldots, m \qquad (2.4)$$

Such is the case in the die-casting experiment if the die is "fair." That is, the probability that any one of the six possible outcomes occurs at a trial is $1/6$.

Let us now consider a more complicated experiment in which two dice are cast and an outcome is any one combination of points showing on the dice. In this experiment there are 36 possible outcomes. As before, each of the outcomes is equally likely. In this experiment we might be interested in the probability that a given sum of points on the faces of the dice occurs. For example, let us examine the occurrence of the sum nine. This can occur in several ways.

Die 1	Die 2
3	6
4	5
5	4
6	3

Any given sum which can occur is called an event. An event, therefore, is defined as some set of outcomes. In this example the sum nine is made up of four different outcomes. If, as with the dice, each of the outcomes is equally likely, the probability of a given event, E_i, may be calculated.

$$P(E_i) = \frac{\text{Number of outcomes leading to } E_i}{\text{Number of possible outcomes}} \qquad (2.5)$$

In the example considered here there are 36 outcomes possible at any trial, but only 11 events. If E_9 is the sum nine,

$$P(E_9) = \frac{4}{36} = \frac{1}{9} \qquad (2.6)$$

The events described here are referred to as mutually exclusive in that the occurrence of a particular event at any trial simultaneously excludes the possibility of any other event occurring on that trial. If the sum nine occurs on a given trial, then any other sum cannot occur on the same trial.

For mutually exclusive events the probability that E_i or E_j occur at a trial of an experiment is given by

$$P(E_i + E_j) = P(E_i) + P(E_j) \tag{2.7}$$

The probability of obtaining a 7 or 11 in tossing a set of dice would then be

$$P(E_7 + E_{11}) = P(E_7) + P(E_{11})$$
$$= \frac{6}{36} + \frac{2}{36} = \frac{2}{9}$$

Consider an experiment in which events are not mutually exclusive, for example, tossing a die and flipping a coin simultaneously. Let the events of interest be obtaining a six on the die, A, and a head, B, on the coin. The occurrence of a six does not exclude the occurrence of a head. Therefore, A and B are not mutually exclusive—they are independent. Events are said to be independent if the occurrence of one event in no way affects the probability of occurrence of the other. For such events, the probability that both A and B occur, denoted $P(AB)$, is given by

$$P(AB) = P(A)P(B) \tag{2.8}$$

Note that mutually exclusive events cannot be independent since the occurrence of one event results in a probability of occurrence of the other of zero. For independent events the probability of A or B is

$$P(A + B) = P(A) + P(B) - P(AB) \tag{2.9}$$

Therefore the probability of a six or a head is given by

$$P(A + B) = \frac{1}{6} + \frac{1}{2} - \left(\frac{1}{6}\right)\left(\frac{1}{2}\right)$$
$$= \frac{7}{12} \tag{2.10}$$

Although the validity of equation (2.9) may not be intuitively obvious, it can be developed with the aid of the notion of the compliment of an event. The compliment of event A is the set of all events which might occur exclusive of A itself and will be denoted by $\bar{A}$. A and $\bar{A}$ comprise the set of all possible events, called the universe, U, or

$$U = A + \bar{A} \tag{2.11}$$

If an experiment consists of tossing a set of dice and recording the sum showing on the dice and simultaneously flipping a coin and recording whether a head or tail occurs, the set of possible events for the toss of dice consists of the integers 2 through 12 inclusive. Similarly the set of events for the toss of the coin is a head and a tail. Therefore, for this experiment there are two universes, the integers 2 through 12 inclusive, and a head and a tail.

Let A and B be two independent events.

$$\begin{aligned} P(A + B) &= P(A\bar{B} + \bar{A}B + AB) \\ &= P(A\bar{B}) + P(\bar{A}B) + P(AB) \end{aligned} \tag{2.12}$$

and

$$P(A) = P(AB + A\bar{B}) \tag{2.13}$$

$$P(B) = P(AB + \bar{A}B) \tag{2.14}$$

Therefore

$$\begin{aligned} P(A + B) &= P(A\bar{B} + AB) + P(\bar{A}B) \\ &= P(A) + P(\bar{A}B) \end{aligned} \tag{2.15}$$

Adding and subtracting $P(AB)$, we get

$$\begin{aligned} P(A + B) &= P(A) + P(\bar{A}B) + P(AB) - P(AB) \\ &= P(A) + P(\bar{A}B + AB) - P(AB) \\ &= P(A) + P(B) - P(AB) \end{aligned} \tag{2.16}$$

The proof of (2.9) is complete.

We have discussed combinations of events such that the occurrence of one event either excludes the possibility of the occurrence of any other events or in no way affects the probability that any other event occurs. Let us now turn our attention to the situation where the occurrence of event A affects the probability that event B will occur, although not rendering that probability zero (as would be true if A and B were mutually exclusive events). For example, suppose two cards are drawn one after another from a standard deck without replacing the first card before the second is drawn. Let A_1 be the event that an ace is drawn on the first selection, A_2 the event that an ace is drawn on the second selection. The probability that A_2 occurs is dependent upon whether A_1 has occurred.

$$P(A_2 \text{ occurs, given } A_1 \text{ has occurred}) = P(A_2 | A_1)$$

$$P(A_2 A_1) = \frac{3}{51}$$

$$P(A_2 | \bar{A}_1) = \frac{4}{51}$$

In general

$$P(A | B) = \frac{P(AB)}{P(B)} \qquad (2.17)$$

or

$$P(AB) = P(A | B)P(B) \qquad (2.18)$$

With reference to the preceding example,

$$P(A_1 A_2) = \left(\frac{4}{52} \times \frac{3}{51} \right)$$

$$P(A_1) = \frac{4}{52}$$

Therefore

$$P(A_2 | A_1) = \frac{P(A_1 A_2)}{P(A_1)}$$

$$= \frac{3}{51}$$

Equations (2.17) and (2.18) hold, in fact, for mutually exclusive events and independent events as well as conditioned events. That is, for mutually exclusive events

$$P(A | B) = 0 \qquad (2.19)$$

since the occurrence of B excludes the possibility of A. Note that (2.17) yields the same result since $P(AB) = 0$ for mutually exclusive events. For independent events

$$P(A | B) = P(A) \qquad (2.20)$$

since the occurrence of B in no way affects the probability that A will occur. But for independent events, A and B, $P(AB) = P(A)P(B)$. Therefore (2.17) and (2.20) lead to identical results.

Example 2.1

Find the probability of obtaining three 7's on three successive tosses of dice.

The probability of a seven on any single toss of the dice is 1/6. Since the probability does not change from one toss of the dice to another, the events are independent.

$$P(\text{Three 7's}) = \left(\frac{1}{6}\right)\left(\frac{1}{6}\right)\left(\frac{1}{6}\right)$$

$$= \frac{1}{216}$$

Example 2.2

Three cards are drawn successively from a standard deck of playing cards without replacement. Find the probability of drawing three aces.

Let A_1, A_2, and A_3 be the events an ace on the first, second, and third draws, respectively.

$$P(\text{Three aces}) = P(A_1 A_2 A_3)$$

$$= P(A_1 A_2)P(A_3 \mid A_1 A_2)$$

$$= P(A_1)P(A_2 \mid A_1)P(A_3 \mid A_1 A_2)$$

$$= \left(\frac{4}{52}\right)\left(\frac{3}{51}\right)\left(\frac{2}{50}\right)$$

$$= \frac{1}{5,525}$$

Example 2.3

Calculate the probability that on drawing three cards from a standard deck (*a*) exactly one ace is drawn, (*b*) exactly two aces are drawn, and (*c*) at least one ace is drawn.

Let A_1, A_2, and A_3 be the events of an ace on the first, second, and third draws.

a) $P(\text{One ace}) = P(A_1 \bar{A}_2 \bar{A}_3 + \bar{A}_1 A_2 \bar{A}_3 + \bar{A}_1 \bar{A}_2 A_3)$

$$= P(A_1 \bar{A}_2 \bar{A}_3) + P(\bar{A}_1 A_2 \bar{A}_3) + P(\bar{A}_1 \bar{A}_2 A_3)$$

$$= \left(\frac{4}{52}\right)\left(\frac{48}{51}\right)\left(\frac{47}{50}\right) + \left(\frac{48}{52}\right)\left(\frac{4}{51}\right)\left(\frac{47}{50}\right) + \left(\frac{48}{52}\right)\left(\frac{47}{51}\right)\left(\frac{4}{50}\right)$$

$$= \frac{1,128}{5,525}$$

b) $P(\text{Two aces}) = P(A_1 A_2 \bar{A}_3) + P(A_1 \bar{A}_2 A_3) + P(\bar{A}_1 A_2 A_3)$

$$= \left(\frac{4}{52}\right)\left(\frac{3}{51}\right)\left(\frac{48}{50}\right) + \left(\frac{4}{52}\right)\left(\frac{48}{51}\right)\left(\frac{3}{50}\right) + \left(\frac{48}{52}\right)\left(\frac{4}{51}\right)\left(\frac{3}{50}\right)$$

$$= \frac{72}{5,525}$$

c) $P(\text{One or more aces}) = 1 - P(\text{No aces})$

$$= 1 - P(\bar{A}_1 \bar{A}_2 \bar{A}_3)$$

$$= 1 - \left(\frac{48}{52}\right)\left(\frac{47}{51}\right)\left(\frac{46}{50}\right)$$

$$= \frac{1,201}{5,525}$$

Example 2.4—Bayes' Theorem

Let the events B_1, B_2, ..., B_n be a set of mutually exclusive events, and let A be another event, the occurrence of which is dependent upon the occurrence of B_i. Further, assume

$$P(A \mid B_i) \neq P(A \mid B_j) \qquad \text{for } i \neq j \tag{2.21}$$

and that if A occurs it must be accompanied or preceded by some B_i.
That is,

$$P(A) = \sum_{i=1}^{n} P(AB_i) \tag{2.22}$$

Suppose A occurs and we wish to calculate the probability that a given B_i also occurred, $P(B_i \mid A)$.

$$P(B_i \mid A) = \frac{P(AB_i)}{P(A)}, \qquad i = 1, 2, \ldots, n \tag{2.23}$$

$$P(A \mid B_i) = \frac{P(AB_i)}{P(B_i)}, \qquad i = 1, 2, \ldots, n \tag{2.24}$$

Solving (2.23) and (2.24) for $P(AB_i)$ leads to

$$P(A \mid B_i)P(B_i) = P(B_i \mid A)P(A) \tag{2.25}$$

$$P(B_i \mid A) = \frac{P(A \mid B_i)P(B_i)}{P(A)} \tag{2.26}$$

From equation (2.22)

$$P(A) = P(AB_1) + P(AB_2) + \cdots + P(AB_n) \tag{2.27}$$

Replacing $P(AB_i)$ by $P(A \mid B_i)P(B_i)$ in (2.27), we get

$$P(A) = \sum_{i=1}^{n} P(A \mid B_i)P(B_i) \tag{2.28}$$

Substituting $P(A)$ in (2.26) by its equivalent, given in (2.28), we have

$$P(B_i \mid A) = \frac{P(A \mid B_i)P(B_i)}{\sum_{i=1}^{n} P(A \mid B_i)P(B_i)} \tag{2.29}$$

Example 2.5

Two tanks, C and D, are firing at one another. The probability that C hits D at any single shot is p, and the probability that D hits C at any single shot is q. If C fires first, what is the probability that D wins?

$$P(D \text{ wins}) = \sum_{i=1}^{\infty} P(D \text{ hits } C \text{ with } i\text{th shot})$$

$$\begin{aligned}
P(D \text{ hits } C \text{ with } i\text{th shot}) &= P(C \text{ misses with first } i \text{ shots}) \\
&\quad \times P[D \text{ misses with first } (i-1) \text{ shots}] \\
&\quad \times P(D \text{ hits } C) \\
&= (1-p)^i (1-q)^{i-1} q
\end{aligned}$$

$$\begin{aligned}
P(D \text{ wins}) &= \sum_{i=1}^{\infty} (1-p)^i (1-q)^{i-1} q \\[6pt]
&= \frac{q}{1-q} \sum_{i=1}^{\infty} [(1-p)(1-q)]^i \\[6pt]
&= \frac{q}{1-q} \frac{(1-p)(1-q)}{1-(1-p)(1-q)} \\[6pt]
&= \frac{q(1-p)}{p+q-pq}
\end{aligned}$$

DISCRETE RANDOM VARIABLES

Discrete random variables are characterized by the fact that the difference between any two finite values which the random variable can assume is finite and nonzero. Examples of such random variables include the number of persons waiting at a bus stop, the number of units of product produced in a given interval of time, the number of vehicles queued at a traffic light, the number of empty parking spaces in a parking lot, the number of students in a classroom, the number of alpha particles recorded by a geiger counter, the number of employees absent from work, and so forth.

The cumulative distribution function, $F_X(k)$, of the random variable X is defined as

$$F_X(k) = \text{Probability that the value of } X \text{ is less than or equal to } k$$
$$= P(X \le k) \tag{2.30}$$

Associated with the cumulative distribution function are the following properties:

1. $0 \le F_X(k) \le 1$
2. $F_X(k)$ is a nondecreasing function
3. $F_X(-\infty) = 0$
4. $F_X(\infty) = 1$

The probability that X lies between a and b $(a<b)$ is calculated by subtracting $F_X(a)$ from $F_X(b)$. That is,

$$P(a < X \le b) = F_X(b) - F_X(a) \tag{2.31}$$

Similarly,

$$P(X = a) = F_X(a) - F_X(a - 1) \tag{2.32}$$

where it is assumed that X can assume only integer values. That is, the difference between any two successive values of the random variable, X, is one. If X could take on values such as 0, 1/2, 1, 1½, 2, 2½, ... , then

$$P(X = a) = F_X(a) - F_X\left(a - \frac{1}{2}\right) \tag{2.33}$$

Hereafter $P(X = a)$ will be denoted $p_X(a)$ and will be referred to as the probability mass function of X.

For the most part the reader need consider only discrete random variables which may assume integer values. If this is true, $F_X(x)$ and $p_X(x)$ may be related by

$$p_X(x) = \Delta F_X(x)$$
$$= F_X(x) - F_X(x - 1) \tag{2.34}$$

which implies

$$F_X(k) = \sum_{x \le k} p_X(x) \tag{2.35}$$

Included in Table 2.1 are several frequently encountered discrete distributions with their probability mass functions, characteristic functions, means, and variances.

If the difference between successive values of the random variables can be other than unity, $p_X(x)$ is given by (2.36) where

$$p_X(x) = F_X(x) - F_X(x - \Delta x) \tag{2.36}$$

Δx is the difference between x and the preceding value of the random variable.

The properties of $F_X(x)$ imply certain properties which $p_X(x)$ must satisfy. Properties 1 and 2 imply $0 \le p_X(x) \le 1$. Properties 3 and 4 imply $p_X(-\infty) = 0$ and $p_X(\infty) = 0$. To summarize,

1. $0 \le p_X(x) \le 1$
2. $p_X(-\infty) = 0$
3. $p_X(\infty) = 0$

CONTINUOUS RANDOM VARIABLES

A continuous random variable possesses the property that on any finite open interval[1] on which it is defined, it can take on an infinite number of values. Continuous random variables with which the systems analyst is concerned usually involve time in some respect. Examples of such random variables include the time between successive demands for a product, production lead time, the time a customer must wait before being served, the time spent by a vehicle in transit between two points, and so forth. Continuous random variables which do not involve time include vehicular velocity, distance between vehicles, fuel consumption, rate of flow of a liquid, percentage of carbon contained in steel, and so forth.

---

[1] An open interval is an interval which does not include its endpoints.

TABLE 2.1

Discrete Probability Distributions

Probability Distribution	Probability Mass Function $p_X(x)$	Characteristic Function $\phi_X(u)$	Mean	Variance	Range of Variable	Parameter Values
Binomial.........	$\dfrac{n!}{x!(n-x)!}p^x(1-p)^{n-x}$	$(pe^{iu}+1-p)^n$	np	$np(1-p)$	$x=0,1,\ldots,n$	$0\le p\le1$
Poisson.........	$\dfrac{(\lambda)^x}{x!}e^{-\lambda}$	$e^{\lambda(e^{iu}-1)}$	λ	λ	$x=0,1,2,\ldots$	$\lambda>0$
Geometric.......	$p(1-p)^{x-1}$	$\dfrac{pe^{iu}}{[1-(1-p)e^{iu}]}$	$\dfrac{1}{p}$	$\dfrac{1-p}{p^2}$	$x=1,2,\ldots$	$0\le p\le1$
Rectangular.......	$\dfrac{1}{b-a+1}$	$\dfrac{e^{iu}}{b-a+1}\left[\dfrac{e^{iub}-e^{iua}}{e^{iu}-1}\right]$	$\dfrac{a+b}{2}$	$\dfrac{(b+a)^2}{12}+\dfrac{b-a}{6}$	$x=a,a+1,\ldots,b$	$a<b$
Hypergeometric.....	$\dfrac{\dfrac{M!}{x!(M-x)!}\dfrac{(N-M)!}{(n-x)!(N-M-n+x)!}}{\dfrac{N!}{n!(N-n)!}}$		$\dfrac{Mn}{N}$	$\dfrac{(N-n)}{(N-1)}\dfrac{(Mn)}{N}\dfrac{(N-M)}{N}$	$x=0,1,\ldots,n$	$N\ge M>n$
Negative binomial ...	$\dfrac{(x-1)!}{(r-1)!(x-r)!}p^r(1-p)^{x-r}$	$\left[\dfrac{p}{1-(1-p)e^{iu}}\right]^r$	$\dfrac{r}{p}$	$\dfrac{r(1-p)}{p^2}$	$x=r,r+1,\ldots$	$0\le p\le1$ $r>0$

The interpretation of the cumulative distribution function, $F_X(k)$, and the properties it must possess are the same for continuous as for discrete random variables. That is,

$$F_X(k) = P(X \leqslant k) \tag{2.37}$$
1. $0 \leqslant F_X(k) \leqslant 1$
2. $F_X(k)$ is a nondecreasing function
3. $F_X(-\infty) = 0$
4. $F_X(\infty) = 1$

The continuous analog of the probability mass function is called the density function, $f_X(x)$, and is related to the cumulative distribution by equation (2.38).

$$f_X(x) = \frac{d}{dx} F_X(x) \tag{2.38}$$

The inverse relationship and continuous analog of (2.34) is given by (2.39) and (2.40).

$$\int_{F_X(-\infty)}^{F_X(k)} dF_X(x) = \int_{-\infty}^{k} f_X(x)\, dx \tag{2.39}$$

Therefore

$$F_X(k) = \int_{-\infty}^{k} f_X(x)\, dx \tag{2.40}$$

$$P(a \leq x \leq b) = \sum_{a \leq x \leq b} p_X(x) \quad \text{discrete case} \tag{2.41}$$

$$P(a \leq x \leq b) = \int_{a}^{b} f_X(x)\, dx \quad \text{continuous case} \tag{2.42}$$

Equations (2.41) and (2.42) lead to an important distinction between the probability mass function, $p_X(x)$, and the density function, $f_X(x)$.

$$P(x = a) = \sum_{x=a}^{a} p_X(x) \quad \text{discrete case}$$
$$= p_X(a) \tag{2.43}$$

$$P(x = a) = \int_{a}^{a} f_X(x)\, dx \quad \text{continuous case}$$
$$= 0 \tag{2.44}$$

Two important conclusions can be drawn from (2.44). First, for continuous random variables the probability that the random variable assumes a unique value is zero. Second, the density function does not represent the probability that a given value of the random variable occurs.

From the properties of the continuous distribution function one may infer certain properties which the density function must possess. Since $F_X(x)$ is a nondecreasing function, $f_X(x)$ must be nonnegative. However, since X is a continuous variable, it is not necessary that $f_X(x)$ take on values less than unity. Also,

$$F_X(-\infty) = 0 \Rightarrow f_X(-\infty) = 0$$
$$F_X(\infty) = 0 \Rightarrow f_X(\infty) = 0$$

In summary,

1. $f_X(x) \geqslant 0$
2. $f_X(-\infty) = 0$
3. $f_X(\infty) = 0$

In Table 2.2 several useful continuous probability distributions are given with their density functions, characteristic functions, means, and variances.

Example 2.6

The probability that a single manufactured item is defective is p. If a random sample of n items is selected, the probability that x of those items are defective follows the binomial distribution. If $p = 0.25$ and n is 10, what is the probability that three or less defective items will be found?

$$P(x \leq 3) = \sum_{x=0}^{3} \frac{n!}{x!(n-x)!} p^x (1-p)^{n-x}$$

$$= (0.75)^{10} + 10(0.25)(0.75)^9 + 45(0.25)^2(0.75)^8 + 120(0.25)^3(0.75)^7$$

$$= 0.7759$$

Example 2.7

Given the probability mass function

$$p_X(x) = \frac{x}{k}, \qquad x = 1, \ldots, 10$$

find
  a) The value of k.

TABLE 2.2
Continuous Probability Distributions

Probability Distribution	Probability Density Function $f_X(x)$	Characteristic Function $\phi_X(x)$	Mean	Variance	Range of Variable	Parameter Values
Normal	$\dfrac{1}{\sigma\sqrt{2\pi}}\,e^{-(x-m)^2/2\sigma^2}$	$e^{ium-\frac{1}{2}u^2\sigma^2}$	m	σ^2	$-\infty < x < \infty$	$-\infty < m < \infty$ $\sigma^2 > 0$
Exponential	$\lambda e^{-\lambda x}$	$\dfrac{\lambda}{\lambda - iu}$	$\dfrac{1}{\lambda}$	$\dfrac{1}{\lambda^2}$	$x > 0$	$\lambda > 0$
Gamma	$\dfrac{\lambda}{\Gamma(n)}(\lambda x)^{n-1}e^{-\lambda x}$	$\left(\dfrac{\lambda}{\lambda - iu}\right)^n$	$\dfrac{n}{\lambda}$	$\dfrac{n}{\lambda^2}$	$x > 0$	$\lambda > 0$ $n > 0$
F	$\dfrac{\Gamma\left(\frac{m+n}{2}\right)}{\Gamma\left(\frac{m}{2}\right)\Gamma\left(\frac{n}{2}\right)}\left(\dfrac{m}{n}\right)^{m/2}x^{m/2-1}\left(1+\dfrac{m}{n}x\right)^{(m+n)/2}$		$\dfrac{n}{n-2}$ $n > 2$ does not exist for $n \le 2$	$\dfrac{2n(m+n-2)}{m(n-2)^2(n-4)}$ $n > 4$ does not exist for $n \le 4$	$x > 0$	$m > 0$ $n > 0$
Uniform	$\dfrac{1}{b-a}$	$\dfrac{e^{iub}-e^{iua}}{iu(b-a)}$	$\dfrac{a+b}{2}$	$\dfrac{(b-a)^2}{12}$	$a < x < b$	$-\infty < a < \infty$ $-\infty < b < \infty$
Laplace	$\tfrac{1}{2}e^{-|x-\lambda|}$	$\dfrac{iue^{iu\lambda}}{u^2-1}$	λ	2	$-\infty < x < \infty$	$-\infty < \lambda < \infty$
Cauchy	$\dfrac{1}{\pi}\dfrac{\beta}{\beta^2+(x-\alpha)^2}$	$e^{i\alpha u-\beta|u|}$	nonexistent	nonexistent	$-\infty < x < \infty$	$-\infty < \alpha < \infty$ $\beta > 0$

b) The cumulative distribution function.

$$a) \sum_{x=1}^{10} p_X(x) = 1$$

$$\sum_{x=1}^{10} \frac{x}{k} = \frac{1}{k} \frac{10(11)}{2}$$

$$k = 55$$

$$b) \ F_X(h) = \sum_{x=1}^{h} \frac{x}{55}$$

$$= \frac{h(h+1)}{110}$$

Example 2.8

Given the following probability mass function, find the cumulative distribution function:

$$p_X(x) = \frac{x}{110}, \qquad x = 1, 2, \ldots, 10$$

$$p_X(x) = \frac{21 - x}{110}, \qquad x = 11, 12, \ldots, 20$$

For $k = 1, 2, \ldots, 10$,

$$F_X(k) = \sum_{x=1}^{k} \frac{x}{110}$$

$$= \frac{k(k+1)}{220}$$

For $k = 11, 12, \ldots, 20$,

$$F_X(k) = \sum_{x=1}^{k} p_X(x)$$

$$= \sum_{x=1}^{10} p_X(x) + \sum_{x=11}^{k} p_X(x)$$

$$= \frac{1}{2} + \sum_{x=11}^{k} \frac{21 - x}{110}$$

$$= \frac{1}{2} + \sum_{x=11}^{k} \frac{21}{110} - \sum_{x=11}^{k} \frac{x}{110}$$

$$F_X(k) = \frac{1}{2} + \frac{21(k-10)}{110} - \frac{k(k+1) - 10(11)}{220}$$

$$= \frac{1}{2} - \frac{(k-31)(k-10)}{220}$$

Example 2.9

Find the median of the exponential distribution. The median of a distribution is defined as that value, M, of the random variable such that $P(x \leqslant M) = 0.5$. From Table 2.2

$$f_X(x) = \lambda e^{-\lambda x}, \qquad 0 < x < \infty$$

$$P(x \leq M) = \int_0^M \lambda e^{-\lambda x}\, dx$$

$$= 0.5$$

$$1 - e^{-\lambda M} = 0.5$$

$$M = -\frac{1}{\lambda} \ln 0.5$$

Example 2.10

Find the cumulative distribution function of the uniform distribution. From Table 2.2

$$f_X(x) = \frac{1}{b-a}, \qquad a < x < b$$

$$F_X(k) = \int_a^k \frac{dx}{b-a}$$

$$= \frac{k-a}{b-a}, \qquad a < k < b$$

JOINT DISTRIBUTION

The joint cumulative distribution function,

$$F_{X_1, X_2, \ldots, X_n}(x_1, x_2, \ldots, x_n)$$

is defined as

$$F_{X_1, X_2, \ldots, X_n}(x_1, x_2, \ldots, x_n) = P(X_1 \leq x_1, X_2 \leq x_2, \ldots, X_n \leq x_n) \quad (2.45)$$

In words, equation (2.45) expresses the probability that the combination of events, $X_1 \leqslant x_1$, $X_2 \leqslant x_2$, $\ldots$, and $X_n \leqslant x_n$, occurs. For example, suppose T_i represents the time, in minutes, between the arrival of the $(i - 1)$st and ith cars at a parking lot. Let us compute the probability that the attendant will have no more than five minutes to park any car without forcing another car to wait. This is the probability that the time between any two arrivals is less than five minutes. Therefore,

$$P(\text{attendant has five minutes or less}) = P(T_2 \le 5, T_3 \le 5, \ldots, T_n \le 5)$$
$$= F_{T_2, T_3, \ldots, T_n}(5, 5, \ldots, 5)$$

Associated with every joint cumulative distribution function is a joint density function or joint probability mass function, depending upon whether the random variables are continuous or discrete. For the continuous case

$$f_{X_1, X_2, \ldots, X_n}(x_1, x_2, \ldots, x_n) = \frac{\partial^n}{\partial x_1 \, \partial x_2 \cdots \partial x_n} F_{X_1, X_2, \ldots, X_n}(x_1, x_2, \ldots, x_n)$$

(2.46)

The analogous relationship for the discrete case is given by

$$p_{X_1, X_2, \ldots, X_n}(x_1, x_2, \ldots, x_n) = \Delta_{X_1} \Delta_{X_2} \cdots \Delta_{X_n} F_{X_1, X_2, \ldots, X_n}(x_1, x_2, \ldots, x_n)$$

(2.47)

where Δ_{X_i} represents the first difference of

$$F_{X_1, X_2, \ldots, X_n}(x_1, x_2, \ldots, x_n)$$

with respect to x_i. The fact that the first difference is taken in (2.47) implies that the random variables assume integer and only integer values over their range of definition.

If the random variables in (2.45) are independent

$$F_{X_1, X_2, \ldots, X_n}(x_1, x_2, \ldots, x_n) = P(X_1 \le x_1)P(X_2 \le x_2), \ldots, P(X_n \le x_n)$$

(2.48)

by a simple extension of equation (2.8). Therefore the joint distribution function for independent variables is given by

$$F_{X_1, X_2, \ldots, X_n}(x_1, x_2, \ldots, x_n) = F_{X_1}(x_1)F_{X_2}(x_2), \ldots, F_{X_n}(x_n) \qquad (2.49)$$

Application of the results of (2.46) and (2.47) to (2.49) leads to

$$f_{X_1, X_2, \ldots, X_n}(x_1, x_2, \ldots, x_n) = f_{X_1}(x_1)f_{X_2}(x_2), \ldots, f_{X_n}(x_n) \qquad (2.50)$$

and

$$p_{X_1, X_2, \ldots, X_n}(x_1, x_2, \ldots, x_n) = p_{X_1}(x_1)p_{X_2}(x_2), \ldots, p_{X_n}(x_n) \qquad (2.51)$$

When one is referring to jointly distributed random variables, $f_{X_i}(x_i)$ and $p_{X_i}(x_i)$ are usually called the "marginal" density and probability mass functions respectively.

In the parking lot problem discussed above, one would expect the random variables, T_i, to be independent. If T_i has an exponential distribution with parameter λ for all i, then

$$f_{T_i}(t_i) = \lambda e^{-\lambda t_i}, \qquad 0 < t_i < \infty$$

and

$$f_{T_1, T_2, \ldots, T_n}(t_1, t_2, \ldots, t_n) = \lambda^n e^{-\lambda(t_1 + t_2 + \cdots + t_n)}, \, 0 < t_i < \infty, \quad \text{for all } i \quad (2.52)$$

Equations (2.50) and (2.51) lead us to a method through which we can determine whether a set of random variables are independently distributed. The marginal density function, $f_{X_i}(x_i)$, and the probability mass function, $p_{X_i}(x_i)$, can be determined from the joint density function and joint probability mass function by equations (2.53) and (2.54).

$$f_{X_i}(x_i) = \int_{X_n} \cdots \int_{X_{i+1}} \int_{X_{i-1}} \cdots \int_{X_1} f_{X_1, \ldots, X_n}(x_1, \ldots, x_n)\, dx_1 \cdots dx_{i-1}\, dx_{i+1} \cdots dx_n$$
$$(2.53)$$

$$p_{X_i}(x_i) = \sum_{X_n} \cdots \sum_{X_{i+1}} \sum_{X_{i-1}} \cdots \sum_{X_1} p_{X_1, X_2, \ldots, X_n}(x_1, x_2, \ldots, x_n) \qquad (2.54)$$

If after deriving $f_{X_i}(x_i)$ for all i [or $p_{X_i}(x_i)$ for all i], we find that equation [2.50 (2.51)] is valid, the n random variables are independently distributed.

To illustrate, let the continuous random variables X and Y have the following joint density function:

$$f_{X,Y}(x, y) = 4x(y - x)e^{-(x+y)}, \qquad 0 < y < \infty, \quad 0 < x < y$$

$$f_X(x) = \int_x^\infty 4x(y - x)e^{-(x+y)}\, dy$$

$$= 4xe^{-2x}, \qquad 0 < x < \infty$$

$$f_Y(y) = \int_0^y 4x(y - x)e^{-(x+y)}\, dx$$

$$= 4e^{-y}(-3ye^{-y} - 2e^{-y} + y + 2), \qquad 0 < y < \infty$$

$$f_X(x)f_Y(y) = 16xe^{-(2x+y)}(-3ye^{-y} - 2e^{-y} + y + 2)$$

$$\neq f_{X,Y}(x, y)$$

Therefore X and Y are not independent random variables.

If the random variables X and Y are not independent, then the probability that a given value of one will occur is dependent upon the value of the other. In such a case it is necessary to know the conditional density function or probability mass function of the random variables which can be developed if $f_{X,Y}(x,y)$ or $p_{X,Y}(x,y)$ are known. Let $f_{X|Y}(x|y)$ be the conditional density function of X for a given value of Y, and let $p_{X|Y}(x|y)$ be the conditional probability mass function of X for a given value of Y.

$$f_{X|Y}(x \mid y) = \frac{f_{X,Y}(x, y)}{f_Y(y)} = \frac{f_{X,Y}(x, y)}{\int_X f_{X,Y}(x, y)\, dx} \tag{2.55}$$

$$p_{X|Y}(x \mid y) = \frac{p_{X,Y}(x, y)}{p_Y(y)} = \frac{p_{X,Y}(x, y)}{\sum_X p_{X,Y}(x, y)} \tag{2.56}$$

As might be expected, if the random variables X and Y are independent,

$$f_{X|Y}(x \mid y) = \frac{f_{X,Y}(x, y)}{f_Y(y)}$$

$$= \frac{f_X(x)f_Y(y)}{f_Y(y)} \tag{2.57}$$

$$= f_X(x)$$

$$p_{X|Y}(x \mid y) = \frac{p_{X,Y}(x, y)}{p_Y(y)}$$

$$= \frac{p_X(x)p_Y(y)}{p_Y(y)} \tag{2.58}$$

$$= p_X(x)$$

Let us develop the conditional density functions of X given Y, and Y given X, for the example above.

$$f_X(x) = 4xe^{-2x}, \qquad 0 < x < \infty$$

$$f_Y(y) = 4e^{-y}(-3ye^{-y} - 2e^{-y} + y + 2), \qquad 0 < y < \infty$$

$$f_{X,Y}(x, y) = 4x(y - x)e^{-(x+y)}, \qquad 0 < y < \infty, \quad 0 < x < y$$

$$f_{X|Y}(x \mid y) = \frac{x(y - x)e^{-x}}{(-3ye^{-y} - 2e^{-y} + y + 2)}, \qquad 0 < x < y$$

$$f_{Y|X}(y \mid x) = (y - x)e^{-y+x}, \qquad x < y < \infty$$

The conditional distribution function, $F_{X|Y}(k|y)$, is the probability that $X \leq k$ given $Y = y$. This function should not be confused with the probability that $X \leq k$, given $Y \leq h$.

$$F_{X|Y}(k|y) = P(X \leq k \mid Y = y) \tag{2.59}$$

$$F_{X|Y}(k|y) = \begin{cases} \displaystyle\int_{-\infty}^{k} f_{X|Y}(x|y)\,dx & \text{continuous case} \\[2ex] \displaystyle\sum_{x=-\infty}^{k} p_{X|Y}(x|y) & \text{discrete case} \end{cases} \tag{2.60}$$

$p(X \leq k | Y \leq h)$ is a conditional probability but is not defined as the conditional distribution function.

$$P(X \leq k \mid Y \leq h) = \begin{cases} \dfrac{\displaystyle\int_{-\infty}^{k}\int_{-\infty}^{h} f_{X,Y}(x,y)\,dy\,dx}{\displaystyle\int_{-\infty}^{h} f_Y(y)\,dy} & \text{continuous case} \\[4ex] \dfrac{\displaystyle\sum_{x=-\infty}^{k}\sum_{y=-\infty}^{h} p_{X,Y}(x,y)}{\displaystyle\sum_{y=-\infty}^{h} p_Y(y)} & \text{discrete case} \end{cases} \tag{2.61}$$

Example 2.11

Let M and N be the weekly demands for a product from customers A and B, respectively. The joint probability mass function of M and N is given by

$$p_{M,N}(m,n) = \frac{(\lambda_1)^m (\lambda_2)^n}{m!\;n!}\, e^{-(\lambda_1 + \lambda_2)}, \qquad \begin{array}{l} m = 0, 1, 2, \ldots \\ n = 0, 1, 2, \ldots \end{array}$$

Show that M and N are independent random variables.

$$p_M(m) = \sum_{n=0}^{\infty} \frac{(\lambda_1)^m (\lambda_2)^n}{m!\;n!}\, e^{-(\lambda_1 + \lambda_2)}$$

$$= \frac{(\lambda_1)^m}{m!}\, e^{-(\lambda_1 + \lambda_2)} \sum_{n=0}^{\infty} \frac{(\lambda_2)^n}{n!}$$

$$= \frac{(\lambda_1)^m}{m!}\, e^{-(\lambda_1 + \lambda_2)} e^{\lambda_2}$$

$$= \frac{(\lambda_1)^m}{m!}\, e^{-\lambda_1}, \qquad m = 0, 1, 2, \ldots$$

$$p_N(n) = \sum_{m=0}^{\infty} \frac{(\lambda_1)^m}{m!} \frac{(\lambda_2)^n}{n!} e^{-(\lambda_1 + \lambda_2)}$$

$$= \frac{(\lambda_2)^n}{n!} e^{-(\lambda_1 + \lambda_2)} \sum_{m=0}^{\infty} \frac{(\lambda_1)^m}{m!}$$

$$= \frac{(\lambda_2)^n}{n!} e^{-\lambda_2}, \qquad n = 0, 1, 2, \ldots$$

$$p_M(m)p_N(n) = \frac{(\lambda_1)^m}{m!} e^{-\lambda_1} \frac{(\lambda_2)^n}{n!} e^{-\lambda_2}$$

$$= p_{M,N}(m, n)$$

Example 2.12

Let X be a Poisson random variable with parameter λ, and let the conditional distribution of Y, given $X = n$ be binomial with parameters n and p. Show that the marginal distribution of Y is Poisson with parameter $p\lambda$.

$$p_X(x) = \frac{\lambda^x}{x!} e^{-\lambda}, \qquad x = 0, 1, 2, \ldots$$

$$p_{Y|X}(y \mid n) = \frac{n!}{y!(n-y)!} p^y(1-p)^{n-y}, \qquad y = 0, 1, 2, \ldots, n$$

$$p_{Y|X}(y \mid n) = \frac{p_{Y,X}(y, n)}{p_X(n)}$$

$$p_{Y,X}(y, n) = p_{Y|X}(y \mid n)p_X(n)$$

$$p_Y(y) = \sum_{n=y}^{\infty} p_{Y,X}(y, n)$$

$$= \sum_{n=y}^{\infty} \frac{n!}{y!(n-y)!} p^y(1-p)^{n-y} \frac{\lambda^n}{n!} e^{-\lambda}$$

$$= \frac{p^y}{y!} e^{-\lambda} \sum_{n=y}^{\infty} \frac{(1-p)^{n-y}\lambda^n}{(n-y)!}$$

Let $m = n - y$.

$$p_Y(y) = \frac{p^y}{y!} e^{-\lambda} \sum_{m=0}^{\infty} \frac{(1-p)^m}{m!} \lambda^{m+y}$$

$$= \frac{(\lambda p)^y}{y!} e^{-\lambda} \sum_{m=0}^{\infty} \frac{[(1-p)\lambda]^m}{m!}$$

$$p_Y(y) = \frac{(\lambda p)^y}{y!} e^{-\lambda} e^{(1-p)\lambda}$$

$$= \frac{(\lambda p)^y}{y!} e^{-p\lambda}, \qquad y = 0, 1, 2, \ldots$$

Example 2.13

The joint density function of X and Y is given by

$$f_{X,Y}(x, y) = \frac{1}{xT}, \qquad 0 < x < T, \quad 0 < y < x$$

Find

a) $f_X(x)$

b) $f_Y(y)$

c) $f_{X|Y}(x \mid y)$

d) $f_{Y|X}(y \mid x)$

a) $f_X(x) = \int_0^x \dfrac{dy}{xT}$

$$= \frac{1}{T}, \qquad 0 < x < T$$

b) $f_Y(y) = \int_y^T \dfrac{dx}{xT}$

$$= \frac{1}{T} \ln(x) \Big|_y^T$$

$$= \frac{1}{T} [\ln(T) - \ln(y)], \qquad 0 < y < T$$

c) $f_{X|Y}(x \mid y) = \dfrac{1}{x[\ln(T) - \ln(y)]}, \qquad y < x < T$

d) $f_{Y|X}(y \mid x) = \dfrac{1}{x}, \qquad 0 < y < x$

Example 2.14

Let T be exponentially distributed with parameter λ. Show that

$$P(T > x + y \mid T > y) = P(T > x)$$

$$f_T(t) = \lambda e^{-\lambda t}, \qquad 0 < t < \infty$$

$$P(T > x + y \mid T > y) = \frac{P(T > x + y)}{P(T > y)}$$

$$= \frac{\int_{x+y}^{\infty} \lambda e^{-\lambda t}\, dt}{\int_{y}^{\infty} \lambda e^{-\lambda t}\, dt}$$

$$= \frac{e^{-\lambda(x+y)}}{e^{-\lambda y}}$$

$$= e^{-\lambda x}$$

$$= P(T > x)$$

As a result of this property, the exponential random variable is said to be a random variable without memory. The exponential random variable is the only continuous random variable possessing this property.

Example 2.15

Show that the geometric random variable is without memory.

$$p_N(n) = p(1 - p)^{n-1}, \qquad n = 1, 2, \ldots$$

$$P(N > x + y \mid N > y) = \frac{\sum_{n=x+y+1}^{\infty} p(1 - p)^{n-1}}{\sum_{n=y+1}^{\infty} p(1 - p)^{n-1}}$$

$$= \frac{(1 - p)^{x+y}}{(1 - p)^{y}}$$

$$= (1 - p)^{x}$$

$$= P(n > x)$$

DERIVED DISTRIBUTIONS

Often the systems analyst is forced to deal with random variables whose values are completely dependent upon the values of other random variables. To illustrate, suppose we are interested in the random variable the number of cars waiting to be washed at a car wash one hour after the car wash opens. This random variable is a function of the number of cars arriving in the first hour and the time to wash a car. If the distribution of arrivals per hour and the distribution of the service time (time to wash) are known, the distribution of the number of cars waiting can be derived. Referring to the same example, we decide the distribution of time between successive arriving cars might also be of interest. Due to the inherent relationship between the number of arrivals per unit time and the distribution of time between arrivals, if one is known the other can be derived.

Functions of a Single Random Variable

Let X be a random variable having density function $f_X(x)$, $a < x < b$, and distribution function $F_X(x)$, and let Y be a function of X defined by the transformation $\phi(x)$. We will first treat transformations which are one-to-one. That is, for each value of X there is one and only one value of Y. The inverse of $\phi(x)$ will be defined as $\psi(y)$. Therefore, $y = \phi(x)$, $x = \psi(y)$, and $\psi[\phi(x)] = x$.

Let $g_Y(y)$ be the density function of Y with distribution function $G_Y(y)$. There exists a value of X, say x, such that when $Y = y$,

$$F_X(x) = G_Y(y)$$

$$\frac{d}{dy} G_Y(y) = \frac{d}{dy} F_X(x)$$

$$= \frac{d}{dx} F_X(x) \frac{dx}{dy}$$

$$= \frac{d}{dx} F_X(x) \frac{d}{dy} \psi(y)$$

$$= f_X(x)\psi'(y)$$

Therefore

$$g_Y(y) = f_X[\psi(y)]\psi'(y) \qquad (2.62)$$

and

$$G_Y(y) = \int_{\phi(a)}^{y} f_X[\psi(z)]\psi'(z)\, dz \qquad (2.63)$$

Equation (2.62) would seem to degenerate when $\psi(y)$ is a monotonically decreasing function. That is, $c < d \Rightarrow \psi(c) > \psi(d)$.

In such a case $\psi'(y)$ would be negative, resulting in negative values for the density function $g_Y(y)$. Further, the limits in (2.63) would be such that $y < \phi(a)$. When we reverse the limits in (2.63), the density function of Y becomes nonnegative. $g_Y(y)$ can then be expressed by (2.64).

$$g_Y(y) = f_X[\psi(y)]\,|\psi'(y)| \qquad\qquad (2.64)$$

Example 2.16

Find the density function of Y where $Y = X - a$ and
$$f_X(x) = \lambda e^{-\lambda x}, \qquad 0 < x < \infty$$
$$\psi(y) = y + a$$
$$\psi'(y) = 1$$

Therefore
$$g_Y(y) = \lambda e^{-\lambda(y+a)}, \qquad -a < y < \infty$$

Example 2.17

Find the density function of Y where $Y = a - X$ and
$$f_X(x) = \lambda e^{-\lambda x}, \qquad 0 < x < \infty$$
$$\psi(y) = a - y$$
$$\psi'(y) = -1$$
$$|\psi'(y)| = 1$$

Therefore
$$g_Y(y) = \lambda e^{-\lambda(a-y)}, \qquad -\infty < y < a$$

It should be noted that in this example when x is equal to its lower limit, y is equal to its upper limit; and when x is equal to its upper limit, y is equal to its lower limit.

Example 2.18

Let X have a uniform distribution on the interval (a,b), and let $Y = 1/X$. Find the density function of Y.
$$f_X(x) = \frac{1}{b-a}, \qquad a < x < b$$

$$\psi(y) = \frac{1}{y}$$

$$\psi'(y) = -\frac{1}{y^2} \qquad |\psi'(y)| = \frac{1}{y^2}$$

$$g_Y(y) = \frac{1}{(b-a)y^2}, \qquad \frac{1}{b} < y < \frac{1}{a}$$

One-to-one transformations involving discrete random variables are somewhat easier to handle. Let X be a discrete random variable having probability mass function $p_X(x)$, and let $y = \phi(x)$ and $x = \psi(y)$. Then

$$p_Y(y) = p_X[\psi(y)] \qquad (2.65)$$

That is, x is replaced by its equivalent in terms of y in the probability mass function of X.

Example 2.19

Let X be Poisson distributed, and let $Y = X + a$. Find the distribution of Y.

$$p_X(x) = \frac{\lambda^x}{x!} e^{-\lambda}, \qquad x = 0, 1, 2, \ldots$$

$$p_Y(y) = \frac{\lambda^{(y-a)}}{(y-a)!} e^{-\lambda}, \qquad y = a, a+1, a+2, \ldots$$

Occasionally it is necessary to deal with transformations other than one-to-one. One example of such a transformation will be presented to illustrate the general approach to this type of problem.

Let X be a random variable with density function of $f_X(x)$ for $-\infty < x < \infty$. We sill derive the density function of Y where $Y = X^2$.

$$X = \pm\sqrt{Y}$$

Thus if Y is less than y, then X must lie between $-\sqrt{y}$ and $\sqrt{y}$.

$$G_Y(y) = \int_{-\sqrt{y}}^{\sqrt{y}} f_X(x)\, dx \qquad (2.66)$$

$$g_Y(y) = \frac{d}{dy} G_Y(y)$$

$$= \frac{f_X(\sqrt{y})}{2\sqrt{y}} + \frac{f_X(-\sqrt{y})}{2\sqrt{y}}$$

$$= \frac{f_X(\sqrt{y}) + f_X(-\sqrt{y})}{2\sqrt{y}} \tag{2.67}$$

Functions of Several Random Variables

Assume that X_1, $X_2 \ldots, X_n$ are random variables with known joint density function $f_{X_1, X_2, \ldots, X_n}(x_1, x_2, \ldots, x_n)$. Let Y_1, $Y_2, \ldots, Y_n$ be random variables, each of which is a function of some subset of $X_1, X_2, \ldots, X_n$. We will develop the density function $g_{Y_1, Y_2, \ldots, Y_n}(y_1, y_2, \ldots, y_n)$. We must first define the following transformations:

$$
\begin{aligned}
Y_1 &= \phi_1(X_1, X_2, \ldots, X_n) \\
Y_2 &= \phi_2(X_1, X_2, \ldots, X_n) \\
&\vdots \qquad \vdots \\
Y_n &= \phi_n(X_1, X_2, \ldots, X_n) \\
X_1 &= \psi_1(Y_1, Y_2, \ldots, Y_n) \\
X_2 &= \psi_2(Y_1, Y_2, \ldots, Y_n) \\
&\vdots \qquad \vdots \\
X_n &= \psi_n(Y_1, Y_2, \ldots, Y_n)
\end{aligned}
\tag{2.68}
$$

An inherent part of every multivariant transformation is the Jacobian of the transformation, defined in (2.69).

$$
J = \begin{vmatrix}
\dfrac{\partial \psi_1}{\partial Y_1} & \dfrac{\partial \psi_1}{\partial Y_2} & \cdots & \dfrac{\partial \psi_1}{\partial Y_n} \\[2mm]
\dfrac{\partial \psi_2}{\partial Y_1} & \dfrac{\partial \psi_2}{\partial Y_2} & \cdots & \dfrac{\partial \psi_2}{\partial Y_n} \\[2mm]
\vdots & \vdots & & \vdots \\[2mm]
\dfrac{\partial \psi_n}{\partial Y_1} & \dfrac{\partial \psi_n}{\partial Y_2} & \cdots & \dfrac{\partial \psi_n}{\partial Y_n}
\end{vmatrix}
\tag{2.69}
$$

The joint density function of Y_1, $Y_2, \ldots, Y_n$ is then given by

$$g_{Y_1, Y_2, \ldots, Y_n}(y_1, y_2, \ldots, y_n) = |J| f_{X_1, X_2, \ldots, X_n}(\psi_1, \psi_2, \ldots, \psi_n) \tag{2.70}$$

No attempt has been made to rigorously develop (2.70), but such a development can usually be found in any text of advanced calculus.

In order to determine the marginal density function of Y_i for any i one need only apply the procedure suggested in (2.53). The following examples will serve to illustrate the use of (2.70).

Example 2.20

The random variables X_1 and X_2 are identically distributed, each following an exponential distribution with parameter λ. Let $Y_1 = X_1 - X_2$ and $Y_2 = X_1 + X_2$. Find the joint density function of Y_1 and Y_2.

$$f_{X_1, X_2}(x_1, x_2) = \lambda^2 e^{-\lambda(x_1 + x_2)}, \qquad 0 < x_1, x_2 < \infty$$

$$x_1 = \frac{y_2 + y_1}{2}, \qquad x_2 = \frac{y_2 - y_1}{2}$$

$$\frac{\partial \psi_1}{\partial y_1} = \frac{\partial x_1}{\partial y_1} = \frac{1}{2} \qquad \frac{\partial \psi_1}{\partial y_2} = \frac{\partial x_1}{\partial y_2} = \frac{1}{2}$$

$$\frac{\partial \psi_2}{\partial y_1} = \frac{\partial x_2}{\partial y_1} = -\frac{1}{2} \qquad \frac{\partial \psi_2}{\partial y_2} = \frac{\partial x_2}{\partial y_2} = \frac{1}{2}$$

$$J = \begin{vmatrix} \dfrac{1}{2} & \dfrac{1}{2} \\[2mm] -\dfrac{1}{2} & \dfrac{1}{2} \end{vmatrix} = \frac{1}{2}$$

$$|J| = \frac{1}{2}$$

$$g_{Y_1, Y_2}(y_1, y_2) = \frac{\lambda^2}{2} e^{-\lambda y_2}$$

We must now find the limits of Y_1 and Y_2. In developing these limits we must remember that the limits of Y_1 and Y_2 must be such that the limits of X_1 and X_2 are not violated. In this example, Y_1 must be less than Y_2 since, if this were not true, X_2 would be forced to assume negative values. Similarly $Y_2 + Y_1$ must be positive. Therefore $Y_2 \geqslant |Y_1|$. The joint density function of Y_1 and Y_2 is then specified by

$$g_{Y_1, Y_2}(y_1, y_2) = \frac{\lambda^2}{2} e^{-\lambda y_2}, \qquad -y_2 < y_1 < y_2, \quad 0 < y_2 < \infty$$

This result can be checked as follows:

$$\int_{Y_2} \int_{Y_1} g_{Y_1, Y_2}(y_1, y_2)\, dy_1\, dy_2 = \int_0^\infty \int_{-y_2}^{y_2} \frac{\lambda^2}{2} e^{-\lambda y_2}\, dy_1\, dy_2$$

$$= \int_0^\infty \lambda^2 y_2\, e^{-\lambda y_2}\, dy_2$$

$$= 1$$

Example 2.21

X_1 and X_2 are random variables with joint density function
$$f_{X_1, X_2}(x_1, x_2) = 1/(x_1{}^2 x_2{}^2), \quad 1 < x_1, x_2 < \infty$$
Let $Y_1 = X_1 X_2$ and $Y_2 = X_1/X_2$. Find the joint density function of Y_1 and Y_2.

$$y_1 = x_1 x_2 \qquad y_2 = x_1/x_2$$

$$x_1 = \sqrt{y_1 y_2} \qquad x_2 = \sqrt{y_1/y_2}$$

$$J = \begin{vmatrix} \dfrac{1}{2}\sqrt{\dfrac{y_2}{y_1}} & \dfrac{1}{2}\sqrt{\dfrac{y_1}{y_2}} \\[3mm] \dfrac{1}{2}\sqrt{\dfrac{1}{y_1 y_2}} & -\dfrac{1}{2}\sqrt{\dfrac{y_1}{y_2{}^3}} \end{vmatrix} = -\frac{1}{4}\frac{1}{y_2} - \frac{1}{4}\frac{1}{y_2}$$

$$|J| = \frac{1}{2y_2}$$

$$g_{Y_1, Y_2}(y_1, y_2) = \frac{1}{2y_2\, y_1{}^2}$$

Obviously Y_2 cannot assume negative values since this would imply $g_{Y_1 Y_2}(y_1, y_2)$ could be negative. Since X_1 must be greater than unity, Y_2 may not be less than $1/Y_1$. Similarly, since X_2 must be greater than unity, Y_2 cannot exceed Y_1. However, Y_1 can assume any value between 1 and ∞. Therefore

$$g_{Y_1, Y_2}(y_1, y_2) = \frac{1}{2y_2\, y_1{}^2}, \qquad \frac{1}{y_1} < y_2 < y_1, \quad 1 < y_1 < \infty$$

Example 2.22

Let X be a standard normal random variable ($m = 0$, $\sigma^2 = 1$), and let Y be a chi-square random variable with r degrees of freedom. Define T as

$$T = \frac{X}{\sqrt{Y/r}}$$

Derive the distribution of T, assuming X and Y are independent random variables.

$$f_X(x) = \frac{1}{\sqrt{2\pi}} e^{-x^2/2}, \qquad -\infty < x < \infty$$

$$f_Y(y) = \frac{1}{2^{r/2}\Gamma(r/2)} y^{(r/2)-1} e^{-y/2}, \qquad 0 < y < \infty$$

Since X and Y are independently distributed,

$$f_{X,Y}(x, y) = \frac{y^{(r/2)-1}}{\sqrt{2\pi}\, 2^{r/2}\Gamma(r/2)} e^{-(x^2+y)/2}, \qquad -\infty < x < \infty, \;\; 0 < y < \infty$$

Let

$$t = \frac{x}{\sqrt{y/r}}$$

$$v = y$$

Therefore

$$x = \sqrt{\frac{v}{r}}\, t$$

$$y = v$$

$$J = \begin{vmatrix} \dfrac{t}{2\sqrt{vr}} & \sqrt{\dfrac{v}{r}} \\ 1 & 0 \end{vmatrix} = -\sqrt{\dfrac{v}{r}}$$

$$|J| = \sqrt{\frac{v}{r}}$$

$$g_{T,V}(t, v) = \frac{\sqrt{v}}{\sqrt{2\pi r}\, 2^{(r/2)}\Gamma(r/2)} v^{(r/2)-1} e^{-[(v/r)t^2+v]/2}$$

Since Y must assume positive values, V must assume positive values; and since X can take on any real values, $-\infty < t < \infty$

$$g_{T,V}(t, v)$$

$$= \frac{1}{\sqrt{2\pi r}\, 2^{(r/2)}\Gamma(r/2)} v^{(r-1)/2} e^{-(v/2)[(t^2/r)+1]}, \quad 0 < v < \infty, \;\; -\infty < t < \infty$$

$$g_T(t) = \int_0^\infty g_{T,V}(t, v) \, dv$$

$$= \frac{1}{\sqrt{2\pi r} \, 2^{(r/2)}\Gamma(r/2)} \int_0^\infty v^{(r-1)/2} e^{-(v/2)[(t^2/r)+1]} \, dv$$

$$= \frac{\Gamma(r+1)/2}{\sqrt{\pi r} \, \Gamma(r/2)} \frac{1}{[(t^2/r)+1]^{(r+1)/2}}, \qquad -\infty < t < \infty \quad (2.71)$$

Example 2.23

X and Y are independent chi-square random variables with a and b degrees of freedom, respectvely. Let $F = (X/a)/(Y/b)$. Derive the density function of F.

$$f_{X,Y}(x, y) = \frac{x^{(a/2)-1} y^{(b/2)-1}}{2^{a/2}\Gamma(a/2) 2^{b/2}\Gamma(b/2)} e^{-(x+y)/2}, \qquad 0 < x, y < \infty$$

$$f = \frac{x/a}{y/b}$$

$$v = y$$

$$x = \frac{avf}{b}$$

$$y = v$$

$$J = \begin{vmatrix} \dfrac{av}{b} & \dfrac{af}{b} \\ 0 & 1 \end{vmatrix} = \frac{a}{b} v$$

$$g_{F,V}(f, v) = \frac{\dfrac{a}{b} v \left(\dfrac{a}{b} fv\right)^{(a/2)-1} v^{(b/2)-1}}{2^{a/2}\Gamma(a/2) 2^{b/2}\Gamma(b/2)} e^{-(v/2)[(a/b)f+1]}, \qquad 0 < f, v < \infty$$

$$g_F(f) = \int_0^\infty g_{F,V}(f, v) \, dv$$

$$= \frac{(a/b)^{a/2} f^{(a/2)-1}}{2^{(a+b)/2}\Gamma(a/2)\Gamma(b/2)} \frac{\Gamma\left(\dfrac{a+b}{2}\right)}{\left[\dfrac{(a/b)f+1}{2}\right]^{(a+b)/2}}$$

$$= \frac{\Gamma\left(\dfrac{a+b}{2}\right)}{\Gamma\left(\dfrac{a}{2}\right)\Gamma\left(\dfrac{b}{2}\right)} \frac{\left(\dfrac{a}{b}\right)^{a/2} f^{(a/2)-1}}{[(a/b)f+1]^{(a+b)/2}}, \qquad 0 < f < \infty \quad (2.72)$$

Example 2.24

Let X_i be the time between $(i-1)$st and ith arrivals at a parking lot with density function given by

$$f_{X_i}(x_i) = \lambda e^{-\lambda x_i}, \qquad 0 < x_i < \infty, \quad i = 1, 2, \ldots$$

Find the distribution of time to the fourth arrival if all arrivals are assumed independent.

If Y_4 is the time until the fourth arrival, $Y_4 = X_1 + X_2 + X_3 + X_4$. Since all the X_i are assumed to be independent random variables,

$$f_{X_1, X_2, X_3, X_4}(x_1, x_2, x_3, x_4) = \lambda^4 e^{-\lambda(x_1 + x_2 + x_3 + x_4)}, \quad \begin{array}{l} 0 < x_i < \infty \\ i = 1, 2, 3, 4 \end{array}$$

Define Y_1, Y_2, Y_3 as follows:

$$Y_1 = X_1$$
$$Y_2 = X_1 + X_2$$
$$Y_3 = X_1 + X_2 + X_3$$

and

$$Y_4 = X_1 + X_2 + X_3 + X_4 \qquad \text{(from above)}$$

Therefore

$$X_1 = Y_1$$
$$X_2 = Y_2 - Y_1$$
$$X_3 = Y_3 - Y_2$$
$$X_4 = Y_4 - Y_3$$

The Jacobian of this transformation is

$$J = \begin{vmatrix} 1 & 0 & 0 & 0 \\ -1 & 1 & 0 & 0 \\ 0 & -1 & 1 & 0 \\ 0 & 0 & -1 & 1 \end{vmatrix} = 1$$

Therefore the joint density function of Y_1, Y_2, Y_3, Y_4 is given by

$$g_{Y_1, Y_2, Y_3, Y_4}(y_1, y_2, y_3, y_4) = \lambda^4 e^{-\lambda y_4}$$

The limits for the Y_i are readily derived if we remember that X_i

must be nonnegative for all i.

$$g_{Y_1, Y_2, Y_3, Y_4}(y_1, y_2, y_3, y_4) = \lambda^4 e^{-\lambda y_4}, \qquad 0 < y_1 < y_2 < y_3 < y_4 < \infty$$

The marginal density function of Y_4 is given by

$$g_{Y_4}(y_4) = \int_0^{y_4} \int_0^{y_3} \int_0^{y_2} \lambda^4 e^{-\lambda y_4} \, dy_1 \, dy_2 \, dy_3$$

$$g_{y_4}(y_4) = \frac{\lambda^4 y_4^3}{3!} e^{-\lambda y_4}, \qquad 0 < y_4 < \infty$$

Example 2.25

Find the distribution of the sum of two independent, identically distributed, Poisson random variables, X_1 and X_2.

$$p_{X_1, X_2}(x_1, x_2) = \frac{\lambda^{(x_1 + x_2)}}{x_1! \, x_2!} e^{-2\lambda}, \qquad \begin{matrix} x_i = 0, 1, 2, \ldots \\ i = 1, 2 \end{matrix}$$

Let

$$Y_1 = X_1 \qquad\qquad X_1 = Y_1$$

$$Y_2 = X_1 + X_2 \qquad X_2 = Y_2 - Y_1$$

$$p_{Y_1, Y_2}(y_1, y_2) = \frac{\lambda^{y_2}}{y_1! \, (y_2 - y_1)!} e^{-2\lambda}, \qquad \begin{matrix} y_1 = 0, 1, \ldots, y_2 \\ y_2 = 0, 1, \ldots \end{matrix}$$

$$p_{Y_2}(y_2) = \sum_{y_1 = 0}^{y_2} \frac{\lambda^{y_2}}{y_1! \, (y_2 - y_1)!} e^{-2\lambda}$$

Multiplying and dividing by $y_2!$, we get

$$p_{Y_2}(y_2) = \frac{\lambda^{y_2}}{y_2!} e^{-2\lambda} \sum_{y_1 = 0}^{y_2} \frac{y_2!}{y_1! \, (y_2 - y_1)!}$$

From the well-known binomial expansion,

$$(a + b)^n = \sum_{k=0}^{n} \frac{n!}{k! \, (n - k)!} a^k b^{n-k} \tag{2.73}$$

The summation in $p_{Y_2}(y_2)$ can be resolved by recognizing its equivalence to (2.73) when a and b are unity:

$$p_{Y_2}(y_2) = \frac{\lambda^{y_2} 2^{y_2}}{y_2!} e^{-2\lambda}$$

or

$$p_{Y_2}(y_2) = \frac{(2\lambda)^{y_2}}{y_2!} e^{-2\lambda}, \qquad y_2 = 0, 1, 2, \ldots$$

Thus the sum of two independent Poisson random variables is another Poisson random variable with parameter equal to the sum of the parameters of the individual Poisson random variables X_1 and X_2.

Expectation

Let $h_X(x)$ be a function of the random variable X. The expected value of $h_X(x)$, denoted $E[h_X(x)]$, is defined as

$$E[h_X(x)] = \begin{cases} \sum_X h_X(x)p_X(x), & X \text{ discrete} \\ \int_X h_X(x)f_X(x)\,dx, & X \text{ continuous} \end{cases} \qquad (2.74)$$

Of paramount importance in probability theory and statistics are the mean, $E(x)$, and the variance, $E[x - E(x)]^2$ because they are the most commonly used measures of central tendency and variability of a random variable. The mean and variance will be denoted henceforth by m and σ^2.

$$m = \begin{cases} \sum_X xp_X(x) & \text{discrete case} \\ \int_X xf_X(x)\,dx & \text{continuous case} \end{cases} \qquad (2.75)$$

The variance, σ^2, can be determined by replacing $h_X(x)$ in (2.74) by $(x - m)^2$. A more convenient form can be developed as follows: If X is a continuous random variable,

$$\sigma^2 = \int_X (x - m)^2 f_X(x)\,dx$$

$$= \int_X (x^2 - 2mx + m^2)f_X(x)\,dx$$

$$= \int_X x^2 f_X(x)\,dx - 2m \int_X xf_X(x)\,dx + m^2 \int_X f_X(x)\,dx$$

$$= E(x^2) - 2mE(x) + m^2$$

$$= E(x^2) - m^2 \qquad (2.76)$$

Equation (2.76) applies equally well for discrete random variables, as can be shown by replacing $f_X(x)$ by $p_X(x)$ and the integrals by summations in the development of (2.76).

To illustrate the use of equations (2.75) and (2.76) let us derive the mean and variance of the gamma and Poisson random variables.

With the gamma random variable

$$
m = \int_0^\infty x \frac{\lambda^k x^{k-1}}{\Gamma(k)} e^{-\lambda x} \, dx
$$

$$
= \frac{\lambda^k}{\Gamma(k)} \int_0^\infty x^k e^{-\lambda x} \, dx
$$

$$
= \frac{k}{\lambda}
$$

Note that $\Gamma(k+1) = k\Gamma(k)$.

$$
\sigma^2 = \int_0^\infty x^2 \frac{\lambda^k x^{k-1}}{\Gamma(k)} e^{-\lambda x} \, dx - \frac{k^2}{\lambda^2}
$$

$$
= \frac{\lambda^k}{\Gamma(k)} \frac{\Gamma(k+2)}{\lambda^{k+2}} - \frac{k^2}{\lambda^2}
$$

$$
= \frac{k}{\lambda^2}
$$

For the Poisson random variable

$$
m = \sum_{x=0}^\infty x \frac{\lambda^x}{x!} e^{-\lambda}
$$

$$
= 0 + \sum_{x=1}^\infty \frac{\lambda^x}{(x-1)!} e^{-\lambda}
$$

Let $n = x - 1$.

$$
m = \lambda e^{-\lambda} \sum_{n=0}^\infty \frac{\lambda^n}{n!}
$$

$$
= \lambda
$$

since

$$
\sum_{k=0}^\infty \frac{a^k}{k!} = e^a
$$

$$
\sigma^2 = \sum_{x=0}^\infty x^2 \frac{\lambda^x}{x!} e^{-\lambda} - \lambda^2
$$

In this development it is helpful to replace x^2 by $x(x-1) + x$.

$$
\sigma^2 = \sum_{x=0}^\infty x(x-1) \frac{\lambda^x}{x!} e^{-\lambda} + \sum_{x=0}^\infty x \frac{\lambda^x}{x!} e^{-\lambda} - \lambda^2
$$

$$\sigma^2 = \sum_{x=0}^{\infty} x(x-1)\frac{\lambda^x}{x!}e^{-\lambda} + \lambda - \lambda^2$$

$$= \sum_{x=2}^{\infty} \frac{\lambda^x}{(x-2)!}e^{-\lambda} + \lambda - \lambda^2$$

since the first two terms of the previous summation are zero. Letting $n = x - 2$, we have

$$\sigma^2 = \sum_{n=0}^{\infty} \frac{\lambda^{n+2}}{n!}e^{-\lambda} + \lambda - \lambda^2$$

$$= \lambda^2 \sum_{n=0}^{\infty} \frac{\lambda^n}{n!}e^{-\lambda} + \lambda - \lambda^2$$

$$= \lambda$$

We have demonstrated a unique property of the Poisson random variable. That is, the mean and variance of the Poisson random variable are equal.

The expected value of a function of several random variables, $h_{X_1, X_2, \ldots, X_n}(x_1, x_2, \ldots, x_n)$, is given by (2.77).

$$E[h_{X_1, X_2, \ldots, X_n}(x_1, x_2, \ldots, x_n)]$$

$$= \begin{cases} \sum_{X_n} \cdots \sum_{X_1} h_{X_1, \ldots, X_n}(x_1, \ldots, x_n) p_{X_1, \ldots, X_n}(x_1, \ldots, x_n) \\ \qquad\qquad\qquad\qquad\qquad\qquad \text{discrete case} \qquad (2.77) \\ \int_{X_n} \cdots \int_{X_1} h_{X_1, \ldots, X_n}(x_1, \ldots, x_n) f_{X_1, \ldots, X_n}(x_1, \ldots, x_n)\, dx_1 \ldots dx_n \\ \qquad\qquad\qquad\qquad\qquad\qquad \text{continuous case} \end{cases}$$

We will illustrate the use of (2.77) for discrete random variables by finding the mean of the sum of n independently and identically distributed Poisson random variables.

$$p_{X_1, \ldots, X_n}(x_1, \ldots, x_n) = \frac{\lambda^{x_1 + x_2 + \cdots + x_n}}{x_1! x_2! \cdots x_n!}e^{-n\lambda}, \qquad x_i = 0, 1, \ldots, \text{for all } i$$

$$E(x_1 + x_2 + \cdots + x_n) = \sum_{x_n=0}^{\infty} \cdots \sum_{x_2=0}^{\infty} \sum_{x_1=0}^{\infty} (x_1 + \cdots + x_n)\frac{\lambda^{x_1 + x_2 + \cdots + x_n}}{x_1! x_2! \cdots x_n!}e^{-n\lambda}$$

$$= \sum_{i=1}^{n} \sum_{x_i=0}^{\infty} (x_1 + x_2 + \cdots + x_n)\frac{\lambda^{x_1 + x_2 + \cdots + x_n}}{x_1! x_2! \cdots x_n!}e^{-n\lambda}$$

$$= \sum_{j=1}^{n} \sum_{i=1}^{n} \sum_{x_i=0}^{\infty} x_j \frac{\lambda^{x_1 + x_2 + \cdots + x_n}}{x_1! x_2! \cdots x_n!}e^{-n\lambda}$$

Therefore

$$E(x_1 + x_2 + \cdots + x_n) = \sum_{j=1}^{n} E(x_j)$$

$$= n\lambda$$

We will demonstate the use of (2.77) for continuous random variables by showing that the variance of the sum of n independent random variables is the sum of the variances of the n random variables. This is also true of discrete random variables but will be proven for continuous random variables only.

$$E[(x_1 - m_1)^2 + (x_2 - m_2)^2 + \cdots + (x_n - m_n)^2]$$

$$= \int_{X_n} \cdots \int_{X_1} [(x_1 - m_1)^2 + \cdots + (x_n - m_n)^2] f_{X_1, \ldots, X_n}(x_1, \ldots, x_n) \, dx_1 \ldots dx_n$$

$$E\left[\sum_{i=1}^{n} (x_i - m_i)^2\right]$$

$$= \sum_{i=1}^{n} \int_{X_n} \cdots \int_{X_1} (x_i - m_i)^2 f_{X_1, \ldots, X_n}(x_1, \ldots, x_n) \, dx_1 \ldots dx_n$$

$$= \sum_{i=1}^{n} \int_{X_n} \cdots \int_{X_1} (x_i - m_i)^2 f_{X_1}(x_1) \ldots f_{X_n}(x_n) \, dx_1 \ldots dx_n$$

$$= \sum_{i=1}^{n} \int_{X_n} f_{X_n}(x_n) \, dx_n \cdots \int_{X_i} (x_i - m_i)^2 f_{X_i}(x_i) \, dx_i \cdots \int_{X_1} f_{X_1}(x_1) \, dx_1$$

$$= \sum_{i=1}^{n} E(x_i - m_i)^2$$

$$= \sum_{i=1}^{n} \sigma_i^{2}$$

Characteristic Function

The characteristic function of a random variable, $\phi_X(\mu)$, is defined as

$$\phi_X(\mu) = E(e^{i\mu x}), \qquad i = \sqrt{-1} \tag{2.78}$$

and is defined for any real number μ. The characteristic function is unique for every random variable as is its density function or probability mass function. For certain purposes the characteristic function is more useful. The characteristic function of n jointly distributed random variables is defined in (2.79).

$$\phi_{X_1, \ldots, X_n}(\mu_1, \mu_2, \ldots, \mu_n) = E[e^{i(\mu_1 x_1 + \cdots + \mu_n x_n)}] \tag{2.79}$$

As we progress further in our discussion of simulation we will find that we are often concerned with the distributions of sums of independent random variables. This is one of the most important areas of application of the characteristic function. Let $X_1, \ldots, X_n$ be n independently and identically distributed random variables, each having characteristic function $\phi_X(\mu)$ and density function $f_X(x)$. If Y is the sum of these n random variables, then the characteristic function of Y is given by

$$\phi_Y(\mu) = E[e^{i\mu y}]$$
$$\phi_Y(\mu) = E[e^{i\mu(x_1 + x_2 + \cdots + x_n)}]$$
$$= E[e^{i\mu x_1} e^{i\mu x_2} \cdots e^{i\mu x_n}]$$

Since we are dealing with independent random variables, the expected value of the product of these random variables is the product of the individual expected values.

$$\phi_Y(\mu) = \prod_{j=1}^{n} E[e^{i\mu x_j}]$$

$$= \prod_{j=1}^{n} \phi_{X_j}(\mu)$$

But since these n random variables are identically distributed, $\phi_{X_j}(\mu) = \phi_X(\mu)$ for all j, and

$$\phi_Y(\mu) = [\phi_X(\mu)]^n \qquad (2.80)$$

If the characteristic function $\phi_Y(\mu)$ is recognized, the distribution of Y is specified.

To illustrate we will determine the distribution of the sum of n independent normal random variables, each having parameters m and σ^2. From Table 2.2 the characteristic function of such a normal random variable is given by

$$\phi_X(\mu) = e^{i\mu m - (1/2)\mu^2 \sigma^2}$$

If

$$Y = \sum_{j=1}^{n} X_j$$

then

$$\phi_Y(\mu) = E(e^{i\mu y})$$

$$= \prod_{j=1}^{n} E(e^{i\mu x_j})$$

$$= [\phi_{X_j}(\mu)]^n$$

$$\phi_Y(\mu) = (e^{i\mu m - (1/2)\mu^2\sigma^2})^n$$
$$= e^{i\mu nm - (1/2)\mu^2 n\sigma^2}$$

Thus Y possesses the characteristic function of a normal random variable with parameters nm and $n\sigma^2$.

Example 2.26

Show that the kth moment about zero, $E(X^k)$, of a random variable can be determined by

$$E(X^k) = \frac{1}{i^k} \frac{d^k}{d\mu^k} \phi_X(\mu) \bigg|_{\mu=0} \qquad (2.81)$$

For continuous random variables

$$\phi_X(\mu) = \int_X e^{i\mu x} f_X(x)\, dx$$

$$\frac{d^k}{d\mu^k} \phi_X(\mu) = \int_X (ix)^k e^{i\mu x} f_X(x)\, dx$$

$$\frac{d^k}{d\mu^k} \phi_X(\mu) \bigg|_{\mu=0} = \int_X (ix)^k f_X(x)\, dx$$

$$= i^k E(X^k)$$

Therefore
$$E(X^k) = \frac{1}{i^k} \frac{d^k}{d\mu^k} \phi_X(\mu) \bigg|_{\mu=0}$$

The argument is similar for discrete random variables.

Equation (2.81) allows us to determine the mean and variance of a random variable from its characteristic function as follows:

$$m = \frac{1}{i} \frac{d}{d\mu} \phi_X(\mu) \bigg|_{\mu=0} \qquad (2.82)$$

$$\sigma^2 = -\frac{d^2}{d\mu^2} \phi_X(\mu) \bigg|_{\mu=0} - m^2 \qquad (2.83)$$

Example 2.27

Show that the sum of two independent, identically distributed, binomial random variables is another binomial random variable.

Let X_1 and X_2 be the binomial random variables of interest.

$$p_{X_j}(x_j) = \frac{n!}{x_j!(n-x_j)!} p^{x_j}(1-p)^{n-x_j}, \qquad \begin{array}{l} x_j = 0, 1, 2, \ldots, n \\ j = 1, 2 \end{array}$$

$$\phi_{X_j}(\mu) = (pe^{i\mu} + 1 - p)^n$$

$$Y = X_1 + X_2$$

$$\phi_Y(\mu) = \phi_{X_1}(\mu)\phi_{X_2}(\mu)$$

$$= (pe^{i\mu} + 1 - p)^{2n}$$

Therefore Y is a binomial variable with parameters p and $2n$ and probability mass function, $p_Y(y)$, given by

$$p_Y(y) = \frac{(2n)!}{y!(2n-y)!}\, p^y(1-p)^{2n-y}, \qquad y = 0, 1, \ldots, 2n$$

Example 2.28

Determine the mean and variance of a binomial random variable with parameters p and n.

We will determine the mean and variance in two ways: from the probability mass function and from the characteristic function.

1. From the probability mass function

$$m = \sum_{x=0}^{n} x p_X(x)$$

$$= \sum_{x=0}^{n} x\, \frac{n!}{x!(n-x)!}\, p^x(1-p)^{n-x}$$

$$= \sum_{x=1}^{n} \frac{n!}{(x-1)!(n-x)!}\, p^x(1-p)^{n-x}$$

let $k = x - 1$.

$$m = \sum_{k=0}^{n-1} \frac{n!}{k!(n-k-1)!}\, p^{k+1}(1-p)^{n-k-1}$$

$$= np \sum_{k=0}^{n-1} \frac{(n-1)!}{k!(n-k-1)!}\, p^k(1-p)^{n-k-1}$$

Replacing $(n-1)$ by r, we get

$$m = np \sum_{k=0}^{r} \frac{r!}{k!(r-k)!}\, p^k(1-p)^{n-r}$$

$$= np$$

$$\sigma^2 = E(x^2) - m^2$$

$$= \sum_{x=0}^{n} x^2\, \frac{n!}{x!(n-x)!}\, p^x(1-p)^{n-x} - (np)^2$$

Let $x^2 = x(x - 1) + x$.

$$\sigma^2 = \sum_{x=2}^{n} \frac{n!}{(x-2)!(n-x)!} p^x(1-p)^{n-x} + E(x) - (np)^2$$

since the first two terms of the summation are zero. Let $k = x - 2$.

$$\sigma^2 = \sum_{k=0}^{n-2} \frac{n!}{k!(n-k-2)!} p^{k+2}(1-p)^{n-k-2} + np - (np)^2$$

$$= n(n-1)p^2 \sum_{k=0}^{n-2} \frac{(n-2)!}{k!(n-2-k)!} p^k(1-p)^{n-k-2} + np + (np)^2$$

$$= n(n-1)p^2 + np - (np)^2$$

$$= np(1-p)$$

2. From the characteristic function

$$m = \frac{1}{i}\frac{d}{d\mu} \phi_X(\mu)\Big|_{\mu=0}$$

$$= \frac{1}{i}\frac{d}{d\mu} (pe^{i\mu} + 1 - p)^n\Big|_{\mu=0}$$

$$m = \frac{1}{i} n(ipe^{i\mu})(pe^{i\mu} + 1 - p)^{n-1}\Big|_{\mu=0}$$

$$= np$$

$$\sigma^2 = -\frac{d^2}{d\mu^2} \phi_X(\mu)\Big|_{\mu=0} - m^2$$

$$= -(i)^2 npe^{i\mu}(pe^{i\mu} + 1 - p)^{n-1}\Big|_{\mu=0}$$

$$- n(n-1)(i)^2 p^2 e^{2i\mu}(pe^{i\mu} + 1 - p)^{n-2}\Big|_{\mu=0} - (np)^2$$

$$= np + n(n-1)p^2 - (np)^2$$

$$= np(1-p)$$

Example 2.29

Derive the characteristic function of the chi-square random variable with n degrees of freedom.

If X has a chi-square distribution,

$$f_X(x) = \frac{1}{2^{n/2}\Gamma(n/2)} x^{(n/2)-1} e^{-x/2}, \qquad 0 < x < \infty \tag{2.84}$$

$$\phi_X(\mu) = \int_0^\infty \frac{1}{2^{n/2}\Gamma(n/2)} \, x^{(n/2)-1} e^{-x(1/2-i\mu)} \, dx$$

$$= \frac{1}{2^{n/2}\Gamma(n/2)} \frac{\Gamma(n/2)}{(\frac{1}{2} - i\mu)^{n/2}}$$

$$= (1 - 2i\mu)^{-n/2} \tag{2.85}$$

Example 2.30

If X_j is normally distributed with a mean of zero and a variance of one for $j = 1, 2, \ldots, n$, show that

$$\sum_{j=1}^n X_j^2$$

has a chi-square distribution with n degrees of freedom.

$$f_X(x) = \frac{1}{\sqrt{2\pi}} e^{-(x^2)/2}, \qquad -\infty < x < \infty$$

Let $Y_j = X_j^2$.

$$\phi \, Y_j(\mu) = E(e^{i\mu x_j^2})$$

$$= \int_{-\infty}^\infty \frac{1}{\sqrt{2\pi}} e^{-x^2(1/2-i\mu)} \, dx$$

Setting $z^2 = 2x^2(\frac{1}{2} - i\mu)$ or $z = x(1 - 2i\mu)^{1/2}$, we get

$$\phi \, Y_j(\mu) = \frac{1}{(1 - 2i\mu)^{1/2}} \int_{-\infty}^\infty \frac{1}{\sqrt{2\pi}} e^{-(z^2)/2} \, dz$$

$$= \frac{1}{(1 - 2i\mu)^{1/2}}$$

If

$$V = \sum_{j=1}^n X_j^2,$$

then

$$\phi_V(\mu) = \prod_{j=1}^n \phi_{x_j}(\mu)$$

$$= [\phi_X(\mu)]^n$$

from equation (2.80) and with the assumption that x is normally distributed with a mean of zero and a variance of one. Then

$$\phi_V(\mu) = (1 - 2i\mu)^{-n/2}$$

From equation (2.85)

$$\sum_{j=1}^{n} X_j^2$$

has a chi-square distribution with n degrees of freedom.

PROBLEMS

1. Five cards are drawn from a standard deck. Find the probability that:
a) All five are of the same suit.
b) Two distinct pairs are included in the five.
c) Three of the five are the same.

2. Three dice are thrown. Find the probability that:
a) The same point value appears on each die.
b) The sum of the points showing is 12.
c) The sum of the points showing is between 12 and 17 inclusive.
d) A different point value appears on each die.

3. There are 30 people at a party. What is the probability that at least two were born on the same day of the year?

4. An interceptor carries five air-to-air missiles. Upon contact with an enemy plane it fires one of its missiles. If the missile destroys the enemy plane, the battle terminates. If the missile misses the enemy plane, the interceptor fires a second missile. If the second missile misses the enemy plane, a third is fired and so on, until the interceptor has fired all five missiles. What is the probability that the enemy plane is destroyed if the probability that any single missile destroys the enemy plane is 0.70?

5. A random sample of three items is selected from a production lot of size N. What is the probability that no more than one item is defective
a) if $N = 1,000$ and there are 10 defective items in the lot and the hypergeometric distribution is used to describe the number of defective items in the sample?
b) if $N \to \infty$, $p = 0.01$ and the binomial distribution is used?
c) if $N \to \infty$, $p = 0.01$ and the Poisson distribution is used?

6. Find the constant k such that the following function is a probability density function:

$$f_X(x) = kx^b(1 - x)^a, \qquad 0 < x < 1$$

7. If the probability density function of the random variable X is

$$f_X(x) = \frac{\lambda}{\Gamma(n)}(\lambda x)^{n-1}e^{-\lambda x}, \qquad 0 < x < \infty, \quad \lambda > 0, \quad n > 0$$

show that

$$F_X(x) = 1 - \sum_{k=0}^{n-1}\frac{(\lambda x)^k}{k!}e^{-\lambda x}, \qquad 0 < x < \infty$$

if n is an integer.

8. The distribution function of the Weibull distribution is given by

$$F_X(x) = 1 - e^{-[(x-a)/(b-a)]^n}, \qquad x \geq a, \quad b \geq a, \quad n > 1$$

Find the density function of the random variable X.

9. Given that the following are density functions, find
a) The value of k.
b) The distribution function.

    i) $f_X(x) = \dfrac{k}{\sqrt{x}}, \qquad 0 < x < 1$

    ii) $f_X(x) = kx, \qquad 0 < x < 1$

    iii) $f_X(x) = \dfrac{k}{\sqrt{1-x^2}}, \qquad 0 < x < 1$

10. Given the following density functions, find the distribution functions:

a) $f_X(x) = \begin{cases} \dfrac{1}{2} e^x, & -\infty < x < 0 \\[2mm] \dfrac{1}{2} e^{-x}, & 0 < x < \infty \end{cases}$

b) $f_X(x) = \dfrac{1}{4} x e^{-x/2}, \qquad 0 < x < \infty$

c) $f_X(x) = \dfrac{4!}{2!\,1!} x^2 (1-x), \qquad 0 < x < 1$

11. Given the following distribution functions, find the corresponding density functions:

a) $F_X(x) = \dfrac{1}{125} x^3, \qquad 0 < x < 5$

b) $F_X(x) = \begin{cases} 0, & x < -2 \\[2mm] \dfrac{1}{2} - \dfrac{x^2}{8}, & -2 < x < 0 \\[2mm] \dfrac{1}{2} + \dfrac{x^2}{8}, & 0 < x < 2 \\[2mm] 1, & x > 2 \end{cases}$

c) $F_X(x) = (n+1)(1-x)^{n+2} - (n+2)(1-x)^{n+1}, \qquad \begin{array}{l} 0 < x < 1 \\ n = \text{positive integer} \end{array}$

d) $F_X(x) = \dfrac{1}{\pi} \tan^{-1}(x - 1), -\infty < x < \infty$

12. Given the following distribution functions, find the corresponding probability mass functions:

a) $F_X(x) = \begin{cases} p, & x = 0 \\ 1, & x = 1 \end{cases}$

b) $F_X(x) = \dfrac{x(x + 1)(2x + 1)}{n(n + 1)(2n + 1)}, \qquad x = 1, 2, 3, \ldots, n$

c) $F_X(x) = \dfrac{1 - p^x}{1 - p^n}, \qquad x = 1, 2, 3, \ldots, n$

13. A sample of 10 items is drawn from a lot of 100. There are 15 defective units in the lot. Using the hypergeometric distribution, find:
   a) The probability that the sample contains three defective items.
   b) The probability that the sample contains three or less defective items.
   c) The probability that the sample contains one, two, or three defective items.

14. Solve problem 13 using the binomial distribution where p is the ratio of the number of defective items in the lot to the lot size.

15. Solve problem 14 using the Poisson distribution where λ is the given by np where n is the sample size.

16. The distribution of monthly demand for a given product is geometrically distributed with probability mass function

$$p_X(x) = p(1 - p)^{x - 1}, \qquad x = 1, 2, 3, \ldots$$

If p is 0.10, what is the distribution of demand for a two-month period?

17. If the random variable X is Poisson distributed with parameter λ, find the distribution of Y where:
   a) $Y = X - 1$
   b) $Y = X + 1$

18. X is a random variable which is exponentially distributed with parameter λ. Find the probability density function of $1/X$.

19. The random variable X has the density function given by $f_X(x) = 1/5$, $0 < x < 5$. Find the density function of X^2.

20. If X has a chi-square distribution, find the distribution of $\sqrt{X}$.

21. A bottling company has several capping machines which fail occasionally. When one of these machines fails it must be repaired and tested after repairs are completed. The time to repair each machine, in hours, is exponentially distributed with parameter 3. The time to test the machine is also exponentially distributed, but with parameter 10. Find the distribution of the total time the

machine is down when it fails. What is the probability that a machine will be down for more than an hour when it fails?

22. The distribution of repair time, in hours, for a particular piece of machinery is exponential with parameter $0.5n$ where n is the number of men in the repair crew. How many men would be required if the probability that the repair takes more than an hour is not to exceed 0.10?

23. Show that the distribution of the sum of two gamma random variables is also gamma.

24. Derive the distribution of XY where X and Y are identically and independently distributed exponential random variables, each with parameter λ.

25. Derive the distribution of $X + Y$ where X and Y are identically and independently distributed geometric random variables, each with parameter p.

26. Derive the distribution $X_1{}^2 + X_2{}^2$ where X_1 and X_2 are normally and independently distributed, each with a mean of zero and a variance of one.

27. If X is an exponential random variable with parameter λ, find the distribution of Y where

$$Y = 1 - e^{-\lambda x}$$

28. Let X be the number of defective units found in a sample of size n. The sample was drawn from a lot which is $100\,p$ percent defective. The joint distribution of X and P is given by

$$f_{X,P}(x, p) = (a + b + 1)\binom{n}{x}\binom{a + b}{a} p^{a+x}(1 - p)^{n+b-x},$$

$$0 < p < 1, \quad x = 0, 1, 2, \ldots, n$$

The constants a and b are both nonnegative. Find

a) The marginal density function of P.

b) The marginal probability mass function of X.

Are X and P independent random variables?

29. Derive the mean and variance of the gamma random variable with parameter λ and n.

30. Show that the mean of the Cauchy random variable does not exist.

31. If the characteristic function of the Poisson random variable is as given in Table 2.1, find the mean of this random variable from the characteristic function.

32. The random variables X_1 and X_2 are identically and independently distributed according to a Cauchy distribution with parameter λ. That is,

$$f_{X_i}(x_i) = \frac{1}{\pi[1 + (x - \lambda)^2]}, \quad -\infty < x_i < \infty, \quad i = 1, 2$$

Find the density function of $\overline{X} = (X_1 + X_2)/2$.

33. Find the mean and variance of the random variable, X, given in problem 32.

34. If X is beta distributed with density function

$$f_X(x) = \frac{(a + b + 1)!}{a!\,b!}\, x^a(1 - x)^b, \qquad 0 < x < 1$$

where a and b are positive integers, find (a) $E(x)$ and (b) $E(x^2)$.

35. The ABC company produces an item which may contain either or both of two defects. The item in question is manufactured in large lots each day, and each unit in the lot is automatically inspected at the end of the day. Each unit which contains one of the defects is rejected at a cost of $0.01 per rejection. The density function of the proportion defective in the day's production for both defects are given by

$$f_{P_1}(p_1) = 24(1 - p_1)^{23}, \qquad 0 < p_1 < 1 \qquad \text{(first defect)}$$

$$f_{P_2}(p_2) = 99(1 - p_2)^{98}, \qquad 0 < p_2 < 1 \qquad \text{(second defect)}$$

Each day's production consists of 100,000 units. Find the expected cost of daily rejection.

36. X and Y are jointly distributed with density function given by

$$f_{X,Y}(x, y) = \frac{1}{2\pi\sqrt{1 - p^2}}\, e^{-\left[\frac{(x^2 - 2pxy + y^2)}{2(1 - p)^2}\right]}, \qquad -\infty < x, y < \infty$$

For what values of p are X and Y independent?

37. The joint density function of the random variables X and Y is given by

$$f_{X,Y}(x, y) = \frac{1}{10}, \qquad 1 \le x \le 6, \quad 1 \le y \le 3$$

Find the density function of Z, where (a) $Z = X/Y$, (b) $Z = XY$, and (c) $Z = (XY)^2$.

38. For each of the following random variables, derive the characteristic function and from the characteristic function of each find the mean: (a) gamma, (b) normal, (c) Laplace, (d) binomial, (e) geometric, and (f) rectangular.

39. A store purchases 1,000 Christmas cards at a cost of $0.10 each. All cards sold before Christmas are sold for $0.15 each. Any cards left after Christmas are sold for $0.05 each. The distribution of demand for Christmas cards is geometric with $p = 0.001$. What profit can the store expect from the sale of these cards?

40. X_1 and X_2 are identically and independently distributed Poisson random variables. Find the distribution of $\overline{X} = (X_1 + X_2)/2$.

41. The probability of finding x defective units in a sample of size n is given by

$$p_X(x \mid p) = \frac{n!}{x!(n-x)!} \, p^x (1-p)^{n-x}, \qquad x = 0, 1, \ldots, n$$

where p is the actual proportion defective in the population from which the sample was selected. The density function of the proportion defective is given by

$$f_P(p) = (b+1)(1-p)^b, \qquad 0 < p < 1$$

where b is a positive integer.

a) Find the joint distribution of X and P.

b) Find the marginal distribution of X.

42. In problem 41, if $n = 10$ and $b = 8$,

a) What is the marginal probability of finding two or less defectives?

b) If the marginal probability of finding two or less defectives is to be 0.10 or less, what is the smallest value that b can assume?

43. A gambler decides to play roulette in the following manner: At each turn of the wheel he will play $1 on black. If a black number wins, the house pays him $1. If a red or green number wins, he loses $1. There are 38 numbers on the wheel. Zero and double zero are green. Eighteen of the remaining 36 numbers are red and 18 are black. The probability that any specified number wins is 1/38.

a) What is the probability that the gambler wins at any turn of the wheel?

b) If the gambler has $100, how many bets would you expect him to make before he goes broke?

44. The density function of the time until failure, T in years, for a particular make of television is given by

$$f_T(t) = 0.25xe^{-0.5x}, \qquad 0 < x < \infty$$

The manufacturer guarantees these television sets for z years. If a television set fails within z years it is repaired free of charge. What should the guaranteed life, z, of the television be if the manufacturer is to expect that only 5 per cent of its sales will require service under the guarantee?

45. X has a normal distribution with mean m and variance σ^2. Find the distribution of $Z = (X - m)/\sigma$.

46. X_1 X_2, and X_3 are uniformly and independently distributed on the interval (0,1). Find the distribution of $X = (X_1 + X_2 + X_3)/3$.

REFERENCES

Feller, W.   *An Introduction to Probability Theory and Its Applications.* Vol. I. New York: John Wiley & Sons, Inc., 1950.

Freeman, H.   *Introduction to Statistical Inference.* Reading, Mass.: Addison-Wesley Publishing Co., Inc., 1963.

Hadley, G.   *Introduction to Probability and Statistical Decision Theory.* San Francisco: Holden-Day, Inc., 1967.

Hogg, R. V. and Craig, A. T.   *Introduction to Mathematical Statistics*. New York: The MacMillan Co., 1959.

Parzen, E.   *Stochastic Processes*. San Francisco: Holden-Day, Inc., 1962.

———.   *Modern Probability Theory and Its Applications*. New York: John Wiley & Sons, Inc., 1960.

Wadsworth, G. P. and Bryan, J. G.   *Introduction to Probability and Random Variables*. New York: McGraw-Hill Book Co., Inc., 1960.

Weiss, L.   *Statistical Decision Theory*. New York: McGraw-Hill Book Co., Inc., 1961.

Wilks, S. S.   *Mathematical Statistics*. New York: John Wiley & Sons, Inc., 1962

CHAPTER
3

QUEUEING THEORY

Delays in the execution of business activity are common, irritating, and at times costly. Whenever possible, such delays should be elimimated or, better still, prevented from occurring in the first place. Where delays cannot be prevented entirely they should be minimized in number and duration as far as is economically possible.

To illustrate the class of problems we will be treating in this chapter, consider the problem of determining the number of check-out counters to be installed in a supermarket. If the number of counters is insufficient to handle the volume of customers attempting to check out at any one time, long waiting lines will form—encouraging the customers to shop elsewhere in the future. On the other hand, installing enough check-out counters to reduce the waiting time in the line to zero would be difficult to justify—considering the number of customers served daily by the average supermarket. We are therefore faced with the problem of finding a balance between too many and too few check-out counters.

In any problem such as this the optimum solution could be found by manipulating the physical system itself—seeking the best solution by trial and error. However, such a method of solution could be extremely expensive and time-consuming. A better approach would be to develop a symbolic model of the system and through appropriate manipulation of this model determine the optimal solution to the problem posed by the modeled system. The models discussed in the remainder of this chapter consist of one or more mathematical relationships which describe the essential characteristics of the modeled system.

SINGLE CHANNEL POISSON QUEUES

Let us consider the simple system described in Figure 3.1. Units arrive at a service facility demanding service. If the service facility or channel is empty, the unit enters the facility and is served. If a unit is already in the service channel, the arriving unit must take its place in the waiting line and wait its turn for service. Service takes place on a first-come first-serve basis.

FIGURE 3.1

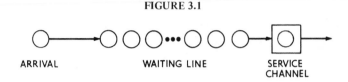

ARRIVAL   WAITING LINE   SERVICE
                                                    CHANNEL

The distribution of time between successive arrivals to the system, T, will be assumed to be exponential with parameter λ. The distribution of time to serve a unit, S, will also be assumed to be exponential with parameter μ.

$$f_T(t) = \lambda e^{-\lambda t}, \qquad 0 < t < \infty \tag{3.1}$$

$$g_S(s) = \mu e^{-\mu s}, \qquad 0 < s < \infty \tag{3.2}$$

In order to develop the required model for the system considered here we will need the probability mass functions of the number of arrivals in time interval of length T and the numbers of services in an interval of length S. The probability of zero arrivals in T, where T is measured from the last arrival, $p_0(T)$, is given by

$$p_0(T) = P(\text{time since last arrival} > T) \tag{3.3}$$

$$= \int_T^\infty \lambda e^{-\lambda t} \, dt \tag{3.4}$$

$$= e^{-\lambda T} \tag{3.5}$$

We calculate the probability of exactly one arrival in T as follows. In order that one and only one arrival occur in T we must have one arrival by some time v between 0 and T, and zero arrivals in the remaining time $T - v$. From (3.5)

$$p_0(T - v) = e^{-\lambda(T - v)} \tag{3.6}$$

The probability that the first arrival occurred between v and $v + dv$

can be expressed as $\lambda e^{-\lambda v}\, dv$. Therefore the combined probability that the first arrival occurred between v and $v + dv$, and no arrivals occurred during the remaining time interval $T - v$, is given by

$$P(\text{One arrival between } v \text{ and } v + dv \text{ and no arrivals in } T - v)$$
$$= \lambda e^{-\lambda v} e^{-\lambda(T-v)}\, dv \tag{3.7}$$

However, to obtain the probability of exactly one arrival in T we must consider all possible points, v, at which the arrival could take place. That is,

$$p_1(T) = \int_0^T \lambda e^{-\lambda v} e^{-\lambda(T-v)}\, dv \tag{3.8}$$

$$= \lambda T e^{-\lambda T} \tag{3.9}$$

We calculate the probability of exactly two arrivals in T in a similar manner. In this case we must have one arrival in v and one arrival in $T - v$ taken over all v, or

$$p_2(T) = \int_0^T \lambda e^{-\lambda v} \lambda (T - v) e^{-\lambda(T-v)}\, dv \tag{3.10}$$

$$= \frac{(\lambda T)^2}{2} e^{-\lambda T} \tag{3.11}$$

Equations (3.5), (3.9), and (3.11) indicate that the probability of n arrivals in T would be given by

$$p_n(T) = \frac{(\lambda T)^n}{n!} e^{-\lambda T}, \qquad n = 0, 1, 2, \ldots \tag{3.12}$$

The validity of (3.12) can be verified by using it to generate the probability of $n + 1$ arrivals in T. To obtain $n + 1$ arrivals in T we must have one arrival in v and n in $T - v$ taken over all v, or

$$p_{n+1}(T) = \int_0^T \lambda e^{-\lambda v} \frac{[\lambda(T - v)]^n}{n!} e^{-\lambda(T-v)}\, dv \tag{3.13}$$

$$= \frac{(\lambda T)^{n+1}}{(n + 1)!} e^{-\lambda T} \tag{3.14}$$

Therefore (3.12) holds for all values of n.

We have established the well-known and useful relationship between the exponential and Poisson distributions. That is, if the time between successive events is exponentially distributed, then the distribution of the number of events occurring in any time interval follows a Poisson distribution.

Since service time is also exponentially distributed, it follows that the distribution of the number of units serviced in a time interval of length s, $q_n(s)$, is Poisson distributed (we assume that there are units available to be serviced).

$$q_n(s) = \frac{(\mu s)^n}{n!} e^{-\mu s}, \qquad n = 0, 1, 2, \ldots \qquad (3.15)$$

We shall now develop several important characteristics of the system previously described for two examples: (1) where the maximum number of units in the system is N, and (2) where there is no limit to the number of units in the system.

Let us first consider the distribution of the number of units in the system (number in the waiting line plus the number in the service channel). Let $P_n(t)$ be the probability that there are n units in the system at an arbitrary point in time, t. We will calculate $P_n(t)$ based on the possible states of the system at time $t - \Delta t$ and the events occurring in the arbitrarily small interval of time Δt. For example, if the system contained five units at $t - \Delta t$ and one service and no arrivals occurred in Δt, the system would contain four units at t. If we choose Δt small enough, we can eliminate the possibility of more than one arrival or more than one service in Δt. We have from (3.12)

$$p_n(\Delta t) = \frac{(\lambda \Delta t)^n}{n!} e^{-\lambda \Delta t} \qquad (3.16)$$

We will choose Δt small enough that $p_n(\Delta t) \to 0$ for $n > 1$. That is, there exists T such that for $\Delta t < T$, $(\lambda \Delta t)^n \to 0$ for $n > 1$. Of course, a similar statement can be made concerning $q_n(\Delta t)$. For $P_n(t)$ we have

$$
\begin{aligned}
P_n(t) = \ & P_{n-1}(t - \Delta t)P(\text{One arrival and no service in } \Delta t) \\
& + P_n(t - \Delta t)[P(\text{No arrivals and no services in } \Delta t) \\
& + P(\text{One arrival and one service in } \Delta t)] \\
& + P_{n+1}(t - \Delta t)P(\text{No arrivals and one service in } \Delta t)
\end{aligned}
\qquad (3.17)
$$

Note that if we considered $n - 2$ or $n + 2$ units in the system at $t - \Delta t$ we would need two arrivals and two services, respectively, to have n units in the system at t. But we have taken Δt small enough to eliminate the possibility of more than one service or arrival in Δt. Therefore, if the system contains less than $n - 1$ units or more than $n + 1$ units at $t - \Delta t$, it cannot contain n units at t.

$$P(\text{One arrival and no service in } \Delta t) = \lambda \, \Delta t e^{-(\lambda + \mu)\,\Delta t} \qquad (3.18)$$

$$P(\text{No arrivals and no services in } \Delta t) = e^{-(\lambda + \mu)\,\Delta t} \qquad (3.19)$$

$$P(\text{One arrival and one service in } \Delta t) = \lambda \mu (\Delta t)^2 e^{-(\lambda + \mu)\,\Delta t} \qquad (3.20)$$

$$P(\text{No arrivals and one service in } \Delta t) = \mu \, \Delta t e^{-(\lambda + \mu)\,\Delta t} \qquad (3.21)$$

Under the conditions specified regarding the magnitude of Δt, (3.20) is zero. Therefore

$$\begin{aligned}
P_n(t) = P_{n-1}(t - \Delta t)\lambda \, \Delta t e^{-(\lambda + \mu)\,\Delta t} &+ P_n(t - \Delta t)e^{-(\lambda + \mu)\,\Delta t} \\
&+ P_{n+1}(t - \Delta t)\mu \, \Delta t e^{-(\lambda + \mu)\,\Delta t}, \qquad n = 1, 2, \ldots, N - 1
\end{aligned} \qquad (3.22)$$

Noting that

$$\begin{aligned}
P(\text{No arrivals and no services in } \Delta t) = 1 &- P(\text{One arrival and} \\
\text{no services in } \Delta t) &- P(\text{No arrivals and one service in } \Delta t)
\end{aligned}$$

We see that (3.22) becomes

$$\begin{aligned}
P_n(t) = P_{n-1}(t - \Delta t)\lambda \, \Delta t e^{-(\lambda + \mu)\,\Delta t} &+ P_n(t - \Delta t) \\
&- P_n(t - \Delta t)\lambda \, \Delta t e^{-(\lambda + \mu)\,\Delta t} - P_n(t - \Delta t)\mu \, \Delta t e^{-(\lambda + \mu)\,\Delta t} \\
&+ P_{n+1}(t - \Delta t)\mu \, \Delta t e^{-(\lambda + \mu)\,\Delta t}, \qquad n = 1, 2, \ldots, N - 1
\end{aligned} \qquad (3.23)$$

Rearranging the terms in (3.23) and dividing by Δt, we get

$$\begin{aligned}
\frac{P_n(t) - P_n(t - \Delta t)}{\Delta t} = P_{n-1}(t - \Delta t)\lambda e^{-(\lambda + \mu)\,\Delta t} &- (\lambda + \mu)P_n(t - \Delta t)e^{-(\lambda + \mu)\,\Delta t} \\
&+ P_{n+1}(t - \Delta t)\mu e^{-(\lambda + \mu)\,\Delta t}
\end{aligned} \qquad (3.24)$$

Taking the limit of both sides of (3.24) as $\Delta t \to 0$, assuming the limit exists, we have

$$\frac{dP_n(t)}{dt} = \lambda P_{n-1}(t) - (\lambda + \mu)P_n(t) + \mu P_{n+1}(t), \qquad n = 1, 2, \ldots, N - 1 \qquad (3.25)$$

For $n = 0$ we have

$$\begin{aligned}
P_0(t) = P_0(t - \Delta t)P(\text{No arrivals in } \Delta t) \\
+ P_1(t - \Delta t)P(\text{No arrivals and one service in } \Delta t)
\end{aligned} \qquad (3.26)$$

$$P_0(t) = e^{-\lambda \Delta t}P_0(t - \Delta t) + P_1(t - \Delta t)\mu \, \Delta t e^{-(\lambda + \mu)\,\Delta t} \qquad (3.27)$$

$$P(\text{No arrivals in } \Delta t) = 1 - \lambda \, \Delta t e^{-\lambda \Delta t}$$

$$P_0(t) = P_0(t - \Delta t) - P_0(t - \Delta t)\lambda \, \Delta t e^{-\lambda \Delta t} + P_1(t - \Delta t)\mu \, \Delta t e^{-(\lambda + \mu)\,\Delta t} \qquad (3.28)$$

Rearranging terms as in (3.24) and taking the limit as $\Delta t \to 0$, we have

$$\frac{dP_0(t)}{dt} = \mu P_1(t) - \lambda P_0(t) \tag{3.29}$$

Equations (3.25) and (3.29) represent transient-state solutions for the distribution of the number of units in the system. We are interested in the steady-state solution, $t \to \infty$, where the incremental change in $P_n(t)$ and $P_0(t)$ with time is zero. That is,

$$\lim_{t \to \infty} \frac{dP_n(t)}{dt} = 0 \tag{3.30}$$

$$\lim_{t \to \infty} \frac{dP_0(t)}{dt} = 0 \tag{3.31}$$

Letting

$$\lim_{t \to \infty} P_n(t) = P_n$$

we have from (3.25) and (3.29)

$$P_1 = \frac{\lambda}{\mu} P_0 \tag{3.32}$$

$$P_{n+1} = \frac{\lambda + \mu}{\mu} P_n - \frac{\lambda}{\mu} P_{n-1} \tag{3.33}$$

Solving recursively for P_2 and P_3, we have

$$P_2 = \frac{\lambda + \mu}{\mu} P_1 - \frac{\lambda}{\mu} P_0$$

$$= \left(\frac{\lambda}{\mu}\right)^2 P_0$$

$$P_3 = \frac{\lambda + \mu}{\mu} P_2 - \frac{\lambda}{\mu} P_1$$

$$= \left(\frac{\lambda}{\mu}\right)^3 P_0$$

This leads to the general solution

$$P_n = \left(\frac{\lambda}{\mu}\right)^n P_0 \tag{3.34}$$

We solve for P_0 as follows:

$$\sum_{n=0}^{N} P_n = 1$$

$$= \sum_{n=0}^{N} \left(\frac{\lambda}{\mu}\right)^n P_0$$

$$= P_0 \sum_{n=0}^{N} \left(\frac{\lambda}{\mu}\right)^n$$

$$P_0 = \frac{1}{\sum_{n=0}^{N} \left(\frac{\lambda}{\mu}\right)^n}$$

$$= \frac{1 - \lambda/\mu}{1 - (\lambda/\mu)^{N+1}} \tag{3.35}$$

Therefore

$$P_n = \left(\frac{\lambda}{\mu}\right)^n \frac{1 - \lambda/\mu}{1 - (\lambda/\mu)^{N+1}}, \qquad n = 0, 1, \ldots, N \tag{3.36}$$

In the above development, λ and μ represent the mean arrival and service rates, respectively. If $\lambda > \mu$, we would expect the number in the system to build up and remain near its maximum value N most of the time. If the number in the system is not restricted, we would expect the waiting line, and therefore the number in the system, to build up indefinitely. Of course, such systems would normally not be feasible and are not of interest here. Henceforth we shall assume $\lambda < \mu$. Therefore

$$P_n = \begin{cases} \left(\frac{\lambda}{\mu}\right)^n \dfrac{1 - \lambda/\mu}{1 - (\lambda/\mu)^{N+1}}, & n = 0, 1, 2, \ldots, N \\[2ex] \left(\frac{\lambda}{\mu}\right)^n (1 - \lambda/\mu), & n = 0, 1, 2, \ldots \end{cases} \tag{3.37}$$

The second of equations (3.37) is obtained by taking the limit of (3.36) as $N \to \infty$.

The distribution of the number in the waiting line, m, is easily derived from the distribution of the number in the system. Let Q_m be the probability that m units are in the waiting line at a random point in time.

$$Q_0 = P_0 + P_1 \tag{3.38}$$

$$Q_m = P_{m+1}, \qquad m = 1, 2, \ldots, N - 1 \tag{3.39}$$

When the total number in the system is limited to N or less,

$$Q_0 = \frac{1 - \lambda/\mu}{1 - (\lambda/\mu)^{N+1}} + \left(\frac{\lambda}{\mu}\right) \frac{1 - \lambda/\mu}{1 - (\lambda/\mu)^{N+1}}$$

$$= \frac{1 - (\lambda/\mu)^2}{1 - (\lambda/\mu)^{N+1}} \tag{3.40}$$

$$Q_m = \left(\frac{\lambda}{\mu}\right)^{m+1} \frac{1 - \lambda/\mu}{1 - (\lambda/\mu)^{N+1}}, \qquad m = 1, 2, \dots, N - 1 \tag{3.41}$$

Taking the limit as $N \to \infty$ in (3.40) and (3.41), we obtain the distribution of the number in the waiting line when the capacity of the system is unrestricted.

$$Q_m = \begin{cases} 1 - (\lambda/\mu)^2, & m = 0 \\ \left(\frac{\lambda}{\mu}\right)^{m+1} (1 - \lambda/\mu), & m = 1, 2, \dots \end{cases} \tag{3.42}$$

Of more importance than the number in the system or waiting line is the total time spent in the waiting line and the total time spent in the system. This is particularly true from a customer's point of view. Let $f_T(t)$ be the density function of total time, T, in the system, and let $g_{T_n}(t_n)$ be the density function of time in the system, given there are n units in the system when the arriving unit enters the waiting line.

$$T_n = \text{(Time to complete service on the unit being served when the arrival occurs)} + \text{(time to serve } n - 1 \text{ units ahead of the arriving unit in the waiting line)} + \text{(time to serve the arriving unit)} \tag{3.43}$$

Let

Z = Time to complete service on the unit being served when the arrival occurs.

V_j = Time to serve jth unit in the waiting line.

S = Time to serve arrival.

$$T_n = Z + \sum_{j=1}^{n-1} V_j + S \tag{3.44}$$

We develop the density function of Z by demonstrating a unique property of the exponential distribution, the service distribution treated here. If X is the random variable representing the total time to serve the unit in service at the time of arrival, and the arriving unit enters the waiting line at time Y after this service began, then

$$Z = X - Y$$

$$P(\text{Service time remaining} > z \mid \text{service time} > y) = H(Z > z \mid Y > y) \quad (3.45)$$

$$H(Z > z \mid Y > y) = P(X > z + y \mid \text{service time} > y)$$

$$= \frac{P(\text{Service time} > z + y)}{P(\text{Service time} > y)} \quad (3.46)$$

Since total service time is exponentially distributed,

$$H(Z > z \mid Y > y) = \frac{e^{-\mu(z+y)}}{e^{-\mu y}}$$

$$= e^{-\mu z} \quad (3.47)$$

$$h_{Z|Y}(z \mid y) = \mu e^{-\mu z}, \qquad 0 < z < \infty \quad (3.48)$$

Therefore the distribution of Z is independent of the time already spent in service and is exponentially distributed. Therefore Z, V_j, and S are all exponentially distributed with parameter μ. T_n is then the sum of $n + 1$ identically distributed random variables. To determine the density function of T_n we will develop the characteristic function of T_n. The characteristic functions of the random variables comprising T_n are

$$\phi_Z(\alpha) = (1 - i\alpha/\mu)^{-1}$$

$$\phi_{V_j}(\alpha) = (1 - i\alpha/\mu)^{-1} \quad , \quad j = 1, 2, \ldots, n - 1$$

$$\phi_S(\alpha) = (1 - i\alpha/\mu)^{-1}$$

In Chapter 2 we showed that $\phi_{T_n}(\alpha)$ is given by

$$\phi_{T_n}(\alpha) = (1 - i\alpha/\mu)^{-1}\left[\prod_{j=1}^{n-1}(1 - i\alpha/\mu)^{-1}\right](1 - i\alpha/\mu)^{-1} \quad (3.49)$$

$$= (1 - i\alpha/\mu)^{-(n+1)} \quad (3.50)$$

The characteristic function specified in (3.50) is that of the gamma random variable. Therefore

$$g_{T_n}(t_n) = \frac{\mu}{\Gamma(n+1)}(\mu t_n)^n e^{-\mu t_n}, \qquad 0 < t_n < \infty \quad (3.51)$$

$$P(T \le t) = \sum_{n=0}^{N} P(T_n \le t)P(n \text{ units in the system upon arrival}) \quad (3.52)$$

$$= \sum_{n=0}^{N} \int_0^t \frac{\mu}{\Gamma(n+1)} (\mu x)^n e^{-\mu x} \left(\frac{\lambda}{\mu}\right)^n \frac{1 - \lambda/\mu}{1 - (\lambda/\mu)^{N+1}} \, dx \qquad (3.53)$$

$$= \int_0^t \frac{\mu(1 - \lambda/\mu)}{1 - (\lambda/\mu)^{N+1}} \sum_{n=0}^{N} \frac{(\lambda x)^n}{n!} e^{-\mu x} \, dx$$

$$= F_T(t)$$

$$f_T(t) = \frac{\mu(1 - \lambda/\mu)}{1 - (\lambda/\mu)^{N+1}} \sum_{n=0}^{N} \frac{(\lambda t)^n}{n!} e^{-\mu x}, \qquad 0 < t < \infty \qquad (3.54)$$

We obtain the density function of total time in the system for unrestricted queue length by taking the limit $N \to \infty$ in (3.54), which yields

$$f_T(t) = (\mu - \lambda)e^{-(\mu - \lambda)t}, \qquad 0 < t < \infty \qquad (3.55)$$

The distribution of total time delayed in the waiting line is of interest not only from a systems point of view, but also because it represents a type of probability distribution which we have not encountered yet. We have discussed distributions which are discrete and distributions which are continuous. The distribution of waiting time is both discrete and continuous. This is demonstrated by considering the probability that an arriving unit will be delayed zero time units in the waiting line. This probability is precisely equal to the probability that there are zero units in the system when the arrival occurs, in which case the unit would immediately enter the service channel. If the number of units in the system, n, is greater than zero, the total time delayed in the waiting line, W_n is given by

$$W_n = Z + \sum_{j=1}^{n-1} V_j \qquad (3.56)$$

where Z and V_j are as defined in (3.44). The density function of W_n is developed by an argument identical to that used in developing the density function of T_n. Therefore

$$g_{W_n}(w_n) = \frac{\mu}{\Gamma(n)} (\mu w_n)^{n-1} e^{-\mu w_n}, \qquad 0 < w_n < \infty \qquad (3.57)$$

The unconditional distribution function of waiting time, W, is then

$$F_W(w) = \sum_{n=1}^{N} \int_0^w \frac{\mu}{\Gamma(n)} (\mu x)^{n-1} e^{-\mu x} \left(\frac{\lambda}{\mu}\right)^n \frac{1 - \lambda/\mu}{1 - (\lambda/\mu)^{N+1}} \, dx \qquad (3.58)$$

which leads to the density function of W given in (3.59).

$$f_W(w) = \frac{\lambda(1 - \lambda/\mu)}{1 - (\lambda/\mu)^{N+1}} \sum_{n=1}^{N} \frac{(\lambda w)^{n-1}}{(n-1)!} e^{-\mu w}, \qquad 0 < w < \infty \qquad (3.59)$$

For unrestricted queue length

$$f_W(w) = \lambda(1 - \lambda/\mu)e^{-(\mu - \lambda)w}, \qquad 0 < w < \infty \qquad (3.60)$$

To summarize

$$f_T(t) = \begin{cases} \dfrac{\mu - \lambda}{1 - (\lambda/\mu)^{N+1}} \displaystyle\sum_{n=0}^{N} \dfrac{(\lambda t)^n}{n!} e^{-\mu t}, & t > 0 \text{ (restricted queue length)} \\[2ex] (\mu - \lambda)e^{-(\mu - \lambda)t}, & t > 0 \text{ (unrestricted queue length)} \end{cases}$$

$$(3.61)$$

$$f_W(w) = \begin{cases} \dfrac{1 - \lambda/\mu}{1 - (\lambda/\mu)^{N+1}}, & w = 0 \\[2ex] \dfrac{\lambda(1 - \lambda/\mu)}{1 - (\lambda/\mu)^{N+1}} \displaystyle\sum_{n=1}^{N} \dfrac{(\lambda w)^{n-1}}{(n-1)!} e^{-\mu w}, & w > 0 \end{cases} \quad \text{(restricted queue length) (3.62)}$$

$$f_W(w) = \begin{cases} 1 - \lambda/\mu, & w = 0 \\ \lambda(1 - \lambda/\mu)e^{-(\mu - \lambda)w}, & w > 0 \end{cases} \quad \text{(unrestricted queue length) (3.63)}$$

Example 3.1

Show that the function given in (3.62) is a probability distribution.

Since the sum of the probabilities must equal unity for every probability distribution,

$$P(W = 0) + P(W > 0) = 1 \qquad (3.64)$$

$$P(W = 0) = \frac{1 - \lambda/\mu}{1 - (\lambda/\mu)^{N+1}} \qquad (3.65)$$

$$P(W > 0) = \int_0^\infty \frac{\lambda(1 - \lambda/\mu)}{1 - (\lambda/\mu)^{N+1}} \sum_{n=1}^{N} \frac{(\lambda w)^{n-1}}{(n-1)!} e^{-\mu w} \, dw$$

$$= \frac{\lambda(1 - \lambda/\mu)}{1 - (\lambda/\mu)^{N+1}} \sum_{n=1}^{N} \int_0^\infty \frac{(\lambda w)^{n-1}}{(n-1)!} e^{-\mu w} \, dw$$

Now

$$\int_0^\infty \frac{(ax)^k}{k!} e^{-bx} \, dx = \frac{a^k}{b^{k+1}} \qquad (3.66)$$

Therefore

$$P(W > 0) = \frac{\lambda(1 - \lambda/\mu)}{1 - (\lambda/\mu)^{N+1}} \sum_{n=1}^{N} \frac{\lambda^{n-1}}{\mu^n}$$

$$= \frac{(1 - \lambda/\mu)}{1 - (\lambda/\mu)^{N+1}} \sum_{n=1}^{N} \left(\frac{\lambda}{\mu}\right)^n \qquad (3.67)$$

and

$$\sum_{n=1}^{N} a^n = \frac{a(1 - a^N)}{1 - a} \qquad (3.68)$$

$$P(W > 0) = \frac{1 - \lambda/\mu}{1 - (\lambda/\mu)^{N+1}} \frac{\lambda}{\mu} \frac{1 - (\lambda/\mu)^N}{1 - \lambda/\mu}$$

$$= \frac{\lambda}{\mu} \frac{1 - (\lambda/\mu)^N}{1 - (\lambda/\mu)^{N+1}} \qquad (3.69)$$

$$P(W = 0) + P(W > 0) = \frac{1 - \lambda/\mu}{1 - (\lambda/\mu)^{N+1}} + \frac{\frac{\lambda}{\mu} - (\lambda/\mu)^{N+1}}{1 - (\lambda/\mu)^{N+1}} \qquad (3.70)$$

$$= \frac{1 - (\lambda/\mu)^{N+1}}{1 - (\lambda/\mu)^{N+1}}$$

$$= 1$$

Example 3.2

Find the mean waiting time in the queue for restricted and unrestricted queue length.

For restricted queue length

$$E(W) = (0)P(W = 0) + \int_0^\infty w \frac{\lambda(1 - \lambda/\mu)}{1 - (\lambda/\mu)^{N+1}} \sum_{n=1}^{N} \frac{(\lambda w)^{n-1}}{(n-1)!} e^{-\mu w} \, dw$$

$$= \frac{1 - \lambda/\mu}{1 - (\lambda/\mu)^{N+1}} \sum_{n=1}^{N} \int_0^\infty \frac{(\lambda w)^n}{(n-1)!} e^{-\mu w} \, dw$$

$$= \frac{1 - \lambda/\mu}{1 - (\lambda/\mu)^{N+1}} \sum_{n=1}^{N} n\left(\frac{\lambda}{\mu}\right)^n \frac{1}{\mu} \qquad (3.71)$$

To resolve this summation, use the following relationship:

$$\sum_{n=1}^{N} na^n = a \frac{d}{da} \sum_{n=1}^{N} a^n \qquad (3.72)$$

$$= a \frac{d}{da} \frac{a(1 - a^N)}{1 - a}$$

$$= a \left(\frac{1 - (N + 1)a^N + Na^{N+1}}{(1 - a)^2} \right) \qquad (3.73)$$

Therefore,

$$E(W) = \frac{\lambda}{\mu^2} \frac{1 - \lambda/\mu}{1 - (\lambda/\mu)^{N+1}} \frac{1 - (N + 1)(\lambda/\mu)^N + N(\lambda/\mu)^{N+1}}{[1 - (\lambda/\mu)]^2}$$

$$= \frac{\lambda}{\mu^2(1 - \lambda/\mu)} \frac{1 - (N + 1)(\lambda/\mu)^N + N(\lambda/\mu)^{N+1}}{1 - (\lambda/\mu)^{N+1}} \qquad (3.74)$$

To obtain $E(W)$ for unrestricted queue length, we take the limit of (3.74) as $N \to \infty$.

$$E(W) = \frac{\lambda}{\mu^2(1 - \lambda/\mu)} \qquad (3.75)$$

The reader should note that in taking the limit of (3.74) as $N \to \infty$ we must apply L'hospital's rule. For example, to evaluate

$$\lim_{N \to \infty} (N + 1)(\lambda/\mu)^N$$

we set $(\lambda/\mu)^N = 1/(\mu/\lambda)^N$. We evaluate the limit as follows.

$$\lim_{N \to \infty} (N + 1)(\lambda/\mu)^N = \lim_{N \to \infty} \frac{N + 1}{(\mu/\lambda)^N}$$

Applying L'Hospital's rule for indeterminate forms, we have

$$\lim_{N \to \infty} \frac{N + 1}{(\mu/\lambda)^N} = \lim_{N \to \infty} \frac{\frac{d}{dN}(N + 1)}{\frac{d}{dN}(\mu/\lambda)^N}$$

$$= \lim_{N \to \infty} \frac{1}{N(\mu/\lambda)^N}$$

$$= 0$$

since we assume $\mu > \lambda$.

Example 3.3

Find the expected number of units in the system for restricted and unrestricted queue length.

For restricted queue length

$$E(n) = \sum_{n=0}^{N} n \frac{1 - \lambda/\mu}{1 - (\lambda/\mu)^{N+1}} \left(\frac{\lambda}{\mu}\right)^n$$

$$= \frac{1 - \lambda/\mu}{1 - (\lambda/\mu)^{N+1}} \sum_{n=0}^{N} n(\lambda/\mu)^n \qquad (3.76)$$

Applying (3.73), we have

$$E(n) = \frac{1 - \lambda/\mu}{1 - (\lambda/\mu)^{N+1}} \frac{\lambda}{\mu} \frac{1 - (N+1)(\lambda/\mu)^N + N(\lambda/\mu)^{N+1}}{[1 - (\lambda/\mu)]^2}$$

$$= \frac{\lambda/\mu}{1 - \lambda/\mu} \left[\frac{1 - (N+1)(\lambda/\mu)^N + N(\lambda/\mu)^{N+1}}{1 - (\lambda/\mu)^{N+1}} \right] \qquad (3.77)$$

Taking the limit of (3.77) as $N \to \infty$, we obtain $E(n)$ for a system with unrestricted queue length.

$$E(n) = \frac{\lambda/\mu}{1 - \lambda/\mu} \qquad (3.78)$$

Example 3.4

Consider a single channel queueing system with unrestricted queue length in which the cost of servicing a unit is $C_1\mu$ and the cost of waiting is $C_2 t$ where t is the waiting time. Develop an equation expressing the total expected cost of operating the service channel per unit served, assuming every unit entering the system is served. Find the value of μ which minimizes the total expected cost per unit of operating the system.

If the unit waits time t to be served, the total cost of serving that unit, C_T, is given by

$$C_T = C_1\mu + C_2 t \qquad (3.79)$$

Taking the expected value of C_T we obtain

$$E(C_T) = C_1\mu + C_2 E(t)$$

$$E(t) = \int_0^{\infty} (\mu - \lambda) t e^{-(\mu - \lambda)t}$$

$$= \frac{1}{\mu - \lambda} \qquad (3.80)$$

$$E(C_T) = C_1 + \frac{C_2}{\mu - \lambda} \qquad (3.81)$$

To determine the optimal value of μ, we differentiate (3.81) with respect to μ, set the derivative equal to zero, and solve for μ.

$$\frac{dE(C_T)}{d\mu} = C_1 - \frac{C_2}{(\mu - \lambda)^2}$$

$$= 0$$

$$(\mu - \lambda)^2 = C_2/C_1$$

$$\mu - \lambda = \sqrt{C_2/C_1}$$

$$\mu = \sqrt{C_2/C_1} + \lambda \tag{3.82}$$

MULTIPLE CHANNELS IN PARALLEL

The system we are concerned with here is similar to that which we discussed previously because as units arrive they take their place in the waiting line if service cannot be obtained immediately. However, here we assume that there is more than one channel available for service. This system is illustrated in Figure 3.2. The first unit in the waiting line enters the first service channel which becomes available.

FIGURE 3.2
Service Channels in Parallel

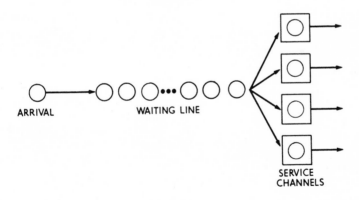

We will assume that the number of arrivals in time t is Poisson distributed with parameter λt and that the number of services per time s is also Poisson distributed with parameter μs for each of the service channels.

Although our discussion of multiple channels in parallel will be limited to unrestricted queue length, we will point out the necessary modifications for restricted queues.

Let K be the number of service channels in parallel. Before developing the probability distribution of the number of units in the system we must recognize that the probability that a service occurs in a small interval of time, Δt, is dependent upon the number of service channels occupied during that interval of time. Let us assume that r of the K channels are occupied. Since the channels are Poisson, the probability of more than one service per channel in Δt is zero. The probability of one service somewhere among the r occupied channels is

$$P(\text{One service in } t) = r\mu \, \Delta t e^{-\mu \Delta t} \tag{3.83}$$

since the service may occur in any one of r channels. For $0 < n < K$

$$
\begin{aligned}
P_n(t) &= P_{n-1}(t - \Delta t)\lambda \, \Delta t e^{-\lambda \Delta t}[1 - (n-1)\mu \, \Delta t e^{-\mu \Delta t}] \\
&+ P_n(t - \Delta t)(1 - \lambda \, \Delta t e^{-\lambda \Delta t})(1 - n\mu \, \Delta t e^{-\mu \Delta t}) \\
&+ P_{n+1}(t - \Delta t)(1 - \lambda \, \Delta t e^{-\lambda \Delta t})(n+1)\mu \, \Delta t e^{-\mu \Delta t}
\end{aligned}
\tag{3.84}
$$

where

$$P(\text{No service in } \Delta t \mid r \text{ in service}) = 1 - r\mu \, \Delta t e^{-\mu \Delta t}$$

$$P(\text{No arrival in } \Delta t) = 1 - \lambda \, \Delta t e^{-\lambda \Delta t}$$

From (3.84) we obtain

$$
\begin{aligned}
\frac{P_n(t) - P_n(t - \Delta t)}{\Delta t} &= P_{n-1}(t - \Delta t)e^{-\lambda \Delta t} - P_{n-1}(t - \Delta t)(n-1)\lambda\mu \, \Delta t e^{-(\lambda + \mu)\Delta t} \\
&- P_n(t - \Delta t)\lambda e^{-\lambda \Delta t} - P_n(t - \Delta t)n\mu e^{-\mu \Delta t} \\
&+ P_n(t - \Delta t)n\lambda\mu \, \Delta t e^{-(\lambda + \mu)\Delta t} \\
&+ P_{n+1}(t - \Delta t)(n+1)e^{-\mu \Delta t} \\
&- P_{n+1}(t - \Delta t)(n+1)\lambda\mu \, \Delta t e^{-(\lambda + \mu)\Delta t}
\end{aligned}
\tag{3.85}
$$

Taking the limit of (3.85) as $\Delta t \to 0$, we have

$$\frac{dP_n(t)}{dt} = \lambda P_{n-1}(t) - \lambda P_n(t) - n\mu P_n(t) + (n+1)\mu P_{n+1}(t) \tag{3.86}$$

Since we are interested in the steady-state distribution,

$$\lim_{t \to \infty} \frac{dP_n(t)}{dt} = 0$$

Therefore in the steady state we have

$$P_{n+1} = \frac{\lambda + n\mu}{(n+1)\mu} P_n - \frac{\lambda}{(n+1)\mu} P_{n-1}, \qquad n = 1, 2, \ldots, K-1 \qquad (3.87)$$

When $n \geq K$, the analog of equation (3.86) is

$$\frac{dP_n(t)}{dt} = \lambda P_{n-1}(t) - \lambda P_n(t) - K\mu P_n(t) + K\mu P_{n+1}(t) \qquad (3.88)$$

which leads to

$$P_{n+1} = \frac{\lambda + K\mu}{K\mu} P_n - \frac{\lambda}{K\mu} P_{n-1}, \qquad n > K \qquad (3.89)$$

For $n = 0$, we have

$$P_0(t) = P_0(t - \Delta t)(1 - \lambda \Delta t e^{-\lambda \Delta t}) + P_1(t - \Delta t)(1 - \lambda \Delta t e^{-\lambda \Delta t})\mu \Delta t e^{-\mu \Delta t}$$
$$(3.90)$$

which leads to

$$\frac{dP_0(t)}{dt} = -\lambda P_0(t) + \mu P_1(t) \qquad (3.91)$$

Therefore in the steady state we have

$$P_1 = (\lambda/\mu)P_0 \qquad (3.92)$$

From equations (3.87) and (3.92) we have

$$P_2 = \frac{\lambda + \mu}{2\mu} P_1 - \frac{\lambda}{2\mu} P_0$$

$$= \frac{1}{2}\left(\frac{\lambda}{\mu}\right)^2 P_0$$

$$P_3 = \frac{\lambda + 2\mu}{3\mu} P_2 - \frac{\lambda}{3\mu} P_1$$

$$= \frac{1}{3!}\left(\frac{\lambda}{\mu}\right)^3 P_0$$

We have for the general solution

$$P_n = \frac{1}{n!}\left(\frac{\lambda}{\mu}\right)^n P_0, \qquad n = 0, 1, \ldots, K \qquad (3.93)$$

Solving (3.89) in a similar manner, we get

$$P_{K+1} = \frac{\lambda + K\mu}{K\mu} P_K - \frac{\lambda}{K\mu} P_{K-1}$$

$$= \frac{\lambda + K\mu}{K\mu} \frac{1}{K!} \left(\frac{\lambda}{\mu}\right)^K P_0 - \frac{\lambda}{K\mu} \frac{1}{(K-1)!} \left(\frac{\lambda}{\mu}\right)^{K-1} P_0$$

$$P_{K+1} = \frac{1}{KK!} \left(\frac{\lambda}{\mu}\right)^{K+1} P_0$$

$$P_{K+2} = \frac{\lambda + K\mu}{K\mu} P_{K+1} - \frac{\lambda}{K\mu} P_K$$

$$= \frac{\lambda + K\mu}{K\mu} \frac{1}{KK!} \left(\frac{\lambda}{\mu}\right)^{K+1} P_0 - \frac{\lambda}{K\mu} \frac{1}{K!} \left(\frac{\lambda}{\mu}\right)^K P_0$$

$$= \frac{1}{K^2 K!} \left(\frac{\lambda}{\mu}\right)^{K+2} P_0$$

Continuing in this fashion, we obtain

$$P_{K+m} = \frac{1}{K^2 K!} \left(\frac{\lambda}{\mu}\right)^{K+m} P_0 \qquad (3.94)$$

or

$$P_n = \frac{1}{K^{n-K} K!} \left(\frac{\lambda}{\mu}\right)^n P_0 \qquad (3.95)$$

We obtain the solution for P_0 by noting that the sum of P_n over all n is unity.

$$\sum_{n=0}^{\infty} P_n = \sum_{n=0}^{K} \frac{1}{n!} \left(\frac{\lambda}{\mu}\right)^n P_0 + \sum_{n=K+1}^{\infty} \frac{1}{K^{n-K} K!} \left(\frac{\lambda}{\mu}\right)^n P_0 \qquad (3.96)$$

The first summation in (3.96) cannot be resolved analytically. For the second, we have

$$\sum_{n=K+1}^{\infty} \frac{1}{K^{n-K} K!} \left(\frac{\lambda}{\mu}\right)^n P_0 = \frac{K^K}{K!} P_0 \sum_{n=K+1}^{\infty} \left(\frac{\lambda}{K\mu}\right)^n$$

$$= \frac{K^K}{K!} P_0 \left[\sum_{n=0}^{\infty} \left(\frac{\lambda}{K\mu}\right)^n - \sum_{n=0}^{K} \left(\frac{\lambda}{K\mu}\right)^n \right]$$

$$= \frac{K^K}{K!} P_0 \left[\frac{1}{1 - \lambda/K\mu} - \frac{1 - (\lambda/K\mu)^{K+1}}{1 - \lambda/K\mu} \right]$$

$$= \frac{K^K}{K!} \frac{(\lambda/K\mu)^{K+1}}{1 - \lambda/K\mu} P_0$$

$$= \frac{(\lambda/\mu)^{K+1}}{KK!(1 - \lambda/K\mu)} P_0$$

Equation (3.96) reduces to

$$\sum_{n=0}^{\infty} P_n = \sum_{n=0}^{K} \frac{1}{n!} \left(\frac{\lambda}{\mu}\right)^n P_0 + \frac{(\lambda/\mu)^{K+1}}{KK!(1 - \lambda/K\mu)} P_0 \qquad (3.97)$$

Solving for P_0, we get

$$P_0 = \frac{1}{\displaystyle\sum_{n=0}^{K} \frac{1}{n!} \left(\frac{\lambda}{\mu}\right)^n + \frac{(\lambda/\mu)^{K+1}}{KK!(1 - \lambda/K\mu)}} \qquad (3.98)$$

The distribution of the total number of units in the system is therefore given by

$$P_n = \begin{cases} \dfrac{1}{n!} \left(\dfrac{\lambda}{\mu}\right)^n P_0, & n = 0, 1, \ldots, K \\[3mm] \dfrac{1}{K^{n-K}K!} \left(\dfrac{\lambda}{\mu}\right)^n P_0, & n = K + 1, K + 2, \ldots \end{cases} \qquad (3.99)$$

where P_0 is given in (3.98).

When the queue length is restricted such that $n < N$ and $N > K$, equation (3.99) still holds. However, equation (3.96) must be modified by taking the second summation from $K + 1$ to N instead of from $K + 1$ to infinity. This modification being accomplished, the solution for P_0 becomes

$$P_0 = \frac{1}{\displaystyle\sum_{n=0}^{K} \frac{1}{n!} \left(\frac{\lambda}{\mu}\right)^n + \frac{K^K}{K!} \frac{(\lambda/K\mu)^{K+1} - (\lambda/K\mu)^{N+1}}{1 - \lambda/K\mu}} \qquad (3.100)$$

In developing the distribution of the number of units in the waiting line, m, we use an argument similar to that in the previous section.

$$Q_0 = P(\text{Number of units in the system} \leq K)$$

$$= \sum_{n=0}^{K} \frac{1}{n!} \left(\frac{\lambda}{\mu}\right)^n P_0 \qquad (3.101)$$

$$Q_0 = 1 - \sum_{n=K+1}^{\infty} \frac{1}{K^{n-K}K!} \left(\frac{\lambda}{\mu}\right)^n P_0 \tag{3.102}$$

$$Q_0 = 1 - \frac{(\lambda/\mu)^{K+1}}{KK!(1 - \lambda/K\mu)} P_0 \tag{3.103}$$

For $m > 0$

$$Q_m = P(\text{Number of units in the system} = K + m) \tag{3.104}$$

$$= \frac{1}{K^m K!} \left(\frac{\lambda}{\mu}\right)^{K+m} P_0 \tag{3.105}$$

If the capacity of the system is limited, $n \leqslant N$, the limits of the summation in (3.102) are $K + 1$ to N.

Example 3.5

Find the expected number of units in the waiting line for a queueing system with K service channels in parallel. Assume the distribution of service time per channel is exponential with mean rate μ.

$$E(m) = 0Q_0 + \sum_{m=1}^{\infty} mQ_m \tag{3.106}$$

$$= \sum_{m=1}^{\infty} \frac{m}{K^m K!} \left(\frac{\lambda}{\mu}\right)^{K+m} P_0$$

$$= \frac{(\lambda/\mu)^K}{K!} \sum_{m=1}^{\infty} m \left(\frac{\lambda}{K\mu}\right)^m P_0 \tag{3.107}$$

To resolve the summation in (3.107), we use equation (3.73), taking the limit as $N \to \infty$.

$$\sum_{m=1}^{\infty} m \left(\frac{\lambda}{K\mu}\right)^m P_0 = \frac{\lambda}{K\mu} \frac{P_0}{(1 - \lambda/K\mu)^2}$$

$$= \frac{\lambda K\mu}{(K\mu - \lambda)^2} P_0 \tag{3.108}$$

Therefore

$$E(m) = \frac{\lambda\mu(\lambda/\mu)^K}{(K-1)!(K\mu - \lambda)^2} P_0 \tag{3.109}$$

Example 3.6

Derive the distribution of waiting time in the queue, W, for a queueing system with K exponential channels in parallel, each with mean rate μ. Arrivals to the system are Poisson distributed with parameter λ.

It is obvious that whenever the number of units in the system is less than K, an arriving unit will not have to wait. Thus we again encounter a distribution which is both discrete and continuous. For $W = 0$,

$$f_W(w) = P(n < K) \tag{3.110}$$

$$= 1 - P(n \geq K)$$

$$= 1 - \frac{1}{K!} \left(\frac{\lambda}{\mu}\right)^K P_0 - \sum_{n=K+1}^{\infty} \frac{1}{K^{n-K}K!} \left(\frac{\lambda}{\mu}\right)^n P_0 \tag{3.111}$$

$$= 1 - \sum_{n=K}^{\infty} \frac{1}{K^{n-K}K!} \left(\frac{\lambda}{\mu}\right)^n P_0 \tag{3.112}$$

$$= 1 - \frac{K^K}{K!} P_0 \sum_{n=K}^{\infty} \left(\frac{\lambda}{K\mu}\right)^n \tag{3.113}$$

The summation in (3.113) is resolved as follows:

$$\sum_{n=K}^{\infty} \left(\frac{\lambda}{K\mu}\right)^n = \sum_{n=0}^{\infty} \left(\frac{\lambda}{K\mu}\right)^n - \sum_{n=0}^{K-1} \left(\frac{\lambda}{K\mu}\right)^n \tag{3.114}$$

$$= \frac{1}{1 - \lambda/K\mu} - \frac{1 - (\lambda/K\mu)^K}{1 - \lambda/K\mu}$$

$$= \frac{(\lambda/K\mu)^K}{1 - \lambda/K\mu} \tag{3.115}$$

Therefore

$$f_W(w) = 1 - \frac{(\lambda/\mu)^K}{K!(1 - \lambda/K\mu)} P_0, \qquad w = 0 \tag{3.116}$$

For $W > 0$, we will use an argument quite different from that used for a single exponential channel. Assume that the arrival occurs at time 0, at which time there are $n \geq K$ units in the system. If we have $n - K$ services in w and one service in a small interval of time Δw then the waiting time of the arrival is between w and $w + \Delta w$.

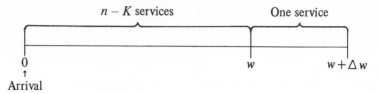

$$P(W < \text{waiting time} < w + \Delta w) = F_W(w + \Delta w) - F_W(w) \qquad (3.117)$$

During the time interval w, each of the K channels is servicing continuously. Since the distribution of service time is exponential with parameter μ for each channel, the distribution of the number of units served in w is Poisson with parameter μ. If X_i is the number of units served by the ith channel in time w, then

$$p_{X_i}(x_i) = \frac{(\mu w)^{x_i}}{x_i!} e^{-\mu w}, \qquad x_i = 0, 1, 2, \ldots \qquad (3.118)$$

However, we are interested in the total number of services in the K channels, Y.

$$Y = \sum_{i=1}^{K} X_i \qquad (3.119)$$

In exámple 2.25 we showed that the distribution of the sum of two Poisson random variables, each with parameter λ, is also Poisson distributed with parameter 2λ. This property can, in fact, be shown to hold for any number of Poisson random variables. Therefore the distribution of Y is Poisson with parameter $K\mu$.

$$P(w < \text{waiting time} < w + \Delta w)$$

$$= \sum_{n=K}^{\infty} P_n P(n - K \text{ services in } w) P(\text{One service in } \Delta w) \qquad (3.120)$$

$$= \sum_{n=K}^{\infty} \frac{1}{K^{n-K}K!} \left(\frac{\lambda}{\mu}\right)^n P_0 \frac{(K\mu w)^{n-K}}{(n-K)!} e^{-K\mu w} K \Delta w e^{-K\mu \Delta w}$$

$$= F_W(w + \Delta w) - F_W(w) \qquad (3.121)$$

$$\frac{F_W(w + \Delta w) - F_W(w)}{\Delta w} = \frac{\mu e^{-K\mu\Delta w}}{(\mu w)^K (K-1)!} P_0 \sum_{n=K}^{\infty} \frac{(\lambda w)^n}{(n-K)!} e^{-K\mu w} \qquad (3.122)$$

Taking the limit of (3.122) as $\Delta w \to 0$, we obtain the density function of W.

$$f_W(w) = \frac{\mu}{(\mu w)^K (K-1)!} P_0 \sum_{n=K}^{\infty} \frac{(\lambda w)^n}{(n-K)!} e^{-K\mu w}, \qquad w > 0 \qquad (3.123)$$

Letting $m = n - K$, we have

$$f_W(w) = \frac{\mu}{(K-1)!} \left(\frac{\lambda}{\mu}\right)^K P_0 \sum_{m=0}^{\infty} \frac{(\lambda w)^m}{m!}$$

$$= \frac{\mu}{(K-1)!} \left(\frac{\lambda}{\mu}\right)^K P_0 e^{-(K\mu - \lambda)w}, \quad w > 0 \qquad (3.124)$$

Therefore the density function of W is completely specified by

$$f_W(w) = \begin{cases} 1 - \dfrac{(\lambda/\mu)^K}{K!(1 - \lambda/K\mu)} P_0, & w = 0 \\[3mm] \dfrac{\mu}{(K-1)!} \left(\dfrac{\lambda}{\mu}\right)^K P_0 e^{-(K\mu - \lambda)w}, & w > 0 \end{cases} \qquad (3.125)$$

Example 3.7

Derive the expected total time in the system for a queueing system with K exponential channels in parallel, each with mean rate μ.

$$E(t) = (\text{Expected waiting time} + \text{expected service time})$$

$$= \int_0^{\infty} \frac{\mu w}{(K-1)!} \left(\frac{\lambda}{\mu}\right)^K P_0 e^{-(K\mu - \lambda)w} \, dw + \frac{1}{\mu} \qquad (3.126)$$

$$= \frac{\mu(\lambda/\mu)^K}{(K-1)!(K\mu - \lambda)^2} P_0 + \frac{1}{\mu} \qquad (3.127)$$

Example 3.8

Find the distribution of the number of units in a system with two service channels in parallel. The distribution of service time is exponential with rate μ_1 for the first channel and μ_2 for the second channel. Arrivals are Poisson with rate λ. The probability that a unit enters either channel, if both are empty, is $\frac{1}{2}$.

$$P_0(t) = P_0(t - \Delta t)(1 - \lambda \, \Delta t e^{-\lambda \Delta t})$$

$$+ P_1(t - \Delta t)(1 - \lambda \, \Delta t e^{-\lambda \Delta t})$$

$$\times \, [P(\text{unit in service in first channel})\mu_1 \, \Delta t e^{-\mu_1 \Delta t}$$

$$+ P(\text{unit in service in second channel})\mu_2 \, \Delta t e^{-\mu_2 \Delta t}] \qquad (3.128)$$

$$= P_0(t - \Delta t)(1 - \lambda \, \Delta t e^{-\lambda \Delta t}) + \frac{P_1}{2} (t - \Delta t)(1 - \lambda \, \Delta t e^{-\lambda \Delta t})$$

$$\times \, (\mu_1 \, \Delta t e^{-\mu_1 \Delta t} + \mu_2 \, \Delta t e^{-\mu_2 \Delta t}) \qquad (3.129)$$

$$\frac{P_0(t) - P_0(t - \Delta t)}{\Delta t} = -\lambda e^{-\lambda \Delta t} P_0(t - \Delta t)$$

$$+ 1/2(\mu_1 e^{-\mu_1 \Delta t} + \mu_2 e^{-\mu_2 \Delta t}) P_1(t - \Delta t)$$

$$- 1/2\lambda \Delta t e^{-\lambda \Delta t}(\mu_1 e^{-\mu_1 \Delta t} + \mu_2 e^{-\mu_2 \Delta t}) P_1(t - \Delta t)$$

$$\frac{dP_0(t)}{dt} = -\lambda P_0(t) + (1/2)(\mu_1 + \mu_2)P_1(t) \tag{3.130}$$

For the steady-state solution, we have

$$P_1 = \frac{2\lambda}{\mu_1 + \mu_2} P_0 \tag{3.131}$$

$$\frac{dP_1(t)}{dt} = \lambda P_0(t) - [\lambda + (\mu_1 + \mu_2)/2]P_1(t) + (\mu_1 + \mu_2)P_2(t) \tag{3.132}$$

$$P_2 = \frac{\lambda}{\mu_1 + \mu_2} P_1 + (1/2)P_1 - \frac{\lambda}{\mu_1 + \mu_2} P_0$$

$$P_2 = 2\left(\frac{\lambda}{\mu_1 + \mu_2}\right)^2 P_0 \tag{3.133}$$

For $n > 1$

$$\frac{dP_n(t)}{dt} = \lambda P_{n-1}(t) - (\lambda + \mu_1 + \mu_2)P_n(t) + (\mu_1 + \mu_2)P_{n+1}(t) \tag{3.134}$$

$$P_{n+1} = \frac{\lambda}{\mu_1 + \mu_2} P_n + P_n - \frac{\lambda}{\mu_1 + \mu_2} P_{n-1}$$

For $n = 2$

$$P_3 = 2\left(\frac{\lambda}{\mu_1 + \mu_2}\right)^3 P_0$$

Solving recursively, we obtain

$$P_n = 2\left(\frac{\lambda}{\mu_1 + \mu_2}\right)^n P_0 \tag{3.135}$$

Solving for P_0, we get

$$\sum_{n=0}^{\infty} P_n = P_0 + 2\sum_{n=1}^{\infty} \left(\frac{\lambda}{\mu_1 + \mu_2}\right)^n P_0 \tag{3.136}$$

$$P_0 = \frac{1}{1 + 2 \sum_{n=1}^{\infty} \left(\dfrac{\lambda}{\mu_1 + \mu_2}\right)^n}$$

$$= \frac{\mu_1 + \mu_2 - \lambda}{3(\mu_1 + \mu_2) - \lambda} \qquad (3.137)$$

The distribution of the number of units in the system is given by

$$P_n = \begin{cases} \dfrac{\mu_1 + \mu_2 - \lambda}{3(\mu_1 + \mu_2) - \lambda}, & n = 0 \\[3mm] 2\left(\dfrac{\lambda}{\mu_1 + \mu_2}\right)^n \dfrac{\mu_1 + \mu_2 - \lambda}{3(\mu_1 + \mu_2) - \lambda}, & n = 1, 2, 3, \ldots \end{cases} \qquad (3.138)$$

Example 3.9

For a service system with K exponential channels in parallel, each having mean rate μ, find the expected number of units in service; Assume arrivals are Poisson distributed with mean rate λ. Let h be the number of units in service.

$$E(h) = \sum_{i=0}^{K} i P(h = i) \qquad (3.139)$$

$P(h = i) = P(\text{Number of units in the system} = i) \quad i = 0, 1, \ldots, K - 1$

$P(h = K) = P(\text{Number of units in the system} \geq K)$

$$E(h) = \sum_{i=0}^{K-1} \frac{i}{i!} \left(\frac{\lambda}{\mu}\right)^i P_0 + K\left[\frac{1}{K!}\left(\frac{\lambda}{\mu}\right)^K + \frac{(\lambda/\mu)^{K+1}}{KK!(1 - \lambda/K\mu)}\right] P_0$$

$$= \sum_{i=1}^{K} \frac{i}{i!} \left(\frac{\lambda}{\mu}\right)^i P_0 + \frac{(\lambda/\mu)^{K+1}}{K!(1 - \lambda/K\mu)} P_0$$

$$E(h) = \frac{\lambda}{\mu} \sum_{i=1}^{K} \frac{1}{(i-1)!} \left(\frac{\lambda}{\mu}\right)^{i-1} P_0 + \frac{(\lambda/\mu)^{K+1}}{K!(1 - \lambda/K\mu)} P_0 \qquad (3.140)$$

The summation in (3.140) is evaluated by recognizing that

$$\sum_{i=0}^{K} \frac{i}{i!} \left(\frac{\lambda}{\mu}\right)^i P_0 + \frac{(\lambda/\mu)^{K+1}}{KK!(1 - \lambda/K\mu)} P_0 = 1$$

Therefore

$$\sum_{i=1}^{K} \frac{1}{(i-1)!} \left(\frac{\lambda}{\mu}\right)^{i-1} P_0 = 1 - \frac{(\lambda/\mu)^{K+1}}{KK!(1 - \lambda/K\mu)} P_0 - \frac{1}{K!}\left(\frac{\lambda}{\mu}\right)^K P_0 \qquad (3.141)$$

Substituting (3.141) in (3.140), we have

$$E(h) = \frac{\lambda}{\mu} - \frac{(\lambda/\mu)^{K+2}}{KK!(1 - \lambda/K\mu)} P_0 - \frac{1}{K!} \left(\frac{\lambda}{\mu}\right)^{K+1} P_0 + \frac{(\lambda/\mu)^{K+1}}{K!(1 - \lambda/K\mu)} P_0$$

$$E(h) = \frac{\lambda}{\mu} \tag{3.142}$$

MULTIPLE CHANNELS IN SERIES

One of the most difficult queueing systems to treat is that in which several service channels and their associated queues are arranged in series. In order for an arriving unit to complete service it must pass through each service channel. The type of queueing system we are considering is illustrated in Figure 3.3.

FIGURE 3.3
Service Channels in Series

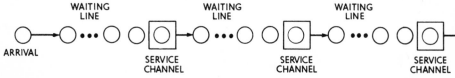

Our discussion of service channels in series will be limited to an attempt to present a general approach which may be employed in analyzing such systems. To illustrate the approach, let us consider a simple system in which two channels are arranged in series with the restriction that no queue is allowed in front of either channel. If a unit arrives and the first channel is full, the unit leaves the system. When service on a unit in the first channel is completed, the unit leaves this channel and immediately enters the second channel if it is empty. If a unit seeks service in the second channel when this channel is full, the unit must wait in the first channel until completion of service in the second channel: the first channel is said to be blocked. Upon completion of service in the second channel, the unit leaves the system. Therefore a blocked condition in the second channel is impossible. We will assume arrivals are Poisson distributed with parameter λ and service times are exponentially distributed with parameter μ for both channels. The system may be in any one of the following five states.

(0, 0) – Both the first and second channels are empty.

(0, 1) – The first channel is empty and the second channel is servicing.

(1, 0) – The first channel is servicing and the second channel is empty.

(1, 1) – Both the first and second channels are servicing.

(b, 1) – The first channel is blocked and the second channel is servicing.

The probability that the system is in a given state at time t is given by $P_{ij}(t)$, $i = 0, 1, b; j = 0, 1$.

$$P_{00}(t) = P_{00}(t - \Delta t)(1 - \lambda \Delta t e^{-\lambda \Delta t})$$
$$+ P_{01}(t - \Delta t)\mu \Delta t e^{-\mu \Delta t}(1 - \lambda \Delta t e^{-\lambda \Delta t})$$

$$\frac{dP_{00}(t)}{dt} = -\lambda P_{00}(t) + \mu P_{01}(t) \tag{3.143}$$

Taking the limit of (3.143) as $t \to \infty$ to obtain the steady-state condition, we have

$$P_{01} = \frac{\lambda}{\mu} P_{00} \tag{3.144}$$

$$P_{01}(t) = P_{10}(t - \Delta t)\mu \Delta t e^{-\mu \Delta t}(1 - \lambda \Delta t e^{-\lambda \Delta t})$$
$$+ P_{b1}(t - \Delta t)\mu \Delta t e^{-\mu \Delta t}(1 - \lambda \Delta t e^{-\lambda \Delta t})$$
$$+ P_{01}(t - \Delta t)(1 - \lambda \Delta t e^{-\lambda \Delta t})(1 - \mu \Delta t e^{-\mu \Delta t}) \tag{3.145}$$

In the steady state

$$0 = \mu P_{10} + \mu P_{b1} - (\lambda + \mu)P_{01} \tag{3.146}$$

By similar argument we have

$$P_{10}(t) = P_{00}(t - \Delta t)\lambda \Delta t e^{-\lambda \Delta t} + P_{10}(t - \Delta t)(1 - \lambda \Delta t e^{-\lambda \Delta t})(1 - \mu \Delta t e^{-\mu \Delta t})$$
$$+ P_{11}(t - \Delta t)\mu \Delta t e^{-\mu \Delta t}$$
$$+ P_{10}(t - \Delta t)\lambda \Delta t e^{-\lambda \Delta t}(1 - \mu \Delta t e^{-\mu \Delta t}) \tag{3.147}$$

In developing equation (3.147) we must remember that if an arrival occurs when the system is in state (1,0), the arriving unit must leave the system because no queue is allowed in front of either channel. The steady-state solution of (3.147) is given by

$$0 = \lambda P_{00} - \mu P_{10} + \mu P_{11} \tag{3.148}$$

$P_{11}(t)$ is expressed by

$$P_{11}(t) = P_{01}(t - \Delta t)\lambda \Delta t e^{-\lambda \Delta t}(1 - \mu \Delta t e^{-\mu \Delta t})$$
$$+ P_{11}(t - \Delta t)(1 - \mu \Delta t e^{-\mu \Delta t})^2 \qquad (3.149)$$

$$0 = \lambda P_{01} - 2\mu P_{11} \qquad (3.150)$$

Solving for P_{01}, P_{10}, P_{11}, and P_{b1} in terms of P_{00} yields

$$P_{01} = \frac{\lambda}{\mu} P_{00} \qquad (3.151)$$

$$P_{10} = \frac{\lambda}{\mu}\left(1 + \frac{\lambda}{2\mu}\right)P_{00} \qquad (3.152)$$

$$P_{11} = \frac{1}{2}\left(\frac{\lambda}{\mu}\right)^2 P_{00} \qquad (3.153)$$

$$P_{b1} = \frac{1}{2}\left(\frac{\lambda}{\mu}\right)^2 P_{00} \qquad (3.154)$$

$$P_{00} + P_{01} + P_{10} + P_{11} + P_{b1} = 1$$

Solving for P_{00}, we have

$$P_{00} = \frac{2}{2 + 4\dfrac{\lambda}{\mu} + 3\left(\dfrac{\lambda}{\mu}\right)^2} \qquad (3.155)$$

$$P_{01} = \frac{2(\lambda/\mu)}{2 + 4\dfrac{\lambda}{\mu} + 3\left(\dfrac{\lambda}{\mu}\right)^2} \qquad (3.156)$$

$$P_{10} = \frac{2(\lambda/\mu)(1 + \lambda/2\mu)}{2 + 4\dfrac{\lambda}{\mu} + 3\left(\dfrac{\lambda}{\mu}\right)^2} \qquad (3.157)$$

$$P_{11} = \frac{(\lambda/\mu)^2}{2 + 4\dfrac{\lambda}{\mu} + 3\left(\dfrac{\lambda}{\mu}\right)^2} \qquad (3.158)$$

$$P_{b1} = \frac{(\lambda/\mu)^2}{2 + 4\dfrac{\lambda}{\mu} + 3\left(\dfrac{\lambda}{\mu}\right)^2} \qquad (3.159)$$

The expected number of units in the system is given by

$$E(n) = \frac{4(\lambda/\mu) + 5(\lambda/\mu)^2}{2 + 4\dfrac{\lambda}{\mu} + 3\left(\dfrac{\lambda}{\mu}\right)^2} \qquad (3.160)$$

As the queue length in front of either or both channels is increased, the solution for P becomes more and more complex. For example, if we allow no queue before the first channel and a maximum queue length of one before the second channel, the resulting steady-state equations are given by

$$\mu P_{01} - \lambda P_{00} = 0$$

$$-(\lambda + \mu)P_{01} + \mu P_{02} + \mu P_{10} = 0$$

$$\lambda P_{00} - \mu P_{10} + \mu P_{11} = 0$$

$$\lambda P_{01} - 2\mu P_{11} + \mu P_{12} = 0 \qquad\qquad (3.161)$$

$$-(\lambda + \mu)P_{02} + \mu P_{11} + \mu P_{b2} = 0$$

$$\lambda P_{02} - 2\mu P_{12} = 0$$

$$P_{00} + P_{01} + P_{02} + P_{10} + P_{11} + P_{12} + P_{b2} = 1$$

The solution to the system of equations given in (3.161) is given below.

$$P_{00} = \frac{4 + \lambda/\mu}{Q}$$

$$P_{01} = \frac{(\lambda/\mu)(4 + \lambda/\mu)}{Q}$$

$$P_{02} = \frac{2(\lambda/\mu)^2}{Q}$$

$$P_{10} = \frac{(\lambda/\mu)[4 + 3(\lambda/\mu) + (\lambda/\mu)^2]}{Q} \qquad\qquad (3.162)$$

$$P_{11} = \frac{(\lambda/\mu)^2[2 + (\lambda/\mu)]}{Q}$$

$$P_{12} = \frac{(\lambda/\mu)^3}{Q}$$

$$P_{b2} = \frac{(\lambda/\mu)^3}{Q}$$

where

$$Q = 4 + 9(\lambda/\mu) + 8(\lambda/\mu)^2 + 4(\lambda/\mu)^3 \qquad\qquad (3.163)$$

OTHER QUEUEING SYSTEMS

The systems discussed in the preceding three sections of this chapter are the most basic encountered in queueing theory. These systems might be considered the basic building blocks of queueing theory to the extent that most of the commonly encountered queueing systems can be developed by altering the conditions governing the basic systems. Usually the solutions for these modified systems are more complex than for the basic systems.

Control of the operation of a service system is governed by the distribution of arrivals, the behaviour of individual arrivals, the servicing mechanism, the queue discipline, and the capacity of the system. We have assumed that the distribution of interarrival time is exponential. Other frequently encountered interarrival time distributions include the gamma, hyperexponential, and normal distributions. The gamma and hyperexponential distributions are not too difficult to deal with since they can be related to the exponential distribution. However, the normal distribution introduces problems which can be extremely difficult to resolve.

When an arrival reaches the system, he may behave in several different ways. He may decide not to enter the system at all because of the length of the waiting line. Such behavior is called balking. The arrival may enter the system and then decide to leave it (reneging), or he may decide to leave one waiting line in the system to enter another shorter line (jockeying). The common denominatior of each of these modes of behavior is that the action of the arrival is completely voluntary.

The serving mechanism in a queueing system is specified by the number of serving channels, their arrangement (parallel, series), and the distribution of service time within each channel. The most difficult serving mechanisms to test mathematically are those involving a sequence of channels (single or multiple in parallel) in series, such as the system shown in Figure 3.4. However, such systems can be simulated, as we shall see in our discussion of the simulation of queueing systems.

The queue discipline of a system controls the order in which arrivals are served. Usually arrivals are served on a first-come first-serve basis, but random service and priority service are not unusual. Priorities are preemptive if an arriving unit may enter service immediately whether another unit is being served or not. That is, if an arriving unit has a higher priority than the unit being served

FIGURE 3.4

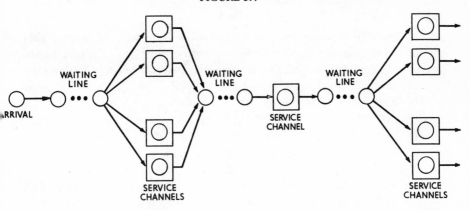

and that priority is preemptive, then the unit in service is immediately replaced by the arrival.

The capacity of a system is determined by the maximum number of units which are allowed in the system at the same time. We usually think of capacity as a constant for a given system, although there are situations in which capacity must be considered a random variable.

Although the mathematical analysis of the systems discussed in this section will not be given, we will discuss simulation of several of these systems.

PROBLEMS
Queueing Theory

1. A supermarket operates one check-out counter. The time to check out a customer is exponentially distributed with mean time three minutes. Customers arrive at the counter according to a Poisson distribution with mean rate 15 per hour. Find:

a) The mean time a customer spends waiting to be checked out.

b) The mean total time a customer spends at the check-out counter (waiting time plus check-out time).

c) The mean number of customers at the check-out counter.

2. How much would the mean service time have to be decreased in problem 1 to cut the mean waiting time in half?

3. It has been suggested that the mean waiting time in problem 1 could be reduced by adding one or more check-out counters to that already in service. How many extra counters would be necessary to reduce the mean waiting time to one third of the value calculated in problem 1? Assume that the extra counters are identical to that described in problem 1.

4. Solve the problem given in example 3.4 if the total cost of serving a unit is given by $C_T = C_1 \mu + C_2 t^2$ where t is the waiting time.

5. The time between successive arrivals at a car wash is exponentially distributed with an average time between arrivals of 0.10 hours. Cars are washed one at a time on a first-come first-served basis. The time taken to wash a car is also exponentially distributed with mean 0.06 hours. Find:

a) The mean time a car spends waiting to be washed.

b) The mean total time in the system.

c) The probability that a car does not wait to be washed.

6. Patients arrive at a small clinic for treatment in a Poisson fashion with mean rate of four per hour. Patients are treated one at a time on a first-come first-served basis. The time spent with a patient is exponentially distributed with mean time 12 minutes. A waiting room is to be provided with seating capacity such that the probability that a patient will have to stand upon arrival is 0.10. What should the seating capacity be?

7. A service station operates four gasoline pumps. The time to serve a customer is exponentially distributed with mean rate of five minutes. Cars arrive for gas in a Poisson fashion with mean rate 30 per hour. If a car arrives and no pumps are available, the sale is lost. If the average gasoline sale is $4 per car, how much can the service station manager expect to lose per day because of driver impatience?

8. An appliance repair shop guarantees that it can repair certain failures in appliances within an hour. The guarantee states that if the customer is forced to wait more than an hour, he gets the repair free. The average charge per repair is $5 and the average cost of the repair to the shop is $3, yielding an average profit of $2 per repair. Appliances are brought to the shop for repair in a poisson fashion with mean rate of eight per hour. Service time per repairman is exponentially distributed with a mean service time of five minutes. The shop employs one repairman. Can the shop operate profitably under this guarantee?

9. In problem 8 suppose that the result of the guarantee was to increase the demand for repairs to 16 per hour. How many repairmen will be required to operate profitably under the guarantee? Assume the costs given in problem 4.

10. Assume that problem 9 is to be solved by increasing the mean service rate rather than the number of repairmen. What mean service rate would be required to operate profitably under the guarantee?

11. In problem 7, if the probability that a driver will refuse to wait for an available pump is 0.5, how much can the manager expect to lose because of driver impatience?

12. A parking lot has space for 100 cars. The time a car spends in the lot is exponentially distributed with a mean of 50 minutes. Arrivals to the lot are poisson distributed with mean arrival rate at 200 per hour. If a car arrives and no space is available, it does not wait for service.

a) What is the average occupancy for the lot?

b) What is the average number of lost sales per day, assuming the parking lot remains open 24 hours a day?

13. Assume that you are to design the parking lot described in problem 12. Each parking space provided costs $300 per year to maintain. Each car is charged $0.75 regarless of how long it remains in the lot. What should the capacity of the parking lot be to maximize annual profit? Ignore the initial cost of constructing the lot.

14. Assuming the capacity specified in problem 13, what is the minimum arrival rate per hour such that the parking lot can be operated profitably?

15. Derive an expression for the expected number of units in the waiting line for a single channel Poisson queueing system for (a) Restricted queue length and (b) Unrestricted queue length.

16. Find the expected number of units in a system with K channels in parallel and a maximum capacity of N units where $N > K$. Interarrival and service time are both exponential.

17. Derive the distribution of the total time a unit spends in a system with K channels in parallel, unrestricted capacity, and exponential service and interarrival times.

18. Suppose that the distribution of time between successive arrivals to a system is gamma with parameters λ and r. Find the distribution of the number of arrivals in T, when $r = 2$. That is, if x is the time between successive arrivals, then $f_X(x) = \lambda^2 x e^{-\lambda x}$, $0 < x < \infty$.

19. A mail-order house receives orders for one of its products in a Poisson fashion with mean rate λ per unit time. The number of units requested per order is geometrically distributed with parameter p. Find the distribution of the number of units demanded per unit time.

(Hint: Derive the distribution of the number of units demanded given n orders were placed and multiply by the probability that n orders occurred.)

20. A company manufactures a certain product. One of two defects may appear in the product, and each is detected as soon as it occurs. The first defect occurs at a rate λ_1 per time unit and the second at a rate λ_2 per time unit. If the occurrence of each defect is Poisson distributed with parameters as given and service for either defect is exponentially distributed with mean rate μ, find the expected number of unrepaired units at any time, assuming repairs occur one at a time and are carried out on a first-come first-served basis.

21. Two service channels are arranged in parallel. The first has service μ_1 and the second μ_2. Service time for both is exponentially distributed. Arrivals are Poisson distributed with parameter λ. Assume that $\mu_1 > \mu_2$ and that if a unit has a choice it will always enter the channel with the highest service rate. Derive the distribution of the number of units in the system and the waiting line, assuming unrestricted queue length.

22. Two channels are arranged in series. No queue is allowed between the two channels. However, a queue of one unit is allowed in front of the first channel. The arrival distribution is Poisson with parameter λ. Service time for both channels is exponentially distributed with mean rate μ. Find the probability mass function of the number of units in the system and the expected number of units in the system.

23. Solve problem 22 if the mean service rates for the first and second channels are μ_1 and μ_2, respectively.

24. The distribution of arrivals to a single channel queue with unrestricted capacity is Poisson with parameter λ. Service time is exponential with mean rate $n\mu$ where n is the number of units in the system. That is, as the queue length increases, the service rate increases proportionally. Find the distribution of the total number of units in the system.

(Hint: Note that the probability of a service in time Δt given n units are in the system is given by $P(\text{service in } \Delta t \,|\, n) = n\mu\Delta t e^{-(\lambda + n\mu)\,\Delta t}$.

25. By noting that

$$e^{-a} = \sum_{k=0}^{\infty} \frac{(-a)^k}{k!}$$

show that $b\Delta t e^{-c\,\Delta t} \to b\Delta t$ as $\Delta t \to 0$. The reader will notice that this relationship could have been used throughout the analyses presented in this chapter.

26. Assume that K channels are arranged in parallel, each with mean service rate μ. If the mean arrival rate is λ and the system has unrestricted capacity, is it necessary that $\lambda/\mu < 1$ if the system is to reach a steady state?

REFERENCES

Bailey, N. T. J. *The Elements of Stochastic Processes with Applications to the Natural Sciences.* New York: John Wiley & Sons, Inc., 1964.

Bhat, V. N. *A Study of the Queueing Systems M/G/1 and GI/M/1.* New York: Springer-Verlag, 1968.

Feller, W. *An Introduction to Probability Theory and Its Applications,* Vol I. New York: John Wiley & Sons, Inc., 1950.

Haight, F. A. *Mathematical Theories of Traffic Flow.* New York: Academic Press, 1963.

Karlin, S. *A First Course in Stochastic Processes.* New York: Academic Press, 1966.

Morris, W. T. *Analysis for Materials Handling Management.* Homewood, Ill.: Richard D. Irwin, Inc., 1962.

Morse, P. M. *Queues, Inventories and Maintenance.* New York: John Wiley & Sons, Inc., 1962.

Parzen, E.   *Stochastic Processes.* San Francisco: Holden-Day, Inc., 1962.

Prabhu, N. V.   *Queues and Inventories.* New York: John Wiley & Sons, Inc., 1965.

Riordan, J.   *Stochastic Service Systems.* New York: John Wiley & Sons, Inc., 1962.

Saaty, T. L.   *Elements of Queueing Theory.* New York: McGraw-Hill Book Co., Inc., 1961.

CHAPTER
4

INVENTORY SYSTEMS

In order for a business to function successfully, inventories of one type or another must be maintained. A retailer must carry a sufficient variety and quantity of the goods he sells to satisfy the desires of his customers. The manufacturer must maintain not only an inventory of the finished product he sells but also a supply of the raw materials required for production and in some cases a supply of partially finished products, called an in-process inventory. Similarly, a service organization must carry an inventory of the items necessary to provide the service. For example, a laundry must maintain a supply of cleaning materials, a repair shop must carry a stock of replacement parts, and an airline must carry enough food to serve its passengers. In analyzing inventory problems such as these, the question to be answered is not whether to carry an inventory but what should the size of the inventory be and how can such an inventory be maintained.

As units are withdrawn from inventory the inventory level will fall and a point will be reached at which it will be necessary to replenish the stock. This point is called the reorder point. When the inventory reaches or falls below the reorder point, an order is placed for a supply of units which will raise the inventory level when it arrives. The number of units requested on each order is called the order quantity. By controlling the reorder point and order quantity we may be able to control, at least in a probabilistic sense, the number of units carried in inventory. Therefore our objective in this chapter will be to develop decision rules or operating policies for inventory systems which specify when and how much to order.

DEMAND AND LEAD TIME

Obviously the demand for a product will influence the size of the inventory maintained. A demand occurs whenever an attempt to purchase an item occurs. It is important that the inventory analyst recognize the distinction between a demand and a sale. A sale occurs only when the customer successfully attempts to purchase an item. For example, if a customer requests an item but none is available, a demand occurs but a sale does not. The customer may take his business elsewhere, in which case the sale is lost, or he may be willing to wait until the stock is replenished to purchase the item, in which case the demand is said to be back ordered.

As the demand rate increases, the frequency with which orders are placed and/or the number of units requested per order will increase. Similarly the predictability of demand will influence the operating policy. If the demand in any period of time can be predicted with certainty (deterministic demand), we can develop an operating policy which will eliminate the possibility of a stock-out or restrict the magnitude of the stock-out to any desired level. However, if we can predict demand only in a probabilistic sense (stochastic demand), the resulting operating policy will require a safety stock to guard against an excessive stock-out should a period of high demand occur. Therefore the average inventory level will be higher with stochastic demand than would be true for deterministic demand, if the only difference between the two is in the nature of demand where the average demand rate per unit time is the same in both cases. We will discuss both deterministic and stochastic demand in this chapter.

Procurement lead time, or merely lead time, is the time delay between the decision to place an order and its receipt. Lead time has a significant bearing upon the point in time at which an order is placed. For example, if an order is to be received in stock on Friday and lead time is three days, the order must be placed on Tuesday. Lead time may be a constant or a random variable. Discussion of the mathematical analysis of inventory systems involving probabilistic lead time is beyond the scope of this text, but we will discuss the simulation of such systems in a subsequent chapter.

PERTINENT COSTS

The costs which arise due to the manner in which an inventory system is operated are among the most significant factors in determining the operating policy for that system. The most obvious cost incurred in operating an inventory system is that of carrying a unit in inventory for a given period of time. The costs which make up the carrying charge include inventory taxes, insurance, product damage during storage, the cost of storage space, and lost return on investment. Although the last cost is not an out-of-pocket expense, it is nonetheless a real cost. Every unit of product which is manufactured or purchased requires an investment of capital. As long as each unit is in inventory it yields no return on the investment. Therefore in every inventory system an attempt should be made to minimize the unit-years of inventory carried. That is, no unit should be carried in inventory for a long period of time.

The inventory carrying cost can be reduced by decreasing the average inventory level. However, as the average inventory level is decreased, the chance of being unable to meet customer demand is increased. As we have already pointed out, if a demand occurs during a stock-out period either a back order or lost sale results. If a stock-out results in a lost sale, the profit which would have been realized from the sale is lost. In addition there will be some loss of goodwill. The cost of lost goodwill is difficult to estimate but is by no means a fictitious cost, since a lost sale today can result in lost demand tomorrow, the customer taking his business elsewhere.

Although there may be no loss of profit when a back order occurs, a loss of goodwill usually occurs. The cost of this loss would, in some way, be proportional to the extent of the delay in filling the customer's order. Further, if the delay is of sufficient extent, the back order may turn into a lost sale.

In addition to carrying costs and stock-out costs, the costs of placing an order and maintaining the inventory system must be recognized. When an order is placed, it must be processed and approved before being issued. If the order is not placed with an outside supplier but, instead, results in an internal production order, the cost of ordering is the cost of setting up production to manufacture the items requested on the order.

Finally we must recognize the cost of carrying out the operating policy once it has been established. The cost of maintaining the inventory system depends upon the system to be established. If the system ties up a computer for long peiods of time, the cost of maintaining the system will be significant. On the other hand, many inventory systems require only a few man-hours per week for effective maintainance.

In this chapter we will attempt to incorporate these costs in a mathematical equation or model such that given any operating policy, the average annual cost of executing that policy can be computed. We will then be in a position to manipulate the model to determine the optimal operating policy.

OPERATING POLICY

We have already pointed out that an inventory system should provide a means for determining when and how much to order. An example of an operating policy in its simplest form would be to place an order for Q units at the end of each week. We could complicate the operating policy slightly by specifying that the order for Q units should be placed at the end of the week only if the inventory level at that time is r units or less. A still more complex operating policy would be to place an order for Q units at the end of the week whenever the sum of the number of units in inventory plus the number of units included in outstanding orders is less than r. In each of these three examples the operating policy clearly indicates when and how much to order.

We will classify inventory systems according to how often the status of the system is reviewed for the purpose of determining whether the inventory should be replenished. If the system is such that a review takes place every time an event occurs which affects the system, we have a reorder point system. If reviews occur at uniform intervals of time, regardless of the number of events which might have taken place between successive reviews, we have a periodic review system. It is important to point out that by "events affecting the system" we mean any event which might affect our decision to place an order, not just events which affect the physical inventory. For example, demands which occur during a stock-out do not affect the physical inventory but may result in a decision to replenish inventory.

Intuitively one might guess that an operating doctrine for either the recorder point or periodic review systems would be to place an order for a given number of units if the inventory level is at or below some predetermined point at the time of the review. However, inventory level is a deceiving basis for the decision to place an order. Let us analyze what might happen if we were to use this intuitive approach in a reorder point system. Suppose the operating policy is to place an order for 100 units whenever the inventory level falls below 25 units. For simplicity we will assume units are demanded one at a time. As soon as the inventory level falls to 24 units we would place an order for 100 units. We will assume that there are no orders outstanding at the time the inventory level falls to 24 units. Suppose 20 more units are demanded between the time the original order was placed and its reception. According to our operating policy we would place 20 more orders, each for 100 units. Therefore we could expect to receive 21 orders in rather rapid succession for a total of 2,100 units received. Obviously if we us inventory level as a basis for ordering excessive inventories can result. To circumvent this situation we might modify the operating policy such that orders are placed whenever the inventory level reaches 24 units, the next order being placed only when the inventory level reaches 24 units again. However, this policy serves only to take us from one extreme to the other—in effect, from the frying pan into the fire. We have specified an operating policy which would eventually lead to a perpetual stock-out condition. For example, suppose 200 units were demanded during the lead time. Net inventory after receipt of the order would be −76 units. Our policy dictates that another order would not be placed because an inventory level of 24 units has not been reached and, under our operating policy, could never again be reached.

To resolve both these problems, inventory position is usually used to determine when to order. Inventory position is the net inventory plus the total number of units included in outstanding orders. Net inventory may be positive (the physical stock of goods has not been exhausted), negative (demand has been back ordered), or zero (nothing in inventory and no back orders). Using inventory position as the basis for placing an order in the above example, we would place an order for 100 units whenever the inventory position falls to or below 24 units. If units are demanded one at a time, inventory position will fluctuate between 24 and 124 units.

There is no guarantee that extensive stock-out periods will not occur when inventory position is used as a basis for ordering in the case of stochastic demand. However, excessive inventories will not result, and the chance that an extensive stock-out period will occur is reduced below what it would be if inventory level were used as the decision variable. A graphical representation of the simultaneous fluctuation of inventory position and net inventory level is shown in Figure 4.1, where the reorder point is 25 units, the reorder quantity is 100 units, lead time is five days, and units are demanded one at a time. Initially, net inventory and inventory position are assumed to be the same.

FIGURE 4.1
Simultaneous Fluctuation of Inventory Position and Net Inventory

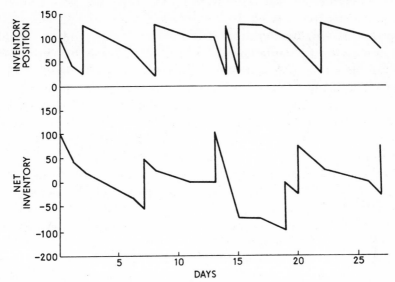

The reordering policies which we shall discuss fall into three categories. The simplest policy is that of ordering Q units whenever an order is placed, where Q can assume any positive integer value. In the second policy the order quantity is constant but must be a multiple of some fixed quantity Q. For example, in purchasing soft drinks from a dealer, we might be restricted to ordering by the case. Here Q would be 24. The order quantity would be designated nQ where n is positive and integer valued. In the last policy we will discuss, the order quantity is not fixed: the order quantity is the number of units necessary to bring inventory position to some predetermined level R. Any of these ordering policies can be used in conjunction with either a reorder point system or a periodic review system.

THE INVENTORY MODEL

In the preceding pages we have discussed the considerations pertinent to the development of an effective inventory system. It now remains to put these concepts together in a fashion which will result in the desired system. We will accomplish this by developing a mathematical representation of the inventory systems under study. The mathematical model will provide a means of measuring the effectiveness of the system developed. The measure of effectiveness will usually be the cost resulting from the use of the derived system, for some specified period of time, although in some instances profit may be used for this purpose. If the mathematical model is reliable, for any given operating policy we should be able to predict the average cost of operating the inventory system for the period of time for which the model was developed and for any given combination of costs, demand distribution, lead time distribution, and so forth. Some of the variables included in the model will be under the control of the system designer. There are usually the variables which determine the operating policy, the reorder quantity, the reorder point, and in the periodic review system, the time between successive reviews. By optimizing the model with respect to these variables, one can obtain the operating doctrine which minimizes the cost of maintaining the system or maximizes the corresponding profit. Usually the analyst would develop mathematical models for several alternative systems, determine the optimal operating policy for each, compare the resulting optimal costs or profits, and select the most economical system for implementation.

DETERMINISTIC INVENTORY SYSTEMS

We will begin our discussion of inventory systems and their associated models with a particularly simple class of systems in which demand and lead time are predictable with certainty and constant over time. Although these systems bear only limited relation to reality (since demand is almost never predictable except in a probabilistic sense), analysis of these systems will provide a foundation for the development of mathematical models for more complicated and realistic inventory systems.

For the models developed in this section we will assume an annual demand rate of λ and lead time Υ. We will further assume that demand occurs uniformly throughout the period under study so that the number of units demanded in any given period of time is constant and independent of the point in time at which the period begins. For those models in which we must account for the rate of production of manufactured units we will assume a constant annual production rate of ψ.

Whenever an order to replenish inventory is placed we will assume a cost C_o is incurred, regardless of the size of the order. The cost of carrying inventory, C_I, will be measured in dollars per unit-year and will therefore be proportional to both the amount in stock and the period of time that that level is maintained. For each lost sale incurred, a cost C_L results. We shall assume that the cost of a back order is linearly dependent upon the interval of time for which the back order exists. As soon as a back order occurs, a cost C_b is incurred. If this back order lasts for a period of time, t, an additional cost, $C_\beta t$ results where t is measured in years. Therefore the total cost of a back order is given by $C_b + C_\beta t$. We shall define the total cost of operation for the period under study as $C_T(a,b,c, \ldots)$ where $a,b,c,$ and so on are the decision variables or variables under the control of the system designer.

In each of the inventory systems analyzed here we will assume that an order for Q units, or nQ (where orders must be in multiples of the basic lot size Q) units, is placed whenever the inventory position reaches r units (reorder point). Sometimes it will be convenient to express the reorder point in terms of time instead of inventory position. For this purpose we will define T_r as the time interval in years between the placement of two successive orders. We will let s be the maximum number of back orders or lost sales accumulated between the receipt of two consecutive orders.

Demand will be treated as a continuous variable in all but one of the models developed in this section. Although this is, for the most part, an approximation to reality, it is usually adequate for practical purposes. To illustrate the manner in which the discrete nature of demand can be accounted for, we will formulate one of the simplest models, taking account of the integrality of demand.

As discussed earlier we will usually use inventory position as a basis for placing an order to replenish inventory. However, for most deterministic systems we could, with equal reliability, use net inventory as a basis for this decision. The problems discussed earlier connected with the use of inventory level or net inventory as a basis for ordering were founded on the assumption that an unusually large number of demands could occur in any given period of time. When demand can be predicted with certainty, the foundation for these problems is removed.

I. Basic lot size model—zero lead time, no back orders or lost sales. If the occurrence of each demand can be predicted with certainty and lead time is known and constant, it is possible to develop an inventory operating policy such that the number and duration of back orders can be controlled with equal certainty. This is also true of the number of lost sales when stock-outs result in lost sales rather than back orders. In the problem we are now considering we wish to develop an operating policy which will prevent stock-outs from occurring. We assume that orders are received as soon as they are placed, resulting in zero lead time. Our inventory operating policy will be to order Q units whenever inventory position reaches r units. We will develop a mathematical model representing the annual cost of operating the system for any values of Q and r and optimize the model by finding the values of Q and r which minimize the annual cost of maintaining the inventory system.

A diagrammatic representation of the fluctuation in inventory position with lead time under a Q,r policy is shown in Figure 4.2.

FIGURE 4.2
Inventory Position (Inventory Level) versus Time

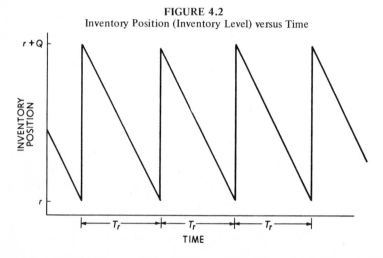

The fact that the time between placing successive orders is constant is the result of the assumption that demand is constant over time. Since lead time is zero, inventory position and inventory level coincide identically.

Since back orders or lost sales are not to be tolerated, we have only two costs involved in this system: the ordering cost and the inventory carrying cost. To determine the total annual cost we must find the annual cost of ordering and the annual cost of carrying stock in inventory and add them together. Each time an order is placed a cost C_0 results. Therefore the annual ordering cost is C_0 times the number of orders placed per year. Since orders are placed every T_r years, the number of orders per year is given by $1/T_r$. Therefore

$$\text{Annual ordering cost} = \frac{C_o}{T_r} \tag{4.1}$$

We can express T_r in terms of Q by recognizing that T_r is the time taken for Q demands. Since the annual demand rate is λ and demand is spread uniformly throughout the year,

$$T_r = \frac{Q}{\lambda} \tag{4.2}$$

Therefore

$$\text{Annual ordering cost} = \frac{\lambda}{Q} C_o \tag{4.3}$$

To obtain the annual inventory carrying cost we must determine the unit-years of inventory per period of length T_r, multiply by C_I, and multiply this product by the number of periods of length T_r per year. The unit-years of inventory in each period of length T_r is given by the area under the inventory position curve in Figure 4.2 for a period T_r.

$$\text{Unit years of inventory per } T_r = \int_0^{Q/\lambda} (Q + r - \lambda t)\, dt \tag{4.4}$$

$$= \frac{rQ}{\lambda} + \frac{Q^2}{2\lambda} \tag{4.5}$$

Since there are λ/Q such periods, the annual carrying cost is given by

$$\text{Annual carrying cost} = \left(\frac{rQ}{\lambda} + \frac{Q^2}{2\lambda}\right) \frac{\lambda}{Q} C_I \tag{4.6}$$

$$= \left(r + \frac{Q}{2}\right) C_I \tag{4.7}$$

Adding (4.3) and (4.7), we have the total annual cost of using the Q,r operating policy.

$$C_T(r, Q) = \frac{\lambda}{Q} C_o + \left(r + \frac{Q}{2}\right) C_I \tag{4.8}$$

It is obvious that the value of r minimizing (4.8) is zero. Since r is the amount of inventory on hand when an order is received (as well as the reorder point here), we are saying that no buffer or safety stock is necessary to guard against unusual demand conditions which might occur just prior to the receipt of an order. This is as would be expected, since demand conditions are known with certainty. Thus (4.8) becomes

$$C_T(Q) = \frac{\lambda}{Q} C_o + \frac{Q}{2} C_I \tag{4.9}$$

To find the value of Q which minimizes (4.9) we must differentiate with respect to Q.

$$\frac{dC_T(Q)}{dQ} = 0 = -\frac{\lambda}{Q^2}C_o + \frac{C_I}{2} \tag{4.10}$$

Solving for Q, we have

$$Q = \sqrt{\frac{2\lambda C_o}{C_I}} \tag{4.11}$$

The optimal value of Q is the positive root given by (4.11) and the resulting minimum annual cost is given by (4.12).

$$C_T(Q) = \sqrt{2\lambda C_o C_I} \tag{4.12}$$

The operating policy is therefore to order

$$\sqrt{\frac{2\lambda C_o}{C_I}}$$

units whenever the inventory position falls to zero.

Example 4.1

A production line requires the supply of a particular chemical at a uniform rate, 24 hours a day, seven days a week. The annual rate of consumption is one million pounds. The chemical is shipped by rail. Each time a shipment is made it costs $500 plus the cost of the chemical, which is $2 per pound. The inventory carrying cost is $0.40 per pound per year. How much should be delivered at each shipment and how often should deliveries be made? What is the annual cost of the inventory system?

It should be noted that the cost of product itself need not be considered a cost of operating the inventory system, since this cost will be incurred no matter how often shipments are made or how much is carried in inventory.

$$Q = \sqrt{\frac{2\lambda C_o}{C_I}} = \sqrt{\frac{2(1,000,000)(500)}{0.40}} = 50,000$$

The time between the receipt of shipments is

$$T_r = \frac{Q}{\lambda} = \frac{50,000}{1,000,000} = 0.05 \text{ years}$$

The total cost of maintaining the inventory system is

$$C_T(Q) = \sqrt{2\lambda C_o C_I} = \sqrt{2(1,000,000)(500)(0.4)} = \$20,000$$

II. Lot size model—constant lead time, no back orders or lost sales. The system under study here is identical to that just discussed, except that we shall now assume that lead time has a constant value Υ. A comparison of the fluctuation of inventory position with inventory level is given in Figure 4.3. As Figure 4.3 indicates, the most economical operating policy will be one such that the receipt of an order occurs just as the inventory level reaches zero. However, since lead time is positive instead of zero, the reorder point, in terms of inventory position, is not zero as in the previous example.

FIGURE 4.3
Fluctuation of Inventory Position with On-Hand Inventory

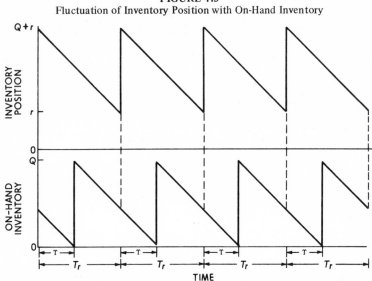

We calculate the annual cost of ordering exactly as in the previous model.

$$\text{Annual ordering cost} = \frac{C_o}{T_r}$$

$$= \frac{\lambda}{Q} C_o$$

(4.13)

The reorder point r can be calculated by recognizing that r must be equal to the number of units demanded in Υ, provided Υ is less than one cycle in length. If $\Upsilon = mT_r + \epsilon$ where m is a nonnegative integer and $0 < \epsilon < 1$, then r is equal to the lead time demand minus the number of units to be received during Υ. Therefore

$$r = \lambda \Upsilon - mQ \qquad (4.14)$$

where m is the largest integer less than $\lambda \Upsilon / Q$.

If an order is placed when the inventory position reaches r, the inventory level will be zero when the order arrives. If we stipulate the value for r given in (4.14), then the inventory carrying cost is calculated as before. Note that the inventory level is Q at the beginning of each cycle[1] and falls to zero after Q/λ years. Since there are λ/Q such cycles, the annual inventory carrying charge is given by

$$\text{Annual carrying cost} = C_I \frac{\lambda}{Q} \int_0^{Q/\lambda} (Q - \lambda t)\, dt \qquad (4.15)$$

$$= \frac{Q}{2} C_I \qquad (4.16)$$

Adding (4.13) and (4.16), we have

$$C_T(Q) = \frac{\lambda}{Q} C_o + \frac{Q}{2} C_I \qquad (4.17)$$

which yields an optimal value of Q

$$Q = \sqrt{\frac{2\lambda C_o}{C_I}} \qquad (4.18)$$

and a total cost of $\quad \sqrt{2\lambda C_o C_I}$.

The ordering policy is to order

$$\sqrt{\frac{2\lambda C_o}{C_I}}$$

units whenever the inventory position falls to $\lambda \Upsilon$.

III. Lot size model with back orders and constant lead time.   In the models already developed we have assumed that it is never economical to allow a stock-out to occur. The system modeled here allows back orders to occur when economical. Of course, the most economical operating policy may be to allow no back orders, in which case we will be led to the operating policy just derived. Therefore the model developed here is more general than the previous two because both of these can be derived from this more generalized model.

---

[1] A cycle is the time between the receipt of two successive orders.

The simultaneous fluctuation of net inventory and inventory position for this system is described in Figure 4.4. The annual ordering cost is computed as in the previous two models and is given in equations (4.3) and (4.13). We calculate the reorder point by noting that upon receipt of the order, net inventory must be $-s$. During the lead time a total of $\lambda\Upsilon$ demands will occur. To provide for the possibility of Υ being greater than T_r, we define r as

$$r = \lambda\Upsilon - mQ - s \qquad (4.19)$$

where m is the largest nonnegative integer less than $\lambda\Upsilon/Q$.

If an order is placed when the inventory position reaches the value given in (4.19), the arrival of an order will coincide with a net inventory of $-s$ units.

FIGURE 4.4
Simultaneous Fluctuation of Net Inventory
and Inventory Position When Back Orders Are Allowed

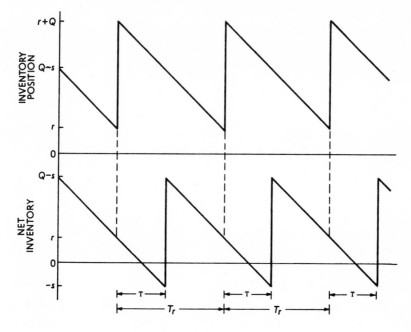

Let us now turn our attention to the annual costs of inventory and back orders. As mentioned previously both of these costs are proportional to time and quantity. To determine the annual value of these costs we will calculate the cost of each per cycle and multiply by the number of cycles per year, λ/Q.

To calculate the unit-years of inventory per cycle we must determine the area per cycle under the positive portion of the net inventory curve in Figure 4.4. The equation of the net inventory curve is

$$\text{Net inventory} = Q - s - \lambda t \qquad (4.20)$$

where $t = 0$ denotes the beginning of the cycle. $Q - s - \lambda t$ is positive for $0 \leqslant t < (Q - s)/\lambda$. Therefore the stock level is positive for $(Q - s)/\lambda$ years each cycle. To obtain the unit-years of inventory per cycle we integrate equation (4.20) from 0 to $(Q - s)/\lambda$. The inventory carrying cost per cycle is given by

$$\text{Carrying cost per cycle} = C_I \int_0^{Q-s/\lambda} (Q - s - \lambda t)\, dt$$

$$= \frac{(Q - s)^2}{2\lambda} C_I \qquad (4.21)$$

and yields the annual carrying cost given in (4.22)

$$\text{Annual carrying cost} = \frac{(Q - s)^2}{2Q} C_I \qquad (4.22)$$

In arriving at the cost of back orders per cycle, we must recognize that this cost is made up of two parts. First, we have a cost which is proportional to the number of units back ordered per cycle, C_b. That is, for each back order which occurs we have a cost C_b. Since s back orders are allowed per cycle, this portion of the back order cost per cycle is given by $C_b s$. The second portion of the back order cost is proportional to both amount and time.

Each back order costs C_β per year in addition to the cost C_b resulting as soon as the back order occurred. Therefore we must determine the unit-years of back orders for each cycle. This is accomplished by calculating the area per cycle above the negative portion of the net inventory curve. The length of time during which back orders occur is equal to the cycle length Q/λ minus the time for which net inventory is positive, $(Q - s)/\lambda$, or s/λ, years. Thus the area above the negative portion of the net inventory curve is given by

$$\text{Unit years of back orders per cycle} = - \int_{(Q-s)/\lambda}^{Q/\lambda} (Q - s - \lambda t)\, dt = \frac{s^2}{2\lambda} \qquad (4.23)$$

The minus sign in front of the integral in (4.23) forces the unit-years of back orders to be positive. The total cost of back orders per cycle is obtained by multiplying (4.23) by C_β and adding $C_b s$.

$$\text{Back order cost per cycle} = C_b s + C_\beta \frac{s^2}{2\lambda} \qquad (4.24)$$

Multiplying (4.24) by λ/Q yields the annual cost of back orders and is given by

$$\text{Annual cost of back orders} = C_b \frac{s\lambda}{Q} + C_\beta \frac{s^2}{2Q} \qquad (4.25)$$

The total annual cost of maintaining the inventory system becomes

$$C_T(Q, s) = \frac{\lambda}{Q} C_o + \frac{(Q - s)^2}{2Q} C_I + \frac{s\lambda}{Q} C_b + \frac{s^2}{2Q} C_\beta \qquad (4.26)$$

There are two variables, s and Q, in (4.26) which are under the control of the system designer. To obtain the optimal operating policy we must minimize (4.26) with respect to s and Q.

$$\frac{\partial C_T(Q, s)}{\partial Q} = -\frac{\lambda}{Q^2} C_o + \frac{(Q - s)}{Q} C_I - \frac{(Q - s)^2}{2Q^2} C_I - \frac{s\lambda}{Q^2} C_b - \frac{s^2}{2Q^2} C_\beta = 0$$

$$(4.27)$$

$$\frac{\partial C_T(Q, s)}{\partial s} = -\frac{(Q - s)}{Q} C_I + \frac{\lambda}{Q} C_b + \frac{s}{Q} C_\beta = 0 \qquad (4.28)$$

Solving (4.27) and (4.28) for the optimal values of s and Q, we have

$$s = \frac{\sqrt{\dfrac{2\lambda C_o C_I (C_\beta + C_I) - C_I (C_b \lambda)^2}{C_\beta}} - C_b \lambda}{C_\beta + C_I} \qquad (4.29)$$

$$Q = \sqrt{\frac{2\lambda C_o (C_\beta + C_I) - (C_b \lambda)^2}{C_\beta C_I}} \qquad (4.30)$$

Care should be exercised in using equations (4.29) and (4.30). Examination of (4.29) indicates that the optimal value of s may be negative. Referring to Figure 4.4, we might conclude that, instead of being out of stock when an order is received, a surplus of stock at this point is optimal. However, if no back orders are to be allowed, equation (4.26) is an invalid model of the inventory system and should be replaced by equation (4.17). The inadequacy of (4.26) in the no back order example is due to the incorporation of a back order cost in this model, which would not arise if back orders were not permitted. Therefore (4.26) is valid for nonnegative values of s.

If (4.29) yields a negative value for s, the optimal value of s is zero. It can also be shown that if $(C_b\lambda)^2 > 2\lambda C_o(C_\beta + C_I)$, implying an imaginery value of s, the optimal value of s is again zero.

Example 4.2

A retail outlet for a photographic film manufacturer sells a particular type of film at a constant rate of 50,000 rolls per year. Inventory carrying costs amount to $0.30 per roll per year. Each time the retailer places an order for a shipment of this film it costs $10, no matter how much he purchases, and it takes three weeks to get the order after it is placed. Each time a demand takes place when there is no film on hand the retailer estimates that it costs him $0.01 plus a cost of $0.05 per roll per year for which the back order lasts. Determine the optimal operating policy, the number of orders placed per year, and the annual cost of operation of the inventory system. Compare this cost with that resulting from a policy of allowing no back orders.

The number of back orders incurred per cycle is given by

$$s = \frac{\sqrt{\dfrac{2\lambda C_o C_I(C_\beta + C_I) - C_I(C_b\,\lambda)^2}{C_\beta}} - C_b\,\lambda}{C_\beta + C_I}$$

$$= \frac{\sqrt{\dfrac{2(50{,}000)(10)(0.30)(0.05 + 0.30) - 0.3(0.01 \times 50{,}000)^2}{0.05}} - (0.01)(50{,}000)}{0.05 + 0.30}$$

$= 784.57$

$\simeq 785$

The optimal order quantity is

$$Q = \sqrt{\frac{2\lambda C_o(C_\beta + C_I) - (C_b\,\lambda)^2}{C_\beta C_I}}$$

$$= \sqrt{\frac{2(50{,}000)(10)(0.05 + 0.30) - (0.01 \times 50{,}000)^2}{(0.05)(0.30)}}$$

$\simeq 2{,}582$ units

resulting in $50{,}000/2{,}582$, or 19.37, orders per year.
Using equation (4.19), we obtain the reorder point $r = \lambda\Upsilon - mQ - s$ where $\Upsilon = 3/52 = 0.0577$ years.

The largest integer less than $\lambda \Upsilon / Q$ is one. Therefore

$$r = (50,000)(0.0577) - 2,582 - 785$$
$$= -482$$

The total cost of maintaining the inventory system is given by

$$C_T(Q, s) = \frac{\lambda}{Q} C_o + \frac{(Q - s)^2}{2Q} C_I + \frac{s\lambda}{Q} C_b + \frac{s^2}{2Q} C_\beta$$

$$= \frac{50,000}{2,582} (10) + \frac{(2,582 - 785)^2}{2(2,582)} (0.30) + \frac{(785)(50,000)}{2,582} (0.01)$$

$$+ \frac{(785)^2}{2(2,582)} (0.05)$$

$$= \$538.74$$

If no back orders were allowed, the cost of operating the inventory system would be

$$C_T(Q) = \sqrt{2\lambda C_o C_I}$$

$$= \sqrt{2(50,000)(10)(0.30)}$$

$$= \$547.72$$

Since there is little difference between the optimal annual cost and the annual cost when back orders are not permitted, the wisdom of allowing any back orders at all might be questioned.

IV. Production Scheduling   So far we have assumed that the inventory level is increased by an amount equal to the order quantity Q whenever an order is received. However, it is easy to visualize an aarrangement with a supplier whereby the order quantity is broken into n parts, with the result that during each cycle n shipments, each of size Q/n, are received and placed in inventory. The limiting case which we will now discuss is that where units are received one at a time.

The system we are concerned with here is a production system in which units are manufactured to inventory at a rate ψ units per year; *i.e.*, manufactured units go directly into inventory. These units are then sold directly from inventory. We will assume that back orders are not to be tolerated. If this is true, then the production rate ψ must be greater than the demand rate λ. If $\lambda > \psi$, it is impossible to meet all demand, even if production continues throughout the year. On the other hand, if $\lambda < \psi$, continuous production would probably be uneconomical since we would produce more during the year than could be sold. The problem is then to determine how often production runs should be set up and how many units should be manufactured during each production run.

We will define lead time Υ as the setup time or the time elapsed between the dispatch of the production order and the startup of the production run. The major portion of the ordering cost, C_o in this example, is the cost of the setup, although certain administrative costs would also be included. Once the production run is started, the inventory level climbs at a rate $\psi - \lambda$ units per year until production is terminated.

As soon as production stops the inventory level declines at a rate of λ units per year. The fluctuation of inventory level with time is shown in Figure 4.5 where it is assumed that Q units are manufactured during each production run. The length of time taken to produce Q units, T_p, is equal to Q/ψ years. Therefore the number of units demanded during production is $(Q/\psi)\lambda$, resulting in a maximum inventory level of $Q[1 - (\lambda/\psi)]$ units at the end of the production period.

FIGURE 4.5
Fluctuation of Inventories with Time

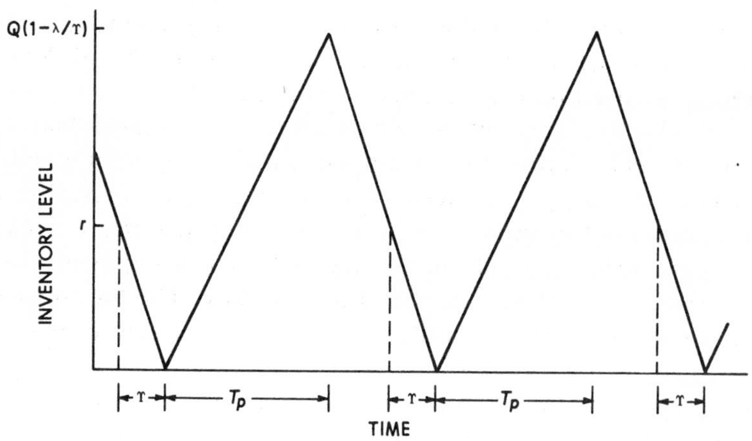

The period of time required for the inventory level to fall from the maximum value of $Q[1 - (\lambda/\psi)]$ units to zero is $(Q/\lambda)[1 - (\lambda/\psi)]$ years. The inventory level can then be expressed by

$$\text{Inventory level} = \begin{cases} (\psi - \lambda)t, & 0 \le t \le \dfrac{Q}{\psi} \\[2mm] Q - \lambda t, & \dfrac{Q}{\psi} < t \le \dfrac{Q}{\lambda} \end{cases} \tag{4.31}$$

That is, from time zero to Q/ψ years during each cycle the inventory level rises from 0 to $Q[1 - (\lambda/\psi)]$ units. From Q/ψ years to $(Q/\psi) + Q[1 - (\lambda/\psi)]$ years the inventory level falls from $Q[1 - (\lambda/\psi)]$ units to zero. To obtain the unit-years of inventory per cycle we must calculate the area under the inventory curve for one cycle. That is, we must find the area under $(\psi - \lambda)t$ for $0 \le t \le (Q/\psi)$ and under $Q - \lambda t$ for $(Q/\psi) < t \le (Q/\lambda)$.

$$\text{Inventory carrying cost per cycle} = C_I \left[\int_0^{Q/\psi} (\psi - \lambda)t \, dt + \int_{Q/\psi}^{Q/\lambda} (Q - \lambda t) \, dt \right]$$

$$= C_I \frac{Q^2}{2} \frac{\psi - \lambda}{\psi \lambda} \tag{4.32}$$

Since the number of cycles per year is λ/Q, the annual inventory carrying cost is

$$\text{Annual inventory carrying cost} = C_I \frac{Q}{2\lambda} \left(1 - \frac{\lambda}{\psi} \right) \tag{4.33}$$

and the annual setup cost is given by

$$\text{Annual set up cost} = C_o \frac{\lambda}{Q} \tag{4.34}$$

resulting in a total annual cost of

$$C_T(Q) = C_o \frac{\lambda}{Q} + C_I \frac{Q}{2} \left(1 - \frac{\lambda}{\psi} \right) \tag{4.35}$$

Differentiating (4.35) with respect to Q, we obtain the optimal value of Q given in (4.36)

$$Q = \sqrt{\frac{2\lambda\psi C_o}{C_I(\psi - \lambda)}} \tag{4.36}$$

To determine the inventory level r at which a production order should be released we will consider the single case where Υ is less than the cycle time. If $\Upsilon < (Q/\lambda)[1 - (\lambda/\psi)]$, the production order is issued between successive production runs, as shown in Figure 4.6. However, if $(Q/\lambda)\,[1 - (\lambda/Q)] < \Upsilon \leqslant (Q/\lambda)$, the production order is issued during the production run. For $\Upsilon < (Q/\lambda)\,[1 - (\lambda/\psi)]$, $r = \lambda\Upsilon$.

FIGURE 4.6

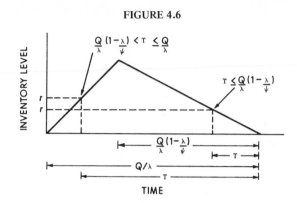

TIME

Let us consider now the example where the production order is released during a production run. Our problem is to calculate the inventory level Υ years from the start of the next production run, or conversely, $(Q/\lambda) - \Upsilon$ years from the beginning of the production run during which the production order is issued. The latter method is the simplest. The inventory level increases at the rate of $\psi - \lambda$ units per year during production. Therefore after $(Q/\lambda) - \Upsilon$ years, the inventory level is $(\psi - \lambda)\,[(Q/\lambda) - \Upsilon]$ units.

$$r = \begin{cases} \lambda\Upsilon & 0 \leq \Upsilon < \dfrac{Q}{\lambda}\left(1 - \dfrac{\lambda}{\psi}\right) \\[2ex] (\psi - \lambda)\left(\dfrac{Q}{\lambda} - \Upsilon\right), & \dfrac{Q}{\lambda}\left(1 - \dfrac{\lambda}{\psi}\right) \leq \Upsilon < \dfrac{Q}{\lambda} \end{cases} \qquad (4.37)$$

We leave the determination of r when Υ is greater than the cycle time as an exercise for the reader.

Example 4.3

Given the conditions stated in example 4.1, with the exception that it will now be assumed that the chemical is manufactured by the user at a production rate of two million pounds per year with a lead time of one day, find the optimal production run length and the inventory level at which a production order should be issued.

From example 4.1 we have $\lambda = 1,000,000$; $C_o = \$500$; and $C_I = \$0.40$.

In addition, $\psi = 2,000,000$ and $\Upsilon = 0.00274$ years.

The optimal order quantity, or production run length, is

$$Q = \sqrt{\frac{2\lambda\psi C_o}{C_I(\psi - \lambda)}}$$

$$= \sqrt{\frac{2(1,000,000)(2,000,000)(500)}{0.4(1,000,000)}}$$

$$\simeq 70,711 \text{ units}$$

Before computing r we must determine whether the lead time is greater than the cycle time

$$T_r = \frac{70,711}{1,000,000} = 0.070711 \text{ yrs}$$

Therefore $\Upsilon < T_r$

$$\frac{Q}{\lambda}\left(1 - \frac{\lambda}{\psi}\right) = 0.070711(1 - 0.5)$$

$$= 0.0353555 \text{ years}$$

Since

$$\Upsilon < \frac{Q}{\lambda}\left(1 - \frac{\lambda}{\psi}\right)$$

production orders are issued during the period when the chemical is not being manufactured.

$$r = \lambda\Upsilon$$

$$= 2740 \text{ units}$$

V. Production scheduling—accounting for raw materials inventories. The production scheduling system we will consider here is the same as that discussed in the preceding section, with one modification. In the system modeled in the last section we assumed that the raw materials necessary for production were somehow available although the cost of maintaining the required supply was not taken into account. Let us assume that two raw materials are necessary for production. We will further assume that one unit of each raw material is required to manufacture one unit of the final product. We must now recognize three inventories in our cost model: two raw material inventories and the inventory of final product. Let C_{o1}, C_{o2}, and C_{of} be the costs of ordering the first and second raw materials and the cost of production setup. Similarly, let C_{I1}, C_{I2}, and C_{If} be the corresponding inventory carrying costs. For simplicity we will consider lead time to be zero for both raw materials.

We will assume $\psi > \lambda$ and no back orders. We have, as before, a situation where continuous production throughout the year would imply excessive final product inventory. Therefore, during any year there will be nonproductive periods. Although we will consider the final product demand rate to be constant for any given time interval, such an assumption for raw material demand is invalid. The number of units of each raw material demanded during a time interval of length t is ψt, provided production continues throughout t. During nonproductive periods there is zero demand for raw materials. Therefore, during each cycle (time between two successive production startups) there is a fixed period, T_p, in which raw materials are demanded at a rate of ψ units per year, and a period during which raw materials are demanded at a rate of zero units per year, T_d. If Q_f is the production run length, then

$$T_p = \frac{Q_f}{\psi} \tag{4.38}$$

and

$$T_d = \frac{Q_f}{\lambda}\left(1 - \frac{\lambda}{\psi}\right) \tag{4.39}$$

The simultaneous fluctuation of both raw materials inventories and the final product inventory is shown in Figure 4.7 where Q_1 and Q_2 are the order quantities for the first and second raw materials. Examination of Figure 4.7 suggests that it is always optimal for raw materials inventories to be zero at the end of each production period. However, when the ordering cost is high in relation to the carrying cost, it may be optimal to carry inventory throughout the nonproductive period as illustrated in Figure 4.8. For simplicity we will assume that the inventory carrying cost is such that the level of the raw material inventories should be zero when production is terminated. We leave consideration of the example illustrated in Figure 4.8 as an exercise for the reader.

FIGURE 4.7
Simultaneous Fluctuation of Raw Materials and Final Product Inventories

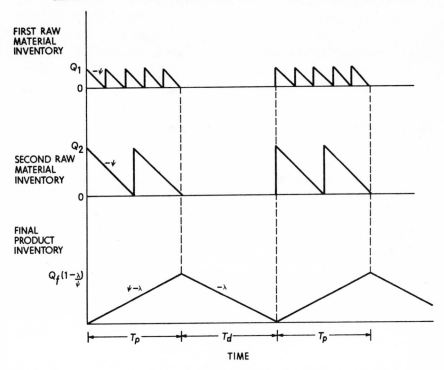

FIGURE 4.8
Raw Material Inventory Fluctuation during Productive and
Nonproductive Periods for the Example with High Ordering Costs

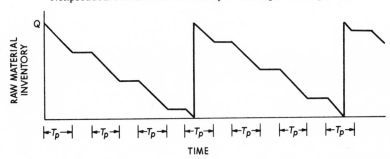

If the number of units of final product manufactured per cycle is Q_f and the number of orders for the ith raw material received per cycle is m_i, then

$$m_i Q_i = Q_f \qquad (4.40)$$

The time between the receipt of two successive raw materials orders of size Q_i is Q_i/ψ. Therefore the inventory carrying cost per cycle for the ith raw material is

$$i\text{th raw material carrying cost per cycle} = C_{Ii} m_i \int_0^{Q_i/\psi} (Q_i - \psi t)\, dt, \quad i = 1, 2$$

$$= C_{Ii} m_i \frac{Q_i^2}{\psi}, \quad i = 1, 2 \qquad (4.41)$$

The final product inventory carrying cost is the same as that given in (4.32).

$$\text{Final product carrying cost per cycle} = C_{If} \frac{Q_f^2}{2} \frac{\psi - \lambda}{\psi\lambda} \qquad (4.42)$$

During each production cycle m_i orders for the ith raw material are placed. Since there are λ/Q_f cycles per year, the annual ordering cost for raw materials is given by

$$\text{Annual raw material ordering cost} = \frac{\lambda}{Q_f} m_i C_{oi}, \quad i = 1, 2 \qquad (4.43)$$

$$\text{Annual setup cost} = \frac{\lambda}{Q_f} C_{of} \qquad (4.44)$$

Therefore

$$C_T(Q_f, m_1, m_2) = \frac{\lambda}{Q_f} C_{of} + \frac{Q_f}{2}\left(1 - \frac{\lambda}{\psi}\right) C_{If} + \sum_{i=1}^{2} \frac{\lambda}{Q_f}\left(m_i C_{oi} + m_i \frac{Q_i^2}{\psi} C_{Ii}\right) \qquad (4.45)$$

Replacing Q_i in (4.45) by its equivalent, Q_f/m_i, we have

$$C_T(Q_f, m_1, m_2) = \frac{\lambda}{Q_f} C_{of} + \frac{Q_f}{2}\left(1 - \frac{\lambda}{\psi}\right) C_{If} + \sum_{i=1}^{2} \frac{\lambda}{Q_f}\left(m_i C_{oi} + \frac{Q_f^2}{m_i \psi} C_{Ii}\right) \qquad (4.46)$$

The decision variables in (4.46) are Q_f, m_1, and m_2. Partial differentiation of (4.46) with respect to these variables yields

$$\frac{\partial C_T(Q_f, m_1, m_2)}{\partial Q_f} = \frac{1}{2}\left(1 - \frac{\lambda}{\psi}\right) C_{If} - \frac{\lambda}{Q_f^2}\left[C_{of} + \sum_{i=1}^{2} m_i C_{oi}\right] + \sum_{i=1}^{2} \frac{\lambda}{m_i \psi} C_{Ii} = 0 \qquad (4.47)$$

$$\frac{\partial C_T(Q_f, m_1, m_2)}{\partial m_i} = \frac{\lambda C_{oi}}{Q_f} - \frac{\lambda Q_f}{\psi m_i^2} C_{Ii} = 0 \qquad (4.48)$$

Solving for the optimal values of Q_f and m_i, we have

$$m_i = Q_f \sqrt{\frac{C_{Ii}}{\psi C_{oi}}} \tag{4.49}$$

Substituting (4.49) in (4.47), we have

$$Q_f = \sqrt{\frac{2\lambda C_{of}}{\left(1 - \dfrac{\lambda}{\psi}\right) C_{If}}} \tag{4.50}$$

and

$$m_i = \sqrt{\frac{2\lambda C_{of} C_{Ii}}{(\psi - \lambda) C_{If} C_{oi}}} \tag{4.51}$$

Example 4.4

An electronics manufacturer requires the supply of a particular part at a rate of 300,000 per year. This part is manufactured internally and is composed of two components which are purchased from another firm. The production rate for the part is 1.2 million per year. Given the following cost information, find the optimal production run length and the optimal order quantities for the two purchased components.

$$C_{o1} = \$25 \qquad C_{o2} = \$10 \qquad C_{of} = \$100$$
$$C_{I1} = \$0.30 \qquad C_{I2} = \$0.90 \qquad C_{If} = \$1.20$$

$$
\begin{aligned}
Q_f &= \sqrt{\frac{2\lambda C_{of}}{\left(1 - \dfrac{\lambda}{\psi}\right) C_{If}}} \\[2mm]
&= \sqrt{\frac{2(300,000)(100)}{(0.75)(1.20)}} \\[2mm]
&= 10,000 \text{ units}
\end{aligned}
$$

$$
\begin{aligned}
m_1 &= Q_f \sqrt{\frac{C_{I1}}{\psi C_{o1}}} \\[2mm]
&= 10,000 \sqrt{\frac{0.30}{(1,200,000)(25)}} \\[2mm]
&= 1
\end{aligned}
$$

$$m_2 = 10,000\sqrt{\frac{0.90}{(1,200,000)(10)}}$$

$$= 2.74$$

Therefore the optimal integer value for m_2 must be either 2 or 3. To determine the minimizing value of m_2 we will evaluate that part of the total cost equation involving m_2 for both of these values.

For $m_2 = 2$,

$$m_2 C_{o2} + \frac{Q_f{}^2}{m_2 \psi} C_{I2} = 2(10) + \frac{(10,000)^2}{2(1,200,000)} (0.90)$$

$$= \$57.50$$

For $m_2 = 3$,

$$m_2 C_{o2} + \frac{Q_f{}^2}{m_2 \psi} C_{I2} = 3(10) + \frac{(10,000)^2}{3(1,200,000)} (0.90)$$

$$= \$55$$

Therefore $m_2 = 3$; $Q_1 = 10,000$ units; and $Q_2 = 3,334$ units.

Accounting for the Discrete Nature of Demand

So far we have treated demand as a continuous variable. However, when the product demanded is manufactured in discrete units, then demand for these units should also be treated as a discrete variable. To illustrate the general approach to be taken when it is necessary to account for the integrality of demand, we will redevelop Model I in two ways. First, we will redevelop Model I as it was originally stated. We will then change the ordering policy from that of ordering Q units (where Q may assume any positive integer value) to a policy of ordering in multiples of Q. That is, the order size is nQ where n may take on any positive integer value while Q is a fixed quantity.

Since demand is assumed deterministic and uniformly distributed throughout the year, an annual demand rate of λ units per year would imply that a demand occurs every $1/\lambda$ years. For the models we shall discuss we will assume that the arrival of an order coincides with the first demand during the cycle.

VI. Discrete demand—model I, order size Q. We are dealing here with an inventory system in which back orders are not allowed, lead time is zero, and orders are received in lots of size Q. Since the arrival of an order is to coincide with the first demand of a cycle, the inventory level at that time is $Q - 1$ as shown in Figure 4.9

FIGURE 4.9
Fluctuation of Inventory Level for Discrete Demand

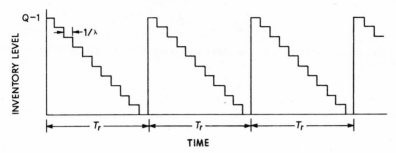

The inventory level at the ith demand during any cycle can be expressed by

$$\text{Inventory level} = Q - i, \qquad i = 1, 2, \ldots, Q \tag{4.52}$$

To obtain the unit-years of inventory per cycle we again calculate the area under the inventory curve during each cycle. To accomplish this we take the sum of the areas of each of the rectangles of width $1/\lambda$.

$$\text{Unit years of inventory per cycle} = \sum_{i=1}^{Q} \frac{Q - i}{\lambda}$$

$$= \frac{Q}{2\lambda}(Q - 1) \tag{4.53}$$

where

$$\sum_{i=1}^{n} i = \frac{n(n+1)}{2}.$$

Since there are an average of λ/Q cycles per year, we have a total average annual cost given by

$$C_T(Q) = \frac{\lambda}{Q} C_o + \frac{C_I}{2}(Q - 1) \tag{4.54}$$

Since Q is a discrete variable, to find the optimal value of Q we must difference (4.54) with respect to Q and determine the largest value of Q such that $\Delta_Q C_T(Q) \leqslant 0$.

$$\Delta_Q C_T(Q) = C_T(Q) - C_T(Q - 1)$$

$$= \frac{\lambda}{Q} C_o + \frac{C_I}{2}(Q - 1) - \frac{\lambda}{Q-1} C_o - \frac{C_I}{2}(Q - 2) \tag{4.55}$$

Solving for Q, we have

$$\lambda C_o\left(\frac{1}{Q} - \frac{1}{Q-1}\right) + \frac{C_I}{2} \leq 0$$

and the optimal value of Q is the largest such value for which

$$Q(Q-1) \leq \frac{2\lambda C_o}{C_I} \qquad (4.56)$$

Example 4.5

Solve example 4.1, taking account of the discrete nature of demand.

From example 4.1,

$\lambda = 1,000,000$ units/year.

$C_o = \$500$

$C_I = \$0.40$.

$$\frac{2\lambda C_o}{C_I} = \frac{2(1,000,000)(500)}{0.4}$$

$$= 2,500,000,000$$

For $Q = 50,000$,

$$Q(Q-1) = 2,499,950,000 \leq \frac{2\lambda C_o}{C_I}$$

For $Q = 50,001$,

$$Q(Q-1) = 2,500,050,000$$

Therefore the optimal value of Q is 50,000 units.

VII. Discrete demand—model I, order size nQ. The system we are concerned with here is identical to Model VI in all respects, except the ordering policy. We are now restricted to ordering in quantities which are multiples of Q. Consequently, when an order is placed, it must be for an amount equal to nQ where n is the decision variable instead of Q. The inventory diagram for such a system is the same as that given in Figure 4.9 if Q is replaced by nQ. Therefore the inventory level during any cycle can be expressed by

$$\text{Inventory level} = nQ - i, \qquad i = 1, 2, \ldots, nQ \qquad (4.57)$$

and the unit-years of inventory per cycle by

$$\text{Unit years of inventory per cycle} = \sum_{i=1}^{nQ} \frac{nQ - i}{\lambda}$$

$$= \frac{nQ}{2\lambda}(nQ - 1) \qquad (4.58)$$

Since there are λ/nQ cycles per year,

$$C_T(n) = \frac{\lambda}{nQ} C_o + \frac{C_I}{2}(nQ - 1) \qquad (4.59)$$

Differencing (4.59) with respect to the decision variable, n, we have

$$\Delta_n C_T(n) = \frac{\lambda}{nQ} C_o + \frac{C_I}{2}(nQ - 1) - \frac{\lambda}{(n - 1)Q} C_o - \frac{C_I}{2}(nQ - Q - 1) \qquad (4.60)$$

Solving for n, we have

$$\Delta_n C_T(n) = \frac{C_I}{2} Q - \frac{\lambda}{n(n - 1)Q} C_o \le 0 \qquad (4.61)$$

The optimal value of n is the largest value such that

$$n(n - 1) \le \frac{2\lambda C_o}{Q^2 C_I} \qquad (4.62)$$

Example 4.6

Solve the problem given in example 4.5 if the order quantity must be a multiple of Q where Q is 20,000 units.

Using equation (4.62) and the data given in example 4.5, we have

$$n(n - 1) \le \frac{2\lambda C_o}{Q^2 C_I}$$

$$\le \frac{2(1,000,000)(500)}{(20,000)^2(0.4)}$$

$$\le 6.25$$

Therefore the optimal value of n is 3 and $nQ = 60,000$ units.

As the reader has undoubtedly noted we have not included consideration of periodic review systems in our discussion of deterministic inventory systems. However, when demand and lead time are known and constant, there is no need for a review of the system in the sense of determining the inventory status and deciding whether to place an order or not. Net inventory and inventory position can be predicted with certainty. Therefore we can schedule the placement of orders in advance and release these orders without reviewing the status of inventory. This is not true when demand is a random variable. Obviously if demand cannot be predicted, the net inventory level and inventory position cannot be predicted. Since inventory position is to be used as the decision variable for placing an order, we will not be able to predict when to order unless we can also predict inventory position. Therefore when demand is a random variable it will be necessary to review inventory position, at least periodically, to determine whether an order should be issued.

STOCHASTIC INVENTORY SYSTEMS

As we have already pointed out, inventory systems are classified as stochastic whenever demand or lead time are random variables. In the sections which follow we shall develop annual cost models for inventory systems in which demand is a random variable and lead time is constant. We shall not treat the example of probabilistic lead time mathematically. However, in Chapter 9 we will develop simulation models which account for the probabilistic nature of both demand and lead time.

In our discussion of deterministic inventory systems we considered several situations in which back orders or lost sales were not permitted. However, when demand is stochastic, the number of demands cannot be predicted except in a probabilistic sense. Therefore if an order for Q units is placed when the inventory level is x and the lead time is Υ, there is no guarantee that demand will not exceed x units during Υ if demand is a random variable. Consequently, when demand is probabilistic, the possibility of the occurrence of demand during a stock-out period must be considered unless lead time is zero. If lead time is zero, we can prevent a stock-out, provided units are demanded one at a time (or in any constant quantity), by placing an order when the inventory level reaches zero.

The mathematical models to be developed in the succeeding sections of this chapter will represent the expected annual cost of the inventory system for a given operating policy. If we are to derive effective inventory models, we must know something about the behavior of demand during any given interval of time, t. Specifically, we must know the probability distribution of demand for any period of time to be considered. For this purpose let $p_D(d,t)$ be the probability that exactly d units are demanded in any time interval of length t. As implied in the definition of $p_D(d,t)$, we are assuming that the probability that d units are demanded in t is a function of the magnitude of t and independent of the point in time at which this interval began. This assumption eliminates the analysis of many inventory systems, such as those in which demand is subject to seasonal variation, but will suffice for the elementary systems to be considered here.

We found it convenient to treat demand as a continuous variable in analyzing deterministic inventory systems, although this was recognized as usually an approximation to reality. However, we shall abandon this approach in discussing stochastic systems, regarding demand as a discrete random variable.

We will adopt the same notation used for deterministic systems with respect to unit costs and system parameters with the obvious exception of the annual demand rate, λ, which can no longer be considered constant. Therefore λ will be redefined as the average annual demand. We will analyze both reorder point and periodic review systems. Although the reorder point system is nothing more than a periodic review system with a review taking place continuously throughout the year, we will consider them separately. For the purpose of the analyses which follow let C_P be the cost of reviewing the inventory status for periodic review systems and let C_R be the annual cost of reviewing the system continuously for reorder point systems. It should be noted that the annual review cost is a function of the period between successive reviews in the periodic review system but is considered a constant in reorder point systems. Therefore the review cost will in part determine the optimum operating policy in the former case, but has no effect on the optimum policy in the latter.

VIII. Reorder point system with zero lead time and no stock-outs.

If an order of size Q units is placed and received whenever inventory position reaches r units (reorder point), then the cycle time, T_Q, is the time for Q units to be demanded and is a random variable since demand is a random variable. Let $f_{T_n}(t)$ be the density function of the time until the nth demand occurs. The density function of T_n can be derived either from the probability mass function of demand, $p_x(x,t)$, or from records which indicate the time between successive demands. Equation (4.63) defines a relationship which can be used to derive $f_{T_n}(t)$ from $p_x(x,t)$ where Q is the order quantity.

$$f_{T_n}(t) = \frac{d}{dt} \sum_{x=n}^{\infty} p_x(x, t) \qquad (4.63)$$

For further discussion of (4.63) the reader should see *Stochastic Processes*, Emanual Parzen, Chapter 4.

We will assume that the Q units demanded during any cycle occur at equally spaced intervals. That is, if the cycle length is t, then the time between successive demands during that cycle is t/Q. An example of the simultaneous fluctuation of inventory position and net inventory is given in Figure 4.10. Since an order can be obtained instantaneously, there is no need to place an order until a demand occurs which reduces the inventory level to $r - 1$. At that instant an order of size Q is received, raising the inventory level to $r + Q - 1$. Intuitively we would expect that the optimal value of r is zero, as in the corresponding deterministic system. We will demonstrate the validity of this intuitive analysis mathematically.

FIGURE 4.10
Simultaneous Fluctuation of Inventory Position and Net Inventory
for Stochastic Demand and Zero Lead Time When Stock-Outs Are Not Allowed

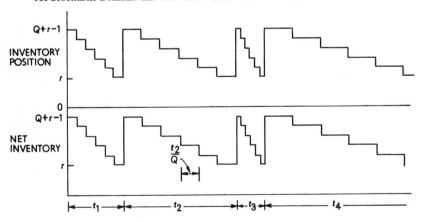

Since stock-outs do not occur, we need consider only the ordering cost, the inventory carrying cost, and the cost of a continuous review of the system. If we can assume that the demand during a given period of time is independent of that in any other period, then we can also assume that the length of any cycle is independent of the length of any other cycle. To compute the expected number of cycles per year we must find the expected length of any cycle, $E(t)$.

$$E(t) = \int_0^\infty t f_Q(t) \, dt \tag{4.64}$$

The expected number of cycles per year is then given by $1/E(t)$ where $E(t)$ is in years. Therefore the annual ordering cost is

$$\text{Expected annual ordering cost} = \frac{C_o}{E(t)} \tag{4.65}$$

If we approach the same problem in another way, we can develop a more useful relationship which will eliminate the need to compute $E(t)$. If d is the number of demands occurring in a year, then the average number of orders per year for years in which there were d demands is d/Q. However, we are interested in the expected value of d/Q. Therefore

$$E\left(\frac{d}{Q}\right) = \frac{1}{Q} E(d)$$

$$= \frac{1}{Q} \sum_{d=0}^\infty d p_D(d, 1) \tag{4.66}$$

But we have defined

$$\sum_{d=0}^\infty d p_D(d, 1)$$

as λ.

$$\text{Expected annual ordering cost} = \frac{\lambda}{Q} C_o \tag{4.67}$$

We will show that $E(t) = Q/\lambda$ in example 4.7 when demand is Poisson distributed.

To calculate the expected annual unit-years of inventory we determine the expected unit-years of inventory per cycle and multiply by the expected number of cycles per year. If the length of the ith cycle is t_i, then the time between successive demands for that cycle is t_i/Q. The net inventory level after the jth demand is given by

$$\text{Net inventory level} = r + Q - j, \qquad j = 1, \ldots, Q \tag{4.68}$$

The unit-years of inventory for the ith cycle is then given by

$$\text{Unit years of inventory for } i\text{th cycle} = \frac{t_i}{Q} \sum_{j=1}^{Q} (r + Q - j)$$

$$= t_i\left(r + \frac{Q-1}{2}\right) \tag{4.69}$$

and

$$\text{Expected unit years of inventory per cycle} = \left(r + \frac{Q-1}{2}\right)E(t_i)$$

$$= \frac{Q}{\lambda}\left(r + \frac{Q-1}{2}\right) \tag{4.70}$$

Since the expected number of cycles per year is λ/Q, we have

$$\text{Expected annual inventory carrying cost} = C_I\left(r + \frac{Q-1}{2}\right) \tag{4.71}$$

Therefore the expected annual cost model is given by

$$C_T(Q, r) = \frac{\lambda}{Q} C_o + \left(r + \frac{Q-1}{2}\right)C_I + C_R \tag{4.72}$$

Inspection of (4.72) indicates that the optimal reorder point is zero. Therefore

$$C_T(Q) = \frac{\lambda}{Q} C_o + \frac{Q-1}{2} C_I + C_R \tag{4.73}$$

Differencing (4.73) with respect to Q, we have

$$\Delta_Q C_T(Q) = -\frac{\lambda C_o}{Q(Q-1)} + C_I \tag{4.74}$$

The optimal value of Q is the largest value satisfying (4.75)

$$Q(Q-1) \leq \frac{2\lambda C_o}{C_I} \tag{4.75}$$

Comparing (4.75) with (4.56), we see that the optimal operating policy when back orders are prevented is determined in the same was whether demand is deterministic or not. Therefore if demand is a random variable but back orders can and are prevented, the system can be treated as deterministic for the purpose of developing an optimal operating policy.

Example 4.7

Show that $E(t) = Q/\lambda$ where t is the cycle length in years and demand is Poisson distributed.

From (4.63) we have

$$f_{T_Q}(t) = \frac{d}{dt} \sum_{d=Q}^{\infty} p_D(d, t)$$

and

$$p_D(d, t) = \frac{(\lambda t)^d}{d!} e^{-\lambda t}$$

Therefore

$$f_{T_Q}(t) = \frac{d}{dt} \sum_{x=Q}^{\infty} \frac{(\lambda t)^x}{x!} e^{-\lambda t}$$

$$= \sum_{x=Q}^{\infty} \frac{d}{dt} \frac{(\lambda t)^x}{x!} e^{-\lambda t}$$

$$f_{T_Q}(t) = \sum_{x=Q}^{\infty} \left(\frac{\lambda(\lambda t)^{x-1}}{(x-1)!} e^{-\lambda t} - \frac{\lambda(\lambda t)^x}{x!} e^{-\lambda t} \right)$$

$$\times \lambda \left(\sum_{x=Q}^{\infty} \frac{(\lambda t)^{x-1}}{(x-1)!} e^{-\lambda t} - \sum_{x=Q}^{\infty} \frac{(\lambda t)^x}{x!} e^{-\lambda t} \right)$$

$$= \frac{\lambda(\lambda t)^{Q-1}}{(Q-1)!} e^{-\lambda t}, \qquad 0 < t < \infty$$

$$E(t) = \int_0^{\infty} \frac{(\lambda t)^Q}{(Q-1)!} e^{-\lambda t} \, dt$$

$$= \frac{\lambda^Q}{(Q-1)!} \frac{Q!}{\lambda^{Q+1}}$$

$$= \frac{Q}{\lambda}$$

Example 4.8

A television repair shop uses a particular electron tube at an average rate of 4,000 per year. Demand for a time period, t, in years is Poisson distributed with parameter $4,000t$ for all t. If one of these tubes is needed and none is available, the serviceman can drive across town to a distributor, pick one up, and return to the job. Such a trip takes about one hour and costs an average of about $20. Such a delay, even for house calls, is not regarded as significant enough to be considered a back order. Since a trip must be made, it would be uneconomical to pick up only one tube. Therefore whenever the stock of tubes reaches zero, the owner decides to purchase Q tubes instead of only one. Find the optimal value of Q if the cost of a tube is $3 and the annual inventory carrying cost is estimated at 10 percent of the value of the tube. Assume an annual cost of continuous review of $100.

$$\lambda = 4,000$$

$$C_o = \$20.$$

$$C_I = (0.10)(\$3) = \$0.30/\text{unit year.}$$

$$C_R = \$100.$$

$$\frac{2\lambda C_o}{C_I} = \frac{(4000)(20)}{0.30} = 533,333$$

The largest value of Q such that $Q(Q-1) < 533,333$ is 730 units. Therefore each time the inventory level falls to zero, 730 tubes are purchased from the distributor. The average annual cost of operating the inventory system is

$$C_T(730) = \frac{(4000)}{(730)}(20) + \frac{(731)}{2}(0.30) + 100$$

$$= \$319.14 \text{ per year}$$

IX.   Reorder point system with back orders and constant but relatively short lead time.   In the last section we discussed a model in which lead time was zero. If lead time is not zero, several problems arise which we have not encountered up to this point. For all of the systems we have discussed, the reorder point could be defined in terms of either inventory position or net inventory with equal propriety. In addition it was possible to predict the number of orders outstanding at any point in time. We have already discussed the problems which can arise when the reorder point is defined in terms of net inventory for stochastic systems with nonzero lead time. With regard to outstanding orders, the number of orders outstanding at any time can be predicted only in a probabilistic sense in the present case. For example, assume that an order of size Q was placed at time zero and that we wish to calculate the probability that n orders are outstanding at time $t < \Upsilon$ where t is measured from the order placed at time zero. If the order was placed at time zero, inventory position at that time was $r + Q$. Since $t < \Upsilon$, at least this original order is outstanding at t. If Q units are demanded by t, then another order must have been placed by t, since inventory position would have fallen to r when Q demands occurred. In order for three orders to be outstanding by t, at least $2Q$ demands had to occur. Therefore two orders are outstanding at t if the demand during t was between Q and $2Q - 1$ inclusive. Three orders are outstanding at t if the demand during t was between $2Q$ and $3Q - 1$ inclusive, and so forth. In general,

$$P(n \text{ orders outstanding at } t) = \sum_{d=(n-1)Q}^{nQ-1} p_D(d, t) \tag{4.76}$$

However, if Υ and the likely range of feasible values of Q are such that the probability of Q or more demands in Υ is insignificant, we can ignore the possibility of two or more outstanding orders at any time. This is the case we will examine here. In the next section we will remove this assumption and develop a generalized reorder point model for arbitrary but constant lead time.

As indicated in Figure 4.11 we again assume that whatever demand takes place in a given cycle is uniformly spread over the cycle. In Figure 4.11 a cycle is shown as the time between the receipt of two successive orders, although we could have defined it as the time between the placement of two successive orders. Since inventory position is the number of units on hand plus the number on order, inventory position and net inventory must be equal when an order is received, there being no units outstanding at this point.

Having defined the beginning of a cycle as the point at which an order is received, we see that a cycle always begins Υ years after the last order was placed. Since net inventory and inventory position are equal upon receipt of an order, the probability that inventory level is x at the start of a cycle is equal to the probability that inventory position is also x at the end of the cycle. Defining the beginning of the cycle as time zero, we get

$$P(\text{Inventory position} = x \text{ at } t = 0) = p_D(r + Q - x, \Upsilon) \tag{4.77}$$

That is, if inventory position is to fall from $r + Q$ when the last order was placed, to x when that order was received, then $r + Q - x$ demands must have occurred during the lead time, Υ. Therefore the

FIGURE 4.11
Fluctuation of Inventory Position and Net Inventory for
Stochastic Demand and Relatively Short but Positive Lead Time

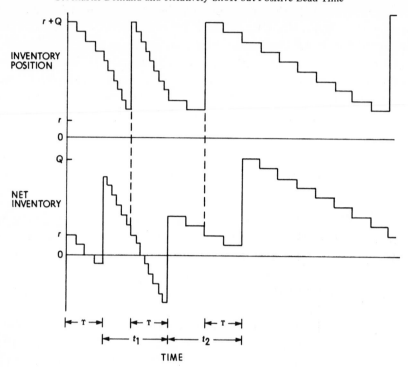

probability that the inventory level is x at the beginning of any cycle, $q_x(x)$, is given by

$$q_x(x) = p_D(r + Q - x, \Upsilon), \qquad x = r, r + 1, \ldots, r + Q \qquad (4.78)$$

We will adopt a new approach in developing a mathematical model of this system. We will choose at random a point in time, t, during the year. Since this point is chosen at random, expected conditions at this point are representative of expected conditions at any other randomly chosen point in time. Therefore if the expected inventory level at t is A and this inventory level is representative of the entire year, then the expected annual unit-years of inventory is A multiplied by one year.

To develop the required model we must know the distribution of inventory position at the random point t. Let $P_{r+j}(t)$ be the probability that inventory position is $r + j$ at t, $j = 1, 2, \ldots, Q$, and let Δt be a small enough interval of time such that the probability of more than one demand in Δt is zero. Therefore if inventory position at $t - \Delta t$ was $r + j + 1$, the probability that inventory position is $r + j$ at t is the probability that one demand occurred in Δt. We can represent the probability that a transition from any inventory position at $t - \Delta t$ to any inventory position at t in the following matrix. The entries in this matrix represent the probability that inventory position changes from any given value at $t - \Delta t$ to any given value at t.

TABLE 4.1

Inventory Position at t

		$r+1$	$r+2$	...	$r+j$	$r+j+1$	...	$r+Q$
	$r+1$	$p(0,\Delta t)$	0	...	0	0	...	$p(1,\Delta t)$
Inventory	$r+2$	$p(1,\Delta t)$	$p(0,\Delta t)$	...	0	0	...	0
Position	.	.	.	.	.	.		.
at	.	.	.	.	.	.		.
$t - \Delta t$	$r+j$	0	0	...	$p(0,\Delta t)$	0	...	0
	$r+j+1$	0	0	...	$p(1,\Delta t)$	$p(0,\Delta t)$	...	0
	.	.	.		.	.		.
	.	.	.		.	.		.
	$r+Q$	0	0	...	0	0	...	$p(0,\Delta t)$

Such a matrix is usually called a probability transition matrix. The reader will notice that the sum of the probabilities across any row or down any column is unity. Such a transition matrix is called doubly stochastic, and for such transition matrices the probability of being in any given state (inventory position in this case) is equal to one over the number of states. Therefore

$$P_{r+j} = \frac{1}{Q}, \qquad j = 1, 2, \ldots, Q \tag{4.79}$$

To calculate the probability that the inventory level is x at t, examine the system at $t - \Upsilon$ and determine what must happen in the intervening period, Υ, if the inventory level is to be x at t. If an order was outstanding at $t - \Upsilon$, it must have arrived by t. In addition any order placed between $t - \Upsilon$ and t cannot arrive until after t and therefore cannot affect the inventory level at t. If an order was outstanding at $t - \Upsilon$, then inventory position exceeded net inventory by Q units at that time. However, this order arrived between $t - \Upsilon$ and t, and upon receipt of the order net inventory and inventory position were equal as shown in Figure 4.12. Let d_1 be the demand between $t - \Upsilon$ and the receipt of the order, and let d_2 be the demand between the order receipt and t. If inventory position at $t - \Upsilon$ is $r + j$, then upon receipt of the order both inventory position and net inventory are $r + j - d_1$. The d_2 demands between the order receipt and t reduce the inventory level to $r + j - d_1 - d_2$ at t. Therefore the demand required in Υ to bring the inventory level to x at t is $r + j - x$.

FIGURE 4.12
Simultaneous Fluctuation of Net Inventory and Inventory Position

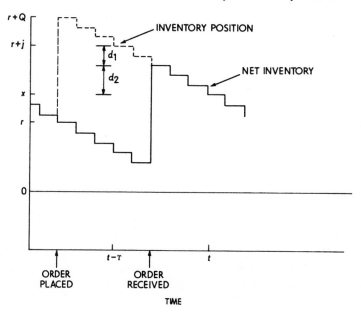

If an order was not outstanding at $t - \Upsilon$, then inventory position and net inventory coincide at this point. If inventory position is $r + j$ at $t - \Upsilon$, then we again need $r + j - x$ demands in Υ to reduce the inventory level to x at t. The placement of an order between $t - \Upsilon$ and t has no effect on net inventory at t since it cannot arrive until after t. Noting that the probability of more than Q demands in Υ is zero, we have the probability that the inventory level (nonnegative) is x, for $x = 0, 1, 2, \ldots, r, r + 1, r + 2, \ldots, r + Q$

$$q_x(0) = \sum_{j=1}^{Q} \sum_{i=r+j}^{Q} P_{r+j} \, p_D(i, \Upsilon)$$

$$q_X(1) = \sum_{j=1}^{Q-r+1} P_{r+j} \, p_D(r+j-1, \Upsilon)$$

$$q_X(2) = \sum_{j=1}^{Q-r+2} P_{r+j} \, p_D(r+j-2, \Upsilon)$$

$$\vdots \qquad\qquad \vdots$$

$$q_X(r) = \sum_{j=1}^{Q} P_{r+j} \, p_D(j, \Upsilon)$$

$$q_X(r+1) = \sum_{j=1}^{Q} P_{r+j} \, p_D(j-1, \Upsilon)$$

$$q_X(r+2) = \sum_{j=2}^{Q} P_{r+j} \, p_D(j-2, \Upsilon)$$

$$\vdots \qquad\qquad \vdots$$

$$q_X(r+Q) = P_{r+Q} \, p_D(0, \Upsilon)$$

(4.80)

Summarizing equations (4.80) and noting that $P_{r+j} = 1/Q$, we have

$$q_X(x) = \begin{cases} \dfrac{1}{Q} \displaystyle\sum_{j=1}^{Q} \sum_{i=r+j}^{Q} p_D(i, \Upsilon), & x = 0 \\[2ex] \dfrac{1}{Q} \displaystyle\sum_{j=1}^{Q-r+x} p_D(r+j-x, \Upsilon), & x = 1, 2, \ldots, r \\[2ex] \dfrac{1}{Q} \displaystyle\sum_{j=x-r}^{Q} p_D(r+j-x, \Upsilon), & x = r+1, r+2, \ldots, r+Q \end{cases}$$

(4.81)

The expected inventory level is given by

$$E(x) = \sum_{x=0}^{r+Q} x q_X(x)$$

$$= \sum_{x=1}^{r+Q} x q_X(x)$$

(4.82)

$$= \frac{1}{Q} \sum_{x=1}^{r} x \sum_{j=1}^{Q-r+x} p_D(r+j-x, \Upsilon) + \frac{1}{Q} \sum_{x=r+1}^{r+Q} x \sum_{j=x-r}^{Q} p_D(r+j-x, \Upsilon)$$

Let y be the number of backorders at t, and let $h_Y(y)$ be the probability mass function of Y. We can develop the expression for $h_Y(y)$, using the same method of analysis applied in deriving $q_X(x)$. If the inventory position at $t - \Upsilon$ is $r+j$, at least $r+j+1$ demands must take place in Υ for a stock-out condition to exist at t. Since the maximum demand during Υ is Q, if inventory position exceeds Q at $t - \Upsilon$, a stock-out at t is not possible. Therefore

$$h_\Upsilon(0) = \sum_{j=1}^{Q-r} \sum_{i=0}^{r+j} P_{r+j} p_D(i, \Upsilon)$$

$$h_\Upsilon(0) = \sum_{j=1}^{Q-1} P_{r+j} p_D(r + j + 1, \Upsilon)$$

$$h_\Upsilon(2) = \sum_{j=1}^{Q-2} P_{r+j} p_D(r + j + 2, \Upsilon) \tag{4.83}$$

$$\vdots \qquad \qquad \vdots$$

$$h_\Upsilon(q = r - 1) = P_{r+1} p_D(r + 1 + Q, \Upsilon)$$

or

$$h_\Upsilon(y) = \begin{cases} \displaystyle\sum_{j=1}^{Q-r} \sum_{i=0}^{r+j} \frac{1}{Q} p_D(i, \Upsilon), & y = 0 \\[2mm] \displaystyle\sum_{j=1}^{Q-y} \frac{1}{Q} p_D(r + j + y, \Upsilon), & y = 1, 2, \ldots, Q - r - 1 \end{cases} \tag{4.84}$$

and

$$E(y) = \frac{1}{Q} \sum_{y=1}^{Q-r-1} y \sum_{j=1}^{Q-y} p_D(r + j + y, \Upsilon) \tag{4.85}$$

Since $E(x)$ and $E(y)$ represent the expected number of units in inventory and back orders at a random point, t, during the year, to obtain the expected annual unit-years of inventory and back orders we multiply $E(x)$ and $E(y)$ by one year.

If P_{so} is the probability that a stock-out exists at any time, t, during the year, then we would expect the number of back orders incurred during the year, z, to be P_{so} multiplied by the annual demand. Since λ is the expected annual demand, the expected number of back orders per year, $E(z)$, is given by

$$E(z) = \lambda P_{so} \tag{4.86}$$

The probability of a stock-out at t is

$$P_{so} = \sum_{y=0}^{Q-r-1} \sum_{j=1}^{Q-y} P_{r+j} p_D(r + j + y, \Upsilon)$$

$$= \frac{1}{Q} \sum_{y=0}^{Q-r-1} \sum_{j=1}^{Q-y} p_D(r + j + y, \Upsilon) \tag{4.87}$$

The expected number of orders per year is λ/Q. Therefore we have the total cost equation given by

$$C_T(Q, r) = \frac{\lambda}{Q} C_o + C_I E(x) + C_b \lambda P_{so} + C_\beta E(y) + C_R \qquad (4.88)$$

or

$$
\begin{aligned}
C_T(Q, r) = \frac{\lambda}{Q} C_o &+ \frac{C_I}{Q} \left(\sum_{x=1}^{r} x \sum_{j=1}^{Q-r+x} p_D(r + j - x, \Upsilon) \right. \\
&+ \left. \sum_{x=r+1}^{r+Q} x \sum_{j=x-r}^{Q} p_D(r + j - x, \Upsilon) \right) \\
&+ \frac{C_b \lambda}{Q} \sum_{y=0}^{Q-r-1} \sum_{j=1}^{Q-y} p_D(r + j + y, \Upsilon) \\
&+ \frac{C_\beta}{Q} \left(\sum_{y=1}^{Q-r-1} y \sum_{j=1}^{Q-y} p_D(r + j + y, \Upsilon) \right) + C_R \qquad (4.89)
\end{aligned}
$$

To find the optimal values of Q and r we could difference (4.89) with respect to r and Q. However, the reader may find it more straightforward to solve (4.89) for the optimal values of r and Q by trial and error. In attempting a trial-and-error solution, we suggest that the reader try the values of r and Q given in equations (4.19) and (4.30) initially. The reader will find that these values are often close to the optimal values. In addition, search techniques, which may be used to optimize this and succeeding models, are presented in Chapter II.

Example 4.9

Develop Model VIII by determining the expected inventory level at a random point in time, t.

In the development of Model VIII we showed that if we knew what inventory position was at $t - \Upsilon$ we could determine the probability that the inventory level was x at t. However, in this case $\Upsilon = 0$; therefore inventory level and inventory position coincide for all t. As we have already shown, the probability that inventory position is $r + j$ at a randomly selected point in time is $1/Q$. That is,

$$P_{r+j} = \frac{1}{Q}, \qquad j = 0, 1, \ldots, Q - 1$$

Since inventory position and inventory level are the same for all t,

$$q_X(x) = 1/Q, \qquad x = r, r+1, r+2, \ldots, r+Q-1$$

and

$$E(x) = \sum_{x=r}^{r+Q-1} \frac{x}{Q}$$

$$= \sum_{i=0}^{Q-1} \frac{r+x}{Q}$$

$$= r + \frac{Q-1}{2}$$

Since there are an average of λ/Q cycles per year, we have

$$C_t(Q, r) = \frac{\lambda}{Q} C_o + \left(r + \frac{Q-1}{2}\right) C_I + C_R$$

which is identical to the cost equation given in (4.72).

Example 4.10

For a reorder point system in which demand is Poisson distributed with mean rate 100 units per year, lead time is 0.08 years and the pertinent unit costs are as follows.

$$C_o = \$100. \qquad C_I = \$20.$$
$$C_b = \$15. \qquad C_\beta = \$10.$$

Find the optimal operating policy and the resulting annual cost of operation. Find and plot the combination of r and Q for which the annual cost of operation is not more than $\$20$, $\$40$, and $\$70$ more than the optimal operating cost.

We will not present the program required to find the values of r and Q which optimize (4.89) but leave this as an exercise for the reader. The optimal values of r and Q are 8 and 34, respectively, yielding an annual cost of operation of $\$694.97$. In the following table we present the values of Q and r for which the annual cost of operation is less than $\$714.97$, $\$734.97$, and $\$764.97$. The information in this table is summarized in Figure 4.13. The curves in Figure 4.13 are called isolines. For any combination of values of r and Q falling inside the curve marked $\$714.97$, the resulting annual cost of operation will be less than or equal to $\$714.97$. For any combination

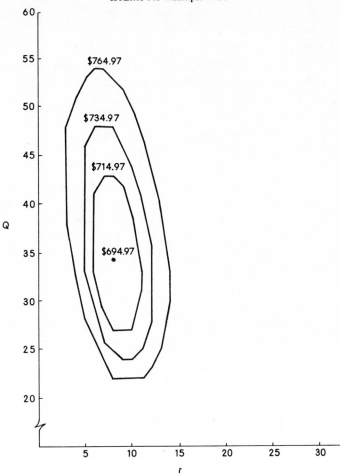

FIGURE 4.13
Isolines for Example 4.10

TABLE 4.2

	Range of Values of Q for Which Total Annual Cost Is Less Than		
r	$714.97	$734.97	$764.97
3			$38 \leqslant Q \leqslant 48$
4			$32 \leqslant Q \leqslant 51$
5		$33 \leqslant Q \leqslant 46$	$28 \leqslant Q \leqslant 53$
6	$33 \leqslant Q \leqslant 41$	$29 \leqslant Q \leqslant 48$	$26 \leqslant Q \leqslant 54$
7	$29 \leqslant Q \leqslant 43$	$26 \leqslant Q \leqslant 48$	$24 \leqslant Q \leqslant 54$
8	$27 \leqslant Q \leqslant 43$	$25 \leqslant Q \leqslant 48$	$22 \leqslant Q \leqslant 53$
9	$27 \leqslant Q \leqslant 42$	$24 \leqslant Q \leqslant 46$	$22 \leqslant Q \leqslant 52$
10	$27 \leqslant Q \leqslant 39$	$24 \leqslant Q \leqslant 44$	$22 \leqslant Q \leqslant 50$
11	$31 \leqslant Q \leqslant 33$	$25 \leqslant Q \leqslant 41$	$22 \leqslant Q \leqslant 47$
12		$28 \leqslant Q \leqslant 36$	$23 \leqslant Q \leqslant 44$
13			$25 \leqslant Q \leqslant 40$
14			$30 \leqslant Q \leqslant 33$

of r and Q falling between the outer and middle isoline, annual cost will be between \$734.97 and \$764.94.

X. Reorder point system with back orders and arbitrary but constant lead time.   The system we are considering here is identical to that described in Model IX, except that we shall not place any restriction on the magnitude of lead time or on the magnitude of lead time demand. The methodology used in this analysis is identical to that used in Model IX, and we shall see that the results of this and the previous analysis are remarkably similar.

We again choose a random point in time, t, and determine the expected number of units in inventory and the expected number of back orders at this point. The distribution of inventory position is the same as that developed in the previous section and is defined in (4.79). Let us examine the relationship between net inventory and inventory position, between $t - \Upsilon$ and t. If there are n orders outstanding at $t - \Upsilon$, all n must have arrived by t, since the lead time on each is Υ. On the other hand, any order placed between $t - \Upsilon$ and t must be received after t. If inventory position is $r + j$ at $t + \Upsilon$ and there are n orders outstanding, then net inventory must be $r + j - nQ$ at that point. If there were d demands during Υ, then net inventory at t is the inventory level at $t - \Upsilon$ plus the number of units which arrived in the orders received between $t - \Upsilon$ and Υ, nQ, minus the demand during Υ. Therefore the inventory level at t is $(r + j - nQ) + nQ - d$ or $r + j - d$. If, then, inventory position is $r + j$ at $t - \Upsilon$ and net inventory is x at t, there were $r + j - x$ demands during Υ. Since demand during Υ must be nonnegative, $j \geqslant x - r$. For $1 \leqslant x \leqslant r$, j may assume any of its permissible values; that is, $1 \leqslant j \leqslant Q$. However, for $r + 1 \leqslant x \leqslant r + Q$, j may assume only values between $x - r$ and Q inclusive. The probability mass function of inventory level is then

$$q_x(x) = \begin{cases} \dfrac{1}{Q} \displaystyle\sum_{j=1}^{Q} \sum_{i=r+j}^{Q} p_D(i, \Upsilon), & x = 0 \\[3mm] \dfrac{1}{Q} \displaystyle\sum_{j=1}^{Q} p_D(r + j - x, \Upsilon), & x = 1, 2, \ldots, r \\[3mm] \dfrac{1}{Q} \displaystyle\sum_{j=x-r}^{Q} p_D(r + j - x, \Upsilon), & x = r + 1, r + 2, \ldots, r + Q \end{cases} \qquad (4.90)$$

We note that inventory level (as distinguished from net inventory) is

FIGURE 4.14
Simultaneous Fluctuation of Net Inventory and Inventory Position

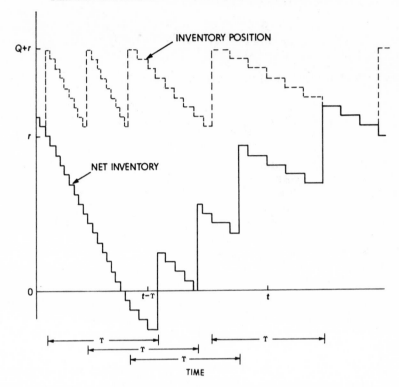

zero whenever demand during Υ is equal to or exceeds inventory position at $t - \Upsilon$. Equation (4.90) differs from equation (4.81) only with respect to the upper limit of summation when $1 \leqslant x \leqslant r$. In (4.81) we took account of the fact that demand during Υ could not exceed Q. However, this restriction does not exist for the system under study here. For the expected inventory level at t we have

$$
\begin{aligned}
E(x) &= \sum_{x=0}^{r+Q} x q_x(x) \\
&= \frac{1}{Q} \sum_{x=1}^{r} x \sum_{j=1}^{Q} p_D(r + j - x, \Upsilon) + \frac{1}{Q} \sum_{x=r+1}^{r+Q} x \sum_{j=x-r}^{Q} p_D(r + j - x, \Upsilon) \quad (4.91)
\end{aligned}
$$

Removing the restriction of Q or less demands in (4.84), we obtain the probability mass function of the number of back orders at t.

$$h_Y(y) = \begin{cases} \dfrac{1}{Q} \sum_{j=1}^{Q} \sum_{i=0}^{r+j} p_D(i, \Upsilon), & y = 0 \\[4mm] \dfrac{1}{Q} \sum_{j=1}^{Q} p_D(r + j + y, \Upsilon), & y = 1, 2, 3, \ldots \end{cases} \tag{4.92}$$

The expected number of back orders is given by

$$E(y) = \frac{1}{Q} \sum_{y=1}^{\infty} y \sum_{y=1}^{Q} p_D(r + j + y, \Upsilon) \tag{4.93}$$

Since the average number of orders per year is λ/Q, we have an expected total cost of

$$C_T(Q,r) = \frac{\lambda}{Q} C_o + \frac{C_I}{Q} \left(\sum_{x=1}^{r} x \sum_{j=1}^{Q} p_D(r + j - x, \Upsilon) + \sum_{x=r+1}^{r+Q} x \sum_{j=x-r}^{Q} p_D(r + j - x, \Upsilon) \right)$$

$$+ \frac{C_b \lambda}{Q} \sum_{y=0}^{\infty} \sum_{j=1}^{Q} p_D(r + j + y, \Upsilon) + \frac{C_\beta}{Q} \sum_{y=1}^{\infty} y \sum_{j=1}^{Q} p_D(r + j + y, \Upsilon)$$

$$+ C_R \tag{4.94}$$

where

$$\frac{1}{Q} \sum_{y=0}^{\infty} \sum_{j=1}^{Q} p_D(r + j + y, \Upsilon)$$

is the probability of a stock-out at t. The reader will notice that the difference between (4.94) and (4.89) is accounted for by altering the upper limits of the summations in (4.89) to remove the restriction that not more that Q demands occur in Υ.

Example 4.11

In example 4.10 we assumed that equation (4.89) provided an adequate representation of the annual cost of the inventory being studied. However, the propriety of (4.89) depends upon the magnitude of lead time, the value of the model decreasing as lead time (or annual demand) increases. When lead time becomes sufficiently large, equation (4.94) should be used to evaluate annual cost. Since we placed no restriction on the magnitude of lead time in the development of equation (4.94), we may use this model whether (4.89) is appropriate or not. Let us now compare the results given by (4.89) and (4.94) for the problem described in example 4.10.

Since equation (4.94) is an exact model for the situation discussed in example 4.10, any discrepancy in the results obtained from this model and those obtained from equation (4.89) must be considered due to the error of approximation in (4.89). Using the data in example 4.10, we find the optimal values of r and Q given by equation (4.94) are 8 and 34 units, respectively, yielding an annual cost of \$694.82. Comparing these results with those obtained in example 4.10, we see that not only do both equations yield the same optimal values of the decision variables, but also the predicted annual costs given by the two models differs by a matter of cents. Obviously the approximate model is appropriate here.

We could have shown that (4.89) was appropriate for the problem in example 4.10 by computing the probability that more than Q demands would occur in Υ. The reader will remember that (4.89) was developed on the assumption that this probability was small. A table of the Poisson distribution will show that the probability that 34 units or more are demanded in 0.08 years is virtually zero when the annual demand rate is 100 units.

Since equation (4.94) provided an exact model for reorder point systems with back orders, stochastic demand, and constant lead time, one might ask why this model would not be used even when the model in equation (4.89) is also appropriate. About the only answer is that the computing time for (4.89) is less than that for (4.94). In writing a generalized program for the back-order model considered here it would be wise to include both (4.89) and (4.94) in the program to take advantage of the saving in computing time which can be realized when (4.89) is appropriate.

XI. Periodic review system with zero lead time and back orders.
In Model VIII we were concerned with a system in which demand was stochastic and lead time was constant, as here. In analyzing that system we presumed that an order for Q units was placed whenever inventory position fell to zero. Of course, such an operating policy implies constant review of the system. Let us now turn our attention to the analysis of an inventory system where reviews take place every T_R years instead of continuously. Each time the system is reviewed we will place an order for enough units to bring the inventory level to R. Such an operating policy is often called an order-up-to-R policy. Although the order quantity is variable, we will again assume an ordering cost, C_o, which is independent of the number of units ordered.

Since lead time is zero, the inventory level is brought up to R at each review if it is not already there. If demand during the time between reviews, T_R, is less than R, then the inventory level is positive at the next review. Otherwise the inventory level is zero at the following review. If we assume that demand during T_R is uniformly distributed over this period of time, then the fluctuation of net inventory is as shown in Figure 4.15. The inventory level, x, after the ith demand during T_R is given by

$$x = \begin{cases} R - i, & i = 0, 1, \ldots, R \\ 0, & i = R + 1, R + 2, \ldots \end{cases} \qquad (4.95)$$

FIGURE 4.15
Fluctuation of Net Inventory for an Order up to R,
Periodic Review System with Zero Lead Time

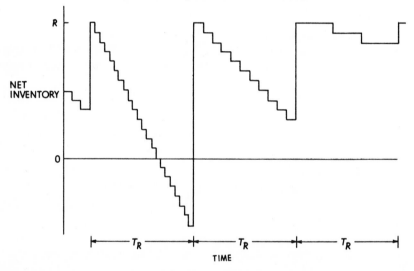

Therefore the unit-years of inventory during T_R, given d demands in T_R, is

$$\text{Unit years of inventory per } T_R = \begin{cases} \dfrac{T_R}{d + 1} \displaystyle\sum_{i=0}^{d} (R - i), & d = 0, 1, \ldots, R \\[3mm] \dfrac{T_R}{d + 1} \displaystyle\sum_{i=0}^{R} (R - i), & d = R + 1, R + 2, \ldots \end{cases} \qquad (4.96)$$

which reduces to

$$\text{Unit years of inventory per } T_R = \begin{cases} T_R \dfrac{(R - d)}{2}, & d = 0, 1, \ldots, R \\[3mm] T_R \dfrac{R(R + 1)}{2(d + 1)}, & d = R + 1, R + 2, \ldots \end{cases} \qquad (4.97)$$

$(T_R/d + 1)$ is the time interval for which inventory remains at any given level. Therefore the expected unit-years of inventory between reviews is given by

Expected unit years of inventory per T_R

$$= \sum_{d=0}^{R} T_R\left(R - \frac{d}{2}\right)p_D(d, T_R) + \sum_{d=r+1}^{\infty} T_R \frac{R(R+1)}{2(d+1)} p_D(d, T_R)$$

$$= T_R\left[\sum_{d=0}^{\infty} \left(R - \frac{d}{2}\right)p_D(d, T_R)\right.$$

$$+ \sum_{d=r+1}^{\infty} \frac{R(R-1) - 2dR + d(d+1)}{2(d+1)} p_D(d, T_R)\right]$$

$$= T_R\left[R - \frac{\lambda T_R}{2} + \sum_{d=r+1}^{\infty} \frac{R(R-1) - 2dR + d(d+1)}{2(d+1)} p_D(d, T_R)\right] \quad (4.98)$$

The number of back orders, y, accumulated after the ith demand during T_R is

$$y = \begin{cases} 0, & i = 0, 1, \ldots, R - 1 \\ i - R, & i = R + 1, R + 2, \ldots \end{cases} \quad (4.99)$$

If there are d demands during T_R,

Unit years of back orders per T_R

$$= \begin{cases} 0, & d = 0, 1, \ldots, R \\ \dfrac{T_R}{d + 1} \displaystyle\sum_{i=R+1}^{d} (i - R), & d = R + 1, R + 2, \ldots \end{cases} \quad (4.100)$$

or

Unit years of back orders per T_R

$$= \begin{cases} 0, & d = 0, 1, \ldots, R \\ \dfrac{T_R}{d + 1} [R(R - 1) - 2dR + d(d + 1)], & d = R + 1, R + 2, \ldots \end{cases} \quad (4.101)$$

Taking the expected value of (4.101), we have

Expected unit years of back orders per T_R

$$= T_R \sum_{d=R+1}^{\infty} \frac{R(R - 1) - 2dR + d(d + 1)}{2(d + 1)} p_D(d, T_R) \quad (4.102)$$

The number of back orders incurred during T_R when demand in that period is i is given by (4.99).

Therefore the expected number of back orders between successive reviews is defined as

$$\text{Expected number of back orders per } T_R = \sum_{d=R+1}^{\infty} (d - R)p_D(d, T_R) \quad (4.103)$$

Each time a review takes place, a review cost of C_p results. However, an ordering cost arises only if an order is placed. Since the inventory level was R after the last review, if one or more demands occurred between the last and the present review, an order will be placed to restore the inventory level to R. Therefore the probability that an order is placed when the system is reviewed, P_o, is the probability that one or more units were demanded in T_R.

$$P_o = \sum_{d=1}^{\infty} p_D(d, T_R) \quad (4.104)$$

The expected ordering cost per review is then $C_o P_o$.

Expected total cost per T_R

$$= C_p + C_o \sum_{d=1}^{\infty} p_D(d, T_R) + C_I T_R$$

$$\times \left[R - \frac{\lambda T_R}{2} + \sum_{d=R+1}^{\infty} \frac{R(R-1) - 2dR + d(d+1)}{2(d+1)} p_D(d, T_R) \right]$$

$$+ C_\beta T_R \sum_{d=R+1}^{\infty} \frac{R(R-1) - 2dR + d(d+1)}{2(d+1)} p_D(d, T_R)$$

$$+ C_b \sum_{d=R+1}^{\infty} (d - R)p_D(d, T_R) \quad (4.105)$$

Since the time between successive reviews, T_R, is measured in years, the number of reviews per year is $1/T_R$. Multiplying (4.105) by $1/T_R$, we obtain the expected total annual cost of operating the periodic review system.

$$C_T(R, T_R) = \frac{C_p}{T_R} + \frac{C_o}{T_R} \sum_{d=1}^{\infty} p_D(d, T_R) + C_I \left(R - \frac{\lambda T_R}{2} \right)$$

$$+ (C_I + C_\beta) \sum_{d=R+1}^{\infty} \frac{R(R-1) - 2dR + d(d+1)}{2(d+1)} p_D(d, T_R)$$

$$+ \frac{C_b}{T_R} \sum_{d=R+1}^{\infty} (d - R) p_D(d, T_R) \qquad (4.106)$$

Example 4.12

Consider a periodic review system where lead time is zero and demand in any time period, t, in years, is Poisson distributed with mean rate $200t$ ($\lambda = 200$). When an order is placed, it is for a quantity sufficient to bring the inventory level to R. Orders are placed every T_R years. Assume that a year is 365 days and that each review takes place at 9am. Therefore T_R must be an integer multiple of $1/365$. If demand during a stock-out is back ordered, find the optimal operating policy given the following cost information.

$$C_p = 60. \quad C_o = 200.$$
$$C_I = 20. \quad C_b = 10.$$
$$C_\beta = 50.$$

Since demand is Poisson distributed,

$$p_D(d, t) = \frac{(\lambda t)^d}{d!} e^{-\lambda t} \qquad (4.107)$$

Let

$$S(z, t) = \sum_{d=z}^{\infty} p_D(d, t) \qquad (4.108)$$

Using (4.107) and (4.108), we see that the last two summations in (4.107) become

$$\sum_{d=R+1}^{\infty} \frac{R(R - 1) - 2dR + d(d + 1)}{2(d + 1)} p_D(d, T_R)$$

$$= \sum_{d=R+1}^{\infty} \frac{R(R - 1)}{2(d + 1)} \frac{(\lambda T_R)^d}{d!} e^{-\lambda T_R}$$

$$- \sum_{d=R+1}^{\infty} \frac{dR}{d + 1} \frac{(\lambda T_R)^d}{d!} e^{-\lambda T_R} + \sum_{d=R+1}^{\infty} \frac{d}{2} \frac{(\lambda T_R)^d}{d!} e^{-\lambda T_R}$$

$$= \frac{R(R - 1)}{2} \sum_{d=R+1}^{\infty} \frac{1}{\lambda T_R} \frac{(\lambda T_R)^{d+1}}{(d + 1)!} e^{-\lambda T_R}$$

$$- R \sum_{d=R+1}^{\infty} \frac{d}{\lambda T_R} \frac{(\lambda T_R)^{d+1}}{(d+1)!} e^{-\lambda T_R} + \frac{1}{2} \sum_{d=R+1}^{\infty} \lambda T_R \frac{(\lambda T_R)^{d-1}}{(d-1)!} e^{-\lambda T_R}$$

$$= \frac{R(R+1)}{2\lambda T_R} S(R+2, T_R) - RS(R+1, T_R) + \frac{\lambda T_R}{2} S(R, T_R)$$

$$\sum_{d=R+1}^{\infty} (d-R)p_D(d, T_R) = \sum_{d=R+1}^{\infty} d \frac{(\lambda T_R)^d}{d!} e^{-\lambda T_R} - R \sum_{d=R+1}^{\infty} \frac{(\lambda T_R)^d}{d!} e^{-\lambda T_R}$$

$$= \lambda T_R \sum_{d=R+1}^{\infty} \frac{(\lambda T_R)^{d-1}}{(d-1)!} e^{-\lambda T_R} - RS(R+1, T_R)$$

$$= \lambda T_R S(R, T_R) - RS(R+1, T_R)$$

Equation (4.106) becomes

$$C_T(R, T_R) = \frac{1}{T_R} [C_p + C_o S(1, T_R)] + C_I \left(R - \frac{\lambda T_R}{2} \right)$$

$$+ \lambda T_R \left(\frac{C_I + C_\beta}{2} + \frac{C_b}{T_R} \right) S(R, T_R)$$

$$- R \left(C_I + C_\beta + \frac{C_b}{T_R} \right) S(R+1, T_R)$$

$$+ \frac{R(R+1)}{2\lambda T_R} (C_I + C_\beta) S(R+2, T_R) \qquad (4.109)$$

The accompanying FORTRAN program computes and prints out the optimal value of R for values of T_R between 1 and 365 days and the optimal R and T_R over the range of values of R and T_R searched. T_R is computed in years and $3 \leqslant R \leqslant 4,997$.

For this problem the optimal values of R and T_R are 92 units and 0.449 years, respectively, with an associated annual cost of $1,510.08.

The following variable definitions are used in this program.

CP = C_p.	CO = C_o.
CI = C_I.	CBETA = C_β.
CB = C_b.	LAMDA = λ.
IR = R.	LR = Maximum value of R.
TR = T_R.	COST = $C_T(R, T_R)$.
IRM = Optimum value of R.	TRM = Optimum value of T_R.

CMIN = Minimum cost.

```
      DIMENSION P(5000),SUM(5000)
      REAL LAMDA
      WRITE(6,3)
      READ(5,1) CP,CO,CI,CBETA,CB,ILAM,LR
      LAMDA=ILAM
      TINC=1./365.
      DO 70 IT=1,365
      TI=IT
      TR=TI*TINC
      PAR=LAMDA*TR
      P(1)=EXP(-PAR)
      SUM(1)=P(1)
      K=0
      DO 30 I=1,4999
      Z=I
      IF(K)10,10,20
10    P(I+1)=(PAR/Z)*P(I)
      SUM(I+1)=SUM(I)+P(I+1)
      IF(SUM(I+1).LE.0.995) GO TO 30
      K=1
      GO TO 30
20    P(I+1)=0
      SUM(I+1)=1.0
30    CONTINUE
      CMIN=10.**30
      COMP=10.**30
      DO 60 IR=1,LR
      RI=IR
      COST=(1./TR)*(CP+CO*(1.-EXP(-PAR)))+CI*(RI-PAR/2.)
      COST=COST+(1./PAR)*(CI+CBETA)*RI*(RI+1.)*0.5*(1.-SUM(IR+2))
      COST=COST-((CI+CBETA)*RI+(RI*CB/TR))*(1.-SUM(IR+1))
      COST=COST+PAR*(((CI+CBETA)/2.)+(CB/TR))*(1.-SUM(IR))
      IF(COST.GT.COMP) GO TO 40
      COMP=COST
      IRC=IR
      TRC=TR
      GO TO 60
40    WRITE(6,2)IRC,TRC,COMP
      IF(IT.GT.1.OR.IR.GT.1) GO TO 50
      CMIN=COMP
      IRM=IRC
      TRM=TRC
      GO TO 60
50    IF(COST.GT.CMIN) GO TO 60
      CMIN=COMP
      IRM=IRC
      TRM=TRC
      GO TO 70
60    CONTINUE
70    CONTINUE
      WRITE(6,3)
      WRITE(6,2)IRM,TRM,CMIN
      STOP
1     FORMAT(5F10.2,2I6)
2     FORMAT(1X3HR =I5,2X4HTR =F10.6,2X6HCOST =F14.2)
3     FORMAT(1H1)
      END
```

XII. Reorder point system with lost sales and constant lead time. We will now consider a system in which customers are impatient and will not wait to have their demands satisfied at a later date. That is, if a demand occurs during a stock-out period, the sale is lost, the consumer taking his business elsewhere. In addition we will assume that no more than one order is outstanding at any point in time. With the exception of these two modifications, the system considered here is the same as that described in Model X.

Let us examine the relationship between net inventory and inventory position. Each time inventory position falls to r, an order for Q units is placed. Net inventory continues to fall with demand until it reaches zero. Net inventory cannot fall below zero since demands occurring during a stock-out are not "made up" at a later date. Therefore net inventory and inventory level are equivalent here. The simultaneous fluctuation of inventory position and inventory level is shown in Figure 4.16. As the reader will note a stock-out is possible only during lead time.

Defining a cycle as the time between the receipt of two successive orders, we see that the inventory level at the beginning of any cycle must lie between Q and $Q + r$ inclusive. Inventory level and inventory position coincide until both fall to r and an order is placed. If r or more demands occur in Υ, a stock-out will occur before the order is received and the order will raise the inventory level to Q when it arrives. Therefore the probability that the inventory level is Q when a cycle begins, $g_x(Q)$, is

$$\sum_{d=r}^{\infty} p_D\,(d,\Upsilon)$$

The probability that the inventory level is x, $Q + 1 < x \leqslant Q + r$, is the probability that $Q + r - x$ demands occurred in Υ.

$$g_x(x) = \begin{cases} \sum_{d=r}^{\infty} p_D(d, \Upsilon) & x = Q \\ p_D(Q + r - x, \Upsilon), & x = Q + 1, Q + 2, \ldots, Q + r \end{cases} \qquad (4.110)$$

The length of a cycle is Υ plus the time taken for the inventory level to fall to r. As we have already pointed out, the density function of the time taken for inventory position to fall to r can be derived from the probability mass function of demand and is defined in (4.63). If the inventory level at the beginning of the cycle is x, then $x - r$ demands must occur before an order is placed. The expected time taken for $x - r$ demands, given an inventory level of x at the beginning of the cycle, is

$$E(t \mid x) = \int_0^{\infty} t f_{T_{x-r}}(t)\, dt \qquad (4.111)$$

FIGURE 4.16
Simultaneous Fluctuation of Inventory Position and Inventory Level
for Reorder Point System with Lost Sales and Constant Lead Time

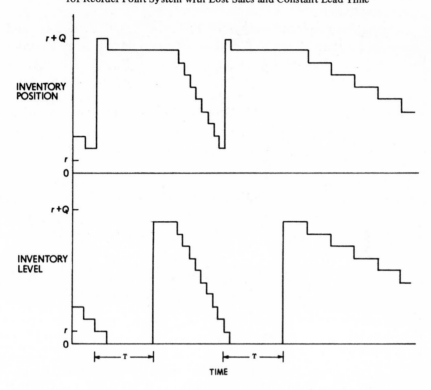

Taking the expected value over x, we have the expected time until an order is placed, T_o.

$$T_o = \sum_{x=Q}^{r+Q} g_X(x) E(t \mid x)$$

$$= \sum_{d=r}^{\infty} p_D(d, \Upsilon) \int_0^{\infty} t f_{T_{Q-r}}(t)\, dt + \sum_{x=Q+1}^{Q+r} p_D(Q + r - x, \Upsilon) \int_0^{\infty} t f_{T_{x-r}}(t)\, dt$$

$$(4.112)$$

Since the mean annual demand is λ, the expected time between successive demands is $1/\lambda$. If the inventory level is x at the beginning of the cycle, the unit-years of inventory carried until an order is placed is $[x(x + 1) - r(r - 1)]/2\lambda$. Taking the expected value over x, we have the expected unit-years of inventory carried in T_o, E_{T_o}.

$$E_{T_o} = \frac{1}{2\lambda} \sum_{x=Q}^{r+Q} [x(x+1) - r(r-1)]g_x(x)$$

$$= \frac{1}{2\lambda}\left[Q(Q+1)\sum_{d=r}^{\infty} p_D(d, \Upsilon) \right.$$

$$\left. + \sum_{x=Q+1}^{r+Q} x(x+1)p_D(Q+r-x, \Upsilon) - r(r+1) \right] \qquad (4.113)$$

Letting $d = Q + r - x$ in the second summation in (4.113), we obtain

$$E_{T_o} = \frac{1}{2\lambda}\left[Q(Q+1)\sum_{d=r}^{\infty} p_D(d, \Upsilon) \right.$$

$$\left. + \sum_{d=0}^{r-1}(Q+r-d)(Q+r-d+1)p_D(d, \Upsilon) - r(r+1) \right]$$

$$= \frac{1}{2\lambda}\left[Q(Q+1) - r(r+1) + r(2Q+r+1)\sum_{d=0}^{r-1} p_D(d, \Upsilon) \right.$$

$$\left. - (2r+2Q+1)\sum_{d=0}^{r-1} dp_D(d, \Upsilon) + \sum_{d=0}^{r-1} d^2 p_D(d, \Upsilon) \right] \qquad (4.114)$$

To calculate the expected unit-years of inventory in the remainder of the cycle, E_Υ, we note that the inventory level may or may not fall to zero during Υ. If the demand in Υ is d, then the inventory level is $r - d$ at the end of the cycle for $d < r$ and zero for $d \geqslant r$. Inventory remains at any given level for $\Upsilon/(d+1)$ years if d is the demand during Υ. Therefore

$$E_\Upsilon = \Upsilon\left[\sum_{d=0}^{r-1}\sum_{i=0}^{d} \frac{r-i}{d+1} p_D(d, \Upsilon) + \sum_{d=r}^{\infty}\sum_{i=0}^{r} \frac{r-i}{d+1} p_D(d, \Upsilon) \right]$$

$$= \frac{\Upsilon}{2}\left[\sum_{d=0}^{r-1}(2r-d)p_D(d, \Upsilon) + \sum_{d=r}^{\infty} \frac{r(r+1)}{d+1} p_D(d, \Upsilon) \right] \qquad (4.115)$$

The expected unit-years of inventory per cycle is then the sum of (4.114) and (4.115).

$$\text{Expected unit-years of inventory per cycle} = E_{T_o} + E_\Upsilon \qquad (4.116)$$

Since lost sales can occur during lead time only, the number of lost sales is $d - r$ for $d > r$ and zero for $d \leqslant r$ where d is lead time demand. The expected number of lost sales per cycle is then given by

$$\text{Expected lost sales per cycle} = \sum_{d=r+1}^{\infty} (d-r)p_D(d, \Upsilon) \qquad (4.117)$$

Since the number of cycles per year is $1/(\Upsilon + T_o)$, the expected annual cost of operating the system is

$$
\begin{aligned}
C_T(Q, r) &= \frac{1}{\Upsilon + T_o} \Bigg\{ C_o + C_L \sum_{d=r+1}^{\infty} (d-r)p_D(d, \Upsilon) \\
&+ C_I \frac{\Upsilon}{2} \Bigg[\sum_{d=0}^{r-1} (2r-d)p_D(d, \Upsilon) + \sum_{d=r}^{\infty} \frac{r(r+1)}{d+1} p_D(d, \Upsilon) \Bigg] \\
&+ \frac{C_I}{2\lambda} \Bigg[Q(Q+1) - r(r+1) + r(2Q+r+1) \sum_{d=0}^{r-1} p_D(d, \Upsilon) \\
&- (2r + 2Q + 1) \sum_{d=0}^{r-1} d p_D(d, \Upsilon) + \sum_{d=0}^{r-1} d^2 p_D(d, \Upsilon) \Bigg] \Bigg\}
\end{aligned}
\qquad (4.118)
$$

Example 4.13

By projecting a trend which has developed over a period of years, an appliance dealer estimates that he will have demand for about 300 television sets in the coming year. Each time he places an order, an ordering cost of $300 results. The inventory carrying cost is $50 per set per year. Stock-outs result in lost sales costing $70 each. Procurement lead time is 0.1 months. If demand per time period Υ is Poisson with mean $300t$, find the optimal reorder point and reorder quantity.

$\lambda = 300.$
$\Upsilon = 0.0083$ years.
$C_o = \$300.$
$C_I = \$50.$
$C_L = \$70.$

$$p_D(d, \Upsilon) = \frac{(300\Upsilon)^d}{d!} e^{-300\Upsilon}$$

In example 4.7 we showed that

$$f_{T_z}(t) = \frac{\lambda(\lambda t)^{z-1}}{(z-1)!} e^{-\lambda t}$$

and $E(t \mid z) = z/\lambda.$

Therefore the expected time between the beginning of the cycle and the placement of an order, T_o, is given by

$$T_o = \sum_{d=r}^{\infty} \frac{Q-r}{\lambda} p_D(d, \Upsilon) + \sum_{x=Q+1}^{Q+r} \frac{x-r}{\lambda} p_D(Q + r - x, \Upsilon)$$

Let

$$S(z, \Upsilon) = \sum_{d=z}^{\infty} p_D(d, \Upsilon)$$

and $m = Q + r - x$.

$$T_o = \frac{Q-r}{\lambda} S(r, \Upsilon) + \frac{1}{\lambda} \sum_{m=0}^{r-1} (Q - m) p_D(m, \Upsilon)$$

$$= \frac{1}{\lambda} \left[Q - rS(r, \Upsilon) - \sum_{m=0}^{r-1} m p_D(m, \Upsilon) \right]$$

We shall find the following relationships useful.

$$\sum_{m=0}^{z} m p_D(m, \Upsilon) = \sum_{m=0}^{z} \frac{m(\lambda\Upsilon)^m}{m!} e^{-\lambda\Upsilon}$$

$$= \sum_{m=1}^{z} \lambda\Upsilon \frac{(\lambda\Upsilon)^{m-1}}{(m-1)!} e^{-\lambda\Upsilon}$$

$$= \lambda\Upsilon[1 - S(z, \Upsilon)] \tag{4.119}$$

$$\sum_{m=0}^{z} m^2 p_D(m, \Upsilon) = \sum_{m=0}^{z} m(m-1) p_D(m, \Upsilon) + \sum_{m=0}^{z} m p_D(m, \Upsilon)$$

$$= \sum_{m=2}^{z} (\lambda\Upsilon)^2 \frac{(\lambda\Upsilon)^{m-2}}{(m-2)!} e^{-\lambda\Upsilon} + \lambda\Upsilon[1 - S(z - 1, \Upsilon)]$$

$$= (\lambda\Upsilon)^2[1 - S(z - 1, \Upsilon)] + \lambda\Upsilon[1 - S(z, \Upsilon)] \tag{4.120}$$

Therefore

$$T_o = \frac{1}{\lambda} [Q - \lambda\Upsilon - rS(r, \Upsilon) + \lambda\Upsilon S(r - 1, \Upsilon)] \tag{4.121}$$

From equation (4.114) we have

$$E_{T_o} = \frac{1}{2\lambda} \{Q(Q + 1) - r(r + 1) + r(2Q + r + 1)[1 - S(r, \Upsilon)]$$

$$- \lambda\Upsilon(2r + 2Q + 1)[1 - S(r - 1, \Upsilon)]$$

$$+ (\lambda\Upsilon)^2[1 - S(r - 2, \Upsilon)] + \lambda\Upsilon[1 - S(r - 1, \Upsilon)]\} \tag{4.122}$$

Equation (4.115) becomes

$$E_T = \frac{T}{2}\left\{ 2r[1 - S(r, T)] - \lambda T[1 - S(r - 1, T)] + \frac{r(r + 1)}{\lambda T}S(r + 1, T)\right\}$$

(4.123)

The expected unit-years of inventory per cycle is given by

$$E_{T_o} + E_T = \frac{Q(Q + 1)}{2\lambda} + \frac{Qr}{\lambda} - QT + QTS(r - 1, T) - \frac{Qr}{\lambda} S(r, T) \quad (4.124)$$

Expected lost sales per cycle

$$= \lambda T S(r, T) - rS(r + 1, T)$$

$$= \lambda T S(r - 1, T) - rS(r, T) + \lambda T p_o(r - 1, T) - rp_o(r, T) \quad (4.125)$$

$$= \lambda T S(r - 1, T) - rS(r, T)$$

The expected annual cost of maintaining the inventory system is

$$C_T(Q, r) = \frac{1}{T + T_o}\left\{ C_o + C_L[\lambda T S(r - 1, T) - rS(r, T)]\right.$$

$$\left. + \frac{C_I}{\lambda}\left[\frac{Q(Q + 1)}{2} + Qr - Q\lambda T + Q\lambda T S(r - 1, T) - QrS(r, T)\right]\right\}$$

(4.126)

where

$$T + T_o = \frac{1}{\lambda}[Q - rS(r, T) + \lambda S(r - 1, T)] \quad (4.127)$$

To find the optimal values of r and Q the accompanying FORTRAN program can be used where $r = 3, 4, \ldots, LR$ and $Q = 1, 2, \ldots, LQ$.

In this program

TAU = T CO = C_o.

CI = C_I.   CL = C_L.

ALAMDA = λ.   LR = Maximum value of r.

LQ = Maximum value of Q.   CYCLE = $E_{T_o} + E_T$.

COST = $C_T(Q, r)$.   ROPT = Optimal value of r.

QOPT = Optimal value of Q.   TCYCLE = Optimal cycle length.

CMIN = Minimum cost

```
REAL LAMDA
READ(5,1)TAU,CO,CI,CL,LR,LQ,ILAM
WRITE(6,3)
LAMDA=ILAM
PAR=LAMDA*TAU
DO 20 IR=3,LR
RI=IR
P=EXP(-PAR)
SUM=P
LRL=IR-2
DO 10 J=1,LRL
Z=J
P=(PAR/Z)*P
10     SUM=SUM+P
SUM1=1-SUM
RLL=LRL
SUM2=1-SUM-(PAR/(RLL+1.))*P
DO 20 IQ=1,LQ
Q=IQ
CYCLE=( Q-RI*SUM2+PAR*SUM1)/LAMDA
COST=(CO+CL*(PAR*SUM1-RI*SUM2)+(CI/LAMDA)*Q*((Q/2)+.5+RI  -PAR+PAR
1*SUM1-RI*SUM2))/CYCLE
WRITE(6,2)IR,IQ,CYCLE,COST,SUM1,SUM2
20     CONTINUE
STOP
1      FORMAT(4F10.5,3I5)
2      FORMAT(1XI5,3XI5,3XF10.2,3XF10.2,3XF10.7,3XF10.7)
3      FORMAT(1H1)
END
```

For this example the optimal values of r and Q are 4 and 61 units, respectively, yielding an expected annual cost of \$3,158.57. The total expected annual cost of the inventory system as a function of Q for three values of r, including the optimal value, is shown in Figure 4.17. As indicated in Figure 4.17, there is little variation in cost from the optimal value for at least minor variations from the optimal values of Q and r. For example, the annual cost of the inventory system lies within 100 of the optimal value for the combinations of values of r and Q given in Table 4.3.

TABLE 4.3

r	Range of Q
3	$51 \leqslant Q \leqslant 76$
4	$48 \leqslant Q \leqslant 78$
5	$48 \leqslant Q \leqslant 76$
6	$50 \leqslant Q \leqslant 72$
7	$57 \leqslant Q \leqslant 64$

The reader will remember that in developing equation (4.118) we assumed that only one order would be outstanding at any point in time. If $r < Q$, this condition holds since inventory position could fall only as low as Q during the lead time. However, if $r > Q$,

FIGURE 4.17

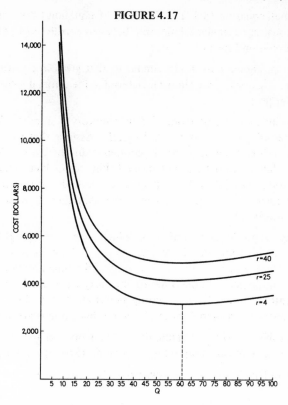

inventory position may fall to r one or more times during lead time, resulting in the placement of one or more orders. Then the model given in equation (4.118) is only approximate. For instance, suppose in the above example, $r = 20$ and $Q = 10$. If the probability of 10 or more demands in the lead time (0.0083 years) is small, we could assume that the present model reasonably approximates reality. Otherwise equation (4.118) should not be used. In this example

$$P(2 \text{ or more orders outstanding at any time}) = P(10 \text{ or more demands in } (0.0083))$$
$$= 0.000277.$$

PROBLEMS

Problems Involving Deterministic Inventory Systems

1. Derive an equation corresponding to (4.37) for the case where the lead time, Υ, is greater than the cycle time (time between the start of two successive production runs).

2. Show that equation (4.17) is the limit of equation (4.35) as ψ tends to infinity. Demonstrate a similar relationship between equations (4.18) and (4.36). Why do these relationships make sense?

3. Develop an annual cost model similar to that given in equation (4.35) for the case where back orders are allowed. Determine the optimal values of Q and s and the reorder point.

4. Develop an annual cost model for an inventory system in which demand during a stock-out period results in a lost sale. Assume that when an order is received, the entire order quantity is contained in the order. Note that net inventory can fall to zero here, but never below zero, since demand during a stock-out period is not fulfilled at a later date. Show that it is optimal either to incur no lost sales or to meet no demand, that is, either allow no lost sales or nothing but lost sales.

5. Consider a production system in which one raw material is used to manufacture the final product. However, assume that two units of raw material are necessary for the manufacture of one unit of the final product. Also assume that the relationship between the ordering and carrying costs is such that the raw material inventory should be zero during nonproductive periods. Develop and optimize the annual cost model for this system if back orders are not allowed.

6. Solve problem 5 without assuming that it is optimal for the raw material inventory to be zero during nonproductive periods. (See Figure 4.8.)

7. Solve problem 5 for the situation where back orders for the final product are allowed.

8. Find the reorder point for problem 5 if the lead time for raw materials is Υ.

Problems with Stochastic Demand

9. A drugstore sells a particular brand of toothpaste at an average rate of λ per year. Past experience indicates that demand for the toothpaste is Poisson distributed within any time period. If demand occurs during a stock-out, the sale is lost at a cost C_L per tube. When the druggist places an order for toothpaste with the supplier, he can expect to receive the shipment in one week. Each order placed results in a cost C_o. In addition, when he purchases toothpaste, he must order in a quantity which is an integer multiple of Q. That is, he must order Q, $2Q$, $3Q$, ... ,nQ tubes on each order. If the inventory carrying cost is C_I and a reorder point system is to be used, develop an annual cost model for this system. Note that the decision variables are r and n (not Q).

10. Find the optimal values of r and n in problem 9 if

$$C_o = \$100. \qquad C_L = \$1.$$
$$C_I = \$0.90. \qquad \lambda = 1{,}000 \text{ units.}$$
$$\Upsilon = 0.02 \text{ years.} \qquad Q = 100.$$

11. In example 4.11, suppose the analyst made a mistake in estimating C_β. If the true value of C_β were $20/year instead of the $10/year, how much would the error cost? The optimal values of r and Q were 8 and 34 units, respectively, using $C_\beta = 10.

12. In example 4.11, what is the probability of a stock-out under the optimum operating policy? What is the expected number of back orders? What is the expected annual cost of back orders?

13. Write a FORTRAN program to compute the expected annual cost given in (4.94) if demand is Poisson distributed with mean annual rate λ. The program should also seek the optimal values of r and Q. Find the optimal values of r and Q for this model if

$$C_o = \$50. \qquad C_I = \$5.$$
$$C_b = \$4. \qquad C_\beta = \$5.$$
$$\lambda = 300 \text{ units}. \qquad \Upsilon = 0.10 \text{ years}.$$

14. Suppose, instead of using equation (4.94) to solve problem 13, equation (4.89) (back-order model for short lead time) had been used. Would the error have been serious? Which model should be used?

15. Solve problem 13 if lead time is 0.01 years. If the analyst assumed lead time was short enough to be considered zero, what would be the magnitude of his error in terms of cost?

16. Solve the problem given in example 4.11 if lead time demand is distributed as follows, where $p = 0.111$. $p_D(d) = p(1 - p)^d$, $d = 0,1,2,\ldots$.

17. A large office building uses fluorescent lamps at an average rate of 1,000 per year. The building manager has decided to install a periodic review system for maintaining the proper supply of lamps. He estimates that each lamp carried in inventory for one year will cost $2. If a lamp burns out and none are available to replace it, a cost of $0.50 is incurred, added to which is another cost of $0.25 for each day the lamp goes unreplaced. Each time an order for flourescent lamps is placed it costs $4. Since the supplier is located near the office building, the building manager decides that he will pick the order up rather than wait for it to be delivered. The resulting lead time is then a matter of hours and can be considered zero for practical purposes. If the order size is to be large enough to bring the inventory level to R and if demand is Poisson, determine the optimal value of R and T_R and the resulting annual cost. Assume that a review takes place at 9am. and that no more than one review can occur per day.

18. For the situation discussed in problem 17, plot isolines for which annual cost will be within 5, 10, and 20 percent of the minimum annual cost.

19. In problem 17, if demand for the year was 1,500 lamps rather than 1,000, how much would the error in estimation cost? Assume demand remains Poisson distributed.

20. For the problem discussed in examples 4.11 and 4.12 find the minimum value of λ for which the approximate back-order model would yield a pseudo-operating policy with an associated annual cost not less than $20 greater than the true optimal cost.

21. Solve the problem given in example 4.14 when

$$\lambda = 300. \quad \Upsilon = 0.083 \text{ years.}$$
$$C_o = \$25. \quad C_I = \$50.$$
$$C_L = \$100.$$

For the optimal solution that you develop, is it not reasonable to assume that no more than one order will be outstanding at a time?

REFERENCES

Buffa, E. S.   *Production-InventorySystems: Planning and Control.* Homewood, Ill.: Richard D. Irwin, Inc., 1968.

Hadley, G.   *Nonlinear and Dynamic Programming.* Reading, Mass.: Addison-Wesley Publishing Co., Inc., 1964.

———.   *Introduction to Probability and Statistical Decision Theory.* San Francisco: Holden-Day, Inc., 1967.

Hadley, G. and Whitin, T. M.   *Analysis of Inventory Systems.* Englewood Cliffs, N.J.: Prentice-Hall, Inc., 1963.

Hanssmann, F.   *Operations Research in Production and Inventory Control.* New York: John Wiley & Sons, Inc., 1962.

Holt, C. C., Modigliani, F., Muth, J. F., and Simon, H. A.   *Planning Production, Inventories, and Work Force.* Englewood Cliffs, N.J.: Prentice-Hall, Inc., 1960.

Morse, P. M.   *Queues, Inventories, and Maintenance.* New York: John Wiley & Sons, Inc., 1958.

Naddor, E.   *Inventory Systems.* New York: John Wiley & Sons, Inc., 1966.

Parzen, E.   *Stochastic Processes.* San Francisco: Holden-Day, Inc., 1962.

Prabhu, N. V.   *Queues and Inventories.* New York: John Wiley & Sons, Inc., 1965.

CHAPTER
5

RELIABILITY, MAINTENANCE,
AND QUALITY CONTROL

In chapters 3 and 4 we discussed the quantitative analysis of production, inventory, and servicing systems. For the most part we were concerned with specification of the mode of operation of the system such that the resulting annual cost of operation would be minimized. We assumed that the system under study was capable of functioning satisfactorily in whatever manner we prescribed without unintended interruption. Such an assumption is an approximation to reality at best.

A system may fail to achieve its intended purpose in two ways. First, the system may fail to function altogether. For example, a jam-up on a production line could cause the line to be shut down completely until appropriate remedial action was taken. The second type of failure occurs when the system continues to perform its function, but not in the intended manner. As an illustration, suppose a soft drink filling line operates such that a large proportion of the bottles which are capped are only half filled. The system is operating, but in such a manner that much of the final product is unacceptable.

In the first part of this chapter we will discuss system failures of the first type. Our objective will be to develop systems which are both as economical and as failure-free as possible. However, having achieved this objective, we have not completely solved the problem. Unless the system is 100 percent reliable, it will eventually fail. When this occurs, corrective action must be taken to render the system operative again. That is, the system must be maintained. Thus our initial discussion will be devoted to the optimal specification of system reliability and to the development of effective maintenance programs to reduce downtime when failures occur.

The final section will be devoted to the development of systems for detecting unacceptable system performance. In the first section we are concerned with the existence of system operation; in the second we are concerned with the quality of that operation. The quality control systems we will deal with will require a quality check of the system at random points in time. Based on the results of this random sample, a decision is made regarding the overall performance of the system for the time period represented in the sample. The objective of our analyses will be to determine the number of inspections to be made and the decision rule to be used in ascertaining the quality of the system's performance.

RELIABILITY AND MAINTENANCE

As we have already noted, system reliability and system maintenance are integrally related. Systems which fail frequently require constant attention and frequent repair. The obvious result is an inflated maintenance cost. In addition we must recognize a cost associated with the loss of the function performed by the system when it is down (inoperative). The cost of downtime can be quite significant, particularly when dealing with manufacturing systems where downtime results in lost production. We can reduce the frequency of repairs and downtime by increasing the reliability of the system, that is, reducing the probability of a failure. However, a price must be paid for the improvements necessary to increase the performance of the system. We are then faced with a trade-off. By increasing the capability of the system to operate for long periods of time without failure we can reduce the frequency of repair as well as downtime. Our problem is to determine the system reliability and associated maintenance program which will minimize the sum of the costs of reliability, maintenance, and downtime.

In the foregoing discussion we dealt with the rather idealized situation in which both system reliability and the maintenance program are under control of the analyst. Unfortunately this is often not true. Frequently the systems analyst must deal with systems with a fixed reliability. Such situations arise when the system under study is well-established and adjustments are not contemplated by management. In these circumstances our investigation is restricted to the determination of the most effective maintenance program under present operating conditions. In this section we will analyze variations of the following three situations:

1. Determination of the optimum system reliability.
2. Determination of the optimum maintenance program.
3. Simultaneous determination of both the optimum system reliability and the optimum maintenance program.

System Reliability

Thus far we have used the term "reliability" to indicate the capacity of the system to function for extended periods of time. However, we have neglected to mention how system reliability can be measured. Any measure of reliability must indicate the ability of the system to perform for a period of time. Four such measures are:

1. Proportion of the time the system is expected to be down.
2. Mean downtime.
3. Probability the system will function without failure for a given interval of time.
4. Mean time between failures.

Note that in each case we have a measure of the ability of the system to operate for a given period of time and in this respect are partially redundant. If we know the proportion of the time the system is down, we also know the proportion of the time the system is in operation. Similarly, if we know the mean time for which the system is down over a given period of time, we also know the mean time of operation. The third and fourth measures of reliability given above are direct measures of the ability of the system to function for any period of time and need no further interpretation here.

In the following example we illustrate the calculation of each of the four measures of reliability defined above, in addition to comparison of the four which will indicate their partial redundancy.

Example 5.1

Consider a system in which the density function of time until failure, measured from the time of the last repair in years, is exponentially distributed with parameter λ. Assume that repairs commence as soon as the system fails and that the time taken to repair the system is also exponentially distributed with parameter μ.

Determine the following measures of the reliability of the system:

a) The expected proportion of the time the system is down during a year.
b) The probability the system will operate without interruption for one year.
c) Mean time between successive failures.
d) Mean downtime per failure.

a) Let $P(t) = P$(System is operating at t). Based on our discussion in Chapter 3, since both time until failure and repair time are exponentially distributed, we have

$$P(t + \Delta t) = (1 - \lambda \, \Delta t)P(t) + \mu \, \Delta t[1 - P(t)] \tag{5.1}$$

which leads to

$$\frac{P(t + \Delta t) - P(t)}{\Delta t} = -\lambda P(t) + \mu[1 - P(t)] \tag{5.2}$$

Taking the limit of (5.2) as $\Delta \, t \to 0$, we obtain the derivative of $P(t)$ with respect to t. In the steady state ($t \to \infty$) this derivative is equal to zero, yielding equation (5.3) where $P = \lim_{t \to \infty} P(t)$

$$-\lambda P + \mu(1 - P) = 0 \tag{5.3}$$

and

$$P = \frac{\mu}{\lambda + \mu} \tag{5.4}$$

Therefore the probability that the system is functioning at an arbitrary point in time is $\mu/(\lambda + \mu)$, which is equivalent to the proportion of the time during a year (or any other period of time for that matter) that the system is operating. The proportion of the time that the system is down is

$$1 - \frac{\mu}{\lambda + \mu}$$

or $\lambda/(\lambda + \mu)$.

b) The probability that the system operates continuously for one year is the probability that the time until failure is greater than one, or

$$P(\text{System operates for one year}) = \int_1^\infty \lambda e^{-\lambda t} \, dt$$

$$= e^{-\lambda} \qquad (5.5)$$

c) The time between two successive failures is made up of the time to repair the system, t_1, and the time until the system fails after that repair, t_2. Therefore

$$\text{Mean time between successive failures} = E(t_1 + t_2)$$

$$= \frac{\mu + \lambda}{\lambda \mu} \qquad (5.6)$$

d) The mean downtime per failure is simply the expected repair time, $1/\mu$.

Let us compare the measures of reliability given in parts a, b, and c by noting what happens to each of these measures when the failure rate, λ, is decreased by an amount $\Delta\lambda$. In part a the difference between the proportion of downtime for failure rates λ and $\lambda - \Delta\lambda$ is given by

$$\frac{\lambda}{\lambda + \mu} - \frac{\lambda - \Delta\lambda}{\lambda - \Delta\lambda + \mu} = \frac{\mu \, \Delta\lambda}{(\lambda + \mu)(\lambda - \Delta\lambda + \mu)} > 0 \qquad (5.7)$$

Therefore the proportion of downtime decreases with decreasing λ, indicating an improvement in the performance of the system. Calculating the difference in the probability of operation without failure for one year for failure rates λ and $\lambda - \Delta\lambda$ leads to

$$e^{-\lambda} - e^{-(\lambda - \Delta\lambda)} = e^{-\lambda}(1 - e^{\Delta\lambda}) < 0 \qquad (5.8)$$

Equation (5.8) indicates that as λ decreases, the probability of successful operation for one year increases. A similar comparison of the mean time between successive failures yields.

$$\frac{\mu + \lambda}{\lambda \mu} - \frac{\mu + \lambda - \Delta\lambda}{(\lambda - \Delta\lambda)\mu} = -\frac{\mu^2 \, \Delta\lambda}{\lambda \mu^2 (\lambda - \Delta\lambda)} < 0 \qquad (5.9)$$

Since the difference given in (5.9) is negative, we conclude that by decreasing the failure rate we increase the mean time between successive failures.

Comparing the measures of system reliability given in parts *a, b,* and *c,* we see that as the failure rate is decreased, the measure of reliability indicates an improvement in the performance of the system.

In part *d* we used mean downtime per failure as our measure of system reliability. The adequacy of this measure alone in assessing system performance is questionable. In order to determine the reliability of the system, we must also know the mean number of failures per year. Multiplying the failures per year by the downtime per failure, we obtain the downtime per year, which is equivalent to the measure of reliability developed in part *a.*

1. *Optimal system reliability.* In this section we shall concern ourselves with the problem of specification of system reliability. For example, suppose a company which manufactures cigarette lighters guarantees these lighters against failure for one year. If a lighter fails within one year, the company agrees to replace the lighter at no cost to the customer. If the manufacturer designs the lighters such that the mean life of a lighter is one year, he can expect a large percentage of replacements. However, if the mean life of the lighter is increased beyond one year, the investment in each lighter will be increased. That is, the more reliable the product, the more expensive it becomes. Therefore the manufacturer is faced with the problem of balancing the costs of replacement and design reliability. In the discussion which follows we will attempt to present an approach to problems of this nature by developing a mathematical model of a simple system of this type. We will then optimize the model with respect to the prescribed measure of reliability.

Assume that a particular product is manufactured at a rate of L units per year, all units eventually being sold. If any unit fails within T years of operation, a cost C_f is incurred by the manufacturer. Let $f_X(x,\tau)$ be the density function of time until failure with mean time until failure τ. As the measure of the reliability of each unit, we will use the mean time until failure, whcih we shall denote by τ. Therefore the reliability of each unit can be increased by increasing τ. Let the cost of a designed reliability of τ be directly proportial to the magnitude of τ, with constant of proportionality, C_τ. That is, the cost of manufacturing a unit with mean time until failure of one year is C_τ.

If the mean time until failure is τ, the probablity that any unit fails before T is

$$P(\text{Failure by } T) = \int_0^T f_X(x,\tau)\, dx \qquad (5.10)$$

The expected number of replacements per year is then

$$L \int_0^T f_X(x,\tau)\, dx.$$

The expected annual cost of operation, $C_T(\tau)$, is given by

$$C_T(\tau) = C_t \tau L + C_f L \int_0^T f_X(x,\tau)\, dx \qquad (5.11)$$

We will demonstrate the optimization of (5.11) in the following example.

Example 5.2

The manufacturer of a particular type of electron tube guarantees its operation for one year. If a tube fails within the guaranteed period, he must replace it at a cost of \$3. Tubes are produced a rate of 50,000 per year. The cost of producing tubes with a mean life τ is directly proportional to τ and is given by $C_t\tau$ per tube where $C_t = \$1$. The distribution of time until failure has been found to be normal with mean τ and standard deviation 0.1 years. To what mean life should the tubes be designed?

From the information given above we have

$$T = 1. \quad C_t = 1.$$
$$C_f = 3. \quad L = 50,000.$$
$$\sigma = 0.1.$$

$$f_X(x, \tau) = \frac{1}{\sigma\sqrt{2\pi}}\, e^{-(x-\tau)^2/2\sigma^2}, \qquad -\infty < x < \infty$$

The normal distribution is defined for all real x, but obviously for our purposes x cannot be negative since this would imply negative time until failure. The assumption that x is normally distributed implies that the parameters τ and σ are such that

$$\int_{-\infty}^0 f_X(x, \tau)\, dx = 0$$

which would be true if $\tau > 0.3$. Since each tube is guaranteed for one year, one could scarcely justify a design which provided a mean life of 0.3 years. If

$$\int_{-\infty}^{0} f_X(x, \tau)\, dx \cong 0$$

then

$$\int_{0}^{T} f_X(x, \tau)\, dx = \int_{-\infty}^{T} f_X(x, \tau)\, dx$$

From equation (5.11)

$$C_T(\tau) = C_\tau \tau L + C_f L \int_{-\infty}^{T} \frac{1}{\sigma\sqrt{2\pi}}\, e^{-(x-\tau)^2/2\sigma^2}\, dx$$

Letting $y = (x - \tau)/\sigma$, we have

$$C_T(\tau) = C_\tau \tau L + C_f L \int_{-\infty}^{\frac{T-\tau}{\sigma}} \frac{1}{\sqrt{2\pi}}\, e^{-y^2/2}\, dy$$

Differentiating with respect to τ, we get

$$\frac{dC_T(\tau)}{d\tau} = C_\tau L - \frac{C_f L}{\sigma\sqrt{2\pi}}\, e^{-(T-\tau)^2/2\sigma^2}$$

$$= 0.$$

Solving for τ, we get

$$\tau = T \pm \sqrt{-2\sigma^2 \ln\left(\frac{C_\tau \sigma\sqrt{2\pi}}{C_f}\right)}$$

and $\tau = 1 \pm 0.223$.

We leave as an exercise for the reader the proof that $\tau = 1.223$ years is the optimal mean time until failure.

II. Systems with zero service delay and service time proportional to size of repair crew. In the systems we are considering here there is no delay between the time at which the system breaks down and the beginning of the required repair. We will also assume that the service time can be reduced by increasing the size of the repair crew. Each time the system fails, the function performed by the system is lost for a period equal to the service time. We will assume that there are two costs associated with each breakdown: one which results every time the system fails and which is independent of the duration of the failure, C_D; and one which is proportional to the duration of the failure, C_P. These costs may account for materials used in repairing the system, lost production, product destroyed by the failure itself, and so forth. We will consider the labor cost separately, assuming that the repair crew must be on stand-by when the system is functioning properly. The annual cost of each repairman is C_L. Let x_i be the service time for the ith service having density function $f_{x_i}(x_i)$, and let y_j be the time until the jth failure measured from the time of the $(j - 1)$st repair and having density function $g_{y_j}(y_j)$. For ease in illustrating the development of the cost model let us assume that x_i and y_j are exponentially distributed with parameters $n\mu$ and λ, respectively, where n is the crew size. Thus we are implying that the service rate is directly proportional to crew size. The expected time between the ith and $(i + 1)$st failure is

$$E(y_{i+1} + x_i) = E(y_{i+1}) + E(x_i)$$

$$= \frac{1}{n\mu} + \frac{1}{\lambda}$$

$$= \frac{n\mu + \lambda}{n\lambda\mu} \tag{5.12}$$

Therefore the expected number of failures per year is

$$\frac{1}{\dfrac{n\mu + \lambda}{n\mu\lambda}}$$

or

$$\frac{n\lambda\mu}{n\mu + \lambda}$$

To calculate the expected annual downtime we note that the expected service time for each failure is $1/(n\mu)$.

$$\text{Expected downtime per year} = \frac{1}{n\mu}\left(\frac{n\lambda\mu}{n\mu + \lambda}\right)$$

$$= \frac{\lambda}{n\mu + \lambda} \tag{5.13}$$

which is equivalent to the result obtained in example 5.1. The expected annual cost of maintaining the system is given by

$$C_T(n) = C_L n + \frac{\lambda}{n\mu + \lambda} C_P + \frac{n\lambda\mu}{n\mu + \lambda} C_D \qquad (5.14)$$

For the purposes of optimizing (5.14) we will treat n as a continuous variable.

$$\frac{dC_T(n)}{dn} = C_L - \frac{\lambda\mu}{(n\mu + \lambda)^2} C_P + \frac{\lambda\mu}{(n\mu + \lambda)} C_D - \frac{n\lambda\mu^2}{(n\mu + \lambda)^2} C_D = 0 \quad (5.15)$$

From which we obtain the solution

$$n = \sqrt{\frac{\lambda}{\mu} \frac{C_P - \lambda C_D}{C_L}} - \frac{\lambda}{\mu} \qquad (5.16)$$

Example 5.3

A production line which automatically fills bottles with a hair-grooming aid also caps and labels them. The company has had a history of trouble with capper jamming. When this occurs, the line must be shut down until the trouble is relieved. The distribution of time until failure has been found to be exponential with mean 0.01 years. Service time is also exponentially distributed with mean $0.001/n$ years where n is the repair crew size. Each time a jam-up occurs, about 10 bottles are destroyed at a cost of $0.70 each. Each bottle is sold for $0.80. The annual production rate is four million bottles per year. Assume $C_L = \$5,000$/year. Find the optimal crew size.

C_D is the cost of bottles lost with each failure, $7. The cost of lost production is the profit which could have been realized if production had continued. The profit per bottle is $0.10. C_P is the annual value of this loss. Therefore

$$C_P = \$400,000.$$

$$\lambda = \frac{1}{0.01} = 100.$$

$$\mu = \frac{1}{0.001} = 1,000.$$

$$n = \sqrt{0.1 \left[\frac{400,000 - 100(7)}{5,000} \right]} - 0.1$$

$$= \sqrt{7.986} - 0.1$$

$$= 2.73$$

Since n must be integer valued, the optimal value must be either 2 or 3. For $n = 2$,

$$C_T(2) = (5,000)(2) + \frac{100}{2,000 + 100}(400,000) + \frac{2(100)(1,000)}{2,000 + 100}(7) = 29,715$$

For $n = 3$,

$$C_T(3) = (5,000)(3) + \frac{100}{3,000 + 100}(400,000) + \frac{3(100)(1,000)}{3,000 + 100}(7) = 28,613$$

Therefore the optimal crew size is three.

III. Systems with zero service delay, service time proportional to repair crew size, and controllable failure rate. The system we will analyze here is similar to the system modeled in the previous section. In this section, however, we will assume that the failure rate can be controlled to some extent if we are willing to make an appropriate investment. Once the investment is made, it will be assumed that the system selected will remain in use without modification for m years. The method used to control the failure rate of the system will be reduction of the mean failure rate, λ (increasing the mean time until failure). Let the investment necessary to obtain a system with failure rate λ be inversely proportional to this rate and given by C_λ/λ. The annual cost of this investment, spread over the m years of service, is $C_\lambda/m\lambda$. The expected annual cost of a system with failure rate λ and repair crew size n is

$$C_T(n, \lambda) = \frac{C_\lambda}{m\lambda} + C_L n + \frac{\lambda}{n\mu + \lambda} C_P + \frac{n\lambda\mu}{n\mu + \lambda} C_D \qquad (5.17)$$

Differentiating (5.17) with respect to n, we obtain the solution given in (5.16). Differentiating with respect to λ, we get

$$\frac{\partial C_T(n, \lambda)}{\partial \lambda} = -\frac{C_\lambda}{m\lambda^2} + \frac{C_P}{n\mu + \lambda} - \frac{\lambda}{(n\mu + \lambda)^2} C_P$$

$$+ \frac{n\mu}{n\mu + \lambda} C_D - \frac{n\lambda\mu}{(n\mu + \lambda)^2} C_D \qquad (5.18)$$

$$= 0$$

or

$$m\lambda^3 C_P + \lambda^2(n^2\mu^2 m C_P + mn\mu C_P - m C_P - C_\lambda) - 2\lambda n\mu C_D - n^2\mu^2 C_\lambda = 0$$
(5.19)

The solution of equations (5.16) and (5.19) for the optimal values of n and λ is left as an exercise for the reader.

Example 5.4

For the problem given in example 5.2, assume that the mean failure rate can be reduced by an increase in the investment in the system. Assume that the investment is inversely proportional to the failure rate and that the system is expected to function for five years.

Let $C_\lambda = \$10,000$. Determine the optimal mean failure rate and repair crew size. What is the initial investment in the system? Suppose the mean failure rate may vary by as much as $\lambda_{opt} \pm 0.25\lambda_{opt}$ where λ_{opt} is the optimal mean failure rate. Find the maximum annual cost of this variation.

Using equations (5.16) and (5.19), we obtain optimal values of n and λ of $n = 1$ and $\lambda_{opt} = 2.2227$, with associated expected annual cost of $\$6,802.44$. Let us now examine the fluctuation in annual cost if λ varies by as much as ± 25 percent from its optimal value.

$$\lambda_{opt} + 0.25\lambda_{opt} = 2.7784$$
$$\lambda_{opt} - 0.25\lambda_{opt} = 1.6670$$

If the crew size remains at its optimal value,

$$C_T(1, 2.7784) = \$6,847.52$$
$$C_T(1, 1.6670) = \$6,877.09$$

Therefore a 25 percent deviation from the optimal value of λ results in a maximum increase in expected annual cost of about 1 percent.

IV. Multiple independent systems with a single repair crew. The system we will analyze here is a generalization of that described in II. We will assume that we now have a system composed of k subsystems which operate independently. The distribution of time until failure for any individual subsystem is exponential with mean rate λ. One repair crew of size n is available, and the distribution of repair time is exponential with parameter $n\mu$. If one of the subsystems fails, the repair crew immediately begins working on that subsystem unless the crew is occupied in repairs elsewhere. If the subsystem which failed cannot obtain immediate service, it must wait its turn for service. That is, subsystems are serviced in the order in which they failed. Let

C_D = Cost per failure, independent of downtime.
C_P = Cost of one failure lasting for one year.
C_L = Labor cost per crew member.
n = repair crew size.
k = number of subsystems.
λ = mean failure rate per subsystem.
$n\mu$ = Mean service rate for a repair crew of size n.

To develop the required annual cost model we must determine the expected total downtime per year for all k subsystems and the expected number of failures per year. Since all of the subsystems may be considered to be identical, we will first determine the expected downtime per year for any one subsystem and multiply by k, the number of subsystems, to obtain the total downtime for the entire system.

Let us examine the system at the point in time, t, at which a failure occurs. If m subsystems are already down at t, the failing unit is down for a period of time equal to the service time remaining on the unit in service plus the time to serve the other $m - 1$ units plus the time to serve the failing subsystem. The reader will note that $m <$ k. In Chapter 3, using equations (3.43) to (3.51), we proved that if service time is exponentially distributed with parameter μ and if there are n units in the system at the time an arrival occurs, the total time that arrival will spend in the system is gamma distributed with parameters n and μ. Therefore the density function of downtime, x, for a subsystem failing at t when m units are already down is

$$f_X(x \mid m) = \frac{n\mu}{\Gamma(m + 1)} (n\mu x)^m e^{-n\mu x}, \qquad 0 < x < \infty \qquad (5.20)$$

and

$$E(x \mid m) = \frac{m + 1}{n\mu} \qquad (5.21)$$

The unconditional expected downtime per failure is given by

$$E(\text{Downtime per failure}) = \sum_{m=1}^{k-1} E(x \mid m)P(m \text{ units down at time of failure})$$

Letting t be a point in time at which a failure occurs, we will determine the probability mass function of the number of units already down, m, at this point, $P_m(t)$. From Chapter 3

$$P_o(t) = P_o(t - \Delta t)(1 - k\lambda \Delta t) + P_1(t - \Delta t)n\mu \Delta t[1 - (k - 1)\lambda \Delta t] \quad (5.22)$$

The probability that any individual unit fails in an interval Δt is $\lambda \Delta t$. Therefore if j subsystems are operating at $t - \Delta t$, the probability of a failure by t is $j\lambda \Delta t$. For $m > 0$ we have

$$P_m(t) = P_{m-1}(t - \Delta t)(k - m + 1)\lambda \Delta t + P_m(t - \Delta t)[1 - (k - m)\lambda \Delta t]$$
$$+ P_{m+1}(t - \Delta t)[1 - (k - m - 1)\lambda \Delta t]n\mu \Delta t, \qquad 0 < m < k - 1 \quad (5.23)$$

From which we obtain

$$\frac{P_o(t) - P_o(t - \Delta t)}{\Delta t} = k\lambda P_o(t - \Delta t) + n\mu[1 - (k - 1)\lambda \Delta t]P_1(t - \Delta t) \quad (5.24)$$

$$\frac{P_m(t) - P_m(t - \Delta t)}{\Delta t} = (k - m + 1)\lambda P_{m-1}(t - \Delta t) - (k - m)\lambda P_m(t - \Delta t)$$
$$- n\mu P_m(t - \Delta t) + (k - m)n\lambda\mu \Delta t P_m(t - \Delta t)$$
$$+ n\mu[1 - (k - m - 1)\lambda \Delta t]P_{m+1}(t - \Delta t) \quad (5.25)$$

Taking the limit of (5.24) and (5.25) as $\Delta t \to 0$, we have

$$\frac{dP_o(t)}{dt} = -k\lambda P_o(t) + n\mu P_1(t) \quad (5.26)$$

$$\frac{dP_m(t)}{dt} = (k - m + 1)\lambda P_{m-1}(t) - [(k - m)\lambda + n\mu]P_m(t)$$
$$+ n\mu P_{m+1}(t), \qquad 0 < m < k - 1 \quad (5.27)$$

To obtain the steady-state solution we take the limit of (5.26) and (5.27) as $t \to \infty$, in which case both derivatives become zero and $P_m(t) \to P_m$.

$$-k\lambda P_o + n\mu P_1 = 0 \quad (5.28)$$

$$(k - m + 1)\lambda P_{m-1} - [(k - m)\lambda + n\mu]P_m + n\mu P_{m+1} = 0,$$
$$0 < m < k - 1 \quad (5.29)$$

We obtain a solution for P_m as follows:

$$P_1 = \frac{k\lambda}{n\mu} P_o \quad (5.30)$$

Letting $m = 1$ in (5.29) yields

$$k\lambda P_o - [(k - 1)\lambda + n\mu]P_1 + n\mu P_2 = 0 \tag{5.31}$$

Substituting the expression P_1 given in (5.30) into (5.31), we get

$$P_2 = \frac{k!}{(k - 2)!} \left(\frac{\lambda}{n\mu}\right)^2 P_o \tag{5.32}$$

Successive solutions lead to

$$P_m = \frac{k!}{(k - m)!} \left(\frac{\lambda}{n\mu}\right)^m P_o, \qquad 0 \le m < k \tag{5.33}$$

$$\sum_{m=0}^{k-1} P_m = 1$$

We can solve for P_o since

$$\sum_{m=0}^{k-1} P_m = \sum_{m=0}^{k-1} \frac{k!}{(k - m)!} \left(\frac{\lambda}{n\mu}\right)^m P_o$$

and

$$P_o = \frac{1}{\displaystyle\sum_{m=0}^{k-1} \frac{k!}{(k - m)!} \left(\frac{\lambda}{n\mu}\right)^m} \tag{5.34}$$

The reader should note the reason that m cannot exceed $k - 1$. Since P_m is the probability that m units are already down when a subsystem fails, m must be less than k. If k units are down at any point in time, there are no subsystems left to fail. Therefore if a subsystem fails at t, there must have been at least one unit operating prior to failure.

$$E(x) = \sum_{m=0}^{k-1} \frac{m + 1}{n\mu} \frac{k!}{(k - m)!} \left(\frac{\lambda}{n\mu}\right)^m P_o \tag{5.35}$$

To determine the number of failures per year we calculate the expected time between successive failures, $E(t)$, in years and divide this quantity into one year.

$$E(t) = E(x) + E(\text{Time until the next failure})$$

$$E(t) = \sum_{m=0}^{k-1} \frac{m + 1}{n\mu} \frac{k!}{(k - m)!} \left(\frac{\lambda}{n\mu}\right)^m P_o + \frac{1}{\lambda} \tag{5.36}$$

E(Number of failures per year per subsystem)

$$= \frac{1}{\sum_{m=0}^{k-1} \frac{m+1}{n\mu} \frac{k!}{(k-m)!} \left(\frac{\lambda}{n\mu}\right)^m P_o + \frac{1}{\lambda}} \qquad (5.37)$$

The total expected downtime for the entire system is

$$E(\text{System downtime}) = k \frac{\sum_{m=0}^{k-1} \frac{m+1}{n\mu} \frac{k!}{(k-m)!} \left(\frac{\lambda}{n\mu}\right)^m P_o}{\sum_{m=0}^{k-1} \frac{m+1}{n\mu} \frac{k!}{(k-m)!} \left(\frac{\lambda}{n\mu}\right)^m P_o + \frac{1}{\lambda}} \qquad (5.38)$$

The expected annual cost equation is given by

$$C_T(n) = C_L n + \left[\frac{C_D + C_P \sum_{m=0}^{k-1} \frac{m+1}{n\mu} \frac{k!}{(k-m)!} \left(\frac{\lambda}{n\mu}\right)^m P_o}{\sum_{m=0}^{k-1} \frac{m+1}{n\mu} \frac{k!}{(k-m)!} \left(\frac{\lambda}{n\mu}\right)^m P_o + \frac{1}{\lambda}} \right] k \qquad (5.39)$$

The reader should recognize that equation (5.39) is a generalization of (5.14) and is equivalent to (5.14) for $k = 1$.

Example 5.5

In example 5.2, suppose there were five filling lines instead of one. Find the optimal crew size. Plot the labor cost, failure cost, and total cost of the maintenance system as a function of crew size.

From example 5.2 we have

$$\lambda = 100. \qquad \mu = 1,000.$$
$$C_L = \$5,000. \qquad C_D = \$7.$$
$$C_P = \$400,000. \qquad k = 5.$$

From equations (5.34) and (5.39)

$$P_o = \frac{1}{\sum_{m=0}^{4} \frac{5!}{(5-m)!} \left(\frac{1}{10n}\right)^m}$$

$$C_T(n) = 5,000n + 5 \left[\frac{7 + (400,000) \sum_{m=0}^{4} \frac{m+1}{1,000n} \frac{5!}{(5-m)!} \left(\frac{1}{10n}\right)^m P_o}{\sum_{m=0}^{4} \frac{m+1}{1,000n} \frac{5!}{(5-m)!} \left(\frac{1}{10n}\right)^m P_o + 0.01} \right]$$

The value of n which minimizes $C_T(n)$ is 23, which yields an expected annual cost of \$ 240,563 as shown in Figure 5.1.

FIGURE 5–1

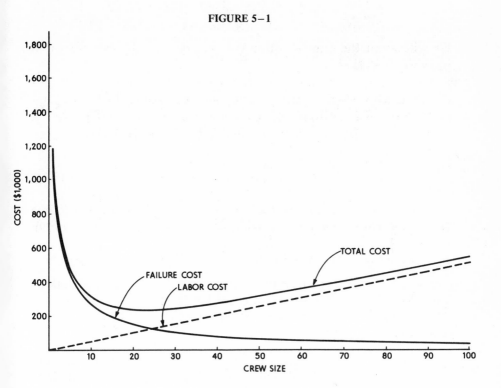

V. Scheduled maintenance, all units repaired or replaced, constant service time.   The maintenance system we are interested in here is similar to that discussed in model IV. We will assume that the operating system is composed of k independent units, or subsystems, and that one crew of n men is available to maintain all k units. Instead of repairing each unit as it fails, we will assume that units are repaired during scheduled maintenance periods and only during these periods. During each such period all k units are shut down. Each unit is inspected and whatever repairs are necessary, are made. We will assume that all units remain down until the end of service on all k units. Let T be the time between the end of one maintenance service period and the beginning of the next. The density functions of time until failure, Y, and service time, X, for each subsystem are $f_Y(y)$ and $g_X(x)$, respectively, and

$$E(x) = \frac{1}{n\mu}$$ (5.40)

$$E(y) = \frac{1}{\lambda}$$ (5.41)

We will adopt the same notation with respect to unit costs as used in previous models.

We will develop the expected annual cost of operating this maintenance system by first deriving the expected cost per cycle and multiplying the resulting cost by the expected number of cycles. A cycle will be the time between the start of two successive service periods.

$$\text{Cycle} = T + \text{service time for } k \text{ units}$$ (5.42)

The downtime per cycle for any given unit is the period of time for which it was down during T plus the length of the service period.

$$E(\text{Downtime per cycle per unit}) = E(\text{downtime during } T) + E(\text{service time})$$ (5.43)

The expected time to service any given unit is $1/(n\mu)$ from (5.40). Therefore

$$E(\text{Service time}) = \frac{k}{n\mu}$$ (5.44)

To compute the expected downtime during T we must recognize two cases. If the time until failure, y, is less than T, the downtime during T is $T - y$. If $y \geqslant T$, the downtime during T is zero.

$$E(\text{Downtime during } T) = \int_0^T (T - y)f_Y(y)\, dy + 0 \int_T^\infty f_Y(y)\, dy$$

$$= \int_0^T (T - y)f_Y(y)\, dy$$ (5.45)

Equation (5.43) becomes

$$E(\text{Downtime per cycle per unit}) = \int_0^T (T - y)f_Y(y)\, dy + \frac{k}{n\mu}$$ (5.46)

The expected downtime per cycle for the entire system of k units is given by equation (5.47)

$$E(\text{System downtime per cycle}) = k \int_0^T (T - y)f_Y(y)\, dy + \frac{k^2}{n\mu} \quad (5.47)$$

Since we have a cost C_D associated with each failure which is independent of the duration of the failure, we must obtain the expected number of failures per cycle. The probability that any individual unit fails during T, that is, p, is given by

$$p = \int_0^T f_Y(y)\, dy \quad (5.48)$$

The probability of m failures in T, that is, P_m, is the probability that any specified combination of m units fails multiplied by the number of possible combinations of m units. The probability that any given combination of m of the k units fails is $p^m(1 - p)^{k-m}$. Since there are $k!/(m!(k - m)!)$ such distinct combinations,

$$P_m = \frac{k!}{m!(k - m)!}\, p^m(1 - p)^{k-m}, \qquad m = 0, 1, \ldots, k \quad (5.49)$$

Equation (5.49) indicates that the number of failures per T is binomially distributed and therefore has mean kp or

$$E(m) = kp \quad (5.50)$$

The total expected cost of downtime per cycle is given by

$$E(\text{Cost of downtime per cycle}) = kpC_D + \left[k \int_0^T (T - y)f_Y(y)\, dy + \frac{k^2}{n\mu} \right] C_P$$

$$(5.51)$$

The expected length of a cycle is $T + (k/n\mu)$. Dividing (5.51) by the cycle length and adding the annual labor cost, we obtain the expected annual cost of the proposed maintenance system, $C_T(n, T)$.

$$C_T(n, T) = C_L N + \frac{kC_D \int_0^T f_Y(y)\, dy}{T + \dfrac{k}{n\mu}} + \frac{C_P\left[k \int_0^T (T - y)f_Y(y)\, dy + \dfrac{k^2}{n\mu} \right]}{T + \dfrac{k}{n\mu}} \quad (5.52)$$

We could determine conditions for the minimization of (5.52) by taking partial derivatives of $C_T(n, T)$ with respect to n and T.

However, the resulting equations are of such complexity that it is generally simpler to work with (5.52) in determining the optimal values of n and T.

Example 5.6

Assuming the distribution of time until failure is exponential with parameter λ, determine the expected annual cost equation corresponding to equation (5.52).

Since time until failure is exponentially distributed, the density function of y is $f_Y(y) = \lambda e^{-\lambda y}$, $0 < y < \infty$.

Therefore

$$\int_0^T f_Y(y)\, dy = 1 - e^{-\lambda t}$$

and

$$\int_0^T (T - y)f_Y(y)\, dy = T - \frac{1 - e^{-\lambda t}}{\lambda}$$

Equation (5.47) becomes

$$C_T(n, T) = C_L n + \frac{kC_D(1 - e^{-\lambda T})}{T + \dfrac{k}{n\mu}} + \frac{C_P\left[kT - \dfrac{k}{\lambda}(1 - e^{-\lambda t}) + \dfrac{k^2}{n\mu}\right]}{T + \dfrac{k}{n\mu}}$$

$$= C_L n + \frac{k(1 - e^{-\lambda t})\left(C_D - \dfrac{C_P}{\lambda}\right)}{T + \dfrac{k}{n\mu}} + kC_P$$

$$= n\left[C_L + \frac{k\mu\left(C_D - \dfrac{C_P}{\lambda}\right)(1 - e^{-\lambda t})}{n\mu T + k}\right] + kC_P$$

Example 5.7

A city owns 100 traffic counters which it keeps in continual operation except during maintenance periods. Since the maintenance required cannot be carried out in the field, all 100 counters are collected and delivered to a central location, where each unit is inspected and repaired or replaced as necessary. Service time per counter is exponentially distributed with parameter 2,000n, where n is the maintenance crew size. The distribution of time until failure is exponential with parameter $\lambda = 10$. Each member of the repair crew costs \$4,000 per year. If any unit is down for one year, a cost of \$1,000 results. Each time a counter fails, it costs \$10, no matter how long the counter is down. Let T be the operating period for each counter before it is picked up for maintenance. Find the values of n and T which minimize the expected annual cost of operation. Plot total expected cost versus T for $n = 1,3,5$.

FIGURE 5–2

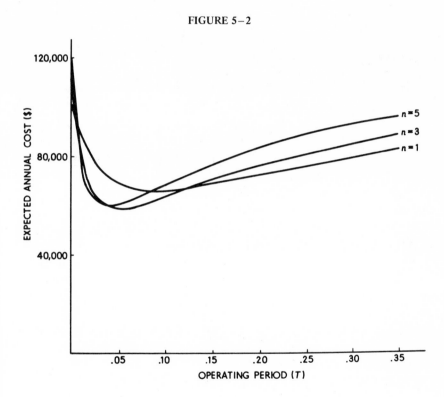

Since the distribution of time until failure is exponential, the expected annual cost of the maintenance system is given by $G(n, T)$ in example 5.5.

$$C_D = \$10. \qquad C_T = \$1,000$$
$$C_L = \$4,000 \qquad \lambda = 10$$
$$\mu = 2,000 \qquad k = 100$$

$$C_T(n, T) = n \left[4,000 + \frac{200,000\left(10 - \frac{1,000}{10}\right)(1 - e^{-10T})}{2,000nT + 100} \right] + 100,000$$

$$= n \left[4,000 - \frac{180,000(1 - e^{-10T})}{20nT + 1} \right] + 100,000$$

The optimal values of n and T are 3.0 and 0.05 years, respectively. The variation of total expected cost with T is shown in Figure 5.2 (page 181) for $n = 1, 3, 5$.

QUALITY CONTROL SYSTEMS

The objective of a quality control system is to determine whether a given quantity of product meets quality specifications. Quality specifications may apply to a measurable variable, such as length, weight, density, hardness, or to a characteristic which is not measured but which is either present or absent. Characteristics of the latter type are usually called attributes and generally refer to the presence or absence of a defect, such as a burned-out filament in a light bulb, a scar on the surface of a table, a hole in a toothpaste tube, or a faulty connection in an electrical circuit. In either case, the quality control system usually consists of the selection of a random sample from the lot of product in question. Based upon results obtained from the sample, a conclusion is drawn regarding the acceptability of the lot represented by the sample. For example, suppose a manufacturing process is to produce 8-inch lead tubes having an inside diameter of 1/2 inch with an allowable tolerance of ±0.01 inches. Assume that these tubes are produced in lots of 10,000. After each production run, an inspection is conducted to determine whether the lot is acceptable with respect to the inside diameter. To ascertain the overall quality of the lot we might select 100 tubes at random, measure the inside diameter of each, and compute mean inside diameter of the sample. Based on the value of the sample mean, we would either accept or reject the lot.

Since lot acceptability is based on a sample, the possibility of making an error in judging the lot must be acknowledged. If the lot is accepted when it contains a large number of substandard units, serious problems may be created when these units are subsequently used. On the other hand, if the lot is rejected when it contains very few defective units, a needless scrap or rework cost will result. The probability of occurrence of either of these errors can be reduced by increasing the sample size. However, a cost is associated with each unit inspected. Therefore to reduce the chance of error and the associated expected cost of these errors we must increase the sampling cost. Consequently we are faced with the problem of balancing opposing costs. In the remainder of this chapter we will derive mathematical models representing the expected cost of operating several commonly encountered quality control systems for attributes. Our objective in each case will be to determine the optimal quality control program. Although models for quality control systems for variables will not be treated here, arguments similar to those used throughout this chapter may be used to develop such models.

VI. Acceptance sampling, all defective units detected. Consider a manufacturing system in which units are produced in lots of size L. In order to determine whether the overall quality of the lot is acceptable, a random sample of N units from the lot will be inspected. If c or less units are found to be unacceptable, the lot will be labeled acceptable. If more than c defective units are found in the sample, the entire lot will be rejected. Since the decision to accept or reject the lot is based on a random sample, one of two errors are possible. First, we might reject a lot which is, in fact, acceptable. Conversely our sampling may result in acceptance of a lot which contains an intolerably large proportion of defective units. The purpose of our analysis will be to develop an economical and effective quality control system.

Let us examine the costs relevant to the quality control system under study here. First, we have the inspection cost per unit, C_I, which is directly proportional to the number of units inspected, N. The magnitude of C_I will depend to a large extent upon whether inspection results in destruction of the inspected unit. For the purpose of this development, destructive testing will be assumed. Therefore the lot size after inspection is $(L - N)$.

In addition to the inspection cost we must also recognize costs associated with acceptance and rejection of the lot. The fact that a lot is accepted does not imply that the lot is defect-free, and each defective unit contained in these lots can cause trouble. For example, if the defective units contained in an accepted lot find their way to a production line, they may cause a shutdown of the line, failure of the final product, or at least replacement after attempting to use them on the line. In each of these situations a cost is attached to the defective unit which is accepted. This is the problem which we will treat here. Let C_d be the cost of accepting a defective unit. The cost of lot rejection is dependent upon the disposition of rejected lots. In some situations rejected lots are 100 percent inspected to screen out defective articles. In other cases it may be more economical to scrap the entire lot. For the purposes of the present analysis we will assume that rejected lots are scrapped in their entirety at a cost of C_r per unit.

If p is the true percent defective for a lot expressed in decimal form, the number of defectives contained in the lot is pL. Assuming that the lot size is large, particularly when compared with the sample size, we find that the distribution of the number of defective units found in the sample of size N is binomial with parameters p and N. That is, if X is the number of defective units in the sample and p is the lot percent defective, the probability mass function of X, $p_X(x|p)$, is given by

$$P_X(x \mid p) = \frac{N!}{x!(N-x)!} \, p^x(1-p)^{N-x}, \qquad x = 0, 1, \ldots, N \qquad (5.53)$$

In practice, the distribution of X is often approximated by the Poisson distribution with parameter Np. This approximation has been found to be quite reliable, the reliability increasing as N increases and p decreases.

Given a lot percent defective of p, the expected cost of rejection is $C_r(L - N)$ multiplied by the probability of rejection where $(L - N)$ is the number of units rejected. The probability of rejection is the probability that the number of defective units found in the sample of size N is greater than c, the acceptance number.

$$\text{Expected cost of rejection, given } p = C_r(L - N) \sum_{x=c+1}^{N} p_X(x \mid p) \qquad (5.54)$$

The expected cost of acceptance is the cost of acceptance, $C_d p(L - N)$, multiplied by the probability of acceptance where $p(L - N)$ is the number of defective units accepted.

$$\text{Expected cost of acceptance, given } p = C_d \, p(L - N) \sum_{x=0}^{c} p_X(x \mid p) \qquad (5.55)$$

Therefore the expected total cost per lot given a lot percent defective p is

Expected total cost, given $p = C_I N + C_d p(L - N) \sum_{x=0}^{c} p_X(x \mid p)$

$$+ C_r(L - N) \sum_{x=c+1}^{N} p_X(x \mid p) \qquad (5.56)$$

Thus far we have assumed a specific lot percent defective. However, if the lot percent defective is constant and known, there is no need for a quality control system, since knowledge of the value of p would automatically tell us whether the lot is acceptable or not. In addition a constant value of p would imply that either every lot is acceptable or every lot is unacceptable. In either case a quality control system would be an unnecessary expense. Therefore the necessity of a quality control system implies that the value of p cannot be predicted with certainty. We will assume that the lot percent defective is a random variable with density function $f_p(p)$. To obtain the unconditional expected total cost per lot, $C_T(N,c)$, we must take the expected value of (5.56) with respect to p.

$$C_T(N, c) = \int_0^1 \left[C_I N + C_d p(L - N) \sum_{x=0}^{c} p_X(x \mid p) \right.$$

$$\left. + C_r(L - n) \sum_{x=c+1}^{N} p_X(x \mid p) \right] f_P(p) \, dp \qquad (5.57)$$

$$C_T(N, c) = C_I N + C_d p(L - N) \sum_{x=0}^{c} \int_0^1 p p_X(x \mid p) f_P(p) \, dp$$

$$+ C_r(L - N) \sum_{x=c+1}^{N} \int_0^1 p_X(x \mid p) f_P(p) \, dp \qquad (5.58)$$

In the development of (5.58) we have made several implicit assumptions. The result of these assumptions is that this model is only approximate for most practical problems. First, we have assumed that N units are inspected without exception. Usually inspection will continue until $c + 1$ defective untis are found. At this point the lot is rejected and there is no need for further inspection.

Therefore the expected sample size per lot will always be less than or equal to N. If, however, the probability of lot rejection is small, the expected sample size will be close to N.

If we assume that the distribution of the number of defective items in a sample of size N is binomially distributed, we are implicitly assuming that the probability that any given unit is defective is independent of whether any other unit in the sample is defective. That is, the probability that a unit is defective remains unchanged as sampling continues. For example, suppose a lot of 500,000 units is 10 percent defective and from this lot we draw and inspect 10 units. The probability that the first item selected is defective is 0.10. Let us now determine the probability that the 10th item is defective under two extreme conditions. First, suppose the first nine items were defective. The probability that the 10th is defective is 49,991/499,991, or 0.09998. Now assume that the first nine items were not defective. The probability that the 10th item is defective is 50,000/499,991, or 0.100002. In this example the probability that any of the 10 items is defective remains substantially constant, and the binomial distribution would be appropriate. Let us now change the lot size from 500,000 units to 100 units, the percent defective and sample size remaining the same. The probability that the first item selected is defective is 10/100, or 0.10. Again we will calculate the probability that the 10th item is defective under the same two conditions described above. If the first nine units are defective, the probability that the 10th is defective also is 1/91, or 0.0109. If the first nine units are not defective, the probability that the 10th is defective is 10/91, or 0.109. Therefore the probability that the 10th item is defective is strongly dependent upon the occurrence of defectives among the first nine items. In circumstances such as this the hypergeometric should be used to describe the probability that x defective units occur in a sample of size N. In general, as N/pL decreases, the propriety of the binomial (or the Poisson) increases.

The third assumption implicit in our development is that the density function of proportion defective per lot remains stable over time. If the system under study tends to become increasingly erratic as the period of operation is extended, the analyst must develop a time-dependent density function of proportion defective.

Example 5.8

Simplify equation (5.58) if the density function of percent defective is given by

$$f_P(p) = (a + 1)(1 - p)^a \qquad 0 \leq p \leq 1, a > -1$$

Also determine the optimal value of c for any given value of N. From equation (5.53) we have

$$p_X(x \mid p) = \frac{N!}{x!(N-x)!} \, p^x(1-p)^{N-x}, \qquad x = 0, 1, 2, \ldots, N$$

We resolve the integrals in (5.58) by noting that

$$\int_0^1 z^k(1-z)^{m-k} \, dz = \frac{\Gamma(k+1)\Gamma(m-k+1)}{\Gamma(m+2)}$$

$$= \frac{k!(m-k)!}{(m+1)!}$$

for integer k and m. Therefore

$$\int_0^1 p p_X(x \mid p) f_P(p) \, dp = \int_0^1 (a+1) \frac{N!}{x!(N-x)!} \, p^{x+1}(1-p)^{N+a-x} \, dp$$

$$= \frac{(a+1)N!}{(N+a+2)!} \frac{(x+1)(N+a-x)!}{(N-x)!}$$

and

$$\int_0^1 p_X(x \mid p) f_P(p) \, dp = \int_0^1 (a+1) \frac{N!}{x!(N-x)!} \, p^x(1-p)^{N+a-x} \, dp$$

$$= \frac{(a+1)N!}{(N+a+1)!} \frac{(N+a-x)!}{(N-x)!}$$

Equation (5.58) becomes

$$C_T(N, c) = C_I N + C_d(L-N) \frac{(a+1)N!}{(N+a+2)!} \sum_{x=0}^{c} \frac{(x+1)(N+a-x)!}{(N-x)!}$$

$$+ C_r(L-N) \frac{(a+1)N!}{(N+a+1)!} \sum_{x=c+1}^{N} \frac{(N+a-x)!}{(N-x)!}$$

$$= C_I N + \frac{(L-N)}{\binom{N+a+1}{N}} \left[\frac{C_d}{(N+a+2)} \sum_{x=0}^{c} (x+1)\binom{N+a-x}{a} \right.$$

$$\left. + C_r \sum_{x=c+1}^{N} \binom{N+a-x}{a} \right] \qquad (5.59)$$

where

$$\binom{z}{v} = \frac{z!}{v!(z-v)!}$$

To optimize (5.59) with respect to c we difference $C_T(N,c)$ with respect to c.

$$\Delta_c C_T(N, c) = C_T(N, c+1) - C_T(N, c)$$

$$= \frac{L-N}{\binom{N+a+1}{N}} \left[\frac{C_d}{(N+a+2)} \sum_{x=0}^{c+1}(x+1)\binom{N+a-x}{a} \right.$$

$$- \frac{C_d}{(N+a+2)} \sum_{x=0}^{c}(x+1)\binom{N+a-x}{a}$$

$$\left. + C_r \sum_{x=c+2}^{N}\binom{N+a-x}{a} - C_r \sum_{x=c+1}^{N}\binom{N+a-x}{a} \right]$$

$$= \frac{L-N}{\binom{N+a+1}{N}} \left[\frac{C_d}{(N+a+2)}(c+2)\binom{N+a-c-1}{a} \right.$$

$$\left. - C_r \binom{N+a-c-1}{a} \right]$$

If c^* is the value of c which minimizes (5.59) for any given value of N, then

$$\Delta_c C_T(N, c^*) \geq 0 \geq \Delta_c C_T(N, c^* - 1) \tag{5.60}$$

is the optimal value of c and is the smallest integer value of c such that $\Delta_c C_T(N,c) \geq 0$ or

$$\frac{C_d}{N+a+2}(c+2) - C_r \geq 0 \tag{5.61}$$

Rearranging equation (5.61), we find that the optimal value of c is the minimum value of c such that

$$c \geq \frac{C_r}{C_d}(N+a+2) - 2 \tag{5.62}$$

We leave the determination of optimal conditions for N as an exercise for the reader.

Example 5.9

The manufacturer of a particular piece of electronic equipment assembles each on a semiautomated line. One of the components of this device is produced internally a a rate of 10,000 units per week. At the end of each week, N units are inspected to determine whether that week's production meets established quality standards. The nature of the defect for which the inspection is conducted is such that if a unit containing this defect reaches the assembly line, it will cause a shutdown of the line at a cost of \$25. The value of each unit is \$2. Each unit inspected is destroyed, and the cost of labor and equipment used in the inspection is \$.50. Therefore the total unit cost of inspection is \$2.50. If the lot is rejected as a result of the weekly inspection, it is scrapped.

Assuming the density function of p is given by

$$f_p(p) = 19(1-p)^{18}, 0 \leq p \leq 1,$$

determine the optimal sampling plan.

From the specified density function we have $a = 18$. Therefore equation (5.62) becomes $c \geq (2N - 10)/25$. Since c cannot assume negative values, the optimal value of c for $N \leq 5$ is zero. The optimal values of c for values of N between 1 and 180 are given in the table below.

TABLE 5.1

Range of N	Optimal c
$1 \leq N \leq 5$	0
$6 \leq N \leq 17$	1
$18 \leq N \leq 30$	2
$31 \leq N \leq 42$	3
$43 \leq N \leq 54$	4
$55 \leq N \leq 67$	5
$68 \leq N \leq 80$	6
$81 \leq N \leq 92$	7
$93 \leq N \leq 105$	8
$106 \leq N \leq 117$	9
$118 \leq N \leq 130$	10
$131 \leq N \leq 142$	11
$143 \leq N \leq 154$	12
$155 \leq N \leq 167$	13
$168 \leq N \leq 180$	14

To determine the optimal solution to (5.59) we must evaluate $C_T(N,c)$ for each N and the corresponding optimal value of c. The accompanying program may be used to accomplish this.

A definition of variables for the program is shown below.

CI = unit cost of inspection.

CR = unit cost of rejection.

CD = unit cost of acceptance.

AL = lot size.

A = parameter of the distribution of proportion defective.

LN = minimum value of *N*.

IN = maximum value of *N*.

AC = acceptance number.

N = sample size.

C(I,J) = combinations of *i* things taken *j* at a time.

ECI = expected inspection cost.

ECR = expected rejection cost.

ECD = expected acceptance cost.

COST = expected total cost.

NMIN = optimal value of N.

MINC = optimal value of AC.

TOTMIN = optimal total cost.

```
      INSPECTION WITH DETECTION OF ALL DEFECTIVE UNITS
      DIMENSION CMIN(500),ICMIN(500)
      READ(5,1) CI,CR,CD,AL,A,LN,IN
      WRITE(6,5)
      TOTMIN=10.**30
      IA=A
      M=IN+IA+1
      DO 100 N=LN,IN
      INT=0
      DO 90 IC=1,N
      ICC=IC-1
      N4=N+IA+1
      AN=N
      N1=N+IA
      SUM1=C(N1,IA)
      IF(ICC)30,30,10
10    DO 20 IX=1,ICC
      X=IX
      N2=N+IA-IX
20    SUM1=SUM1+(X+1.)*C(N2,IA)
30    SUM2=0
      DO 40 IX=IC,N
      N3=N+IA-IX
40    SUM2=SUM2+C(N3,IA)
      ECI=CI*AN
      ECD=CD*(AL-AN)*SUM1/((AN+A+2.)*C(N4,N))
      ECR=CR*(AL-AN)*SUM2/C(N4,N)
      COST=ECI+ECR+ECD
      WRITE(6,2) ICC,N,ECI,ECR,ECD,COST
      IF(ICC)60,60,50
50    IF(COST.GE.CMIN(N)) GO TO 80
60    ICMIN(N)=ICC
      CMIN(N)=COST
70    IF(COST.GE.TOTMIN) GO TO 90
      TOTMIN=COST
      NMIN=N
      MINC=ICC
      GO TO 90
```

```
80    INT=INT+1
      IF(INT.GT.5) GO TO 100
90    CONTINUE
      ICM1=ICMIN(N)
      IF(ICM1.GT.1) GO TO 100
      ICM1=1
100   CONTINUE
      DO 110 I=LN,IN
      WRITE(6,3) I,ICMIN(I),CMIN(I)
110   CONTINUE
      WRITE(6,4)  NMIN,MINC,TOTMIN
      WRITE(6,1) CI,CR,CD,AL,A
      STOP
1     FORMAT(5F6.2,2I8)
2     FORMAT(1X2I8,4F14.2)
3     FORMAT(1X2HN=I8,2X6HICMIN=I8,2X5HCMIN=F14.2)
4     FORMAT(1X16HOPTIMUM SOLUTION/1X2HN=I8,3X2HC=I8,3X5HCOST=E14.8)
5     FORMAT(1H1)
      END
      FUNCTION C(I,J)
      AI=I
      AJ=J
      C=AI/AJ
      JJ=J-1
      IF(JJ)30,30,10
10    DO 20 K=1,JJ
      AK=K
20    C=C*(AI-AK)/(AJ-AK)
30    RETURN
      END
```

FIGURE 5.3
Sample Size

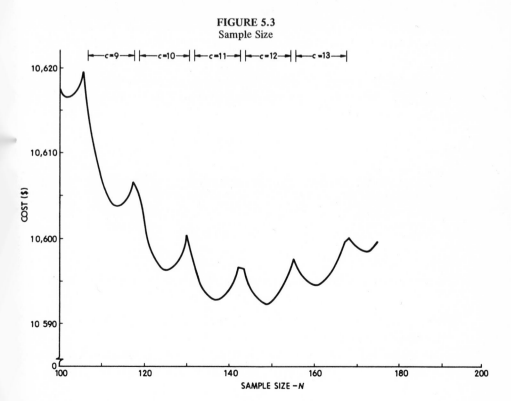

The optimal sampling plan is to select a sample of 149 units and reject the lot if 13 or more defective units are found. The expected total cost, $C_T(149.13)$ is \$10,592.58. In Figure 5.3 (page 191) a graph of the variation of $C_T(N,c)$ with N is presented for the optimal values of c.

VII. Acceptance sampling with subsequent customer inspection.

In the preceding section we discussed the development of an acceptance sampling system when all defective units contained in accepted lots are eventually detected at a cost C_d for defective unit. The problem we will analyze here is identical to that described in Model VI with one modification. As in Model VI, we will assume destructive testing. Therefore the lot size after producer inspection is $(L - N)$ where N is the sample size. However, in the development which follows we will not assume that all defective units that were included in lots accepted by the producer are necessarily detected at a cost to the producer. Such a case arises when accepted lots are delivered to a consumer who then conducts an inspection of the lot for his own protection. If the consumer's inspection indicates that the lot conforms to his quality specifications, he accepts the lot. Once the consumer accepts the lot, the producer is released from the responsibility for any defective units which may subsequently appear in the lot. However, if the consumer rejects the lot, the entire lot is returned to the producer. Therefore the cost of producer acceptance of the lot is either zero; the consumer also accepts the lot; or $C_d(L - N)$, the consumer rejects the lot.

The cost of producer rejection is zero if the producer accepts the lot and $C_r(L - N)$ if he rejects it. The cost of inspection is again simply $C_I N$. Let M be the sample size for inspection by the consumer and let c_1 and c_2 be the acceptance numbers for the producer and consumer, respectively.

If p is the proportion defective for a given lot, the expected cost of rejection is computed as in (5.54) and is given by

$$\text{Expected cost of rejection, given } p = C_r(L - N) \sum_{x=c_1+1}^{N} p_X(x \mid p) \quad (5.63)$$

where $p_X(x|p)$ is the probability the producer finds x defective units in the sample of size N.

The expected cost of acceptance $C_d(L - N)$ multiplied by the probability of acceptance by the producer and rejection by the consumer is as follows:

Expected cost of rejection, given $p = C_d(L - N)P$(producer acceptance)
$$\times P(\text{consumer rejection})$$

$$= C_d(L - N) \sum_{x=0}^{c_1} p_X(x \mid p)$$

$$\times \sum_{y=c_2+1}^{M} p_Y(y \mid p) \tag{5.64}$$

where $p_X(y|p)$ is the probability the consumer finds y defective units in the sample of size M.

Expected total cost, given $p = C_I N + (L - N)\left[C_r \sum_{x=c_1+1}^{N} p_X(x \mid p) \right.$

$$\left. + C_d \sum_{x=0}^{c_1} \sum_{y=c_2+1}^{M} p_X(x \mid p) p_Y(y \mid p) \right] \tag{5.65}$$

As we have already discussed, the need for a quality control system implies that p is not a constant. Let $f_P(p)$ be the density function of the proportion defective per lot. Taking the expected value of (5.65) with respect to p, we obtain the unconditioned expected total cost per lot, $C_T(N, c_1)$.

$$C_T(N, c_1) = C_I N + (L - N)\left[C_r \sum_{x=c_1+1}^{N} \int_0^1 p_X(x \mid p) f_P(p) \, dp \right.$$

$$\left. + C_d \sum_{x=0}^{c_1} \sum_{y=c_2+1}^{M} \int_0^1 p_X(x \mid p) p_Y(y \mid p) f_P(p) \, dp \right] \tag{5.66}$$

The reader should recognize that the assumptions implicit in the development of equation (5.58) also apply to the development of the expected cost equation given in (5.66).

Example 5.10

If the density function of P, proportion defective, $f_P(p)$ is given by

$$f_P(p) = \frac{\Gamma(a + b + 2)}{\Gamma(a + 1)\Gamma(b + 1)} p^b(1 - p)^a, \qquad 0 \le p \le 1, a > -1, b > -1$$

simplify equation (5.66). Assume that the probability mass functions of X and Y are binomial.

If X and Y are binomially distributed, then

$$p_X(x \mid p) = \frac{N!}{x!(N-x)!} \, p^x(1-p)^{N-x}, \qquad x = 0, 1, 2, \ldots, N$$

$$p_Y(y \mid p) = \frac{M!}{y!(M-y)!} \, p^y(1-p)^{M-y}, \qquad y = 0, 1, 2, \ldots, M$$

From example 5.8

$$\int_0^1 p_X(x \mid p) f_P(p) \, dp = \frac{(a+1)N!}{(N+a+1)!} \frac{(N+a-x)!}{(N-x)!}$$

We evaluate the second integral in (5.66) as follows: We will assume that a and b are integers

$$\int_0^1 p_X(x \mid p) p_Y(y \mid p) f_P(p) \, dp = \int_0^1 \frac{N!}{x!(N-x)!} \frac{M!}{y!(M-y)!} \frac{(a+b+1)!}{a!b!}$$

$$\times \, p^{x+y+b}(1-p)^{M+N+a-x-y} \, dp$$

$$= \frac{N!M!(a+b+1)!}{x!(N-x)!\,y!(M-y)!\,a!\,b!}$$

$$\times \int_0^1 p^{x+y+b}(1-p)^{M+N+a-x-y} \, dp$$

Since

$$\int_0^1 z^k(1-z)^{m-k} \, dz = \frac{k!(m-k)!}{(m+1)!}$$

for integer m and k, we have

$$\int_0^1 p_X(x \mid p) p_Y(y \mid p) f_P(p) \, dp = \frac{N!M!(a+b+1)!}{x!(N-x)!\,y!(M-y)!\,a!\,b!}$$

$$\times \, \frac{(x+y+b)!(M+N+a-x-y)!}{(M+N+a+b+1)!}$$

$$= \frac{a+b+1}{M+N+a+b+1} \frac{\binom{N}{x}\binom{M}{y}\binom{a+b}{a}}{\binom{M+N+a+b}{x+y+b}}$$

Equation (5.66) becomes

$$C_T(N, c_1) = C_I N + (L - N)\left[C_r \sum_{x=c_1+1}^{N} \frac{\binom{N+a-x}{a}}{\binom{N+a+1}{a+1}} \right.$$

$$\left. + C_d \frac{a+b+1}{M+N+a+b+1} \binom{a+b}{a} \sum_{x=0}^{c_1} \sum_{y=c_2+1}^{M} \frac{\binom{N}{x}\binom{M}{y}}{\binom{M+N+a+b}{x+y+b}} \right] \quad (5.67)$$

Example 5.11

Given the following parameters, find the values of N and c_1 which optimize equation (5.67). For each value of N between 1 and 20 find the optimal value of c_1 and plot for these combinations of N and c_1, the total expected cost and the expected costs of inspection, rejection, and acceptance.

$$C_I = \$10. \quad C_r = \$9.$$
$$C_d = \$14. \quad a = 8.$$
$$b = 0. \quad M = 5.$$
$$c_2 = 1. \quad L = 10,000.$$

The accompanying FORTRAN program can be used to carry out the calculations required in this example.

A definition of program variables is shown below.

NMI = minimum value of N, 2 for this example.
NMA = maximum value of N, 20 for this example.
C(I,J) = combinations of i things taken j at a time.
CMIN(N) = minimum cost for a given N.
ICMIN = optimal c_1 for a given N.
TCOST = minimum cost over all permissible N.
NMIN = optimal N.
ICTOT = optimal c_1.
ECI = expected cost of inspection.
ECR = expected cost of rejection.
ECD = expected cost of acceptance.

```
C       OUTGOING INSPECTION WITH CUSTOMER INSPECTION
        DIMENSION C(100,100),CMIN(100)
        READ(5,1) CI,CR,CD,A,B,IC2,M,NMI,NMA,L
        WRITE(6,4)
        WRITE(6,1) CI,CR,CD,A,B,IC2,M,L .
        IA=A
        AL=L
        IB=B
        IABMN=M+NMA+IA+IB
        AM=M
        DO 30 I=1,IABMN
        DO 30 J=1,I
        AI=I
        AJ=J
        C(I,J)=AI/AJ
        JJ=J-1
        IF(JJ)30,30,10
10      DO 20 K=1,JJ
        AK=K
        C(I,J)=C(I,J)*(AI-AK)/(AJ-AK)
20      CONTINUE
30      CONTINUE
        DO 130  N=NMI,NMA
        DO 100  IC=1,N
        IC1=IC-1
        AN=N
        SUM1=0
        DO 40 IX=IC,N
        N3=IA+1
        N1=N+IA-IX
        N2=N+IA+1
40      SUM1=SUM1+C(N1,IA)/C(N2,N3)
        IYY=IC2+1
        SUM2=0
        DO 70 IY=IYY,M
        CON=C(M,IY)
        N4=N+M+IA+IB
        N5=IY+IB
        SUM3=1./C(N4,N5)
        IF((IC1)70,70,50
50      DO 60 IX=1,IC1
        N6=IX+IY+IB
        SUM3=SUM3+C(N,IX)/C(N4,N6)
60      CONTINUE
70      SUM2=SUM2+CON*SUM3
        N7=IA+IB
        ECO=(AL-AN)*CD*(A+B+1.)*C(N7,IA)*SUM2/(AM+AN+A+B+1.)
        ECR=(AL-AN)*CR*SUM1
        ECI=AN*CI
        COST=ECI+ECR+ECO
        WRITE(6,2) IC1,N,COST,ECI,ECR,ECO
        IF((IC1)90,90,80
80      IF(COST-CMIN(N)) 90,100,100
90      CMIN(N)=COST
        ICMIN=IC1
100     CONTINUE
        WRITE(6,2) ICMIN,N,CMIN(N),ECI,ECR,ECO
        IF(N.LE.NMI) GO TO 120
        IF(CMIN(N).GE.TCOST) GO TO 130
120     TCOST=CMIN(N)
        NMIN=N
        ICTOT=ICMIN
130     CONTINUE
        WRITE(6,3) NMIN,ICTOT,TCOST
        STOP
1       FORMAT(1X5F8.2,5I6)
2       FORMAT( 1X2HC=I5,3X5HCMIN(I6,2H)=F14.2,3X4HECI=F14.2,3X4HECR=F14.2,
       1 3X4HECD=F14.2)
3       FORMAT(1X16HOPTIMAL SOLUTION/1X2HN=I8,3X2HC=I8,3X5HCOST=F14.2)
4       FORMAT(1H1)
        END
```

In Table 5.2 we summarize the pertinent expected costs for each N and the corresponding optimal value of c_1. Examination of this table indicates that the optimal sampling plan is to select a sample of five units and reject the lot only if all five units are defective. However, for this and all of the other plans analyzed, the cost of acceptance is extremely high and probably prohibitively so. The question is what can the supplier do to reduce the cost of acceptance. Since we have developed a sampling plan which minimizes total cost, there is no point in searching for another plan. About the only alternative available to the supplier is to improve the production process so that the number of defective units produced is reduced to a tolerable level. Figure 5.4 shows the data given in the table.

TABLE 5.2

N	c_1	Expected Cost of Inspection	Expected Cost of Rejection	Expected Cost of Acceptance	$C_T(n, c_1)$
2 . . 1		20	1,727	14,452	16,199
3 . . 2		30	432	15,080	15,541
4 . . 3		40	133	15,269	15,441
5 . . 4		50	47	15,333	15,430
6 . . 5		60	19	15,356	15,435
7 . . 6		70	8	15,365	15,443
8 . . 6		80	4	15,368	15,450
9 . . 7		90	2	15,368	15,459
10 . . 7		100	1	15,368	15,465
11 . . 7		110	1	15,367	15,473
12 . . 8		120	0	15,366	15,479
13 . . 8		130	0	15,364	15,486
14 . . 9		140	0	15,363	15,494
15 . . 9		150	0	15,361	15,500
16 . . 9		160	0	15,360	15,508
17 . . 10		170	0	15,358	15,514
18 . . 10		180	0	15,357	15,520
19 . . 11		190	0	15,355	15,528
20 . . 11		200	0	15,354	15,534

In this case the supplier might have guessed that he was in for trouble. The probability that the consumer rejects a lot of product of proportion defective p is

$$P(\text{Reject} \mid p) = \sum_{x=2}^{5} \frac{5!}{x!(5-x)!} p^x(1-p)^{5-x}$$

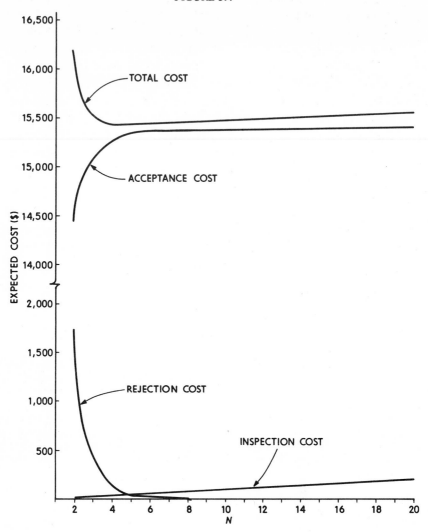

FIGURE 5.4

Let

$$P(p) = P(\text{proportion defective} > p)$$

In Figure 5.5 we see that when $p = 0.20$, the probability of lot rejection by the consumer is about 0.25. In addition the probability that a lot will have a proportion defective of 0.20 or greater is about 0.15. Consequently the supplier should not be surprised at a total rejection (consumer and supplier) of 5 to 15 percent.

This example emphasizes an important point to be considered in the design of a quality control system. A quality control system cannot improve the quality of the manufactured product. If the manufacturing process turns out a large proportion of defective units, the likelihood of rejection somewhere is high. In this example the supplier could employ a very rigid quality control system so that bad lots would not get to the consumer. However, he would also reject a larger number of acceptable lots than would be rejected by a less rigid plan with the often encountered result that the saving in consumer rejection is more than offset by increased supplier rejection. In any case the saving which can be realized from the quality control system above is limited. Savings beyond this point must be accomplished elsewhere, usually within the manufacturing process itself.

FIGURE 5.5

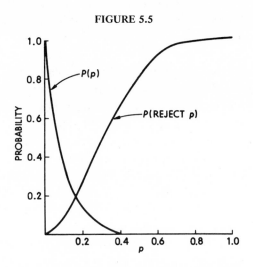

VIII. Acceptance sampling, incoming product. So far we have looked at quality control models from the point of view of the supplier or producer. Let us now consider the problem the consumer faces in determining whether the product he has received is of acceptable quality. As we suggested in the preceding model, each lot received is usually inspected according to a sampling plan which the consumer feels will give him protection against the acceptance of too many defective products. Let C_d be the cost of accepting one defective unit. If we assume nondestructive testing, the cost of accepting a lot of size L and proportion defective p is $C_d p(L - y)$ where C_d is the cost of accepting one defective unit and y is the number of defective units found in the consumer's sample. Therefore each defective unit found in the sample is discarded, reducing the accepted lot size to $L - y$.

The cost of accepting defective product can be reduced by adopting a powerful sampling plan, that is, a sampling plan which will reject a very small proportion defective. However, the consumer must exercise caution in applying such a plan. If a rigid quality control plan is adopted, the supplier may be forced to increase the overall quality of the product he ships to reduced the chance of having lots returned. This means that the cost of the product will increase. Such an increase in cost will ultimately be passed on to the consumer. This implies the obvious: the consumer will have to pay for the quality he demands. In addition each time the consumer rejects a lot of product he deprives himself of product which we presume he needs.

For the purpose of the present analysis we will assume that the consumer returns rejected lots to the supplier. The supplier then conducts a 100 percent inspection of the lots, removing all defective units. If the supplier finds that the actual proportion defective is less than p_a, he charges the cost of the 100 percent inspection to the consumer. Therefore a lot having a proportion defective p_a is considered acceptable by the consumer, and he accepts the responsibility for any such lots which he rejects. Let C_r be the unit cost of rejecting an acceptable lot.

If we assume that M units are inspected whether the lot is rejected or not, the cost of inspection per lot is $C_I M$ where C_I is the unit cost of inspection. The costs of acceptance and rejection given a lot proportion defective, p, are computed as follows.

$$\text{Expected cost of acceptance, given } p = \sum_{y=0}^{c} C_d\, p(L - y) p_Y(y \mid p) \quad (5.68)$$

$$\text{Expected cost of rejection, given } p = \begin{cases} C_r L \sum_{y=c+1}^{M} p_Y(y \mid p), & p < p_a \\ 0, & p \geq p_a \end{cases} \quad (5.69)$$

In equations (5.68) and (5.69), c is the consumer's acceptance number and $p_Y(y \mid p)$ is the probability mass function of the number of defective units found in a sample of size M and for a proportion defective p. If $f_P(p)$ is the density function of proportion defective, the expected cost per lot is given by (5.70).

$$C_T(M, c) = C_I M + C_d \sum_{y=0}^{c} (L - y) \int_0^1 p p_Y(y \mid p) f_P(p) \, dp$$

$$+ C_r L \sum_{y=c+1}^{M} \int_0^{p_a} p_Y(y \mid p) f_P(p) \, dp \qquad (5.70)$$

The reader may wonder why we have considered p_a a constant rather than a decision variable. As a matter of fact a more complete model would include p_a as a decision variable. To develop such a model, equation (5.70) would have to be modified to reflect the increase in product cost which would undoubtedly result from a reduction in p_a. Unfortunately quality control and manufacturing are not well enough integrated in many companies to permit simultaneous specification of p_a, c, and M. Often the acceptable quality level, p_a, is established by manufacturing or marketing and without consultation with the quality control department. Quality control is therefore forced to live with the value of p_a so specified.

Example 5.12

Modify equation (5.70) given

$$p_Y(y \mid p) = \frac{M!}{y!(M - y)!} p^y (1 - p)^{M-y}, \qquad y = 0, 1, 2, \ldots, M$$

$$f_P(p) = \frac{\Gamma(a + b + 2)}{\Gamma(a + 1)\Gamma(b + 1)} p^b (1 - p)^a, \qquad 0 \le p \le 1, a > -1, b > -1$$

To resolve the second integral in (5.70) we present the following relationship without proof:

$$\int_0^w z^m (1 - z)^n \, dz = \frac{m!n!}{(m + n + 1)!} \sum_{j=0}^{n} \frac{(m + j)!}{m!j!} w^{m+1}(1 - w)^j \qquad (5.71)$$

Therefore we have for integer a and b

$$\int_0^{p_a} p_Y(y \mid p) f_P(p) \, dp = \int_0^{p_a} \frac{M!(a + b + 1)!}{y!(M - y)!a!b!} p^{y+b}(1 - p)^{M+a-y} \, dp$$

$$\int_0^{P_a} p_Y(y|p) f_P(p)\, dp = \frac{a+b+1}{M+a+b+1} \frac{\binom{M}{y}\binom{a+b}{a}}{\binom{M+a+b}{y+b}}$$

$$\times \sum_{j=0}^{M+a-y} \binom{y+b+j}{j} p_a^{y+b+1}(1-p_a)^j \qquad (5.72)$$

and

$$\int_0^1 p\, p_Y(y\,|\,p) f_p(p)\, dp = \int_0^1 \frac{M!(a+b+1)!}{y!(M-y)!a!b!}\, p^{y+b+1}(1-p)^{M+a-y}\, dp$$

$$= \binom{M}{y}\binom{a+b}{a}(a+b+1)$$

$$\times \int_0^1 p^{y+b+1}(1-p)^{M+a-y}\, dp$$

$$= \frac{a+b+1}{M+a+b+2} \frac{\binom{M}{y}\binom{a+b}{a}}{\binom{M+a+b+1}{y+b+1}} \qquad (5.73)$$

Equation (5.70) becomes

$$C_T(M,c) = C_I M + C_d \frac{a+b+1}{M+a+b+2}\binom{a+b}{a}\sum_{y=0}^{c}(L-y)\frac{\binom{M}{y}}{\binom{M+a+b+1}{y+b+1}}$$

$$+ C_r L \frac{a+b+1}{M+a+b+1}\binom{a+b}{a}\sum_{y=c+1}^{M}\frac{\binom{M}{y}}{\binom{M+a+b}{y+b}}$$

$$\times p_a^{y+b+1}\sum_{j=0}^{M+a-y}\binom{y+b+j}{j}(1-p_a)^j \qquad (5.74)$$

IX. Inspection for several defects.   The quality control models we have developed so far apply when we are concerned with only one type of defect. Usually, however, both supplier and consumer are forced to control the occurrence of several different defects in the same product. As one would expect, as the number of defects to be controlled increases, the cost of quality control increases. First, the inspection cost per unit must increase since it will take longer to inspect one unit for n defects than for one defect. Therefore, at least the labor cost of inspection will increase. There may also be other factors which inflate the inspection cost, such as the use of additional testing equipment. Since each unit may be defective for one or more of n reasons, the lot can be rejected by either supplier or consumer for one or more of n reasons. Consequently the cost of rejection increases as n increases. For similar reasons the cost of lot acceptance would also be greater when we are forced to control several defects rather than only one.

Let us reformulate the model developed in Model VI, assuming inspection for two defects. Let N_i and c_i be the sample size and acceptance number for the ith defect. Assuming destructive testing, let C_{Ii} be the cost of inspecting one unit of product for the ith defect. The nature of inspection is such that a single item cannot be inspected for both defects. That is, in inspecting for either defect the unit is destroyed to the extent that it is impossible to properly inspect for the other defect.

$$\text{Inspection cost per lot} = \sum_{i=1}^{n} C_{Ii} N_i \qquad (5.75)$$

If p_i is the proportion defective for the ith defect and $p_{x_i}(x_i | p_i)$ is the probability that x_i defective units are found in a sample of size N_i, the probability of lot rejection is

$$P(\text{Lot rejection} \mid p_1, p_2) = 1 - P(\text{Lot acceptance} \mid p_1, p_2)$$

$$P(\text{Lot rejection} \mid p_1, p_2) = 1 - \sum_{x_1=0}^{c_1} p_{x_1}(x_1 | p_1) \sum_{x_2=0}^{c_2} p_{x_2}(x_2 | p_2) \qquad (5.76)$$

Therefore

Expected cost of rejection, given p_1 and p_2

$$= C_r(L - N_1 - N_2)\left[1 - \sum_{x_1=0}^{c_1} p_{x_1}(x_1 | p_1) \sum_{x_2=0}^{c_2} p_{x_2}(x_2 | p_2)\right] \qquad (5.77)$$

and

Expected cost of acceptance, given p_1 and p_2 =

$$C_a(L - N_1 - N_2)(p_1 + p_2 - p_1 p_2) \sum_{x_1=0}^{c_1} p_{x_1}(x_1 | p_1) \sum_{x_2=0}^{c_2} p_{x_2}(x_2 | p_2) \qquad (5.78)$$

In equation (5.78), $p_1 + p_2 - p_1 p_2$ is the probability that any unit contains the first defect or the second or both [see equation (2.10)].

Let $f_{P_1, P_2}(p_1, p_2)$ be the joint density function of P_1 and P_2. If the occurrence of either defect is independent of the occurrence of the other, the joint density function can be represented by the product of the individual density functions, $f_{P_1}(p_1)$ and $f_{P_2}(p_2)$. We will assume that this is true here.

Summing equations (5.75), (5.77), and (5.78) and taking the expected value of the sum with respect to p_1 and p_2, we have

$$C_T(N_1, N_2, c_1, c_2) = \sum_{i=1}^{2} C_{Ii} N_i + (1 - N_1 - N_2)$$

$$\times \left\{ C_r + \sum_{x_1=0}^{c_1} \sum_{x_2=0}^{c_2} \int_0^1 \int_0^1 [C_d(p_1 + p_2 - p_1 p_2) - C_r] \right.$$

$$\left. \times p_{X_1}(x_1 \mid p_1) p_{X_2}(x_2 \mid p_2) f_{P_1}(p_1) f_{P_2}(p_2) \, dp_1 \, dp_2 \right\} \qquad (5.79)$$

where C_r, C_d, and L are as defined in Model VI.

Example 5.13

Evaluate equation (5.79), given the following functions for $p_{X_i}(x_i \mid p_i)$ and $f_{P_i}(p_i)$.

$$p_{X_i}(x_i \mid p_i) = \binom{N_i}{x_i} p_i^{x_i}(1 - p_i)^{N_i - x_i}, \qquad x_i = 0, 1, 2, \ldots, N_i \qquad (5.80)$$

$$f_{P_i}(p_i) = (a_i + b_i + 1)\binom{a_i + b_i}{a_i} p_i^{b_i}(1 - p_i)^{a_i},$$

$$0 \le p_i \le 1, \qquad a_i > -1, \qquad b_i > -1 \quad (5.81)$$

To simplify the evaluation of the double integral in (5.79) we note the following:

$$p_1 + p_2 - p_1 p_2 = 1 - (1 - p_1)(1 - p_2)$$

and

$$[C_d(p_1 + p_2 - p_1 p_2) - C_r] = [(C_d - C_r) - C_d(1 - p_1)(1 - p_2)].$$

We break the double integral into the following two parts

$$\int_0^1 \int_0^1 p_{X_1}(x_1 \mid p_1) p_{X_2}(x_2 \mid p_2) f_{P_1}(p_1) f_{P_2}(p_2) \, dp_1 \, dp_2$$

$$= \int_0^1 p_{X_1}(x_1 \mid p_1) f_{P_1}(p_1) \, dp_1 \int_0^1 p_{X_2}(x_2 \mid p_2) f_{P_2}(p_2) \, dp_2$$

$$= \prod_{i=1}^2 \frac{a_i + b_i + 1}{a_i + b_i + N_i + 1} \frac{\dbinom{N_i}{x_i}\dbinom{a_i + b_i}{a_i}}{\dbinom{a_i + b_i + N_i}{x_i + b_i}}$$

where $\displaystyle\prod_{i=1}^n$ indicates the product of n terms. That is,

$$\prod_{i=1}^n A_i = A_1 A_2 \ldots A_n \; .$$

$$\int_0^1 \int_0^1 (1 - p_1)(1 - p_2) p_{X_1}(x_1 \mid p_1) p_{X_2}(x_2 \mid p_2) f_{P_1}(p_1) f_{P_2}(p_2) \, dp_1 \, dp_2$$

$$= \int_0^1 (1 - p_1) p_{X_1}(x_1 \mid p_1) f_{P_1}(p_1) \, dp_1 \int_0^1 (1 - p_2) p_{X_2}(x_2 \mid p_2) f_{P_2}(p_2) \, dp_2$$

$$= \prod_{i=1}^2 (a_i + b_i + 1) \dbinom{N_i}{x_i}\dbinom{a_i + b_i}{a_i} \int_0^1 p_i^{x_i + b_i}(1 - p_i)^{a_i + N_i - x_i + 1} \, dp_i$$

$$= \prod_{i=1}^2 \frac{a_i + b_i + 1}{a_i + b_i + N_i + 2} \frac{\dbinom{N_i}{x_i}\dbinom{a_i + b_i}{a_i}}{\dbinom{a_i + b_i + N_i + 1}{x_i + b_i}}$$

Total expected cost per lot is given by

$$C_T(N_1, N_2, c_1, c_2)$$

$$= \sum_{i=1}^2 C_{Ii} N_i + (L - N_1 - N_2)\left[C_r + (C_d - C_r)\prod_{i=1}^2 \frac{a_i + b_i + 1}{a_i + b_i + N_i + 1} \right.$$

$$\times \dbinom{a_i + b_i}{a_i} \frac{\dbinom{N_i}{x_i}}{\dbinom{a_i + b_i + N_i}{x_i + b_i}}$$

$$\left. - C_d \prod_{i=1}^2 \frac{a_i + b_i + 1}{a_i + b_i + N_i + 2} \dbinom{a_i + b_i}{a_i} \sum_{x_i=0}^{c_i} \frac{\dbinom{N_i}{x_i}}{\dbinom{a_i + b_i + N_i + 1}{x_i + b_i}} \right] \qquad (5.82)$$

Example 5.14

The *XYZ* Company manufactures glue which it sells in collapsible metal tubes. The closures for these tubes are plastic caps which are produced internally. The company has found that two defects can occur in the caps which cause brief stoppages on the tube filling line. The first is an incomplete or short-shot cap, that is, a cap which has not been completely formed. The second is a crack in the cap.

The value of the cap is $0.001. Each defective cap which reaches the filling line costs the company about $0.01. To inspect a cap for a short-shot costs about $0.001, while inspection for cracks costs about $0.005 per cap. Caps are manufactured in lots of 100,000. All rejected lots will be scrapped.

The Quality Control Department has suggested the following sampling plans for these defects.

TABLE 5.3

Defect Type	Sample Size	Acceptance Number
Short-shots 20		1
Cracks 15		0

Find the expected cost of this proposed quality control system if the density function of proportion defective for these defects is given by

$$f_{P_1}(p_1) = 24(1 - p_1)^{23}, \qquad 0 \le p_1 \le 1$$
$$f_{P_2}(p_2) = 19(1 - p_2)^{18}, \qquad 0 \le p_2 \le 1$$

where P_1 and P_2 are the proportions defective for short-shots and cracks.

We will compute the expected costs of inspection, rejection, and acceptance individually and sum these together to obtain the expected cost per lot.

$$\text{Expected sampling cost} = C_{I1}N_1 + C_{I2}N_2$$
$$= 0.02 + 0.075$$
$$= \$.095$$

Expected rejection cost

$$= C_r(L - N_1 - N_2)\left[1 - \prod_{i=1}^{2} \frac{a_i + 1}{a_i + N_i + 1} \sum_{x_i=0}^{c_i} \frac{\binom{N_i}{x_i}}{\binom{a_i + N_i}{x_i}}\right]$$

$$= C_r(L - N_1 - N_2)\left\{1 - \left[\frac{24}{45}\sum_{x_1=0}^{1}\frac{\binom{20}{x_1}}{\binom{43}{x_1}}\right]\left[\frac{19}{34}\frac{\binom{20}{0}}{\binom{43}{0}}\right]\right\}$$

$$= 0.001(99{,}965)\left[1 - \frac{24}{45}\left(1 + \frac{20}{43}\right)\frac{19}{34}\right]$$

$$= 99.965(0.563)$$

$$= \$55.18$$

Expected cost of acceptance

$$= C_d(L - N_1 - N_2)\left[\prod_{i=1}^{2}\frac{a_i + 1}{a_i + N_i + 1}\sum_{x_i=0}^{c_i}\frac{\binom{N_i}{x_i}}{\binom{a_i + N_i}{x_i}}\right.$$

$$\left. - \prod_{i=1}^{2}\frac{a_i + 1}{a_i + N_i + 2}\sum_{x_i=0}^{c_i}\frac{\binom{N_i}{x_i}}{\binom{a_i + N_i + 1}{x_i}}\right]$$

$$= C_d(L - N_1 - N_2)\left\{\frac{24}{45}\left(1 + \frac{20}{43}\right)\frac{19}{34} - \frac{24}{46}\left[1 + \frac{20}{44}\right]\left[\frac{19}{35}\right]\right\}$$

$$= 0.005(99{,}965)0.025$$

$$= \$12.50$$

Expected total cost = \$67.87

We leave determination of the optimal sampling plan as an exercise for the reader.

In each of the quality control examples we have used the beta distribution to represent the variability of proportion defective, and it is expressed in its generalized form in example 5.10. The authors have found this distribution to be useful, particularly when the mean proportion defective is less than 0.10. The reader may also find the normal distribution useful for this purpose, but the reliability of this distribution for a mean proportion defective less than 0.10 is questionable. In any case the adequacy of the proposed distribution should be checked against experimental data by means of either the Kolmogorov–Smirnov or chi-square goodness-of-fit tests.

In examples 5.9 and 5.11 we have presented computer programs which can be used to optimize the expected cost equations developed in examples 5.8 and 5.10. Caution should be exercised in using these programs to avoid overflows. In particular, before using either of these programs the reader should determine the maximum value of

$$\binom{A}{B}$$

and check this against the capacity of the computer he is using. Should the maximum value of

$$\binom{A}{B}$$

indicate the occurrence of an overflow condition, the following modification may be used to eliminate this problem. We will demonstrate this technique by modifying the term

$$\frac{\binom{N}{x}\binom{M}{y}}{\binom{M+N+a+b}{x+y+b}}$$

which appears in equation (5.67) in example 5.10.

Let us assume that one or more of the combinatorial terms,

$$\binom{N}{x}, \; \binom{M}{y}, \; \text{or} \; \binom{M+N+a+b}{x+y+b}$$

would cause the occurrence of an overflow. We can express each of these combinatorial terms as follows:

$$\binom{N}{x} = \prod_{i=0}^{x-1} \frac{(N-i)}{(x-i)}, \qquad x > 0 \tag{5.83}$$

$$\binom{M}{y} = \prod_{j=0}^{y-1} \frac{(M-j)}{(y-j)}, \qquad y > 0 \tag{5.84}$$

$$\binom{M+N+a+b}{x+y+b} = \prod_{k=0}^{x+y+b-1} \frac{(M+N+a+b-k)}{(x+y+b-k)}, \qquad x+y > 0$$

$$= \prod_{i=0}^{x-1} \frac{(M+N+a+b-i)}{(x+y+b-i)}$$

$$\times \prod_{j=0}^{y-1} \frac{(M+N+a+b-x-j)}{(y+b-j)}$$

$$\times \prod_{k=0}^{b-1} \frac{(M+N+a+b-x-y-k)}{(b-k)} \tag{5.85}$$

We can therefore express the required ratio by

$$\frac{\binom{N}{x}\binom{M}{y}}{\binom{N+M+a+b}{a+y+b}} = \prod_{i=0}^{x-1} \frac{(N-i)(x+y+b-i)}{(x-i)(M+N+a+b-i)}$$

$$\times \prod_{j=0}^{y-1} \frac{(M-j)(y+b-j)}{(y-j)(M+N+a+b-x-j)}$$

$$\times \prod_{k=0}^{b-1} \frac{(b-k)}{(M+N+a+b-x-y-k)} \qquad (5.86)$$

Although the formulation given in (5.86) is not guaranteed to eliminate overflows, it will certainly reduce the possibility of their occurrence.

PROBLEMS

Reliability

1. Find the optimal value of n corresponding to that given in equation (5.11) when

a) $C_P < \lambda C_0$

b) $\sqrt{\dfrac{\lambda \, (C_P - \lambda C_0)}{u} \cdot \dfrac{1}{C_L}} < \dfrac{\lambda}{u}$ but $C_P > \lambda C_0$

2. Show that 1.223 years is the optimal value of τ for the problem given in example 5.2.

3. For the problem discussed in example 5.5, break the expected failure cost into the cost of downtime and the cost of breakdowns (independent of downtime) for $1 \leqslant n \leqslant 100$. Plot both of these costs as a function of n. Explain why the breakdown cost increases with increasing n while the cost of downtime decreases as n increases.

Reliability and Maintenance

4. For the problem given in example 5.3 how much can C_D change without changing the optimal crew size of three?

5. Solve the problem given in example 5.5 when $C_D = 0$.

6. How would equation (5.14) have to be modified if the cost of the repair crew was proportional to the annual repair time? Let C_L be the cost of one

repairman working continuously for one year. Find the optimal crew size, n, for this situation.

7. Solve the problem given in example 5.4 if the annual investment cost is given by $C_\lambda/[m(1+\lambda)]$ and $C_\lambda=\$100,000$.

8. A transit company has K buses which require repair from time to time. The average number of failures per year per bus is λ, and the distribution of the number of times a bus fails in t years, x, is given by

$$P_X(x) = (\lambda t)^x e^{-\lambda t}/x! \quad ,x = 0,1,2,....$$

The company has n servicemen to repair the buses as they fail. It takes one man to repair a bus. Therefore it is possible that up to n buses may be under repair at one time. The distribution of service time per bus is exponential with mean service time $1/u$ years. Each time a bus fails, a cost C_D is incurred, and if the bus is down for t years, an additional cost $C_P t$ is incurred. It costs the company C_L to carry one repairman for one year. Develop an equation expressing the expected annual cost of the maintenance system. Assume that K is large enough that the probability that y buses fail in time t is unaffected by the number of buses already down.

(Hint: This system may be viewed as a system of n service channels in parallel. The probability of one failure in Δt is $K\lambda\Delta t$ for large K.)

9. Find the optimal crew size for problem 8 when .

$$K = 1,000 \qquad \lambda = 5$$
$$u = 300 \qquad C_L = \$8,000$$
$$C_P = \$20,000 \qquad C_D = \$100$$

10. Solve the problem given in example 5.7 when

$$f_Y(y) = p^2 \lambda e^{-p\lambda y} + (1 - p)^2 \lambda e^{-(1-p)\lambda y}, 0 < y < \infty \text{ where } p = 0.2.$$

11. What modification of equation (5.52) must be made if $k = 3$ and each unit is put back into service as soon as maintenance on that unit is completed?

12. Solve the problem given in example 5.3 under the restriction that the probability that the filling line is down for more than 0.0005 years at any failure is less than 0.05.

13. Solve the problem given in example 5.2 where $f_X(x, \tau) = 1/\tau \; e^{-x\tau}$, $0 < x < \infty$.

Quality Control

1. By differencing equation (5.59) with respect to N, determine the condition or conditions under which equation (5.59) is optimized for a given value of c.

2. Determine the optimal sampling plan for the problem given in example 5.14.

3. In example 5.11 we assumed that a sampling plan was desirable and determined the optimum such plan. Develop a cost model for the case where no sampling is carried out. Is the solution given in example 5.11 actually optimal?

4. A particular product is to be inspected for two different defects, A and B. The product is manufactured in lots of size L. C_{I_1} and C_{I_2} are the unit inspection costs for defects A and B, respectively. If, upon inspection, too many units contain defects of type A, the lot is scrapped at a cost C_S per unit. If too many units contain type B defects, the lot is reprocessed at a cost C_R per unit. If the lot passes both inspections, it is sent to final product inventory and units are sold from this point. Any unit which is sold containing either defect costs the manufacturer C_A per unit. Develop an expected total cost equation for this quality control system.

5. Given that the distributions of proportion defective for defects A and B in problem 4 are both beta with parameters $a_1 > 0$, $b_1 = 0$ and $a_2 > 0$, $b_2 = 0$, modify the expected cost equation developed in problem 4.

6. Find the optimal sampling plans for the model developed in problem 5 when

$$C_{I1} = C_{I2} = \$.20 \quad C_3 = \$1.00$$
$$C_R = \$.40. \qquad C_A = \$4.00.$$
$$a_1 = 48. \qquad a_2 = 98.$$

7. An engineer has developed a sampling plan which he believes is appropriate for use in the problem given in example 5.9. The plan was developed such that the probability of rejecting a lot with proportion defective less than 0.06 is very low while the probability of rejecting a lot having proportion defective greater than 0.15 is high. His plan is to select a sample of size 200 and accept the lot whenever 21 or less defectives are found. How much will his error cost per lot?

8. Develop a model corresponding to that given in (5.82) when three defects are to be controlled. Assume that proportion defective is beta distributed for all three defects.

9. Solve the problem given in example 5.11 if the density function of proportion defective is given by

$$f_P(p) = \begin{cases} 800p, & 0 < p < .05 \\ 0, & p > .05 \end{cases}$$

10. How much can the unit cost of acceptance, C_a, vary in example 5.9 without changing the optimal solution of $N = 149$ and $c = 12$?

11. Develop a model for two defects corresponding to that for a single defect given in (5.66).

[Hint: If N_1 and N_2 are the supplier sample sizes for the two defects and s_1 and s_2 are the corresponding acceptance numbers, then

Probability of supplier rejection =

$$1 - \int_0^1 \int_0^1 \sum_{x_2=0}^{s_2} \sum_{x_1=0}^{s_1} p_{X_1}(x_1 \mid p_1) p_{X_2}(x_2 \mid p_2) f_{P_1}(p_1) f_{P_2}(p_2) \, dp_1 \, dp_2$$

12. In the quality control models developed in this chapter we have assumed that if the sample size is N, all N units are inspected even if the lot is rejected before all N units have been inspected. Let c be the acceptance number and assume that inspection ceases as soon as $c + 1$ defective units are detected. Determine the expected number of units inspected where $P_X(x \mid p)$ and $F_P(p)$ assume their usual definitions.

REFERENCES

Barnard, G. A. "Sampling Inspection and Statistical Decisions," *J. R. Statistical Society, B,* Vol. 16, pp. 151–74.

Cowden, Dudley J. *Statistical Methods in Quality Control.* Englewood Cliffs, N. J.: Prentice-Hall, Inc., 1957.

Dodge, H. F. "Administration of a Sampling Inspection Plan," *Industrial Quality Control,* Vol. 4, No.3 (1948), pp. 12–19.

Dodge, H. F. and Romig, H. G. "A Method of Sampling Inspection," *Bell System Technical Journal,* (Oct. 1929), pp. 613–31.

——— *Sampling Inspection Tables Single and Double Sampling.* 2d ed. New York: J. W. Wiley & Sons, Inc., 1959.

Duncan, Acheson J. *Quality Control and Industrial Statistics.* Homewood, Ill.: Richard D. Irwin, Inc., 1965.

Hamaker, H. C. "Economic Principles in Industrial Sampling Problems: A General Introduction," *Bulletin of International Statistics,* Vol. 33, No. 5, pp. 105–22.

Horsnell, G. "Economic Acceptance Sampling Schemes," *Journal,* Royal Statistical Society, A, 120, (1957), pp. 99–121.

Schmidt, J. W. and Byrd, Jack. "Quality Control Models for Attributes Sampling Systems," Engineering Experiment Station, West Virginia University, Morgantown, West Virginia, Report 2, October 1968.

Shewhart, Walter A. *Industrial Quality Control,* (July 1947), p. 23.

——— *Economic Control of Quality of Manufactured Product* New York: D. Van Nostrand Co., 1931.

Sittig, J. "The Economic Choice of Sampling System in Acceptance Sampling," *Bulletin of International Statistics,* Vol. 33, No. 5, pp. 51–84.

Smith, Robert D. "Quality Assurance in Government and Industry: A Bayesian Approach," *Journal of Industrial Engineering,* (May 1966), pp. 254–59.

Van der Waerden, B. L. "Sampling Inspection as a Minimum Loss Problem," *Annals of Mathematical Statistics,* Vol. 31, (1960), pp. 369–84.

Wetherill, G. B. , "Some Remarks on the Bayesian Solution of the Single Sample Inspection Scheme," *Technometrics,* (August 1960), pp. 351–52.

SECTION TWO

Simulation Modeling

CHAPTER
6

RANDOM NUMBER GENERATION

INTRODUCTION

In any simulation experiment as well as in most sampling experiments there exists a need for a source of random numbers. Random numbers as discussed here refer to numbers or variates which follow the uniform distribution as presented in Chapter 3. The purpose of this chapter is to discuss the desirable properties of random numbers used in simulation experiments, to present some methods which can be used to generate these random numbers, and finally to discuss some statistical tests which can be applied to a given set of these random numbers to determine which properties exist.

There is a long history associated with the generation of random elements. Earliest methods for this were developed about the creation of some physical device which performed in such a manner as to cause, say, a pointer to stop on a number which was then written down in a table. The advent of electronic computers opened completely new vistas for methods to generate these random numbers.

Random numbers are useful in many types of computations, such as in problems of probability and statistics. Say, for example, we wish to investigate some process in which two equiprobable outcomes are possible, such as the flipping of a coin. Further assume that we had a bowl containing 10 beads numbered from 1 to 10. We make the rule that when a bead numbered from 1 to 5 is drawn, we will consider that we have flipped a head on our hypothetical coin. Similarly, when a bead numbered from 6 to 10 is drawn, we will consider that a tail has been flipped. Now by successively drawing a bead, recording its value and replacing it we have in effect designed a very simple random number generator. Further, as a point of interest, we have created a simple simulation study of probabilistic physical phenomonon, namely, that of flipping a coin. At any rate, after we continue this process 200 times, we summarize the results and find that 98 times the bead drawn was between 1 and 5 and 102 times the bead drawn was between 6 and 10. We could then say that for this sample 98 heads were flipped and 102 tails were flipped. Theoretically, if we were to continue the process an infinite number of times, we would draw exactly the same number of beads between 1 and 5 as between 6 and 10.

The next chapter will be devoted to the creation of "process generators," of which the simple bead examination process is a member. In this chapter we will discuss the aspects of the more basic process of producing the initial random numbers. As mentioned above, the bowl containing the beads has become a device which supplies uniformly distributed random numbers. The act of drawing a bead and recording its value is, in this sense, a random number generation method, and the entire process could be called a random number generator. The numbers we work with from this generator are uniformly distributed. If we were to use 100 beads numbered consecutively from 00 to 99, we would be able to evaluate the process at a more "microscopic" level because of the added digit of significance. In effect, however, we are concerned with producing random variables from the uniform distribution whose density function for the continuous case is defined as follows:

$$f_X(x) = \begin{cases} \dfrac{1}{b-a}, & a < x < b \\ 0, & \text{otherwise} \end{cases} \tag{6.1}$$

where the random variable X is defined over the interval (a, b). Although other values may be used, for this discussion we will concern ourselves with the generation of variates over the interval $(0, 1)$.

In effect, then, in this chapter we will concern ourselves with both practical and theoretical considerations regarding the process of creating numbers which follow the uniform distribution. The use of these numbers, once created, is, of course, dependent upon the process under study. Further, many methods are available for obtaining these random numbers. These are listed below:

1. Manual Methods.
2. Random number tables.
3. Analog computer methods.
4. Digital computer methods.

The example discussed above with the beads illustrates the manual method of creating random numbers. Several statistical textbooks contain large random number tables which can be used as needed. The techniques for the creation of random variables with analog computers are presented in other texts, such as the one by Korn (1966). Hence, this chapter will discuss random numbers only in relation to their creation and use with digital computers. Random number generators will then be defined for this discussion to mean some mathematical relationship which can be represented or manifested through a series of digital computer language statements which when executed will cause a number to be created from the uniform probability distribution.

PROPERTIES OF UNIFORMLY DISTRIBUTED RANDOM NUMBERS

As a simulation experiment proceeds in time, uniformly distributed random numbers are continously being generated. In that the major portion of the text is devoted to digital computer simulation experiments, we will consider that the random numbers are being supplied to us by some random number generator in the form of a computer program or subprogram. It is often easy to forget that we must concern ourselves with the actual series of consecutively generated numbers. The random number generator which supplies these numbers is designed to produce variables which follow the uniform distribution. The question we must answer is "What properties should this series of uniformly distributed random variables possess?"

First, let us examine the uniform probability distribution and define the properties it possesses. The density function for the uniform distribution defined over the range $(0,1)$ is shown in Figure 6.1.

Ideally the properties of the uniform distribution were presented in Table 3.2 for the continuous case. For purposes of this discussion, unless otherwise noted, let us assume that we are dealing with the continuous uniform distribution defined over the range $(0,1)$.

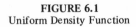

FIGURE 6.1
Uniform Density Function

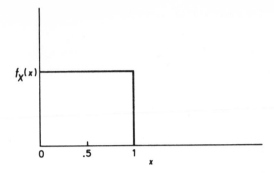

The mean of this distribution should be 1/2. Further, for any given sample the second moment or average sum of squares should be 1/3; and the third moment or average sum of cubes should be 1/4. These values can easily be derived by using the techniques of expected value theory discussed in chapter 3.

If we were to divide the interval (0,1) into n classes or subintervals, then the ith subinterval should contain T/n observations where T is the total number of observations taken. That is, if we had taken 1,000 observations of the variables from the uniform distribution and placed these into a frequency distribution containing, say, 10 equally spaced intervals, we would expect to have a frequency of 1,000/10 = 100 observations in each interval. This property should hold regardless of the size of the interval. In fact, theoretically, if we were to divide the interval (0,1) into 1,000 subintervals or classes, this property will hold.

Let us view this particular property in terms of the discrete uniform distribution. If we were to reduce the interval in the discrete case to a single value, then we would expect to have exactly the same number of observations recorded for each value in the range. In the example about the beads in the first section of this chapter we would expect to draw exactly the same number of 1's as we do 10's, and so on.

This property can be further extended to mean that the probability of observing a value in a particular interval remains constant and is independent of the previous value drawn. Again let us view this particular property in terms of the discrete distribution. This says that in the discrete case the probability of any given number being observed is exactly the same for each different number and is independent of the previous number recorded. That is,

$$P(x_i = X) = \text{constant for all } i \qquad (6.2)$$

In the example about the beads discussed in the first section of this chapter this probability is 0.10 for each possible value of the random variable. This was obtained by dividing the number of possible values of the random variable into one. Remember we replaced the bead each time it was drawn. This is done so that on successive observations each number has an equal chance of being drawn, independent of the number previously drawn. Note that in the example about the beads only one place significance need have been used (because we could have used the numbers 0 through 9 instead of 1 through 10). It is important to point out that the property of equiprobable independent events must ideally hold to whatever level of significance we might be using. That means if we were using the numbers 000 through 999, then the probability of any given number being drawn is 1/1,000. Remember, this property must necessarily hold independently of time and previous observations,

Finally, the properties mentioned above regarding random variables from the uniform distribution should hold true regardless of the sample size. That is, no matter if we only take 20 observations or 2,000 observations, the properties of the sample should reflect those of the throretical distribution.

In the above discussion we used both the discrete and continuous uniform probability distributions to illustrate properties of the uniform distribution. It is important to realize some practical aspects about the use of the discrete distribution for the generation of uniformly distributed random variables. In the random number generator we will be using in our computer simulation model we will always be limited to a certain number of digits of significance for our calculations. When we impose a limit upon the number of places to work with, we, in effect, say that we will be working with discrete data with some finite number of values. This will allow us to work in discrete terms to some extent. In our random number generator we may, in fact, generate numbers between 000 and 999. We determine our resultant continuous random number by dividing by 1,000 and hence have then a set of values over the range (0,1) to three decimal places.

In real world examples when we attempt to precisely model the characteristics of the uniform distribution through a random number generator we fall short of perfection. That is, our generator usually will not create perfect uniform random variables in time. There will be some errors introduced into our distribution, and some of the ideal characteristics cited above will not be included. Let us now discuss what some of these errors might be. These errors occur in the form of a series of generated numbers which do not reasonably follow all of the characteristics of the theoretical uniform distribution. As we shall see later, some errors may not greatly affect the results of one particular study, and the criterion for acceptance of a given random number generator must be based upon the application for which it will be used. Later we shall discuss some statistical tests which may be applied to a given sample to measure how well these properties have been met. Further, usually we shall see that more than one test should be applied to any sample to examine any given set of characteristics required in the series of random numbers we will be using.

The mean of a given sample may turn out either high or low. Further examination of the sample may indicate that the series of numbers being tested are consistently above or below $1/2$. On the other hand, the fact that a calculated value of $1/2$ occurs may not indicate an acceptable series of numbers for the dispersion about that mean may be great. That is, our series may contain a large number of values far above and below the mean which when averaged will produce a reasonable sample mean. Hence, examination of the second and third moments as well as testing the frequency distribution of the sample will shed light on this aspect.

Remember again that we are dealing with a series of numbers which are being generated successively in time. Theoretically, we must expect independent events, and for any given interval, a constant probability that a given value will fall in that interval. It may turn out that our particular generator does not in fact produce these numbers independently and has a cyclic variation that causes, say, several numbers below the mean to be generated then several numbers above the mean to be generated, and so on. Standard frequency tests may indicate a good fit. However, when we consider the order in which the numbers occurred, we see that the generator was not truly random and hence we did not create truly independent events.

In that these properties ideally exist to any level of significance, we should be able to partition the numbers and test each digit or group of digits for randomness. If random numbers to three decimal places are desired, then it is useless to test the generator to five places. At any rate, the series of numbers which are produced should be tested at each digit if the application dictates this. At any given digit in the random number the probability of observing the numbers zero through nine is 0.1. For example, the probability of observing the number three in the second decimal place of our random number is 0.1 for each number generated. This property was mentioned earlier and, as cited above, should be tested for each digit in the number.

In summary of this section remember that variables from the uniform distribution have several properties which ideally should be characterized in any sequence or sample of numbers taken. In that we rarely are able to deal with generators which create variables perfectly we must know how numbers may deviate from the true random variables. The next section of this chapter will present methods for creating random number generators for digital computers.

RANDOM NUMBER GENERATION

Before we discuss any methods for designing random number generators or show any examples of them, let us examine the desirable properties which a random number generator should possess. For our purposes we must consider these properties in terms of a computer program. Let us simply ask ourselves "What are the desirable properties of this computer program which generates uniformly distributed random variables?"

Obviously, the first answer we would offer to our own question is that the series of numbers this generator produces should follow the ideal uniform distribution as nearly as possible. This is a rather subjective answer, but suffice it to say at this point that based upon the application for which we will use our random number generator we shall require that certain characteristics be as nearly followed as possible. To illustrate this point briefly, consider again the bead example. The necessary characteristics we must require would not include randomness at the third decimal place. Further, this random number generator is adequate with only one digit significance, so we only need test it at one place. Keep in mind at all times to always base the acceptance criterion upon the application.

For the moment let us assume that the random number generator program does produce acceptable numbers for our application. What other properties should we reasonably expect this program to have? The other desirable properties are listed below.

1. It should be fast. That is, it should generate a number in the minimum amount of time. This random number generator is only a facet of a computer simulation model and, hence, should not consume large amounts of time. Since computer time is often very expensive, one should always attempt to attain speed in generation in our random number generators.

2. The program itself should be short. That is, it should not require large amounts of core storage.

3. It should have a long period. The period of a random number generator is a measure of how many numbers are generated before the same sequence of numbers reappears. When the same sequence of numbers begins to reappear, the generator is said to begin cycling. Hence, to say that a particular random number generator has a period of N numbers means that N terms will be generated before the generator begins cycling. The generator will not necessarily cycle back to the first number it generated. For example, the generator may cycle and begin reproducing the series which began at the 10th number generated.

4. Since we may wish to duplicate the experiment several times, the generator should be able to reproduce the same series of numbers as desired. On the other hand, it should have the ability to produce a distinctly different set or series of numbers at will.

5. The generator should be nondegenerate in nature. Degeneracy is defined to mean that the same number is continuously produced by the generator. If there is a degenerate quality in the generator, the program should be able to make corrections and continue.

In general, then, we could say that a random number generator should be a short, fast program which produces a long sequence of random numbers (which pass the standard tests) before beginning to cycle and which is algorithmic in nature. As we shall see, for any particular experiment there may be several different programs which meet these criteria.

We initially made the statement that a random number generator was usually a computer program or subprogram. It should be obvious to the reader that if only five random numbers are required for a given simulation experiment, it might be much more economical to read these in on data cards after the values were taken from a set of tables. Further, if a particular random number generator just happened to generate 30 perfectly random numbers before cycling (that is, it has a period of 30 terms) and we only needed 20 for our experiment, then this generator would be adequate for our purposes. There is no utility in having a period of thousands of terms if only 20 are used for the experiment.

We stated previously that the generator should be algorithmic in nature. This is a very practical requirment to place upon our generator program. Being algorithmic in nature indicates that the results of the previous calculation will be used in determining the next calculation. That is, the Ith term in the sequence is used in the expression to calculate the $(I + 1)$st term; the $(I + 1)$st term is used to calculate the $(I + 2)$d term, and so on. It so happens that most current methods for generating random numbers involve these recursive, or algorithmic-type, calculations. Indeed, it is a useful quality, for it allows the generator to operate independently of all other parts of the simulation program. Generally, all we need do is supply an initial or starting value to a generator and it "takes over" from there and continues to generate a sequence from that initial value.

To be precise we should note that the methods presented here for the creation of random number generators are very deterministic in that they all involve a recursive technique or congruence relation as expressed in some formula. Any series of numbers created in this manner cannot be "truly random." Theoretically, only some physical phenomenon can be a truly random process. In light of this, many authors refer to "pseudo-random number generators" instead of "random number generators." However, we shall adopt the less rigorous term for ease and understand that we may lack some precision in terminology.

The history of the generation of random sequences is documented in several works. It is not within the scope of this chapter to reiterate this history in detail. However, we will begin our discussion by reviewing some of the earlier techniques for random number generation.

The earliest method proposed for the generation of random numbers is known as the "midsquare" technique. It was proposed by

Von Newmann and Metropolis about 1946. In the midsquare method each successive number is generated by taking the middle n-digits of the square of the previous n-digit number. For example, assume that we wish to generate three-digit random numbers. Our first value is 239. This leads to the following sequence of numbers: $239 \to 712 \to 694 \to 163 \to 656 \to 033 \to 108 \to 166 \to 755 \ldots$. The problems which exist with this method are that it has the tendency to degenerate rapidly. Depending upon the initial value, the method can degenerate within 20 numbers. For example, let us assume that we wish four-digit random numbers to be generated and that the nth number generated was 3,500. Look at the resulting sequence

$$r_n{}^2 = 12,250,000 \qquad r_{n+1} = 2,500$$
$$r_{n+1}^2 = 0,625,000 \qquad r_{n+2} = 2,500$$

Notice that we have reached a degenerate condition. Hence, we must always test our number series as it is being generated to protect against this.

In this method the repitition of some series will eventually occur and the random number sequence will cycle. Further, to carry this scheme out in a compiler-level language we need at least two multiplications and possibly three divisions to be able to access the middle four digits in a fixed word binary computer. Consequently, this method is not very fast.

Another method for generation of random numbers is called the midproduct techniqe and is very similar to the midsquare technique in that the resultant random number is taken as the middle n-digits of the result of a previous multiplication. In mathematical notation

$$r_{m+1} = r_m \times r_{m-1} \qquad \text{mid four digits} \qquad (6.3)$$

The technique for the midproduct involves selecting two random numbers r_1 and r_2, each containing P digits. Now multiply r_1 by r_2 to get U. Set r_3 equal to the middle P digits of U. Now r_4 equals r_3 multiplied by r_2, and so forth. A modification of this method is to use a constant multiplier instead of random numbers. That is,

$$r_{m+1} = K \times r_m \qquad \text{mid four digits} \qquad (6.4)$$

This method is similar to the midsquare method. However, both have longer periods, and the numbers they produce seem to be more uniformly distributed. But as with the midsquare method, this technique seems to eventually degenerate to some constant value. Both the midsquare and midproduct methods have a relatively short period which is greatly affected by the initial values chosen.

Figure 6.2 shows a flow chart for a random number generator which seems to overcome the problem to some degree. It returns a four digit random number. It can be coded as a FUNCTION subprogram called RANDNO. Originally one must declare in the first two positions of COMMON two random numbers (which correspond to N and N1 in the subprogram).

FIGURE 6.2
A Random Number Generator Using
Perturbation and Midsquare

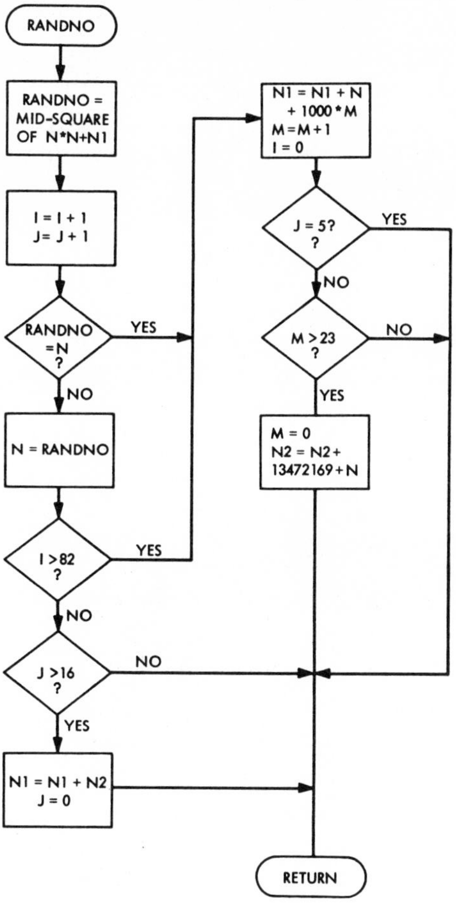

The method used combines a pertubation method with the midsquare method but also includes a stabilizing factor. Tests have shown that it creates less variation from the uniform distribution for a moderate number of generations. It permits generation of the same number for any number of times without degeneration of the sequence. It permits generation of all zeros without degeneration. The usual midsquare method seems to have very poor distribution with respect to zeros, but this method is stable in this respect. Study of the pertubation used should intuitively convince one that the method has a long period. The parameters of pertubation are cycling irregularly in approximate periods of 14, 83, and 2,000 for N1, M, and N2, respectively. The obvious disadvantage is less speed.

Another point should be noted about Figure 6.2. Block number 10 says RANDNO = MID SQUARE OF N*N + N1. This would have to be executed by a series of multiplications and division if used in a FORTRAN program to get the middle four digits of the number. The exact method would be dependent upon the particular computer being used.

These methods, once widely used, have given way to congruential methods based on the relation

$$r_{i+1} \equiv ar_i + C(\text{mod } m), \qquad 0 \le r_i \le m \qquad (6.5)$$

This relation means that the sum $ar_i + C$ is to be divided by m, and r_{i+1} is to be set equal to the remainder. The relation reads "r_{i+1} is congruent to $ar_i + C$ modulo m." To illustrate, let $m = 25$, $a = 6$, and $C = 1$; also let $r_0 = 1$.

$$r_1 \equiv 6 \times 1 + 1(\text{mod } 25) \qquad r_1 \equiv 7$$
$$r_2 \equiv 6 \times 7 + 1(\text{mod } 25) \qquad r_2 \equiv 18$$
$$r_3 \equiv 6 \times 18 + 1(\text{mod } 25) \qquad r_3 \equiv 9$$

The method was initially proposed in 1949 by Lehmer. With $C = 0$, it is called multiplicative congruential method. The form shown with $C \ne 0$ is called the mixed congruential method. Another form,

$$r_{i+1} \equiv r_i - r_{i-1}(\text{mod } m) \qquad (6.6)$$

is known as the additive congruent method. This is actually a Fibonacci sequence when $r_0 = 0$ and $r_1 = 1$.

The multiplicative congruent method where

$$r_{i+1} \equiv ar_i(\text{mod } m) \qquad (6.7)$$

has been shown to behave very well statistically (Gorenstein 1967). Usually, on a binary computer we pick m to be some power of 2 while on a decimal computer we pick m as some power of 10. Many books and articles discuss the detailed mathematics of the development of these congruence relationships, (Hull and Dobell, 1962; Naylor *et al.*, 1966; IBM, 1959). We will not spend time developing the theory of these congruence relationships. The reader is advised to consult the references for background.

With the multiplicative method on binary machines the maximum period is $m/4$ where $m = 2^b (b > 2)$ and is achieved with r_0 odd, and $a = 8t \pm 3$ where $t = 1, 2, 3$ (Hull and Dobell, 1962; IBM, 1959). In this method it is usually convenient to set $m = 2^b$ where b is equal to the number of bits in a binary word on the particular computer.

In a decimal machine with $m = 10^d$ (for $d > 3$) the maximum period is $m/20$ and is achieved with

r_0 not divisible by 2 or 5.

$a = 200t \pm Z$.

$t = 1, 2, 3, \ldots$.

C odd.

$Z = 3, 11, 13, 19, 21, 27, 29, 37, 53, 59, 61, 67, 69, 77, 83$, or 91.

For purposes of this text most examples will use the multiplicative congruential method. A FORTRAN IV program for this method with a 35-bit word binary computer is shown in Figure 6.3.

FIGURE 6.3
FORTRAN IV Random Number Generator

```
FUNCTION RANDU (IX,IY)
IY = IX * 03125
IF (IY) 5,6,6
5 IY = IY + 2 * * 35
6 YFL = IY
RANDU = YFL * 2.0 * * (-35)
IX = IY
RETURN
END
```

All we need to do is supply the first random number and make sure it is five digit odd. The routine takes over and continues by itself. Note that this method is rather fast and takes little storage.

The following subroutine, written by IBM,[1] will function for the IBM System/360. It will compute uniformly distributed numbers over the unit interval. The routine is accessed by the statement CALL RANDU (IX,IY,YFL). The definition of variables is as follows:

IX – For the first entry this must contain any odd integer number with nine or less digits. After the first entry, IX should be the previous value of IY computed by the subroutine.

IY – A resultant integer random number required for the next entry to this subroutine. The range of this number is between zero and 2 * * 3 1.

YFL – The resultant uniformly distributed, floating point random number in the range zero to 1.0.

The subroutine listing is given in Figure 6.4.

FIGURE 6.4
System/360 Random Number Generator

```
SUBROUTINE RANDU (IX,IY,YFL)
IY = IX * 65539
IF (IY) 5,6,6
5  IY = IY + 2147483647 + 1
6  YFL = IY
YFL = YFL * .4656613E-9
RETURN
END
```

MacLaren and Marsaglia (1965) have proposed a combination of two congruential generators to produce random sequences. In this method one generator is used to shuffle the sequence produced by the other. For example, one generator produces the sequence $x_L \ldots x_N$, and the other generator produces the sequence $y_L \ldots y_N$. The process begins by creating a table of random numbers $x_L \ldots x_j$. Then to generate (on a binary computer) r_K, the Kth random number, we obtain the first L bits from y_K where $2^L = j$. These first L bits are then used as a pointer into the table initially created from which r_K was taken. The table is then refilled with a number from the first random number generator.

In their research MacLaren and Marsaglia, used the relations

---

[1] Reprinted by permission from H20-0205-0 – System/360 Scientific Subroutine Package. 1966 by International Business Machines Corporation.

$$x_{K+1} = (2^{17} + 3) x_K (\text{mod } 2^{35}) \tag{6.8}$$

$$y_{K+1} = (2^7 + 1) y_K (\text{mod } 2^{35}). \tag{6.9}$$

They found that this method produced a quite acceptable series of random numbers. In this method the time to produce a random number is just about twice that required by a single congruential generator.

Most scientifically oriented compiler-level computer languages have built-in functions which will perform the remaindering operation. This makes it rather easy to construct a random number generator in FORTRAN. The functions commonly used for this operation in FORTRAN are called MOD and AMOD.

TESTING A RANDOM NUMBER GENERATOR

The requirements to be placed upon a particular set of random numbers must be based primarily upon the intended application of those numbers in the simulation experiment. Several different tests have been proposed by various mathematicians and statisticians which provide the tools to statistically validate the randomness of the set of numbers for a given set of conditions. It is incumbent upon the analyst to decide which of the tests he must use, and the decision must necessarily rest upon a synthesis of the answers to several basic questions. These questions must be asked at the outset of the experiment and must be considered pertinent in the design phase. Some of these questions which are pertinent are listed below:

1. How many numbers will be needed for one simulation run?
2. How many decimal places must the random number contain?
3. What will the effect be upon the results if the generator produces an inadequate sequence of numbers?

Other considerations must also be made when establishing the adequacy of a random number generator for a particular study. These considerations will be pointed out as the various statistical tests are discussed.

TESTS FOR UNIFORMITY OF DISTRIBUTION

One basic analysis which should always be performed is that of validation of the uniformity of the distribution. Two basic tests may be applied for this application, namely, the chi-square test and the Kolmogorov-Smirnov test. Both of these statistical tests are concerned with the degree of agreement between the distribution of a sample of generated random numbers and the theoretical uniform distribution. Further, both tests are based upon a null hypothesis of no detectable difference between the sample distribution and the theoretical distribution. Both tests are based upon the grouping of sample data into classes within the interval (0,1).

Goodness-of-Fit Tests

The hypothesis that there exists no difference between the sample frequency distribution and the theoretical uniform distribution is under test. This null hypothesis specifies the proportion of observations falling in each of the classes in our presumed population. That is, from the null hypothesis we may deduce what are the expected frequencies. The chi-square goodness-of-fit test allows us to determine whether the observed frequencies are sufficiently close to those expected under our null hypothesis.

Essentially the null hypothesis may be tested by

$$\chi^2 = \sum_{i=1}^{n} \frac{(O_i - E_i)^2}{E_i} \tag{6.10}$$

where O_i = observed number in ith class, E_i = expected number in ith class, and n = number of classes.

For the uniform distribution

$$E_i = \frac{T}{n} \tag{6.11}$$

for equally spaced classes where T is the total number of observations recorded.

It can be shown that the sampling distribution of χ^2, as calculated from (6.10), follows the chi-square distribution with $df = n - 1$.

Because this test has been presented in a myriad of textbooks, no specific example will be presented here. However, some general considerations regarding the application of this technique are listed below.

1. The choice of the size of class interval may be chosen in several ways. Mann and Wald (1942) present a method for choosing

the class interval based upon the significance level of the test. However, keeping the application in mind will aid the analyst in choosing this interval. For instance, if the simulation model utilizes the random number several times to make one of several possible choices, say K, then the interval should be establised to reflect this by placing $n = K$.

2. The interval should further be selected such as to reflect the level of significance to be required of the random number in the simulation model.

3. As Cochran (1954) points out, when $n > 2$, the chi-square test should not be used when more than 20 percent of the expected frequencies are smaller than five or when any expected frequency is smaller than one. In addition, when $n = 2$, each expected frequency should be at least five.

4. The total number of observations to take, again, should be based upon the application itself.

Although we shall not present an example of the use of the chi-square test for goodness-of-fit at this point, examples of its application will be presented in conjunction with several other tests which we shall discuss.

Another goodness-of-fit test is the Kolmogorov-Smirnov test. Again, we are concerned with the degree of agreement between our sample frequency distribution and the theoretical uniform distribution under the hypothesis that no difference, in fact, exists. The test involves the use of a cumulative frequency distribution.

Let $F_x(x)$ be the continuous cumulative distribution function for the uniform distribution. That is, for any value of x, the value of $F_x(x)$ is the proportion of observations expected to have values less than or equal to x. Let $S_T(x)$ be the observed cumulative frequency distribution of a sample of T observations. For any given observation x, $S_T(x) = m/T$ where m is the number of observations less than or equal to x.

The Kolmogorov-Smirnov test concerns itself with the largest single deviation between $F_x(x)$ and $S_T(x)$ over the range. Remember that under the null hypothesis we expect these deviations to be small and within the limits of random errors. In the Kolmogorov-Smirnov test, the largest deviation, D, between $F_x(x)$ and $S_T(x)$ is called the maximum deviation where

$$D = \max |F_X(x) - S_T(x)| \qquad (6.12)$$

The sampling distribution of D is known and is dependent upon T.

distribution. The general procedure for performing this test is then to (a) specify the cumulative distribution function for the uniform distribution based upon the number of classes, (b) arrange the observed sample of random numbers into a cumulative frequency distribution with these same classes, (c) find the max$|F_X(x) - S_T(x)|$ using formula (6.12) to find D, (d) refer to Table 4 to find the critical value of D corresponding to the specified alpha error. If the tabular value, $D_{1-\alpha}$, is less than D, then the hypothesis that the data came from the postulated distribution is rejected.

Example 6.1

Suppose we had generated 100 random numbers and wished to test their uniformity over 10 equidistant intervals using the Kolmogorov-Smirnov test. We shall set our alpha level at 0.05 and follow the procedure outlined in the paragraph above. Table 6.1 shows $F_X(x)$, $S_T(x)$, and the difference between them for this sample.

TABLE 6.1
Hypothetical Random Number Generator Outcome
Interval Number

	1	2	3	4	5	6	7	8	9	10
$F_X(x)$	0.10	0.20	0.30	0.40	0.50	0.60	0.70	0.80	0.90	1.00
$S_T(x)$	0.08	0.25	0.30	0.35	0.47	0.65	0.70	0.84	0.97	1.00
$|F_X(x) - S_T(x)|$	0.02	0.05	0.00	0.05	0.03	0.05	0.00	0.04	0.07	0.00

From this table $D = 0.07$. The critical value of D, from Table 4 is $1.36/\sqrt{100}$, or 0.136. Since $D < 0.136$, we cannot reject our null hypothesis and, hence, must conclude that the sample taken from our random number generator is uniformly distributed over (0,1).

A few points should be made regarding the Kolmogorov-Smirnov test.

1. In that we are dealing with individual class differences as opposed to a sum of values we do not lose information as in the chi-square test.

2. Further, since there is no restriction upon class size, the Kolmorgorov-Smirnov test can be applied for smaller samples.

3. As Siegel (1956) points out, "the Kolmorgorov-Smirnov test

may in all cases be more powerful that its alternative, the chi-square test."

4. Siegel says "the Kolmogorov-Smirnov test should be used when the variable under consideration has a continuous distribution. However, if the test is used when the population distribution is discontinuous, the error which occurs in the resulting probability statement is in the 'safe' direction." In other words, if the null hypothesis is rejected by that test, we have real confidence in that decision.

5. In light of the above, the selection for class intervals should be based solely upon the application. Further, the total number of samples should also be based upon the application.

These two methods are both applicable for testing the uniformity of the distribution of the sequence of random numbers. Essentially, neither take into account the ordering of the data, and hence, additional tests will be discussed for that purpose. It appears that the Kolmogorov-Smirnov test is more powerful in almost all instances than the chi-square test. For practical purposes with large number of observations, both will suffice. Both are very easy to program on a digital computer and can be designed as subroutines for testing purposes.

It should be noted that if only two classes over the interval (0,1) are to be tested, the binomial test as presented in Siegel (1956, p. 36) can be used, especially when the sample size is too small for the chi-square test. However, all in all the Kolmogorov-Smirnov test seems to be the most powerful goodness-of-fit test presented.

We now turn our attention to a series of statistical tests which allow us to investigate various facets of the ordering of our sequence of random numbers. In these tests we are concerned with the time sequence ordering of the numbers as they are produced by the generator. In that we are dealing with a deterministic process or pseudo-random process we must be concerned not only with merely the uniformity of our sample but also with the order in which the numbers in our sample were produced. A glaring example of how the chi-square or Kolmogorov-Smirnov test would fail us by neglecting the order can be presented as follows: Assume that we were going to generate 1,000 numbers on the interval (0,1) and group them into 10 classes. Say our generator produced all of the numbers in the first class first, all of the numbers in the second class next, and so on for each of the 10 classes, culminating its process by having 100 numbers in each class. Both the chi-square test and the Kolmogorov-Smirnov test would indicate excellent fits. However, are these even remotely random? At any rate the following tests will provide us with the statistical tools necessary to cope with this problem.

RUNS TESTS

The tests discussed in the previous section may suggest that a sequence of numbers can be assumed to have been generated from a uniform population, and yet the arrangement of the numbers within the sequence may be such that doubt is cast upon the "randomness" of the numbers. For example, consider the following sequence of 40 single-digit numbers: 0, 1, 2, 3, 4, 5, 6, 7, 8, 9, 0, 1, 2, 3, 4, 5, 6, 7, 8, 9, 0, 1, 2, 3, 4, 5, 6, 7, 8, 9, 0, 1, 2, 3, 4, 5, 6, 7, 8, 9.

Either the chi-square or the Kolmogorov-Smirnov tests would attest to the uniformity of distribution of these numbers; but one would hardly characterize them as random numbers. However, if we rearrange these same numbers as follows 2, 4, 7, 8, 4, 2, 4, 7, 3, 6, 3, 7, 2, 9, 7, 1, 9, 9, 8, 5, 0, 3, 5, 9, 0, 3, 8, 5, 2, 6, 6, 0, 1, 1, 4, 5, 8, 1, 0, 6 — we have less reason to doubt their randomness. Thus we are interested in the particular arrangement of the numbers within a sequence in determining their randomness. The purpose of the runs test is to assess the random character of a sequence of numbers.

Before defining a run we must break the possible occurrences into a set of three mutually exclusive outcomes or events. One of these events is always no event at all. For example, suppose we flip a coin 10 times with the following result: H T H H T H T T T H.

The first head is preceded by "no event," and the last head is succeeded by "no event." Therefore we might say that every sequence of events begins and ends with no event. The other two mutually exclusive categories are heads and tails. A run is thus defined as a succession of similar events preceded and followed by a different event. The length of a run is the number of events which occur in the run. In the coin flipping example we have seven runs; the first and second of length one, the third of length two, and fourth and fifth of length one, the sixth of length three, and the seventh of length one. The reader will note that proper application of a runs analysis requires that the events which may occur be classified in one of two mutually exclusive categories.

In assessing the randomness of a sequence of numbers we may be interested in either the number or the length of the runs which occur. We will be interested in two types of runs here—runs up and runs down. If we have a sequence of numbers such that each number in the sequence is succeeded by a larger number, the sequence will be called an upward run. If the sequence is such that each number is succeeded by a smaller number, the sequence will be called a downward run. To illustrate consider the following sequence of 20 single-digit numbers: 3, 1, 2, 3, 6, 4, 5, 4, 1, 2, 6, 8, 9, 7, 5, 2, 3, 1, 5, 1. We first give each number in the sequence a sign (+, −). If the number is followed by a larger number, it is assigned a +. If the number is followed by a smaller number, it is given a −. Since the last number in any sequence is followed by "no event," it is not given either a + or a −. Therefore we have: − + + + − + − − + + + + − − − + − + −.

Each succession of +'s and −'s constitutes a run, its length denoted by the number of like signs contained in the run. Therefore the first run is down and of length one, the second is up and of length three, and so on. In this example we have 11 runs—5 up and 6 down.

A sequence of numbers can be nonrandom if we have either too few or too many runs. For example, consider the following two sequences of 10, two-digit numbers:

Sequence A 28, 47, 49, 63, 77, 82, 87, 91, 96, 99
Sequence B 01, 61, 32, 94, 21, 78, 39, 42, 17, 34

In the first sequence we have only one run—that being up. In the second sequence we have nine runs—five up and four down. Since we would not expect truly random numbers to continually increase, we would question the proposition that the first sequence is composed of random numbers. On the other hand, we would not expect the other extreme exhibited in sequence B, where the numbers increase, decrease, increase, decrease, and so on. Therefore we expect the number of runs found in a sequence of random numbers to be something between the maximum and the minimum number possible.

If we have a sequence of N numbers, the maximum number of runs possible is N-1. The minimum number of runs is always one. Let a_1 be the total number of runs in a sequence. The mean and variance of a_1, m_{a_1}, and $\sigma_{a_1}^2$, are given by

$$m_{a_1} = \frac{2N - 1}{3} \tag{6.13}$$

$$\sigma_{a_1}^2 = \frac{16N - 29}{90} \tag{6.14}$$

For $N > 20$, the distribution of a_1 can be reasonably approximated by a normal distribution with mean and variance given by (6.13) and (6.14). This approximation would normally be appropriate for testing the randomness of the numbers generated by a random number gene..tor since one would usually generate several hundred numbers before applying a runs test. For $N \leqslant 20$, the reader should consult Siegel (1956).

As we have already pointed out, the hypothesis that a sequence of numbers is random may be rejected because there are either too few or too many runs. Thus we require a two-tailed test to determine whether either of these two extremes has occurred. As our test statistic we use

$$Z = \frac{a_1 - m_{a_1}}{\sigma_{a_1}}$$

$$= \frac{a_1 - \frac{2N - 1}{3}}{\sqrt{\frac{16N - 29}{90}}} \tag{6.15}$$

where Z is normally distributed with a mean of zero and a variance of unity. If the level of significance is defined by α and $Z_{1-\alpha/2}$ is that value of Z such that

$$P(Z \geq Z_{1-\alpha/2}) = \frac{\alpha}{2} \tag{6.16}$$

then if

$$|Z| \geq Z_{1-\alpha/2} \tag{6.17}$$

the hypothesis of randomness if rejected.

Example 6.2

Determine whether the number of runs exhibited in the following sequence is such that the hypothesis that the numbers are random can be rejected. Let $\alpha = 0.05$.

59, 12, 19, 05, 59, 58, 83, 18, 36, 00, 61, 47, 24, 41, 42, 98, 23, 67, 84, 43, 29, 71, 88, 74, 60, 10, 46, 23, 15, 11, 78, 31, 11, 91, 99, 57, 28, 18, 32, 21, 12, 95, 38, 76, 07, 96, 33, 63, 10, 05

The sequence of runs up and down is as follows:

$$- + - + - + - + - + - - + + + - + + - - + + - - - + - - - + - - + + - - - + - - + - + - + - + - -$$

Therefore $a_1 = 33$.

Since $N = 50$, for the mean and variance of a_1, we have

$$m_{a_1} = 33$$
$$\sigma^2_{a_1} = 8.57$$

and

$$Z = \frac{33 - 33}{\sqrt{8.57}}$$

$$= 0.00$$

$$Z_{0.975} = 1.96$$

Since $|Z| < Z_{0.975}$, the randomness of the numbers cannot be rejected on the basis of this test.

The runs test just discussed is not completely adequate in assessing the randomness of a sequence of numbers. To illustrate, consider the following sequence of 50 numbers.

59, 52, 78, 61, 98, 54, 97, 84, 91, 60, 78, 71, 54, 55, 63, 68, 53, 82, 88, 63, 58, 67, 92, 90, 84, 42, 47, 10, 07, 00, 35, 21, 14, 41, 48, 33, 29, 08, 18, 10, 02, 41, 32, 33, 21, 48, 21, 29, 17, 11

If we were to apply the runs analysis described above, we would obtain the following sequence of pluses and minuses.

$$- + - + - + - + - + - - + + + - + + - - + + - - - + - - - + - - + + - - - + - - + - + - + - + - -$$

The reader will notice that this sequence is identical to that found in example (6.2). Therefore the preceding analysis would suggest that these numbers are truly random. However, this assertion is obviously questionable since the first 25 numbers fall above the mean (49.5) while the remaining 25 fall below the mean. The nonrandom character of this sequence is suggested by the fact that we have one run of numbers above the mean followed by one run below the mean.

If we modify our definition of a run, we can apply a variation of the previously discussed runs analysis to test for the property just described. For this purpose we will describe runs as being above or below the mean. A plus sign will denote an observation above the mean and a minus an observation below the mean. For example, for the following sequence of single-digit numbers

9, 4, 5, 6, 1, 0, 6, 6, 4, 9, 2, 8, 4, 0, 3, 7, 5, 5, 5, 5, 7, 1, 8, 9, 1, 0

we have an assignment of pluses and minuses as follows, where the mean is 4.5.

+ − + + − − + + − + − + − − − + + + + + − + + − −

Here we have a run of one above the mean followed by a run of one below the mean, followed by a run of two above the mean, and so on. Or, we have seven runs above the mean and seven below the mean.

Let n_1 and n_2 be the number of individual observations above and below the mean, respectively. Again a_1 will be defined as the total number of runs. For the test for runs above and below the mean, the mean and variance of a_1 are given by

$$m_{a_1} = \frac{2n_1 n_2}{n_1 + n_1} + 1 \tag{6.18}$$

$$\sigma_{a_1}^2 = \frac{2n_1 n_2 (2n_1 n_2 - n_1 - n_2)}{(n_1 + n_2)^2 (n_1 + n_2 - 1)} \tag{6.19}$$

For either n_1 or n_2 greater than 20, a_1 is normally distributed, and for this case the test statistic is given by

$$Z = \frac{a_1 - \dfrac{2n_1 n_2}{n_1 + n_2} - 1}{\sigma_{a_1}} \tag{6.20}$$

Since we are interested in the occurrence of either too few or too many runs, a two-tailed test is again in order. If the level of significance is specified by α, we reject the hypothesis of randomness if

$$|Z| > Z_{1-\alpha/2} \tag{6.21}$$

Example 6.3

Determine whether there is an excessive number of runs above or below the mean for the sequence of numbers given in example 6.2. Let $\alpha = 0.05$.

We assign +'s and −'s to the numbers in example 6.2 as follows: (Note that the mean of two-digit random numbers is 49.5.)

+ − − − + + + − − − + − − − − + − + + − − + + + + − − − − − + − − + + + − − − − − + − + − + − + − −

For this sequence we have

$$n_1 = 20$$

$$n_2 = 30$$

$$a_1 = 24$$

$$m_{a_1} = \frac{2(20)(30)}{50} + 1 = 23$$

$$\sigma_{a_1}^2 = \frac{2(20)(30)[2(20)(30) - 20 - 30]}{(20 + 30)^2(20 + 30 - 1)}$$

$$= 11.27$$

Since $n_2 > 20$, the normal approximation is appropriate.

$$Z = \frac{24 - 23}{\sqrt{11.27}}$$

$$= 0.298$$

$$Z_{0.975} = 1.96$$

Therefore, since $|Z| < 1.96$, we cannot reject the hypothesis of randomness on the basis of this test.

Thus far our concern has been with the number of runs appearing in a particular sequence of numbers without regard to the length of those runs. For example, suppose that within a sequence of 1,000 numbers, 250 runs were observed above the mean and 250 below the mean. Further, suppose that each run was of length two. For this situation the expected number of runs above and below the mean is 501 by equation (6.18). Thus observing 500 runs in the sequence, we would be forced to accept the hypothesis of randomness. However, we would expect to find runs of length other than two within such a long series of numbers. Let R_i be the number of runs of length i in a sequence of N numbers. For the expected value of R_i we have

$$E(R_i) = 2N \left(\frac{n_1}{N}\right)^i \left(\frac{n_2}{N}\right)^2 \tag{6.22}$$

for runs above and below the mean and large N and

$$E(R_i) = \frac{2}{(i + 3)!} [N(i^2 + 3i + 1) - (i^3 + 3i^2 - i - 4)], \qquad i \leq N - 2$$

$$= \frac{2}{N!}, \qquad i = N - 1 \tag{6.23}$$

for runs up and down. Using the chi-square test already presented, we can compare the observed number of runs of a given length with the expected number. That is, if O_i is the observed number of runs of length i, we have as our test statistic

$$\chi^2 = \sum_{i=1}^{L} \frac{[O_i - E(R_i)]^2}{E(R_i)} \tag{6.24}$$

where $L = N$ for runs above and below the mean and $L = N-1$ for runs up and down.

Example 6.4

Given the following sequence of numbers, can the hypothesis that the numbers are random be rejected on the basis of the distribution of run length above and below the mean? Let $\alpha = 0.05$.

0.44, .04, .12, .22, .64, .55, .43, .92, .65, .24, .69, .86, .48, .78, .47, .20, .80, .04, .67, .28, .17, .99, .02, .55, .59, .66, .01, .29, .47, .06, .31, .72, .17, .48, .74, .05, .92, .15, .80, .22, .86, .96, .35, .29, .36, .32, .51, .74, .33, .78, .99, .77, .57, .35, .81, .53, .78, .61, .52, .95, .26, .21, .99, .01, .95, .30, .88, .80, .37, .00, .01, .28, .21, .34, .86, .67, .67, .32, .78, 0.76

For this sequence of numbers we have

```
- - - - + + - + + - + + - + - - + - + - - + - + + + - - - - - + - - + - + - + -
+ + - - - - + + - + + + + - + + + + + - - + - + - + + - - - - - + + + - + +
```

Since we are interested in the length of runs above and below the mean, we use equation (6.22) to determine the expected number of runs of length i. For example, $E(R_1)$ is given by

$$E(R_1) = 2(80)\left(\frac{40}{80}\right)\left(\frac{40}{80}\right)^2 = 20$$

where $n_1 = 40$, $n_2 = 40$. The remaining calculations are summarized in Table 6.2.

TABLE 6.2

Run Length i	Observed Runs (O_i)	Expected Runs $E(R_i)$	$\dfrac{[O_i - E(|R_i|)]^2}{E(R_i)}$
1. 23		20	0.45
2. 11		10	0.10
3. 6		5	1.80
4 or more 2		5	0.20

The experimental chi-square value is given by

$$\chi^2 = 2.55$$

and

$$\chi^2_{0.95}(3) = 7.81$$

Since $\chi^2 < \chi^2_{0.95}(3)$, we cannot reject the hypothisis that the numbers given are not random on the basis of this test.

TESTS FOR AUTOCORRELATION

Tests for autocorrelation examine the tendency of numbers to be followed by other numbers. To illustrate what we mean let us examine the following series of random numbers:

0.20, .96, .78, .18, .92, .90, .80, .02, .53, .05, .30, .70, .59, .98, .90, .03, .37, .86, .73, .06, .53, .25, .67, .78, .33, .97, .63, .25, .33, .72, .91, .00, .24, .64, .90, .08, .33, .94, .33, .16, .45, .70, .18, 0.07

At first glance these numbers might appear to be random and may well pass all of the tests discussed so far. However, as one examines these numbers closely one will note a distinct relationship between every sixth number starting with the second. Each of these numbers varies in magnitude successively from very large to very small. Although we would scarcely reject the random number generator which produced these numbers for this reason on the basis of an analysis of only 44 numbers, this example serves to illustrate the property we are about to investigate.

Suppose that we wish to determine whether there is any relationship among the random numbers $r_i, r_{i+m}, r_{i+2m}, \cdots, r_{i+(M+1)m}$, that is, the extent of the autocorrelation among every mth random number starting with the ith. Under the assumption that the random numbers are uniformly and independently distributed on the internal (0, 1) we have for the probability density function of r_{i+km}

$$f_{R_{i+km}}(r_{i+km}) = 1, \qquad 0 < r_{i+km} < 1 \tag{6.25}$$

The test we will develop is based upon an analysis of successive pairs of the random numbers. Considering the pair of numbers r_{i+km} and $r_{i+(k+1)m}$, let us derive the distribution of the product of these two random variables. Assuming independence and uniformity of distribution, we have

$$f_{X,Y}(x, y) = 1, \qquad 0 < x < 1, \qquad 0 < y < 1 \tag{6.26}$$

where $R_{i+km} = X$ and $R_{i+(k+1)m} = Y$. Let $Z = XY$ and $W = X$, $X = W$ and $Y = Z/W$.

The Jacobian of the transformation is given by

$$J = \begin{vmatrix} 1 & 0 \\ -\dfrac{z}{w^2} & \dfrac{1}{w} \end{vmatrix} = \dfrac{1}{w}$$

$$f_{Z,W}(z, w) = \frac{1}{w}, \qquad z < w < 1, \qquad 0 < z < 1 \tag{6.27}$$

and

$$f_Z(z) = \int_z^1 \frac{dw}{w}$$

$$= -\,ln(z), \qquad 0 < z < 1 \tag{6.28}$$

The mean and variance of the product of two random numbers are given by

$$E(r_{i+km}\, r_{i+(k+1)m}) = \frac{1}{4} \tag{6.29}$$

$$\mathrm{Var}(r_{i+km}\, r_{i+(k+1)m}) = \frac{7}{144} \tag{6.30}$$

To analyze the overall correlation for all successive pairs of random numbers we will use the statistic

$$\rho_{im} = \frac{1}{M+1} \sum_{k=0}^{M} [r_{i+km}\, r_{i+(k+1)m}] \tag{6.31}$$

where N is the total number of random numbers in the entire sequence and M is the largest integer such that $i + (M + 1)\, m < N$. From equation (6.26) we have

$$E(\rho_{im}) = 0.25 \tag{6.32}$$

The expression for the variance of ρ_{im} is complicated by the fact that all the terms in the sum in equation (6.28) are not uncorrelated. For example, the first and second terms in the sum, $r_i r_{i+m}$ and $r_{i+m} r_{i+2m}$, contain r_{i+m}, and therefore these two terms are not independent. We take account of this condition as follows:

$$\text{Var}(\rho_{im}) = E\left\{\frac{1}{M+1}\sum_{k=0}^{M}[r_{i+km}\,r_{i+(k+1)m}] - 0.25\right\}^2 \tag{6.33}$$

$$= \frac{1}{(M+1)^2}\,E\left\{\sum_{k=0}^{M}[r_{i+km}\,r_{i+(k+1)m}] - 0.25\right\}^2$$

Expanding the squared term, we have the sum of each term squared plus twice the cross-product of each term within the original sum.

$$\text{Var}(\rho_{im}) = \frac{1}{(M+1)^2}\,E\left\{\sum_{k=0}^{M}[r_{i+km}\,r_{i+(k+1)m} - 0.25]^2\right.$$

$$\left. + 2\sum_{k=0}^{M-1}\sum_{j=k+1}^{M}[r_{i+km}\,r_{i+(k+1)m} - 0.25][r_{i+jm}\,r_{i+(j+1)m} - 0.25]\right\} \tag{6.34}$$

Taking each summation separately, we have

$$E\sum_{k=0}^{M}[r_{i+km}\,r_{i+(k+1)m} - 0.25]^2 = \sum_{k=0}^{M}E[r_{i+km}\,r_{i+(k+1)m} - 0.25]^2$$

$$= \sum_{k=0}^{M}\text{Var}[r_{i+km}\,r_{i+(k+1)m}]$$

$$= \frac{7(M+1)}{144} \tag{6.35}$$

$$2E\sum_{k=0}^{M-1}\sum_{j=k+1}^{M}[r_{i+km}\,r_{i+(k+1)m} - 0.25][r_{i+jm}\,r_{i+(j+1)m} - 0.25]$$

$$= 2\sum_{k=0}^{M-1}\sum_{j=k+1}^{M}E[r_{i+km}\,r_{i+(k+1)m} - 0.25][r_{i+jm}\,r_{i+(j+1)m} - 0.25] \tag{6.36}$$

The expected value of each of the cross-product terms in (6.36) is given by

$$E[r_{i+km}\,r_{i+(k+1)m} - 0.25][r_{i+jm}\,r_{i+(j+1)m} - 0.25] = \begin{cases} \dfrac{3}{144}, & j = k + 1 \\ 0, & j \neq k + 1 \end{cases} \tag{6.37}$$

The proof of (6.37) is left as an exercise for the reader. Inspection of (6.36) indicates that there are M cross-products within the double summation for which $j = k + 1$. Therefore

$$2E \sum_{k=0}^{M-1} \sum_{j=k+1}^{M} [r_{i+km} r_{i+(k+1)m} - 0.25][r_{i+jm} r_{i+(j+1)m} - 0.25] = \frac{6M}{144} \quad (6.38)$$

and

$$\text{Var}(\rho_{im}) = \frac{13M + 7}{144(M + 1)^2} \quad (6.39)$$

For large M the distribution of ρ_{im} is approximately normal if the variables $r_i, r_{i+m}, \cdots, r_{i+(M+1)m}$ are uncorrelated. The test statistic for determining the significance of autocorrelation for the proposed sequence of $M + 1$ numbers is

$$Z = \frac{\rho_{im} - 0.25}{\sqrt{\dfrac{13M + 7}{12(M + 1)}}} \quad (6.40)$$

which is normally distributed with a mean of zero and a variance of unity under the assumption of independence. Since we are interested in the detection of both large and small values of ρ_{im}, a two-tailed test is required. Therefore the hypothesis of independence is rejected if

$$|Z| \geq Z_{1-(\alpha/2)}$$

where α is the significance level of the test.

Example 6.5

Determine whether the 2d, 7th, 12th, 17th, and 22d randon numbers in the following sequence are autocorrelated. Let $\alpha = 0.10$.

0.13, .91, .11, .02, .65, .33, .86, .63, .05, .25, .28, .80, .82, .10, .78, .88, .76, .29, .20, .66, .17, .71, .45, .40, 0.35

Since we are interested in the degree of autocorrelation for every fifth number starting with the second, $i = 2$, $m = 5$, $N = 25$, and $M = 3$

$$\rho_{25} = \frac{1}{4} \sum_{k=0}^{3} r_{2+5k} r_{2+5(k+1)}$$

$$= \frac{1}{4} [(0.91)(0.86) + (0.86)(0.80) + (0.80)(0.76) + (0.76)(0.71)]$$

$$= 0.6546$$

$$\sigma_{\rho_{25}} = \frac{\sqrt{13(3) + 7}}{12(4)}$$

$$= 0.141$$

$$Z = \frac{0.6546 - 0.25}{0.141}$$

$$= 2.87$$

Since $|Z| > Z_{0.95}$, we must reject the hypothesis that the numbers analysed are not significantly autocorrelated.

In the preceding discussion we concentrated our attention on the analysis of one particular set of numbers within the total sequence of N numbers. A more generalized and useful analysis is to examine the autocorrelation for every sequence of the type r_i, r_{i+m}, r_{i+2m}, ..., $r_{i+(M+1)m}$. To obtain such a test we define ρ_m as

$$\rho_m = \frac{1}{N-m} \sum_{i=1}^{N-m} r_i r_{i+m} \tag{6.41}$$

For N large relative to m, ρ_m is approximately normally distributed with mean and variance given by

$$E(\rho_m) = 0.25 \tag{6.42}$$

$$\text{Var}(\rho_m) = \frac{13N - 19m}{144(N - m)^2} \tag{6.43}$$

Example 6.6

Determine the significance of autocorrelation for every 10th number in the sequence of random numbers given in example 6.4. Let

$$\alpha = 0.10$$

$$\rho_m = \frac{1}{15} \sum_{i=1}^{15} r_i r_{i+10}$$

$$= \frac{1}{15} [(0.13)(0.28) + (0.91)(0.80) + (0.11)(0.82) + (0.02)(0.10)$$

$$+ (0.65)(0.78) + (0.33)(0.88) + (0.86)(0.76) + (0.63)(0.29) + (0.05)(0.20)$$

$$+ (0.25)(0.66) + (0.28)(0.17) + (0.80)(0.71) + (0.82)(0.45) + (0.10)(0.40)$$

$$+ (0.78)(0.35)]$$

$$= 0.264$$

$$\sigma_{\rho_{10}} = \frac{\sqrt{13(25) - 190}}{180}$$

$$= 0.065$$

Using Z as our test statistic, we have

$$Z = \frac{0.264 - 0.25}{0.0625}$$

$$= 0.215$$

As before, a two-tailed test is appropriate, and since $|Z| < Z_{0.95}$, we cannot reject the hypothesis that the data, as analyzed, are not autocorrelated.

The reader should note that examples 6.4 and 6.5 contradict one another with respect to the indicated degree of autocorrelation among the numbers analyzed. This raises a question regarding the relative propriety of the two tests discussed. That is, should we have analyzed each of the 15 possible sequences of, r_i, r_{i+10}, and so on, separately or as a group? Let us point out one difficulty which arises when multiple tests are run on the same set of data. Let us suppose that we had analyzed each of the 15 sequences using α of 0.10. Further, we will assume that, in fact, there is no autocorrelation within each of these sequences. The probability that we will reach the correct conclusion, no significant autocorrelation, in any single test is 0.90. The probability that we would reach this conclusion in all 15 tests is $(0.90)^{15}$, or about 0.2. Stated another way, the chance that significant autocorrelation will be found in one or more sequences is about 80 per cent. Therefore the apparent disparity of the results obtained in examples 6.4 and 6.5 is not completely unexpected.

To this point we have been concerned with the analysis of a sequence of numbers from the point of view of the uniformity of distribution and randomness of the numbers taken as whole quantities. We have not discussed properties related to the individual digits comprising a given number. For example, the following numbers would be judged to be random on the basis of all of the tests we have discussed so far:

0.599, .122, .199, .055, .599, .588, .833, .188, .366, .000, .611, .477, .244, .411, .422, .988, .233, .677, .844, .433, .299, .711, .888, .744, .600, .100, .466,

.233, .155, .111, .788, .311, .111, .911, .999, .577, .288, .188, .322, .211, .122, .955, .388, .766, .077, .966, .333, .633, .100, 0.055

However, only a cursory examination of this sequence indicates that the third digit in each number is by no means random.

Gap Test

The gap test is used to determine the significance of the intervals between the recurrence of a given digit. If the digit k is followed by x non$k$ digits before k occurs again, then a gap of size x is said to exist. To illustrate let us examine the gaps which occur between successive 0's in the following set of digits:

4, 8, 9, 7, 9, 8, 3, 3, 3, 9, 9, 0, 6, 3, 0, 3, 3, 4, 3, 5, 5, 8, 2, 9, 5, 5, 2, 5, 1, 5, 4, 8, 7, 9, 0, 6, 4, 8, 9, 2, 3, 9, 6, 0, 1, 5, 6, 8, 7, 7, 0, 9, 9, 7, 6, 3, 6, 3, 3, 5, 2, 7, 4, 0, 3, 1, 1, 4, 4, 2, 3, 4, 0, 4, 6, 0, 2, 7, 8, 5, 6, 8, 4, 0, 8, 8, 5, 0, 6, 5, 2, 7, 6, 6, 3, 9, 4, 6, 9, 1, 8, 9, 4, 5, 0, 2, 0, 4, 8, 1, 4, 4, 5, 0, 2, 8

Zero occurs 13 times; therefore there will be 12 gaps. The first gap is of length 2, the second of length 19, the third of length 8, and so on. For the purpose of this test we are concerned with the frequency with which the various gaps occur. In general, for any given digit k, the probability that the digit is followed by x non k digits before k occurs again is given by

$$P(x|k) = P(k \text{ followed by exactly } x \text{ non } k \text{ digits})$$
$$= (0.9)^x(0.1), \quad x = 0, 1, 2, \ldots \qquad (6.44)$$

For a given sequence of digits we record the number of times gaps of length 0, 1, 2, ... occur. We can apply this procedure to a single digit between 0 and 9. The latter alternative is usually the more appropriate of the two. After recording the frequency with which each gap occurs we compare the observed relative cumulative frequency with the theoretical cumulative frequency via the Kolmogorov-Smirnov test. Under the assumption that the digits are randomly ordered, the theoretical cumulative frequency distribution is given by

$$F_X(x) = \sum_{n=0}^{x} (0.1)(0.9)^n$$
$$= 1 - (0.9)^{x+1} \qquad (6.45)$$

Example 6.7

Based on the frequency with which gaps occur, determine whether the following digits can be assumed to be randomly ordered. Let α = 0.05

2, 9, 3, 1, 6, 3, 0, 4, 6, 3, 2, 8, 7, 0, 8, 1, 3, 1, 8, 3, 6, 0, 7, 9, 6, 1, 3, 4, 8, 6, 3, 4, 9, 1, 4, 2, 8, 1, 0, 5, 5, 9, 2, 3, 1, 4, 0, 5, 8, 8, 9, 8, 3, 9, 9, 3, 3, 5, 9, 1, 1, 5, 3, 6, 8, 4, 7, 7, 9, 6, 0, 4, 0, 6, 0, 5, 7, 3, 1, 5, 9, 5, 4, 0, 1, 4, 6, 0, 0, 5, 4, 6, 2, 4, 8, 4, 2, 0, 5, 4, 4, 1, 0, 2, 0, 5, 4, 1, 3, 7, 5, 3, 3, 1, 6, 7, 1, 0, 2, 9, 6, 7, 0, 1, 7

The number of gaps recorded will be the number of numbers analyzed minus 10 since each digit must occur a last time.

$$\text{Total gaps} = N - 10$$
$$= 115$$

We summarize the test in the Table 6.3:

TABLE 6.3

Gap Length	Frequency	Relative Cum Frequency	$F_X(x)$	|Difference|
0–2 27		0.234	0.271	0.027
3–5 30		0.495	0.469	0.026
6–8 23		0.695	0.613	0.082
9–11 11		0.792	0.718	0.074
12–14 8		0.860	0.794	0.066
15–17 3		0.888	0.850	0.038
18–20 2		0.905	0.891	0.014
21–23 3		0.931	0.920	0.011
24–26 1		0.940	0.942	0.002
27–29 1		0.948	0.958	0.010
30–32 2		0.965	0.969	0.004
33–35 1		0.974	0.978	0.004
36–38 1		0.983	0.984	0.001
39–41 0		0.983	0.988	0.005
42–44 1		0.990	0.991	0.001
45–47 0		0.990	0.994	0.004
48–50 1		1.000	0.995	0.005
115				

For the maximum absolute difference we have $D = 0.082$ and

$$D_{0.95} = \frac{1.36}{\sqrt{115}}$$
$$= 0.127$$

Since $D < D_{0.95}$, we reject the hypothesis that the digits are randomly ordered.

Poker Test

The poker test is used to analyze the frequency with which digits repeat in individual random numbers. For example, if we are dealing with five-digit random numbers, we would be interested in examining the frequency with which the following occur in individual numbers.

1. All five digits different.
2. Exactly one pair (one digit repeated exactly once in a random number).
3. Two different pairs.
4. Three like digits.
5. Three like digits plus a pair.
6. Four like digits.
7. Five like digits

Of course the number of such combinations which can occur depends upon the number of digits making up each of the random numbers.

To apply the poker test we first select a level of significance, α, and enumerate all of the different combinations indicating the degree of digit repetition. Next we compute the probability of occurrence of each of these combinations. We then examine the frequency with which each combination occurs in the sequence of numbers analyzed. The observed frequency with which each combination occurs can then be compared with the expected frequency by application of the chi-square test.

To illustrate, suppose we are to apply the poker test to N five-digit random numbers. The possible combinations indicating the degree of repetition of digits in a given random number are given above. Let us compute the probability of occurrence of each of these combinations under the assumption that digits occur in a completely random fashion.

P (five different digits) = P(second digit different from the first)
$$\times P \text{ (third digit different from first and second)}$$
$$\times P \text{ (fourth digit different from first, second, and third)}$$
$$\times P \text{ (fifth digit different from the first four)}$$
$$= (0.9)(0.8)(0.7)(0.6)$$
$$= 0.3024 \tag{6.46}$$

$$P(\text{exactly one pair}) = \binom{5}{2}(0.9)(0.8)(0.7)(0.1)$$
$$= 0.5040 \tag{6.47}$$

$$P(\text{two pairs}) = \binom{5}{1}\binom{3}{2}(0.1)^2(0.9)(0.8)$$

$$= 0.1080 \tag{6.48}$$

$$P(\text{three like digits}) = \binom{5}{3}(0.9)(0.8)(0.1)^2$$

$$= 0.0720 \tag{6.49}$$

$$P(\text{three like digits plus one pair}) = \binom{5}{2}(0.9)(0.1)^3$$

$$= 0.0090 \tag{6.50}$$

$$P(\text{four like digits}) = \binom{5}{4}(0.9)(0.1)^3$$

$$= 0.0045 \tag{6.51}$$

$$P(\text{five like digits}) = (0.1)^4$$
$$= 0.0001 \tag{6.52}$$

To obtain the number of times each of these combinations would be expected to occur we multiply each probability by N.

Example 6.8

A random number generator has been developed which is said to produce numbers such that the digits comprising each number occur randomly.

Out of a sequence of 1,000 numbers generated, 460 were found with four different digits, 480 containing exactly one pair, 16 with two pairs, 40 containing three like digits, and 4 with four like digits. Using the poker test, determine whether this series of numbers is random. Let $\alpha = 0.05$.

The repetitive combinations which could occur in any of these 50 numbers are

1. Four different digits.
2. One pair.
3. Two pairs.
4. Three like digits.
5. Four like digits.

The probability that each of these outcomes occurs is given by

$$P(\text{four different digits}) = (0.9)(0.8)(0.7)$$
$$= 0.504$$

$$P(\text{one pair}) = \binom{4}{2}(0.1)(0.9)(0.8)$$

$$= 0.432$$

$$P(\text{two pairs}) = \binom{3}{2}(0.1)^2(0.9)$$

$$= 0.027$$

$$P(\text{three like digits}) = \binom{4}{3}(0.1)^2(0.9)$$

$$= 0.036$$

$$P(\text{four like digits}) = 0.001$$

We summarize the results of the poker analysis in Table 6.4:

TABLE 6.4

Combination i	Observed Frequency O_i	Expected Frequency E_i	$\dfrac{(O_i-E_i)^2}{E_i}$
4 different digits	460	504	3.841
1 pair	480	432	5.333
2 pairs	16	27	4.481
3 like digits	40	36	0.444
4 like digits	4	1	9.000
	1,000	1,000	23.099

Since $\chi^2_{0.95}(4) = 9.488 < 23.099$, we cannot reject the assertion that the digits within the random numbers are randomly ordered.

Yule's Test

Let r be a four-digit random variable such that each of the four digits is uniformly distributed on the interval 0 to 9. Let r_i be the ith digit of the random variable

$$p_{R_i}(r_i) = 0.1, \qquad r_i = 0, 1, \ldots, 9 \qquad (6.53)$$
$$i = 1, 2, 3, 4$$

Define y as the sum of the four digits in r

$$y = \sum_{i=1}^{4} r_i \qquad (6.54)$$

The probability mass function of Y, $p_Y(y)$, is given by

$$
p_Y(y) = \begin{cases}
\dfrac{(y+3)!}{3!\,y!}\left(\dfrac{1}{10}\right)^4, & y = 0, 1, \ldots, 9 \\[2ex]
\left[\dfrac{(y+3)!}{y!\,3!} - \dfrac{4(y-7)!}{(y-10)!\,3!}\right]\left(\dfrac{1}{10}\right)^4, & y = 10, 11, \ldots, 18 \\[2ex]
\left[\dfrac{(39-y)!}{(36-y)!\,3!} - 4\dfrac{(29-y)!}{(26-y)!\,3!}\right]\left(\dfrac{1}{10}\right)^4, & y = 19, 20, \ldots, 26 \\[2ex]
\dfrac{(39-y)!}{(36-y)!\,3!}\left(\dfrac{1}{10}\right)^4, & y = 27, 28, \ldots, 36
\end{cases}
$$

$$(6.55)$$

If N random numbers are drawn, each number being comprised of four digits and if the random numbers are uniformly distributed on the interval 0 to 9,999, then the expected number of times the sum y occurs is given by $Np_Y(y)$.

The function of Yule's test is to determine whether the observed number of times the sum y occurs is significantly different from $Np_Y(y)$. Let

E_y = expected number of times the sum y occurs = $Np_Y(y)$, $y = 0, 1, \ldots, 36$
O_y = observed number of times the sum y occurs

If the random numbers are uniformly distributed on the interval 0 to 9,999, then the quantity T is distributed as the χ^2 with 36 degrees of freedom

$$T = \sum_{y=0}^{36} \frac{(O_y - E_y)^2}{E_y} \tag{6.56}$$

If $T > \chi^2_{(1-\alpha)}(36)$, then we must conclude that the digits do not occur randomly within the individual random numbers generated.

Example 6.9

Apply Yule's test to the sequence of numbers given in example 6.8. Let $\alpha = 0.10$

The calculations necessary for this analysis are summarized in Table 6.5 where $N = 50$.

TABLE 6.5

Sum y	$P_Y(y)$	$Np_Y(y)$	Sum y	$P_Y(y)$	$Np_Y(y)$
0. . . . .0.0001	0.0050		19. . . . .0.0660	3.3000
1. . . . .0.0004	0.0200		20. . . . .0.0633	3.1650
2. . . . .0.0010	0.0500		21. . . . .0.0592	2.9600
3. . . . .0.0025	0.1000		22. . . . .0.0540	2.7000
4. . . . .0.0035	0.1750		23. . . . .0.0480	2.4000
5. . . . .0.0056	0.2800		24. . . . .0.0415	2.0750
6. . . . .0.0084	0.4200		25. . . . .0.0348	1.7400
7. . . . .0.0120	0.6000		26. . . . .0.0282	1.4100
8. . . . .0.0165	0.8250		27. . . . .0.0220	1.1000
9. . . . .0.0220	1.1000		28. . . . .0.0165	0.8250
10. . . . .0.0282	1.4100		29. . . . .0.0120	0.6000
11. . . . .0.0348	1.7400		30. . . . .0.0084	0.4200
12. . . . .0.0415	2.0750		31. . . . .0.0056	0.2800
13. . . . .0.0480	2.4000		32. . . . .0.0035	0.1750
14. . . . .0.0540	2.7000		33. . . . .0.0020	0.1000
15. . . . .0.0592	2.9600		34. . . . .0.0010	0.0500
16. . . . .0.0633	3.1650		35. . . . .0.0004	0.0200
17. . . . .0.0660	3.3000		36. . . . .0.0001	0.0050
18. . . . .0.0670	3.3500			
				1.0000	50.0000

In the above table each expected frequency, $Np_Y(y)$, is less than five. Since not more than 20 per cent of the categories should contain expected frequencies of less than five, we combine categories as in Table 6.6.

TABLE 6.6

Sum Interval	Expected Frequency E_y	Observed Frequency O_y	$\dfrac{(O_y - E_y)^2}{E_y}$
0–11. . . . . . . 6.7250	12	4.152
12–15. . . . . . .10.1350	12	0.343
16–20. . . . . . .16.2800	9	3.255
21–24. . . . . . .10.1350	11	0.074
25–36. . . . . . . 6.7250	6	0.078
50.0000	50	7.902

Since $T = 7.902 > \chi^2_{0.90}(4)$, (where $\chi^2_{0.90}(4) = 7.78$) we would be justified in questioning the random character of the digits occurring in these numbers.

LEVEL OF SIGNIFICANCE

If we are to apply n different tests to a series of numbers and the level of significance for each test is to be α, then the composite level of significance, α_T, is given by

$$\alpha_T = 1 - (1 - \alpha)^n \qquad (6.57)$$

That is, if the null hypothesis for each test is in fact true, then the probability that one or more of these hypotheses will be rejected is given by α_T. Therefore for a given α_T the α error for each of the individual tests is given by

$$\alpha = 1 - (1 - \alpha_T)^{1/n} \qquad (6.58)$$

For example, if five different tests are to be applied to a series of random numbers such that the probability of rejection incorrectly on one or more of the tests is to be 0.05, then α error for each test is $\alpha = 1 - (0.95)^{0.2} \simeq 0.01 \cdot$

PROBLEMS

1. Write a program to generate random numbers employing the method of MacLaren and Marsaglia and compare it to a single congruential generator.

2. Write a FORTRAN program to generate a series of random numbers based upon the number system to the base 3.

3. In the random number generator shown in Figure 6.3 change the multiplier to 67499 and test the generator.

In the following problems all random numbers were generated sequentially in rows from left to right.

4. Determine whether the following sequence of 60, two-digit random numbers is uniformly distributed.

0.38, .33, .25, .05, .69, .35, .98, .52, .12, .79, .50, .46, .95, .42, .49, .11, .78, .34, .02, .02, .43, .07, .50, .20, .91, .77, .18, .21, .04, .17, .62, .66, .18, .19, .91, .36, .13, .26, .21, .11, .88, .12, .60, .31, .21, .76, .63, .48, .07, .73, .38, .97, .90, .32, .78, .77, .30, .67, .52, 0.03,

5. For the sequence of random numbers given in problem 4 determine whether there is significant autocorrelation exhibited by
a) The first, fourth, eighth, etc. numbers.
b) The third, sixth, ninth, etc. numbers.

6. Given the following sequence of 60 two-digit random numbers, determine
a) Whether the number of runs exhibited indicates that the sequence of numbers is not random.
b) Whether there is an excessive number of runs above or below the mean.

c) Whether the numbers in the sequence are uniformly distributed.

0.39, .04, .02, .45, .24, .37, .49, .10, .05, .36, .04, .24, .16, .65, .87, .57, .59, .64, .63, .64, .63, .84, .99, .92, .74, .53, .77, .62, .13, .44, .25, .45, .45, .44, .41, .35, .35, .15, .08, .29, .13, .00, .44, .02, .47, .30, .20, .48, .09, .38, .93, .66, .55, .91, .61, .90, .81, .72, .22, 0.27

7. By applying the gap test determine whether the following sequence of digits is random.

3, 5, 4, 9, 0, 0, 5, 1, 6, 7, 6, 1, 6, 9, 5, 2, 7, 0, 1, 7, 1, 9, 5, 6, 2,
1, 8, 2, 6, 3, 2, 3, 3, 1, 7, 2, 7, 3, 2, 3, 0, 2, 2, 1, 7, 3, 5, 1, 2, 0,
5, 3, 5, 5, 9, 3, 6, 9, 2, 0, 0, 6, 7, 6, 1, 6, 1, 0, 1, 0, 7, 2, 3, 3, 3,
5, 9, 0, 2, 7, 2, 1, 0, 3, 5, 3, 5, 9, 9, 1, 3, 7, 1, 0, 9, 7, 3, 1, 9, 1,
6, 0, 7, 0, 0, 1, 1, 0, 7, 3, 2, 6, 0, 6, 6, 7, 7, 6, 6, 9, 7, 2, 9, 3, 6,
9, 6, 5, 4, 1, 2, 0, 9, 7, 7, 9, 3, 1, 6, 6, 7, 0, 6, 5, 2, 1, 9, 1, 4, 8

8. Determine whether the sequence of digits given in problem 7 is uniformly distributed.

9. Test the randomness of the following sequence of numbers by (*a*) testing for uniformity of distribution, and (*b*) testing for runs above and below the mean.

0.876, .344, .288, .663, .177, .459, .352, .910, .323, .949, .029, .785, .357, .990, .236, .228, .742, .299, .416, .279, .822, .779, .360, .813, .665, .688, .324, .500, .881, .133, .169, .947, .784, .689, .637, .351, .453, .241, .256, .419, .671, .332, .002, .127, .199, .440, .153, .272, .631, .135, .732, .906, .365, .699, .669, .522, .585, .340, .364, .709, .844, .462, .758, .197, .607, 0.745

10. Test the hypothesis that the digits contained in the following random numbers are random using the poker test.

0.58722, .07823, .18437, .40214, .75350, .90178, .62913, .65879, .29054, .81416, .27009, .29308, .32770, .32848, .02153, .17290, .84363, .50564, .44122, .09652, .60812, .78099, .20742, .22374, .47562, .84011, .76004, .99925, .15520, .93793, .23076, .94317, .58217, .00448, .78734, .68372, .01620, .94378, .51686, .60713, .99105, .48209, .97311, .49980, .24082, .94673, .51300, .55747, .72779, 0.34953

11. Construct the poker test for three-digit random numbers.

12. Use the poker test developed in problem 11 to test the following sequence of random numbers.

0.547, .136, .896, .150, .829, .623, .281, .073, .909, .795, .585, .358, .878, .045, .369, .807, .521, .858, .458, .023, .017, .893, .204, .189, .295, .065, .729, .792, .187, .991, .260, .638, .487, .180, .697, .555, .055, .339, .534, .148, .085, .169, .252, .988, .654, .034, .317, .592, .699, 0.866

13. Develop Yule's test for (*a*) three-digit random numbers, and (*b*) five-digit random numbers.

14. Apply the gap test to the following sequence of random digits.

9, 6, 5, 6, 4, 5, 9, 1, 2, 2, 3, 3, 1, 4, 3, 6, 1, 3, 0, 9, 0, 5, 8, 7, 9,
1, 6, 2, 4, 3, 2, 5, 7, 0, 0, 0, 8, 8, 3, 7, 9, 7, 9, 4, 0, 5, 0, 6, 9, 9

15. It has been suggested that the last four digits of telephone numbers constitute a reasonable source for random numbers. Test this assertion.

16. What is the minimum number of five-digit random numbers which must be generated to carry out the poker test?

17. What is the minimum number of four-digit random numbers which must be generated to carry out Yule's test?

18. A random number generator is to be tested for (a) uniformity of distribution, (b) runs above and below the mean, and (c) autocorrelation between the first, fifth, ninth, etc. numbers. The probability of rejecting the generator as nonrandom if in fact it is random, is to be 0.02. At what α level should each of the tests be conducted?

19. Write a FORTRAN program which will determine whether a sequence of N numbers is uniformly distributed on the interval $(0,1)$ using the chi-square goodness-of-fit test.

20. Write a FORTRAN program which will carry out the poker test for random numbers containing two, three, four, or five digits.

REFERENCES

Cochran, W. G.   "Some Methods for Strengthening the Common Tests," *Biometrics,* Vol. 10, (1954), pp. 417–51.

Good, I. J.   "The Serial Test for Sampling Numbers and Other Tests of Randomness," *Proceedings of the Cambridge Philosophic Society,* Vol. 49, (1953), pp. 276–84.

——   "On the Serial Test for Random Sequences," *Annals of Mathematical Statistics,* Vol. 28, (1957), pp. 262–64.

Goodman, L. A.   "Kolmogorov-Smirnov Tests for Psychological Research," *Psychological Bulletin,* Vol. 51, (1944), pp. 160–68.

Gorenstein, Samuel.   "Testing a Random Number Generator," *Communications of ACM,* Vol. 10, No. 2, (February 1967), pp. 111–18.

Hull, T. E. and Dobell, A. R.   "Random Number Generators," *Society for Industrial and Applied Mathematics,* Vol 4, No. 3, (July 1962), p. 230.

International Business Machines Corporation. *Random Number Generation and Testing.* Form C20–8011. White Plaines, New York, 1959.

International Business Machines Corporation. *System/360 Scientific Subroutine Package* (360A–CM–03X) Form H20–0205–0. White Plaines, New York, 1966.

Korn, Granino, A.   *Random Process Simulation and Measurements.* New York: McGraw-Hill, 1966.

Levene, H. and Wolfowitz, J.   "The Covariance Matrix of Runs Up and Down," *Annals of Mathematical Statistics,* Vol. 15, (1944), pp. 58–59.

Maclaren, M. D. and Marsaglia, George.   "Uniform Random Number Generators." *Journal of ACM,* Vol. 12, No. 1, (January 1965), pp. 83–89.

Mann, H. B., and Wald, A.   "On the Choice of the Number of Class Intervals in the Application of the Chi-Square Test," *Annals of Mathematical Statistics,* Vol. 13, (1942), pp. 306–17.

Naylor, T. H. *et al.*   *Computer Simulation Techniques.* New York: John Wiley & Sons, 1966.

Siegel, S.   *Nonparametric Statistics.* New York: McGraw-Hill, 1956, pp. 42–60.

CHAPTER
7

PROCESS GENERATION

We have discussed the generation of random numbers (uniformly distributed random variables). However, it would be unrealistic to believe that we need concern ourselves only with uniformly distributed random variables in systems simulation. For example, suppose we were simulating traffic flow at an intersection and one of the random variables we were interested in was the number of cars making a left turn between 4 p.m. and 5 p.m.. At a busy intersection the value of this random variable could range between zero and several thousand. Let N be the number of left turns during the one hour period under study. It would be difficult to imagine any busy intersection for which all values of N would be equally likely.

To consider a simpler example, when a man buys a tube of toothpaste he will find it either contains toothpaste or something else. Suppose we were to conduct a simulation of the purchase of tubes of toothpaste and an examination of the contents of the tube. If the tube contains toothpaste a "one" is recorded, otherwise a "zero" is recorded. Thus there are two outcomes possible in the experiment, zero and one. If the random variables were uniformly distributed, then $P(0) = P(1)$, that is the probability that one finds something other than toothpaste in the tube is the same as the probability that one finds toothpaste in the tube (a rather disconcerting prospect were this actually the case).

MONTE CARLO METHOD

Suppose we wish to generate binomially distributed random variables with parameters $p = 0.5$ and $n = 5$.

$$p_X(x) = \frac{5!}{x!(5-x)!} (0.5)^5$$

The probabilities associated with this distribution are summarized in Table 7.1.

TABLE 7.1
Binomial Distribution

x	$p_X(x)$	$F_X(x)$
0	0.03125	0.03125
1	0.15625	0.18750
2	0.31250	0.50000
3	0.31250	0.81250
4	0.15625	0.96875
5	0.03125	1.00000

If the method employed to generate this random variable is reliable then out of 100,000 random variables generated we would expect to obtain 3,125 zero's, 15,625 one's, 31,250 two's, and so on. However, this can be accomplished by generating five digit random numbers and placing a decimal before the first digit. If these random numbers are uniformly distributed, the probability that such a number will fall between 0.00000 and 0.03125 is 0.03125. The probability that the random variable falls between 0.03126 and 0.18750 is 0.15625. The same holds true for each of the remaining intervals. Thus if the random number generated lies between 0.50001 and 0.81250, the value of the variable generated is three. An example of this process repeated 200 times is illustrated in Table 7.2.

The results of this experiment (Table 7.3) indicate reasonable correspondence to the expected probabilities. As the number of repetitions of the experiment is increased, the difference between the estimated and theoretical probabilities would decrease.

The procedure for generating continuous random variables is basically the same as that for discrete random variables. However, it is usually more convenient to utilize a graph of the cumulative distribution function for continuous random variables than to tabulate the various intervals since an accurate simulation would require a very large number of intervals. As a simple example let us attempt to generate an exponential random variable with $\lambda = 0.5$. Let $y = F_X(x)$.

We first generate a random number between 0.0 and 1.0 and set y equal to this number. We then locate this value of y in Figure 7.1 and

TABLE 7.2

Generation of 200 Binomial Random Variables

R.N.	x	R.N.	x	R.N.	x	R.N.	x	R.N.	x	R.N.	x	R.N.	x	R.N.	x
13689	1	82922	4	99668	5	92020	4	03091	0	18623	1	45523	2	32757	2
59539	3	75342	3	02614	0	11265	1	84957	4	30282	2	08926	1	83345	4
72269	3	37519	2	55698	3	60337	3	65728	3	29351	2	95183	4	03666	1
88833	4	88272	4	59446	3	88118	4	05075	1	50206	3	47551	2	88388	4
74044	3	71864	3	66944	3	80142	3	18623	1	82868	4	61368	3	53033	3
02440	0	28006	2	01486	0	89637	4	58320	3	38515	2	57343	3	26085	2
36954	2	18807	2	29553	2	24125	2	06282	1	28493	2	49719	2	21998	2
19253	2	88182	4	47617	2	75289	3	15650	1	29621	2	28160	2	78583	3
46174	2	16194	1	06833	1	53549	3	68008	3	27012	2	82611	4	42855	2
18288	1	02482	0	31398	2	24741	2	92823	4	59970	3	72711	3	75321	3
27415	2	29198	2	72734	3	22065	2	45946	2	14578	1	33092	2	67692	3
31014	2	71937	3	17332	1	51026	3	07138	1	78644	3	16697	1	70427	3
91924	4	34688	2	48673	2	14364	1	47073	2	23752	2	82384	4	97423	5
85632	4	45523	2	74304	3	19611	2	28788	2	85546	4	29832	2	83584	4
73877	3	91532	4	05303	1	72291	3	35283	2	90960	4	15087	1	28386	2
00508	0	47786	2	92448	4	37691	2	97728	5	55690	3	14903	1	65902	3
53933	3	76861	3	15706	1	88265	4	12544	1	71828	3	93531	4	99496	5
68094	3	63804	3	80296	3	53461	3	76900	3	33894	2	33408	2	87400	4
06119	1	61825	3	21063	2	40099	2	29991	2	38494	2	20825	2	09749	1
88940	4	30469	2	99095	5	57016	3	21359	2	56118	3	77044	3	13202	1
94029	4	93783	4	01548	0	21550	2	32517	2	68063	3	76783	3	61730	5
87827	4	63959	3	95321	4	74798	3	17897	1	93787	4	63409	3	97316	5
97347	5	20661	2	30541	2	41250	2	97372	5	72131	3	88204	4	63256	3
88923	4	40110	2	88789	4	80532	3	09166	1	86749	4	10868	1	96448	4
21759	2	76718	3	80047	3	03372	1	49883	2	87469	4	36252	2	50457	3

TABLE 7.3

x	Frequency	Estimated Probability	Theoretical Probability
0 7		0.035	0.03125
1 29		0.145	0.15625
2 61		0.305	0.31250
3 58		0.290	0.31250
4 37		0.185	0.15625
5 8		0.040	0.03125
200		1.000	1.00000

move horizontally across the graph until the cumulative distribution function is intersected. At that point we drop down to the x-axis and record the value of x as the value of the random variable generated. Examples of random variables generated in this fashion are given in Table 7.4 and in Figure 7.1.

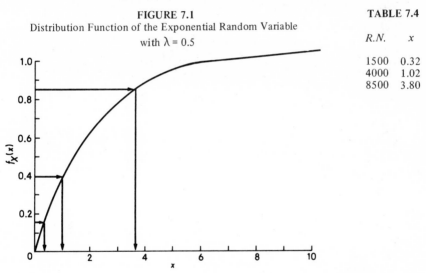

FIGURE 7.1
Distribution Function of the Exponential Random Variable
with $\lambda = 0.5$

TABLE 7.4

R.N.	x
1500	0.32
4000	1.02
8500	3.80

Example 7.1

Estimate, by simulation, the average number of lost sales per week for an inventory system which functions as follows:

1. Whenever the inventory level falls to or below five units, an order is placed.
2. The size of each order is equal to $20 - x$ where x is the inventory level when the order is placed.
3. If a demand occurs during a period when the inventory level is zero, the sale is lost.

TABLE 7.5
Estimation of Lost Sales by Simulation of 55 Days of Operation

Day	R.N. Demand	R.N. Lead Time	Demand	Lead Time	Sales	Lost Sales	Inventory Level	Amount Received
0							20	
1	389		2		2		18	
2	366		2		2		16	
3	812		3		3		13	
4	113		1		1		12	
5	751		3		3		9	
6	547		3		3		6	
7	085		1		1		5	
7		318		2				
8	726		3		3		2	
9	465		2		2		0	
9							15	15
10	913		4		4		11	
11	942		4		4		7	
12	549		3		3		4	
12		649		3				
13	388		2		2		2	
14	207		2		2		0	
15	103		1			1	0	
15							16	16
16	758		3		3		13	
17	299		2		2		11	
18	628		3		3		8	
19	742		3		3		5	
19		095		1				
20	470		2		2		3	
20							18	15
21	367		2		2		16	
22	338		2		2		14	
23	145		1		1		13	
24	046		1		1		12	
25	678		3		3		9	
26	197		2		2		7	
27	727		3		3		4	
27		971		5				
28	982		5		4	1	0	
29	133		1			1	0	
30	114		1			1	0	
31	821		4			4	0	
32	471		2			2	0	
32							16	16
33	569		3		3		13	
34	550		3		3		10	
35	592		3		3		7	
36	455		2		2		5	
36		367		2				
37	641		3		3		2	
38	314		2		2		0	
38							15	15
39	130		1		1		14	
40	279		2		2		12	
41	804		3		3		9	
42	854		4		4		5	
42		514		3				
43	064		1		1		4	
44	198		2		2		2	
45	560		3		2	1	0	
45							15	15
46	668		3		3		12	
47	955		4		4		8	
48	225		2		2		6	
49	886		4		4		2	
49		316		2				
50	399		2		2		0	
51	450		2			2	0	
51							18	18
52	264		2		2		16	
53	368		2		2		14	
54	456		2		2		12	
55	078		1		1		11	

4. Daily demand is binomially distributed with $p = 0.5$ and $n = 5$.
5. The distribution of time, in days (called lead time), between placing an order and the receipt of that order is also binomial with $p = 0.5$ and $n = 5$.
6. The simulation will start with 20 units in inventory.
7. For simplicity it will be assumed that all demands occur at 12 noon and all orders are placed at the same time. It will be further assumed that orders are received at 5 p.m. or after the demand which occured on that day.

If we assume a five day week, the 11-week simulation resulted in 13 lost sales, or 1.19 lost sales per week.

As in all simulations, it is important to note the sequence of events in this example. Before an order can take place on any given day, one or more demands must occur on that day in order to bring the inventory level to or below the reorder point (five units in this case). Similarly, since orders arrive at 5p.m., if a demand occurs on the day on which an order is received, the demand must occur before the receipt of the order.

The methods we have discussed for generating random variables require either a table or graph of the cumulative distribution function of the random variable. If the simulation is carried out on a digital computer, the resulting table check or graphical interpolation required may be time-consuming and cumbersome to program, to say nothing of the computer time required to execute the program. These problems can be overcome if a relationship between the random variable, x, and the distribution function, $F_X(x)$, can be established. That is,

$$x = \phi[F_X(x)] \tag{7.1}$$

CONTINUOUS PROCESS GENERATORS

Let us assume that an equation, or equations, defining the cumulative distribution function $F_X(x)$, can be defined either exactly or approximately and let $r = F_X(x)$ where r is a uniformly distributed random variable such that $0 < r < 1$. We must find a relationship of the form

$$x = \phi(r) \tag{7.2}$$

As we shall see, exact relationships of this form are sometimes impossible to define so that we will be forced to resort to approximations.

Exponential Process Generator

The density and cumulative distribution functions of the exponential random variable with parameter λ are given by

$$f_X(x) = \lambda e^{-\lambda x}, \qquad 0 < x < \infty \tag{7.3}$$

$$F_X(x) = \int_0^x \lambda e^{-\lambda t}\, dt$$

$$= 1 - e^{-\lambda x} \tag{7.4}$$

We can easily solve (7.4) for x in terms of $F_X(x)$.

$$e^{-\lambda x} = 1 - F_X(x)$$

Letting $r = F_X(x)$, we have

$$-\lambda x = \ln(1 - r)$$

$$x = \frac{-1}{\lambda} \ln(1 - r) \tag{7.5}$$

To generate exponentially distributed random variables we select a random number, r, between 0 and 1 and solve (7.5) for x. For example, let $\lambda = 0.5$ and $r = 0.40$.

$$x = -2 \ln(0.60)$$

$$= 1.02$$

This result can be verified in Figure 7.1. In equation (7.5), $1 - r$ may be replaced by r since both $1 - r$ and r are identically distributed.

Gamma Process Generator

Let X be gamma distributed with parameters λ and K where K is an integer greater than zero. Then

$$f_X(x) = \frac{\lambda^K}{(K-1)!}\, x^{K-1} e^{-\lambda x}, \qquad 0 < x < \infty \tag{7.6}$$

$$F_X(x) = \int_0^x \frac{\lambda^K}{(K-1)!} t^{K-1} e^{-\lambda t} \, dt$$

$$= 1 - e^{-\lambda x} \sum_{m=0}^{K-1} \frac{(\lambda x)^m}{m!} \qquad (7.7)$$

It is difficult at best to solve (7.7) for x. However, if we examine the characteristic function of x, we find a useful relationship between the gamma random variable and the exponential random variable.

$$\phi_X(\mu) = \left(1 - \frac{i\mu}{\lambda}\right)^{-K}$$

$$= \prod_{j=1}^K \left(1 - \frac{i\mu}{\lambda}\right)^{-1} \qquad (7.8)$$

But

$$\left(1 - \frac{i\mu}{\lambda}\right)^{-1}$$

is the characteristic function of an exponentially distributed random variable with parameter λ. Thus from equation (2.82), the gamma random variable X can be represented by the sum of K identically distributed exponential random variables each with parameter λ. To generate a gamma random variable we merely generate K exponential random variables each with parameter λ and sum the resulting values. The gamma process generator is given by

$$x = \frac{-1}{\lambda} \sum_{i=1}^K \ln(1 - r_i) \qquad (7.9)$$

where r_i is the ith random number generated. This relationship is more conveniently expressed in (7.10).

$$x = \frac{-1}{\lambda} \ln \left[\prod_{i=1}^K (1 - r_i) \right] \qquad (7.10)$$

Normal Process Generator

If x is normally distributed with mean λ and variance σ^2, the cumulative distribution function of x is given by

$$F_X(x) = \int_{-\infty}^x \frac{1}{\sigma\sqrt{2\pi}} e^{-(t-\lambda)^2/2\sigma^2} \, dt \qquad (7.11)$$

The integral in (7.11) cannot be evaluated analytically but can be evaluated with the help of a table of the distribution function of the standard normal random variable (mean 0 and variance 1). To use such a table we must first employ the following transformation:

$$z = \frac{t - \lambda}{\sigma} \tag{7.12}$$

$$dt = \sigma \, dz$$

$$F_X(x) = \int_{-\infty}^{(x-\lambda)/\sigma} \frac{1}{\sqrt{2\pi}} e^{-z^2/2} \, dz \tag{7.13}$$

The equivalence of (7.11) and (7.13) leads us to the conclusion that if x is normally distributed with mean λ and variance σ^2, and z is normally distributed with mean 0 and variance 1, then

$$P[X \le x] = P\left[z \le \frac{x - \lambda}{\sigma}\right] \tag{7.14}$$

The problem is then to find the value of y such that

$$\int_{-\infty}^{y} \frac{1}{\sqrt{2\pi}} e^{-z^2/2} \, dz = F_X(x) = r \tag{7.15}$$

To solve (7.15) for y we will utilize the following approximation. If

$$w = \int_{G(w)}^{\infty} \frac{1}{\sqrt{2\pi}} e^{-z^2/2} \, dz, \qquad 0 < w < 0.5 \tag{7.16}$$

and

$$v = \sqrt{\ln \frac{1}{w^2}} \tag{7.17}$$

then

$$G(w) = v - \left(\frac{2.515517 + 0.802853v + 0.010328v^2}{1 + 1.432788v + 0.189269v^2 + 0.001308v^3} \right) \tag{7.18}$$

From (7.15) and the symmetry of the normal distribution

$$r = 1 - \int_{y}^{\infty} \frac{1}{\sqrt{2\pi}} e^{-z^2/2} \, dz, \qquad y > 0, \quad 0.5 < r < 1.0 \tag{7.19}$$

$$r = \int_{|y|}^{\infty} \frac{1}{\sqrt{2\pi}} e^{-z^2/2} \, dz, \qquad y < 0, \quad 0 < r < 0.5 \tag{7.20}$$

and

$$\int_{y}^{\infty} \frac{1}{\sqrt{2\pi}} e^{-z^2/2} \, dz = 1 - r, \qquad y > 0, \quad 0 < 1 - r < 0.5 \qquad (7.21)$$

If we let $y = (x - \lambda)/\sigma$, then

$$\frac{x - \lambda}{\sigma} = v - \left(\frac{2.515517 + 0.802853v + 0.010328v^2}{1 + 1.432788v + 0.189269v^2 + 0.001308v^3} \right)$$

and

$$v = \begin{cases} \sqrt{\ln(1/r^2)}, & 0 < r \leq 0.5 \\ \sqrt{\ln 1/(1 - r)^2}, & 0.5 \leq r < 1 \end{cases}$$

From the symmetry of the normal distribution if $r \leq 0.5$, then $(x - \lambda)/\sigma \leq 0$, and if $r \geq 0.5$, then $(x - \lambda)/\sigma \geq 0$. Therefore for $r \leq 0.5$

$$x = \lambda - \sigma \left(v - \frac{2.515517 + 0.802853v + 0.010328v^2}{1 + 1.432788v + 0.189269v^2 + 0.001308v^3} \right) \qquad (7.22)$$

where $v = \sqrt{-2\ln(r)}$, and for $r \geq 0.5$

$$x = \lambda + \sigma \left(v - \frac{2.515517 + 0.802853v + 0.010328v^2}{1 + 1.432788v + 0.189269v^2 + 0.001308v^3} \right) \qquad (7.23)$$

where $v = \sqrt{-2\ln(1 - r)}$. A more convenient expression that condenses equations (7.22) and (7.23) is given by (7.24).

$$x = \lambda + \frac{r - 0.5}{|r - 0.5|} \sigma \left(v - \frac{2.515517 + 0.802853v + 0.010328v^2}{1 + 1.432788v + 0.189269v^2 + 0.001308v^3} \right) \qquad (7.24)$$

where

$$v = \sqrt{-2 \ln 0.5(1 - |1 - 2r|)}$$

Chi-Square Process Generator

The density function of the chi-square random variable is given by

$$f_X(x) = \frac{1}{2^{n/2}\Gamma(n/2)} x^{(n/2)-1} e^{-x/2}, \qquad 0 < x < \infty \qquad (7.25)$$

Equation (7.6) defines the density function of the gamma random variable for the case where K is an integer greater than zero. A more generalized definition of the density function of this random variable, permitting noninteger values of K, is given in (7.26).

$$f_x(x) = \frac{\lambda K}{\Gamma(K)} x^{K-1} e^{-\lambda x}, \qquad \begin{matrix} 0 < x < \infty \\ \lambda > 0, \quad K > 0 \end{matrix} \qquad (7.26)$$

If we let $K = n/2$ and $\lambda = 1/2$, equation (7.26) becomes equivalent to (7.25), demonstrating that the family of chi-square distributions is a subset of the family of gamma distributions. We have already developed a method for generating random variables with density function given by (7.26) when K is an integer. This method may then be used to generate chi-square random variables when n is even. However, this method does not apply for odd n.

In example 2.30 we demonstrated that a chi-square random variable with n degrees of freedom can be expressed as the sum of squares of n standard normal random variables. This example suggests that a chi-square random variable with n degrees of freedom may be generated by generating n normal random variables each having mean zero and variance unity, squaring the value of each, and taking the sum of the squares. Let z_i be the value of the ith standard normal random variable generated, and let x be the value of the chi-square random variable with n degrees of freedom.

$$x = \sum_{i=1}^{n} z_i^2 \qquad (7.27)$$

F Process Generator

From example (2.23) if X and Y are chi-square random variables with a and b degrees of freedom, respectively, then

$$F = \frac{X/a}{Y/b} \qquad (7.28)$$

From equation (7.17) the chi-square random variable with n degrees of freedom can be represented as the sum of squares of n unit normal random variables. Therefore the process generator for the F random variable is given by

$$f = \frac{b}{a} \frac{\sum\limits_{i=1}^{a} z_i^2}{\sum\limits_{i=a+1}^{a+b} z_i^2} \tag{7.29}$$

where z_i is normally distributed with mean zero and variance unity.

T Process Generator

The T random variable is defined in example (2.22) as

$$T = \frac{Z}{\sqrt{Y/a}} \tag{7.30}$$

where Z is normally distributed with a mean of zero and a variance of unity and Y is a chi-square random variable with a degrees of freedom. Therefore the T process generator is defined by

$$t = \frac{\sqrt{a}\, z_1}{\sqrt{\sum\limits_{i=2}^{a+1} z_i^2}} \tag{7.31}$$

where z_i is a standard normal random variable.

Example 7.2

Develop a process generator for a uniformly distributed random variable, X, where $a < x < b$.

$$f_X(x) = \frac{1}{b - a}, \qquad a < x < b$$

$$r = \int_a^x \frac{dz}{b - a}$$

$$= \frac{x - a}{b - a}$$

Therefore

$$x = a + r(b - a) \tag{7.32}$$

Example 7.3

Let X be a random variable having a Weibull distribution with density function given by

$$f_X(x) = \frac{a}{b-c}\left(\frac{x-c}{b-c}\right)^{a-1} \exp\left[-\left(\frac{x-c}{b-c}\right)^a\right], \qquad c < x < \infty \qquad (7.33)$$

and $a > 1, b > c$

Derive a process generator for this random variable.

$$r = \int_c^x \frac{a}{b-c}\left(\frac{z-c}{b-c}\right)^{a-1} \exp\left[-\left(\frac{z-c}{b-c}\right)^a\right] dz$$

Let

$$y = \left(\frac{z-c}{b-c}\right)^a$$

$$r = \int_0^{[(x-c)/(b-c)]^a} e^{-y}\, dy$$

$$= 1 - \exp\left[-\left(\frac{x-c}{b-c}\right)^a\right]$$

$$-\left(\frac{x-c}{b-c}\right)^a = \ln(1-r)$$

Therefore a process generator for x is given by

$$x = c + (b-c)[-\ln(1-r)]^{1/a} \qquad (7.34)$$

Example 7.4

Develop a process generator for the random variable having the following density function:

$$f_X(x) = \begin{cases} 0.1, & 0 < x < 4 \\[2mm] \dfrac{1}{x^2}, & 4 < x < 10 \\[2mm] \dfrac{3}{1000}\, x, & 10 < x < 20 \end{cases} \qquad (7.35)$$

For $0 < x < 4$

$$r = \int_0^x 0.1\, dz$$

$$= 0.1x$$

$$x = 10r, \qquad 0 < r < 0.4$$

For $4 < x < 10$

$$r = \int_0^4 0.1 \, dz + \int_4^x z^{-2} \, dz$$

$$= 0.4 + 0.25 - \frac{1}{x}$$

$$x = \frac{1}{0.65 - r}, \qquad 0.4 < r < 0.55$$

For $10 < x < 20$

$$r = \int_0^4 0.1 \, dz + \int_4^{10} z^{-2} \, dz + \int_{10}^x \frac{3}{1000} z \, dz$$

$$= 0.4 + 0.15 + 0.0015x^2 - 0.15$$

$$= 0.0015x^2 + 0.4$$

$$x = 25.84\sqrt{r - 0.4}, \qquad 0.55 < r < 1$$

Summarizing, we have

$$x = \begin{cases} 10r, & 0 < r < 0.4 \\ (0.65 - r)^{-1}, & 0.4 < r < 0.55 \\ 25.84(r - 0.4)^{1/2}, & 0.55 < r < 1 \end{cases}$$

Example 7.5

We wish to develop a process generator which will simulate the distribution of time to travel between two points. There are two routes which might be taken, A and B. The probability that route A is taken is p. The density functions of time over each route are

$$f_X(x) = \begin{cases} \lambda_1 e^{-\lambda_1 x}, & 0 < x < \infty \quad \text{route } A \\ \lambda_2 e^{-\lambda_2 x}, & 0 < x < \infty \quad \text{route } B \end{cases} \tag{7.36}$$

The process generators for each route are given by

$$x = \begin{cases} -\dfrac{1}{\lambda_1} \ln(1 - r), & \text{route } A \\[2mm] -\dfrac{1}{\lambda_2} \ln(1 - r), & \text{route } B \end{cases}$$

It is easily seen that two random numbers must be drawn, the first to determine which route is taken and the second to determine the time over that route. If r_1 and r_2 are the two random numbers

$$x = \begin{cases} -\dfrac{1}{\lambda_1} \ln(1 - r_2), & r_1 < p \\[2em] -\dfrac{1}{\lambda_2} \ln(1 - r_2), & r_1 > p \end{cases} \tag{7.37}$$

Example 7.6

Show that

$$\sum_{i=1}^{N} r_i$$

can be used to generate a normal random variable for large N.

From the central limit theorem if y is a random variable with finite mean, a, and variance, b, then

$$\sum_{i=1}^{N} y_i$$

has an approximate normal distribution with mean Na and variance Nb for large N. Since r_i is uniformly distributed on the interval $(0,1)$,

$$E(r_i) = 1/2$$

$$\text{Var}(r_i) = 1/12$$

Therefore for large N,

$$\sum_{i=1}^{N} r_i$$

has an approximate normal distribution with mean $N/2$ and variance $N/12$. This immediately leads to a process generator for the standard normal random variable, z, and is given in (7.38).

$$z = \frac{\sum_{i=1}^{N} r_i - N/2}{\sqrt{N/12}} \tag{7.38}$$

To generate a normal random variable, x, with mean λ and variance σ^2, we need only note the relationship between the general normal and standard normal random variable.

$$z = \frac{x - \lambda}{\sigma}$$

Using this relationship and equation (7.38), we arrive at the process generator given in (7.39) for a normal random variable with mean λ and variance σ^2.

$$x = \sigma \frac{\sum_{i=1}^{N} r_i - N/2}{\sqrt{N/12}} + \lambda \qquad (7.39)$$

DISCRETE PROCESS GENERATORS

In generating values for discrete random variables certain problems are introduced which did not exist when dealing with continuous random variables. In the continuous case for each value of the random variable X there was one and only one value of the random number r which would generate that value of X. This is not true with the discrete random variables. Consider the simple case where X has the probability mass function

$$p_X(x) = 1/3, \qquad x = 1, 2, 3$$

and distribution function

$$F_X(x) = x/3, \qquad x = 1, 2, 3$$

The process generator is readily seen to be given by

$$x = \begin{cases} 1, & 0 < r < 1/3 \\ 2, & 1/3 < r < 2/3 \\ 3, & 2/3 < r < 1 \end{cases} \qquad (7.40)$$

Thus, theoretically, there are an infinite number of values of r which yield a given value of x.

As we shall see, relationships of the type given in (7.40) are often difficult to develop or so cumbersome to use once they are developed that it becomes more useful to relate the random variable we are trying to generate to some other random variable which can be generated in a more straightforward manner. For example, the binomial random variable can be easily generated upon recognition of the fact that the binomial random variable can be represented as the sum of Bernouli random variables, which are easily generated.

The general problem which must be resolved in generating discrete random variables is similar to that encountered in generating continuous random variables in the sense that a relationship between r and $F_X(x)$ must be established.

$$F_X(x) = \sum_{y \leq x} p_X(y) \tag{7.41}$$

If we assume X is integer valued, X takes on the value x whenever

$$F_X(x-1) < r \leq F_X(x) \tag{7.42}$$

To illustrate, let X have the following probability mass function.

$$p_X(x) = \frac{1}{K+1}, \qquad x = 0, 1, 2, \ldots, K$$

$$F_X(x) = \frac{x+1}{K+1}, \qquad x = 0, 1, 2, \ldots, K$$

X assumes the value x whenever

$$\frac{x}{K+1} < r \leq \frac{x+1}{K+1}$$

or

$$x < (K+1)r \leq x+1$$

which reduces to

$$(K+1)r - 1 \leq x < (K+1)r$$

Let $K = 10$ and $r = 0.5$; then $4.5 \leq x \leq 5.5$. Since x is integer valued, $x = 5$.

Bernoulli Process Generator

The probability mass function of the Bernoulli random variable is

$$p_X(x) = p^x(1-p)^{1-x}, \qquad x = 0, 1 \tag{7.43}$$

Since the Bernoulli random variable can only assume two values, its process generator is simply given by

$$x = \begin{cases} 0, & r > p \\ 1, & r < p \end{cases} \tag{7.44}$$

Geometric Process Generator

The geometric random variable has the probability mass function defined by

$$p_X(x) = p(1 - p)^{x-1}, \qquad x = 1, 2, \ldots, \quad 0 < p < 1$$

and the distribution function given by

$$F_X(x) = 1 - (1 - p)^x$$

From equation (7.43) X has the value x whenever

$$1 - (1 - p)^{x-1} < r \le 1 - (1 - p)^x$$

or

$$(1 - p)^x \le 1 - r < (1 - p)^{x-1}$$

Taking the natural logarithm, we get

$$x \ln(1 - p) \le \ln(1 - r) < (x - 1) \ln(1 - p)$$

or

$$x \ge \frac{\ln(1 - r)}{\ln(1 - p)} > x - 1$$

which reduces to

$$0 \ge \frac{\ln(1 - r)}{\ln(1 - p)} - x > -1$$

$$\frac{\ln(1 - r)}{\ln(1 - p)} \le x < \frac{\ln(1 - r)}{\ln(1 - p)} + 1 \tag{7.45}$$

To generate a geometrically distributed random variable, one must generate r and find the value of x satisfying (7.45).

Binomial Process Generator

Let X be a binomial random variable with parameters p and n. In order to develop the required process generator by the methods employed for the Bernoulli and geometric random variables we must be able to find the value of x such that

$$F_X(x) = \sum_{y=0}^{x} \frac{n!}{y!(n - y)!} p^y(1 - p)^{n-y}, \qquad x = 0, 1, \ldots, n \tag{7.46}$$

We are fortunate to be able to generate binomially distributed random variables without solving for x in (7.46) because such a solution is by no means easy to derive.

Let X and Y be binomial and Bernoulli random variables, respectively, with characteristic functions given by (7.47) and (7.48)

$$\phi_X(\mu) = (pe^{i\mu} + 1 - p)^n \qquad (7.47)$$

$$\phi_Y(\mu) = pe^{i\mu} + 1 - p \qquad (7.48)$$

Then

$$\phi_X(\mu) = [\phi_Y(\mu)]^n \qquad (7.49)$$

In Chapter 3 we showed that (7.49) implies

$$X = \sum_{j=1}^{n} Y_j \qquad (7.50)$$

where Y_j, is Bernoulli distributed with parameter p for all j. Equation (7.50) defines the process generator for the binomial random variable with parameters p and n. That is, we need only generate n Bernouli random variables, each having parameter p and take the sum of these n values.

Due to the well-known normal approximation to the binomial it is possible to generate binomial random variables by this approximation. This approximation can be useful since only one random number is needed to generate a normal random variable, while n are needed for generation using (7.50).

Hypergeometric Process Generator

A hypergeometric random variable can best be generated by noting the mechanism which produces such a random variable. We take this approach since we are unable to analytically resolve the summation involved in the cumulative distribution function of this random variable.

To characterize the hypergeometric random variable assume we have a bowl containing N chips of which M are black, the remaining $N - M$ are white. We select a sample of size n where $n < M$. Let x be the number of black chips in the sample. The random variable X is then hypergeometrically distributed with probability mass function given in (7.51).

$$p_X(x) = \cfrac{\cfrac{M!}{x!(M-x)!}\cfrac{(N-M)!}{(n-x)!(N-M-n+x)!}}{\cfrac{N!}{n!(N-n)!}}, \qquad x = 0, 1, \ldots, n \quad (7.51)$$

When the first chip is drawn, the probability that it is black is M/N. If the first chip was black, the probability that the second is also black is $(M-1)/(N-1)$. If the first chip was white, the probability that the second is black is $M/(N-1)$. This process continues until a sample of size n has been selected.

A mathematical expression for the hypergeometric process generator is difficult to develop, but the procedure for generating these random variables is simply described by the following flow chart:

K_i = Population size when ith chip is selected.

L_i = Number of black chips remaining when ith chip is selected.

N = Original population size.

M = Initial number of black chips in the population.

Poisson Process Generator

In the literature on systems analysis no random variable has received more attention than the Poisson random variable. Its applications in such areas as inventory control, queueing theory, quality control, traffic flow theory, replacement theory, and so forth, are well-known. The importance of the Poisson process will be more clearly demonstrated in succeeding chapters in which it will be extensively applied in many of the examples we shall consider.

To characterize the Poisson process, we consider the problem of counting the number of α-rays, X, emitted from a radioactive source in an interval of time t. If the mean number of emissions per unit time is λ, then the random variable X would have a Poisson distribution with parameter λt (or at least could be nearly approximated by a Poisson distribution). Therefore the probability mass function of X is given by

$$p_X(x) = \frac{(\lambda t)^x}{x!} e^{-\lambda t}, \qquad x = 0, 1, 2, \ldots \qquad (7.52)$$

Again we encounter the problem of having to resolve the summation involved in the distribution function, $F(x)$.

$$F_X(x) = \sum_{y=0}^{x} \frac{(\lambda t)^y}{y!} e^{-\lambda t} \qquad (7.53)$$

We will circumvent this problem in a manner similar to that employed for the binomial random variable, except that instead of relating the Poisson random variable to another discrete random variable (as with the binomial), we shall relate it to a continuous random variable, the exponential.

To demonstrate this relationship let us consider a time interval, t, in which events occur according to a Poisson process. The probability that x events occur in t is given by (7.52). We will assume that at time zero an event occurred, but we will not include this event in x. Let us develop the density function of time until the first event occurs after time zero, $f_V(v)$.

$$f_V(v) = \frac{dF_V(v)}{dv} \qquad (7.54)$$

$$F_V(v) = P(V \leq v)$$
$$= 1 - P(V > v) \qquad (7.55)$$

We can relate $P(V > v)$ to $p_X(x)$ by (7.56).

$$P(V > v) = P(\text{no events in } v)$$
$$= e^{-\lambda v} \qquad (7.56)$$

Therefore by (7.55)

$$F_V(v) = 1 - e^{-\lambda v}$$

and

$$f_V(v) = \lambda e^{-\lambda v}, \qquad 0 < v < \infty \qquad (7.57)$$

Equation (7.57) implies that if the number of events occurring on an interval of time is Poisson distributed with parameter λ, then the distribution of time between successive events is exponentially distributed with parameter λ.

This relationship between the Poisson and exponential random variables leads us to a process for generating Poisson random variables. If x events occurred in time t, then the sum of the times between the x events must be less than t. That is, let v_i be the time

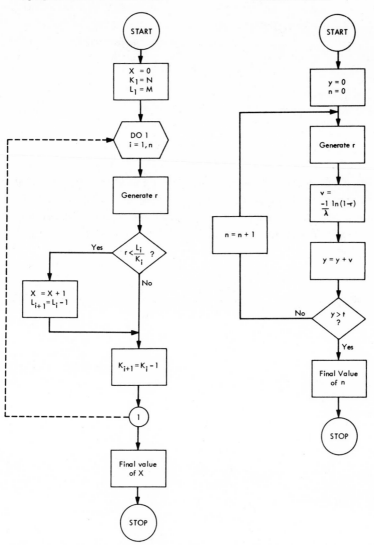

FIGURE 7.2
Process Generator for the
Hypergeometric Random Variable

FIGURE 7.3
Process Generator for the Poisson
Random Variable

between the $(i - 1)$st and ith events $(v_0 = 0)$; then

$$\sum_{i=1}^{x} v_i \leq t \qquad (7.58)$$

if x events are to occur in t.

We know from (7.57) that v_i is exponentially distributed with parameter λ for all i. To generate the value of x we merely generate successive values of v_i. Since we are specifying that x events occur in t, we continue to generate v until

$$\sum_{i=1}^{K} v_i > t \tag{7.59}$$

That is, K is the number of events such that

$$\sum_{i=1}^{K-1} v_i \leq t < \sum_{i=1}^{K} v_i \tag{7.60}$$

or, $K - 1$ events occurred in t, but the Kth event did not occur until a point in time beyond t, this fact implying $x = K - 1$. Since v_i is exponentially distributed, this random variable can be generated by equation (7.5). Figure 7.3 summarizes this process generator.

Example 7.7

Develop a process generator for X where $p_X(x)$ is given by

$$p_X(x) = \frac{2x}{K(K + 1)}, \qquad x = 1, 2, \ldots, K \tag{7.61}$$

The distribution function of X is given by

$$F_X(x) = \sum_{n=1}^{x} \frac{2n}{K(K + 1)}$$

$$= \frac{x(x + 1)}{K(K + 1)}, \qquad x = 1, 2, \ldots, K \tag{7.62}$$

$X = x$ whenever

$$\frac{x(x - 1)}{K(K + 1)} < r \leq \frac{x(x + 1)}{K(K + 1)} \tag{7.63}$$

or

$$x(x - 1) < K(K + 1)r \leq x(x + 1) \tag{7.64}$$

We must then find the smallest integer value of x such that

$$K(K + 1)r \leq x(x + 1)$$

or the smallest integer value of x such that

$$x \geq 1/2[-1 + \sqrt{1 + 4K(K+1)r}] \qquad (7.65)$$

Example 7.8

Let X be a random variable having probability mass function given by

$$p_X(x) = \begin{cases} \dfrac{x}{K(K+1)}, & x = 1, 2, \ldots, K \\[2mm] \dfrac{2K+1-x}{K(K+1)}, & x = K+1, K+2, \ldots, 2K \end{cases} \qquad (7.66)$$

Develop a process generator for X.

$$F_X(x) = \begin{cases} \dfrac{x(x+1)}{2K(K+1)}, & x = 1, 2, \ldots, K \\[2mm] \dfrac{x(4K+1-x) - 2K^2}{2K(K+1)}, & x = K+1, K+2, \ldots, 2K \end{cases} \qquad (7.67)$$

$0 < r < 0.5$ implies x lies between 1 and K. By an argument similar to that in example 7.7, x is generated by determining the smallest value of x such that

$$2K(K+1)r \leq x(x+1)$$

or

$$x \geq 1/2[-1 + \sqrt{1 + 8K(K+1)r}] \qquad (7.68)$$

If $0.5 < r < 1$, then x lies between $K+1$ and $2K$. $X = x$ where $K+1 \leq x \leq 2K$, whenever $0.5 < r < 1$ and

$$\frac{x(4K+2-x) - 2K^2}{2K(K+1)} < r \leq \frac{x(4K+1-x) - 2K^2}{2K(K+1)} \qquad (7.69)$$

or

$$x(4K+2-x) < 2K(K+1)r + 2K^2 \leq x(4K+1-x)$$

Therefore we must find the smallest value of x such that

$$x(4K+1-x) \geq 2K[(K+1)r + K] \qquad (7.70)$$

Solving (7.70) for x, we must find the smallest value of x satisfying (7.71).

$$x \geq 1/2[4K + 1 \pm \sqrt{8K(K + 1)(1 - r) + 1}] \qquad (7.71)$$

Equation (7.71) implies two values of x for any $0.5 < r < 1$. From equation (7.67), $r = 1$ implies $x = 2K$. Let us examine (7.71) when the sign before the radical is positive and $r = 1$.

$$x \geq 1/2(4K + 2) \qquad (7.72)$$

Then $x \geq 2K + 1$. The smallest integer value of x satisfying (7.72) is then $2K + 1$, forcing us to reject (7.72) as a solution. Let us try the solution given in (7.73).

$$x \geq 1/2[4K + 1 - \sqrt{8K(K + 1)(1 - r) + 1}] \qquad (7.73)$$

When $r = 1$, (7.73) reduces to $x \geq 2K$, which satisfies the required conditions. We might test (7.73) further by setting $r = 0.5 + \epsilon$ where ϵ is an arbitrarily small positive number such that the resulting value of x should be $K + 1$. Substituting $r = 0.5 + \epsilon$ in (7.73), we obtain

$$x \geq 1/2[4K + 1 - \sqrt{8K(K + 1)(0.5 - \epsilon) + 1}]$$

or

$$2x - 4K - 1 \geq - \sqrt{8K(K + 1)(0.5 - \epsilon) + 1}$$

If $x = K + 1$, we have

$$-2K + 1 \geq - \sqrt{8K(K + 1)(0.5 - \epsilon) + 1}$$

Multiplying by -1 and squaring both sides lead to

$$4K^2 - 4K + 1 \leq 8K(K + 1)(0.5 - \epsilon) + 1$$

or

$$-1 + (K + 1)\epsilon \leq 0$$

Therefore whenever

$$\epsilon \leq \frac{1}{K + 1}$$

$x = K + 1$ satisfies (7.73).

The process generator for X is given by finding the smallest value of x such that

$$x \geq \begin{cases} 1/2[-1 + \sqrt{1 + 8K(K + 1)r}], & 0 < r < 0.5 \\ 1/2[4K + 1 - \sqrt{8K(K + 1)(1 - r) + 1}], & 0.5 < r < 1 \end{cases} \quad (7.74)$$

EMPIRICAL DATA

We have discussed methods for generating random variables, given that the underlying mechanism or probability law governing those random variables is known. However, it is indeed rare for a systems analyst to have a priori knowledge of the nature of the distributions of the random variable affecting the system he is studying. The analyst would first have to collect data of sufficient volume to adequately describe the probability mass function, density function, or distribution function. At this point, he might attempt to determine whether the distribution of the variable in question can be described by one of the better known probability distributions, such as those discussed in Chapter 2. Several statistical tests, known as tests of goodness-of-fit, are available which provide the researcher with the tools necessary to determine whether the distribution of the random variable he is studying can be described by a given known distribution specified by the researcher. Two of the more commonly used tests of goodness-of-fit are the chi-square and Kolmogorov-Smirnov tests. A detailed discussion of these tests was given in Chapter 6.

If after applying a goodness-of-fit test the analyst finds that he is able to explicitly describe the density function or probability mass function by a mathematical relationship, he can then develop a process generator for this random variable by the methods already discussed. Unfortunately such attempts often result in failure, leaving the analyst with the problem of developing a process generator for a random variable whose distribution function is unknown. In this case the methods already discussed do not apply.

Polynomial Approximation

The relationship we are trying to establish is of the form

$$x = \phi[F_X(x)] \quad (7.75)$$

In this section we will attempt to approximate (7.75) by a polynomial. The first step would be to plot x versus $F_X(x)$. To illustrate this method, consider the data on demand collected in example 7.1. From this example we have the following data (Table 7.6):

TABLE 7.6

Demand (x)	Frequency	Relative Frequency	$F_X(x)$
0. 0		0.0000	0.0000
1. 10		0.1818	0.1818
2. 21		0.3818	0.5636
3. 17		0.3091	0.8727
4. 6		0.1091	0.9818
5. 1		0.0182	1.0000
	55	1.0000	

A graph of x versus $F_X(x)$ is given in Figure 7.4.

FIGURE 7.4
Empirical Process Generator for x

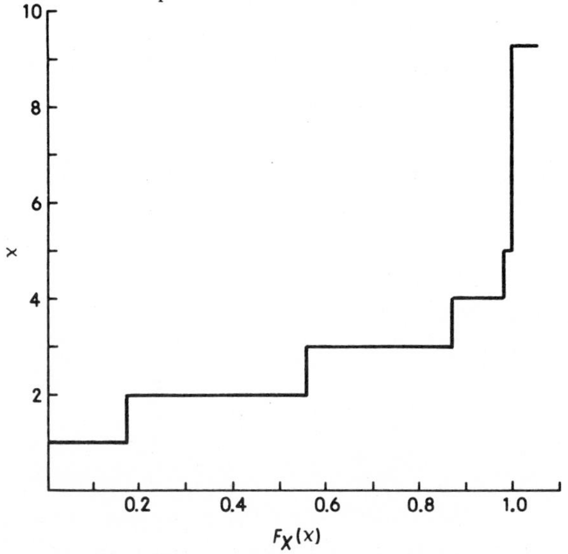

We wish to approximate the function in Figure 7.4 by a polynomial. We might start by fitting a straight line, then a quadratic, cubic, and so on, until a satisfactory relationship is found. The method we shall use for fitting curves to experimental data is called the method of least squares. A general expression for x as a polynomial function of r is given by (7.76)

$$x = a_0 + \sum_{n=1}^{m} a_n r^n \tag{7.76}$$

where m is the degree of the polynomial and a_n is the coefficient of r^n. There are six possible values of x, and corresponding to each is a value of r. Let x_i be the ith value of x, and r_i be the corresponding value of r.

TABLE 7.7

i	x_i	r_i
1........0		0.0000
2........1		0.1818
3........2		0.5636
4........3		0.8727
5........4		0.9818
6........5		1.0000

In using the method of least squares the researcher derives those values of $a_0, a_1, \ldots, a_m$ such that

$$\sum_{i=1}^{K} \left(x_i - a_0 - \sum_{n=1}^{m} a_n r_i^n \right)^2 = \text{minimum} \qquad (7.77)$$

K represents the number of combinations of x_i and r_i recorded. The values of the coefficients, a_n satisfying (7.77) can be determined by taking partial derivatives with respect to a_n, $n = 0, 1, \ldots, m$; setting each of the resulting derivatives equal to zero; and solving for a_n, $n = 0, 1, \ldots, m$. The system of equations which must be solved is given in (7.78).

$$\sum_{i=1}^{K} \left(x_i - a_0 - \sum_{n=1}^{m} a_n r_i^n \right) = 0$$

$$\sum_{i=1}^{K} r_i \left(x_i - a_0 - \sum_{n=1}^{m} a_n r_i^n \right) = 0$$

$$\vdots \qquad \qquad \vdots \qquad (7.78)$$

$$\sum_{i=1}^{K} r_i^m \left(x_i - a_0 - \sum_{n=1}^{m} a_n r_i^n \right) = 0$$

The system of equations in (7.78) can be expressed in matrix form by (7.79).

$$
\begin{pmatrix}
K & \sum_{i=1}^{K} r_i & \sum_{i=1}^{K} r_i^2 & \cdots & \sum_{i=1}^{K} r_i^m \\
\sum_{i=1}^{K} r_i & \sum_{i=1}^{K} r_i^2 & \sum_{i=1}^{K} r_i^3 & \cdots & \sum_{i=1}^{K} r_i^{m+1} \\
\vdots & \vdots & \vdots & & \vdots \\
\sum_{i=1}^{K} r_i^m & \sum_{i=1}^{K} r_i^{m+1} & \sum_{i=1}^{K} r_i^{m+2} & \cdots & \sum_{i=1}^{K} r_i^{2m}
\end{pmatrix}
\begin{pmatrix}
a_0 \\
a_1 \\
\vdots \\
a_m
\end{pmatrix}
=
\begin{pmatrix}
\sum_{i=1}^{K} x_i \\
\sum_{i=1}^{K} r_i x_i \\
\vdots \\
\sum_{i=1}^{K} r_i^m x_i
\end{pmatrix}
$$

$$(7.79)$$

Expressing the matrices in (7.79) from left to right more concisely as R, A, and X, respectively, we have

$$RA = X \qquad (7.80)$$

Matrix A is then given by

$$A = R^{-1}X \qquad (7.81)$$

where R^{-1} is the inverse of R.

In attempting to develop a process generator for demand, x, we will try only linear and quadratic solutions.

$$K = 6 \qquad \sum_{i=1}^{6} r_i = 3.60 \qquad \sum_{i=1}^{6} r_i^2 = 3.08 \qquad \sum_{i=1}^{6} r_i^3 = 2.79$$

$$\sum_{i=1}^{6} r_i^4 = 2.59 \qquad \sum_{i=1}^{6} x_i = 15 \qquad \sum_{i=1}^{6} r_i x_i = 12.85 \qquad \sum_{i=1}^{6} r_i^2 x_i = 11.79$$

For the linear solution (7.79) becomes

$$\begin{pmatrix} 6.00 & 3.60 \\ 3.60 & 3.08 \end{pmatrix} \begin{pmatrix} a_0 \\ a_1 \end{pmatrix} = \begin{pmatrix} 15.00 \\ 12.85 \end{pmatrix}$$

Solving for a_0 and a_1 we have

$$\begin{pmatrix} a_0 \\ a_1 \end{pmatrix} = \frac{1}{5.52} \begin{pmatrix} 3.08 & -3.60 \\ -3.60 & 6.00 \end{pmatrix} \begin{pmatrix} 15.00 \\ 12.85 \end{pmatrix}$$

$$= \begin{pmatrix} -.0109 \\ 4.1848 \end{pmatrix}$$

or

$$x = -0.011 + 4.185r \qquad (7.82)$$

For the quadratic solution we have

$$\begin{pmatrix} 6.00 & 3.60 & 3.08 \\ 3.60 & 3.08 & 2.79 \\ 3.08 & 2.79 & 2.59 \end{pmatrix} \begin{pmatrix} a_0 \\ a_1 \\ a_2 \end{pmatrix} = \begin{pmatrix} 15.00 \\ 12.85 \\ 11.79 \end{pmatrix}$$

The solution for a_0, a_1, a_2 is given by

$$a_0 = 0.086$$
$$a_1 = 1.125$$
$$a_2 = 3.000$$

Therefore

$$x = 0.286 + 1.125r + 3.000r^2 \qquad (7.83)$$

The linear and quadratic equations are compared with the actual relationship in Figure 7.5.

FIGURE 7.5
Linear and Quadratic Process Generators

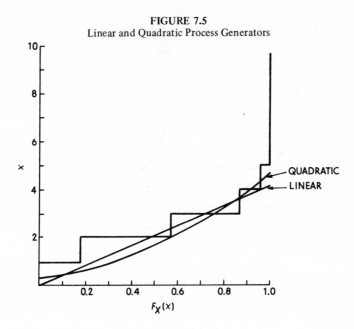

Since we are dealing with a discrete random variable we must adopt some scheme whereby the linear and quadratic relationships yield integer values of x. For example, we might adopt the convention of raising the value of x generated from (7.82) or (7.83) to its next higher integer value. To illustrate, let $r = 0.5$.

$$x = 2.08 \quad \text{from (7.82)}$$
$$x = 1.60 \quad \text{from (7.83)}$$

Raising each value of x to its next higher integer value, we get values of demand of three and two, respectively; the actual value being two.

TABLE 7.8

x	Range of Values of r Generating x		
	Exact	Linear	Quadratic
0	none	$0.0000 < r < 0.0026$	none
1	$0.0000 < r < 0.1818$	$0.0026 < r < 0.2416$	$0.0000 < r < 0.3341$
2	$0.1818 < r < 0.5636$	$0.2416 < r < 0.4805$	$0.3341 < r < 0.6241$
3	$0.5636 < r < 0.8727$	$0.4805 < r < 0.7194$	$0.6241 < r < 0.7808$
4	$0.8727 < r < 0.9818$	$0.7194 < r < 0.9584$	$0.7808 < r < 0.9400$
5	$0.9818 < r < 1.0000$	$0.9584 < r < 1.0000$	$0.9400 < r < 1.0000$

A more exact comparison of the linear, quadratic, and exact process generators is given in Table 7.8. It is obvious that both of the polynomial generators derived leave much to be desired in approximating the actual probability distribution. To improve the approximation we might try increasing the degree of the polynomial or we might try a nonpolynomial approximation.

Nonpolynomial Approximation

A relationship which has proven most useful in approximating inverse distribution functions is given in (7.84).

$$x = a + br + cr^2 + \alpha(1 - r)^2 \ln(r) + \beta r^2 \ln(1 - r) \tag{7.84}$$

As we shall soon see, this equation is not only valuable in dealing with empirical distributions but is also useful in approximating many of the distributions discussed in Chapter 3.

The values of a, b, c, α, β can be developed by the same method used to evaluate the parameters of the polynomials discussed in the previous section. That is, if x_i and r_i are the ith observed values of the random variable and the cumulative distribution function, respectively, then we wish to find the values of a, b, c, α, β such that

$$\sum_{i=1}^{K} [x_i - a - br_i - cr_i^2 - \alpha(1 - r_i)^2 \ln(r_i) - \beta r_i^2 \ln(1 - r_i)]^2$$

$$= \min \tag{7.85}$$

Setting each of the first partial derivatives with respect to a, b, c, α, β equal to zero, we develop the system of equations in (7.86) which is represented in matrix form in (7.87).

$$\sum_{i=1}^{K} x_i = Ka + b \sum_{i=1}^{K} r_i + c \sum_{i=1}^{K} r_i^2 + \alpha \sum_{i=1}^{K} (1 - r_i)^2 \ln(r_i)$$

$$+ \beta \sum_{i=1}^{K} r_i^2 \ln(1 - r_i)$$

$$\sum_{i=1}^{K} r_i x_i = a \sum_{i=1}^{K} r_i + b \sum_{i=1}^{K} r_i^2 + c \sum_{i=1}^{K} r_i^3 + \alpha \sum_{i=1}^{K} r_i(1 - r_i)^2 \ln(r_i)$$

$$+ \beta \sum_{i=1}^{K} r_i^3 \ln(1 - r_i)$$

$$\sum_{i=1}^{K} r_i^2 x_i = a \sum_{i=1}^{K} r_i^2 + b \sum_{i=1}^{K} r_i^3 + c \sum_{i=1}^{K} r_i^4 + \alpha \sum_{i=1}^{K} r_i^2(1 - r_i)^2 \ln(r_i)$$

$$+ \beta \sum_{i=1}^{K} r_i^4 \ln(1 - r_i)$$

$$\sum_{i=1}^{K} (1 - r_i)^2 \ln(r_i)x_i = a \sum_{i=1}^{K} (1 - r_i)^2 \ln(r_i) + b \sum_{i=1}^{K} r_i(1 - r_i)^2 \ln(r_i)$$

$$+ c \sum_{i=1}^{K} r_i^2(1 - r_i)^2 \ln(r_i) + \alpha \sum_{i=1}^{K} (1 - r_i)^4 [\ln(r_i)]^2$$

$$+ \beta \sum_{i=1}^{K} r_i^2(1 - r_i)^2 \ln(r_i) \ln(1 - r_i)$$

$$\sum_{i=1}^{K} r_i^2 \ln(1 - r_i)x_i = a \sum_{i=1}^{K} r_i^2 \ln(1 - r_i) + b \sum_{i=1}^{K} r_i^3 \ln(1 - r_i)$$

$$+ c \sum_{i=1}^{K} r_i^4 \ln(1 - r_i) + \alpha \sum_{i=1}^{K} r_i^2(1 - r_i)^2 \ln(r_i) \ln(1 - r_i)$$

$$+ \beta \sum_{i=1}^{K} r_i^4 [\ln(1 - r_i)]^2 \tag{7.86}$$

$$\begin{pmatrix} K & R_1 & R_2 & R_3 & R_4 \\ R_1 & R_2 & R_5 & R_6 & R_7 \\ R_2 & R_5 & R_8 & R_9 & R_{10} \\ R_3 & R_6 & R_9 & R_{11} & R_{12} \\ R_4 & R_7 & R_{10} & R_{12} & R_{13} \end{pmatrix} \begin{pmatrix} a \\ b \\ c \\ \alpha \\ \beta \end{pmatrix} = \begin{pmatrix} X_1 \\ X_2 \\ X_3 \\ X_4 \\ X_5 \end{pmatrix} \tag{7.87}$$

where K is the number of observations of x and

$$R_1 = \sum r_i$$
$$R_2 = \sum r_i^2$$
$$R_3 = \sum (1 - r_i)^2 \ln(r_i)$$
$$R_4 = \sum r_i^2 \ln(1 - r_i)$$

$$R_5 = \sum r_i^3$$
$$R_6 = \sum r_i(1 - r_i)^2 \ln(r_i)$$
$$R_7 = \sum r_i^3 \ln(1 - r_i)$$
$$R_8 = \sum r_i^4$$

$$R_9 = \sum r_i^2(1 - r_i)^2 \ln(r_i)$$
$$R_{10} = \sum r_i^4 \ln(1 - r_i)$$
$$R_{11} = \sum (1 - r_i)^4 [\ln(r_i)]^2$$
$$R_{12} = \sum r_i^2(1 - r_i)^2 \ln(r_i)\ln(1 - r_i)$$
$$R_{13} = \sum r_i^4 [\ln(1 - r_i)]^2$$

$$X_1 = \sum x_i$$
$$X_2 = \sum r_i x_i$$
$$X_3 = \sum r_i^2 x_i$$
$$X_4 = \sum (1 - r_i)^2 \ln(r_i)x_i$$
$$X_5 = \sum r_i^2 \ln(1 - r_i)x_i$$

To illustrate the applicability of (7.84) let us consider several examples. Since the purpose of the following examples is to demonstrate the versatilitv of (7.84), step-by-step calculation of the coefficients a, b, c, α, β will not be given. The reader may find it instructive to verify these calculations on his own. However, hand calculation of a, b, c, α, β is quite tedious, and a digital computer is highly recommended for this purpose.

Example 7.9

Develop a process generator for x using equation (7.84) based on the data in Table 7.9. Determine the accuracy of the generator.

TABLE 7.9

Interval	Interval Midpoint	Frequency	Cumulative Frequency	Relative Cumulative Frequency
$-3.5 < x \leqslant -2.5$ . . . . -3.0		0	0	0.000
$-2.5 < x \leqslant -1.5$ . . . . -2.0		13	13	0.065
$-1.5 < x \leqslant -0.5$ . . . . -1.0		58	71	0.355
$-0.5 < x \leqslant 0.5$ 0.0		70	141	0.705
$0.5 < x \leqslant 1.5$ 1.0		43	184	0.920
$1.5 < x \leqslant 2.5$ 2.0		15	199	0.995
$2.5 < x \leqslant 3.5$ 3.0		1	200	1.000

For this example the process generator in (7.84) becomes

$$x = 0.412 - 5.433r + 7.090r^2 + 0.88(1 - r)^2 \ln r + 0.094r^2 \ln(1 - r) \quad (7.88)$$

FIGURE 7.6
Experimental and Approximate Process Generator for
Example 7.9

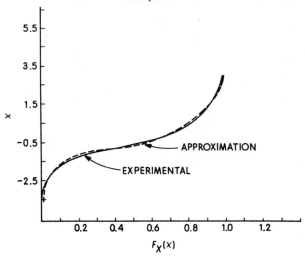

It is easily seen in Figure 7.6 that the approximate process generator given by (7.88) provides an adequate representation of the experimental generator.

Example 7.10

Determine the adequacy of (7.84) in generating an exponential random variable when the parameter, λ, of the exponential distribution is three.

$$f_X(x) = 3e^{-3x}$$
$$F_X(x) = 1 - e^{-3x} \qquad (7.89)$$

The approximate process generator is given by

$$x = +0.333 - 0.562r + 0.585r^2 + 0.119(1 - r)^2 \ln r - 0.254r^2 \ln(1 - r) \qquad (7.90)$$

The exact process generator is

$$x = -\tfrac{1}{3} \ln(1 - r) \qquad (7.91)$$

A comparison of the values of x generated by the two generators for common values of r is given in Table 7.10 and Figure 7.7. The approximate generator seems reasonable for $r > 0.05$. For $r < 0.05$ equation (7.90) generates negative values of x, which are not permitted if x is exponentially distributed.

TABLE 7.10
Accuracy of Equation (7.84) as a Generator of Exponential Random Variables

r	x Exact	x Approximate
0.01 . . .	0.0033	−0.2150
0.05 . . .	0.0169	−0.0181
0.10 . . .	0.0347	0.0586
0.30 . . .	0.1177	0.1544
0.50 . . .	0.2287	0.2214
0.70 . . .	0.3973	0.3780
0.90 . . .	0.7600	0.7760
0.95 . . .	0.9887	1.0157
0.99 . . .	1.5197	1.4890

Figures 7.6 and 7.7 provide a hint as to the type of distributions for which equation (7.84) can be used as an approximate process generator. In both figures 7.6 and 7.7 the process generator is of the form shown in Figure 7.8. Thus when the cumulative distribution function is of the general form given in Figure 7.9, equation (7.84)

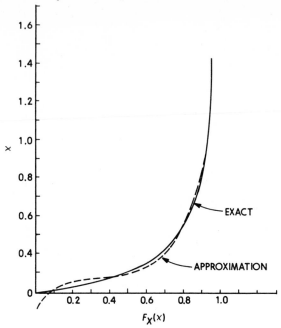

FIGURE 7.7
Exact and Approximate Process Generators for the
Exponential Random Variable with $\lambda = 3$

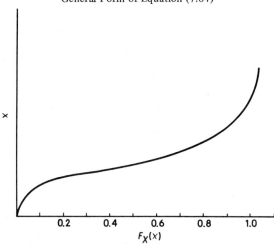

FIGURE 7.8
General Form of Equation (7.84)

will usually serve quite well as a process generator. However,
difficulties will probably be encountered in attempting to use this

approximating function when the observed cumulative distribution function is similar to that in Figure 7.10.

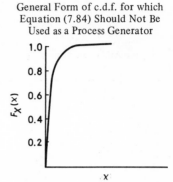

FIGURE 7.9
General Form of c.d.f. for which
Equation (7.84) Can Be Used as
a Process Generator

FIGURE 7.10
General Form of c.d.f. for which
Equation (7.84) Should Not Be
Used as a Process Generator

NUMERICAL INVERSE INTERPOLATION

Occasionally a probability distribution is encountered whose distribution function, $F_X(x)$, can be evaluated exactly for any x but whose inverse cannot be evaluated exactly. That is, if

$$x = \phi[F_X(x)]$$

it is either impossible or difficult to evaluate x, given $F_X(x)$. We will assume that (7.92),

$$F_X(x) = \int_{-\infty}^{x} f_X(x)\, dx \qquad (7.92)$$

can be evaluated exactly. Our problem is to find the value of x corresponding to r, a uniformly distributed random number on the interval (0,1,). This method can be summarized as follows:

1. Generate r.
2. Find, by trial and error, two values of x, a, and b such that $F_X(a) < r < F_X(b)$.
3. By interpolation determine the value of x between a and b such that $F_X(x) = r$. If a and b are chosen such that $F_X(a)$ and $F_X(b)$ closely "bracket" r, linear interpolation will suffice.

We will illustrate this procedure when X is exponentially distributed with $\lambda = 1$. Of course, we would not ordinarily use this method for a distribution such as the exponential since its inverse cumulative distribution function is easily derived, but it will serve to illustrate the step-by-step procedure.

$$F_X(x) = 1 - e^{-x}, \qquad 0 < x < \infty$$

TABLE 7.11
Generation of an Exponential Random Variable through Numerical Inverse Interpolation

a	$F_X(a)$	$F_X(a) < r$	b	$F_X(b)$	$F_X(b) > r$	x (lin. inter)
0.50. . .0.393		no				
0.30. . .0.259		yes	0.50	0.393	yes	0.3910
0.35. . .0.295		yes	0.45	0.362	yes	0.3873
0.38. . .0.316		yes	0.42	0.343	yes	0.3859

Let $r = 0.32$ and $a = 0.5$, yielding $F_X(a) = 0.393$. Since $F_X(a) > r$, we must select another value of a. We summarize the procedure in Table 7.11. Using the exact process generator given in (7.5), we arrive at the solution $x = 0.38566$. The reader will notice that the first interpolated value of x was temporarily rejected in favor of narrowing the difference $F_X(b) - F_X(a)$—resulting in a more exact value of a. The number of iterations required before a value of x is accepted depends upon the degree of accuracy required. In general, the smaller $F_X(b) - F_X(a)$, the more accurate the interpolated value of x.

Example 7.11

Let X be a continuous random variable having density function given by

$$f_X(x) = 3x^2, \qquad 0 < x < 1 \tag{7.93}$$

By numerical inverse interpolation find the values of x corresponding to values of r of 0.05, 0.5, and 0.90. In each case let a and b be defined such that $F_X(b) - F_X(a) = 0.01$. Compare the resulting values of x with those generated by the exact generator given in (7.94).

$$x = r^{1/3} \tag{7.94}$$

To illustrate how process generators are used in simulation we will present several simple examples. It is not our purpose at this time to delve into the analysis of the data generated by a simulator but rather to develop a means of generating the data. We will defer our discussion of the analysis of simulation results until chapter 11.

TABLE 7.12
Numerical Inverse Interpolation for Example 7.11

r	a	$F_X(a)$	$F_X(b) < r$	b	$F_X(b)$	$F_X(b) > r$	x
0.05. . .0.01	0.000001	yes	0.30	0.0270	no		
. . .0.30	0.0270	yes	0.40	0.0640	yes	0.3622	
. . .0.36	0.0467	yes	0.37	0.0507	yes	0.3683	
		exact value	x = 0.3684				
0.50. . .0.70	0.3430	yes	0.80	0.5120	yes	0.7929	
. . .0.79	0.4930	yes	0.80	0.5120	yes	0.7937	
		exact value	x = 0.7937				
0.90. . .0.95	0.8574	yes	0.99	0.9703	yes	0.9651	
. . .0.96	0.8847	yes	0.97	0.9127	yes	0.9655	
		exact value	x = 0.9655				

Example 7.12 — A Transportation Problem

Each day a delivery truck leaves A and makes stops at B, C, and D in that order. However, the truck does not always take the same route. In Figure 7.11 □ represents a delivery point, ○ represents a route intersection, and → represents a route the truck might take. The number under each route is for identification. The number above each route is the probability that that route is taken. The time elapsed in traversing each route will be assumed to be normally distributed with mean and standard deviation given below for each route. We will assume that no delay is experienced at each intersection but a delay does occur at each delivery point. The distribution of delay time at each delivery point will be assumed to be exponentially distributed with means as follows:

Delivery Point	Mean Delay (minutes)
B	40
C	20
D	15

Let us now develop a simulator which will generate the total time taken to make all three deliveries and return to A.

At A and at each intersection two random numbers must be generated. The first is used to determine which route is to be taken

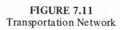

FIGURE 7.11
Transportation Network

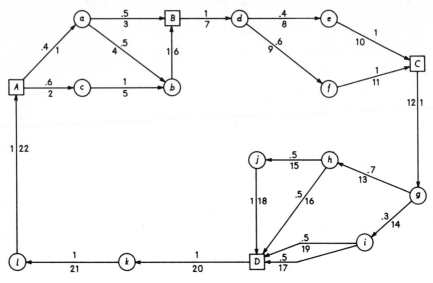

TABLE 7.13
Route Times

Route	Mean (minutes)	Standard Dev. (min).
1	5	1.00
2	3	0.50
3	10	1.00
4	2	0.25
5	8	0.50
6	3	0.25
7	12	0.50
8	5	0.20
9	7	0.40
10	9	0.30
11	4	0.60
12	9	1.00
13	6	0.40
14	4	0.10
15	2	0.10
16	4	0.30
17	8	0.20
18	3	0.30
19	6	1.00
20	7	1.00
21	5	0.50
22	3	0.30

away from the point in question. Once the route is decided upon, another random number is required to determine the time taken to traverse that route. Of course, if only one route leads away from a given point, a random number is not required to determine that that route is taken. For example, if the truck is at A, we generate a random number, R, and compare it with 0.4. If R is less than or equal to 0.4, route 1 is taken. Otherwise, route 2 is taken. On the other hand, if the truck reaches intersection b, a random number is not needed to determine what route is taken at that point, since only one route is available, 6.

Flow Chart

The following flow chart indicates the sequence of events which occur in one full trip. In this flow chart ROUTIM (L,M,X,N) is a subroutine which determines the route to be taken where more than one route is possible. Once the route has been determined, the subroutine computes the time taken to traverse the route selected. The route selected, N, and the travel time on that route, X, are transferred back to the mainline program. L and M are the alternative routes which may be taken. The values of L and M must be defined in the mainline program and transferred to ROUTIM (L,M,X,N). GENNOR(I) generates the time taken to travel the length of route I. The variables used in the program are defined as follows:

NSIM – Number of trips simulated.
SUMTIM – Total travel time for all NSIM trips.
TIM(K) – Travel time for Kth trip simulated.
X(I) – Travel time over route I.
A(I) – Mean travel time over route I.
B(I) – Standard deviation of travel time over route I.
P(I) – Probability route I is taken
C(J) – Mean delay at Jth delivery point.
Y(J) – Delay at Jth delivery point.

Here we have an example of a problem which can be resolved as easily by mathematical methods as by simulation. Let us compare the two solutions. To compute the expected time through the network analytically we note that there are 24 distinct combinations of routes which might be taken. These combinations are enumerated in the table below. To compute the expected total time through the network we compute the expected time "on the road" and add this

FIGURE 7.12
Flow Chart for Example 7.12

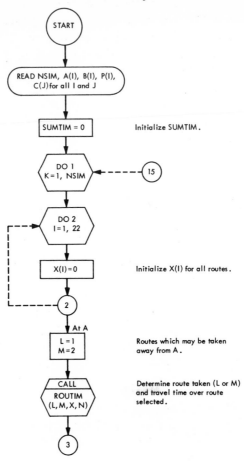

to the sum of the expected delays at the delivery points. To compute the expected time "on the road" we compute the probability that each of the combinations given below is taken, multiply this probability by the expected time over that combination of routes, and sum these products over all combinations.

For example, the probability that the first combination is taken is given by

$$P(1-3-7-8-10-12-13-15-18-20-21-22)$$
$$= (0.4)(0.5)(1)(0.4)(1)(1)(0.7)(0.5)(1)(1)(1)(1) = 0.028$$

The expected time taken to traverse this combination of routes is the sum of the mean time over each of the individual component routes.

FIGURE 7.12 *(continued)*

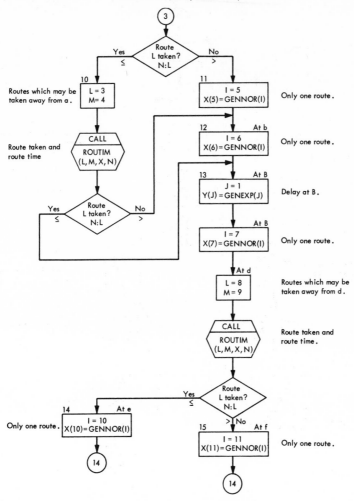

The expected time over the above combination is given by

$$E(\text{time}) = 5+10+12+5+9+9+6+2+3+7+5+3 = 76 \text{ minutes}$$

If m_i is the mean time over the ith combination and P_i is the probability that that combination is taken

$$E(\text{time on the road}) = \sum_{i=1}^{24} P_i m_i = 72.25 \text{ minutes}$$

FIGURE 7.12 *(continued)*

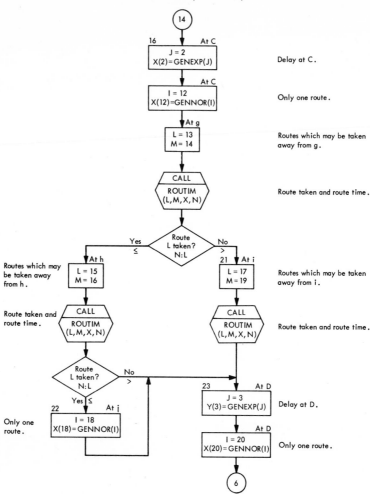

The expected delay time at each delivery point is the sum of the individual expected delays.

$$E \text{ (delay in delivery)} = 40 + 20 + 15 = 75 \text{ minutes}$$

Therefore

$$E \text{ (total time through the system)} = 72.25 + 75 = 147.25 \text{ minutes}$$

Using the program already presented, we obtain a mean time through the system of 149.70 minutes based on the first 500 trips simulated and 147.72 minutes based on a total of 1000 trips

FIGURE 7.12 *(concluded)*

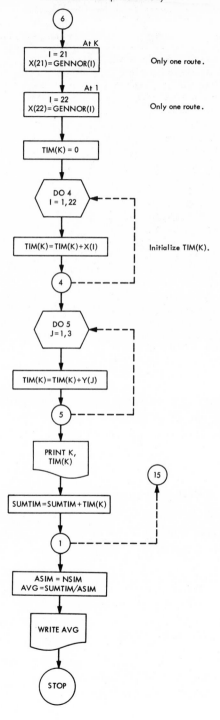

TABLE 7.14

Combination of Routes Taken	Mean Time per Combination (min.)	P (Combination)
1–3–7–8–10–12–13–15–18–20–21–22	76	0.028
1–3–7–8–10–12–13–16–20–21–22	75	0.028
1–3–7–8–10–12–14–19–20–21–22	75	0.012
1–3–7–8–10–12–14–17–20–21–22	77	0.012
1–3–7–9–11–12–13–15–18–20–21–22	73	0.042
1–3–7–9–11–12–13–16–20–21–22	72	0.042
1–3–7–9–11–12–14–19–20–21–22	72	0.018
1–3–7–9–11–12–14–17–20–21–22	74	0.018
1–4–6–7–8 –10–12–13–15–18–20–21–22	71	0.028
1–4–6–7–8 –10–12–13–16–20–21–22	70	0.028
1–4–6–7–8 –10–12–14–19–20–21–22	70	0.012
1–4–6–7–8 –10–12–14–17–20–21–22	72	0.012
1–4–6–7–9 –11–12–13–15–18–20–21–22	68	0.042
1–4–6–7–9 –11–12–13–16–20–21–22	67	0.042
1–4–6–7–9 –11–12–14–19–20–21–22	67	0.018
1–4–6–7–9 –11–12–14–17–20–21–22	69	0.018
2–5–6–7–8 –10–12–13–15–18–20–21–22	75	0.084
2–5–6–7–8 –10–12–13–16–20–21–22	74	0.084
2–5–6–7–8 –10–12–14–19–20–21–22	74	0.036
2–5–6–7–8 –10–12–14–17–20–21–22	76	0.036
2–5–6–7–9 –11–12–13–15–18–20–21–22	72	0.126
2–5–6–7–9 –11–12–13–16–20–21–22	71	0.126
2–5–6–7–9 –11–12–14–19–20–21–22	71	0.054
2–5–6–7–9 –11–12–14–17–20–21–22	73	0.054

simulated. In general, as the number of trips simulated is increased, the average time through the system should approach the expected time through the system as demonstrated by increasing the number of trips simulated from 500 to 1000.

Example 7.13 – A Maintenance Problem

A production line is to be maintained by a single repair crew. The production line may fail for three reasons. When the system fails, the maintenance crew corrects the problem causing the failure and makes adjustments in the line to reduce the probability that the line will fail for either of the remaining two reasons. In other words, when an adjustment is made for one problem it is made for all three. Let T_i be the time in hours until failure for the ith failure, measured from the last adjustment. The density function of T_i is given by

$$f_{T_i}(t_i) = \frac{\lambda_i}{(n_i - 1)!} (\lambda_i t_i)^{n_i - 1} e^{-\lambda_i t_i}, \qquad 0 < t_i < \infty, i = 1, 2, 3$$

where

$$n_1 = 4 \qquad \lambda_1 = 0.25$$
$$n_2 = 8 \qquad \lambda_2 = 0.10$$
$$n_3 = 2 \qquad \lambda_3 = 0.05$$

The density function of the time to complete the required repairs, X is given by

$$g_X(x) = 5e^{-5x}, \qquad 0 < x < \infty$$

where the repair time is independent of the type of failure. Let us simulate the downtime for a one-year period. We will assume that the period simulated starts immediately after the completion of a repair. The system will then be simulated for 200 eight-hour working days, or for 1,600 hours.

TABLE 7.15
Simulation of One Year of Operation of the
Maintenance System in Example 7.13

Failure	Frequency of Failure	Mean Time To Failure
1.	. 83	15.40
2.	. 1	28.52
3.	. 20	13.77

After each repair we must generate the time until each of the failure occurs, t_1, t_2, and t_3. The smallest t_i represents the time until the next failure. For example, if $t_2 < t_1 < t_3$, the next failure is of the second type and occurs t_2 hours after the last repair. We then generate the repair time, x, and accumulate the total elapsed time until we have simulated 1,600 hours of operation. We summarize the procedure in the following flow chart. The variables used are:

TOTTIM = Total hours simulated.
ALAM (I) = λ_i.
N(I) = n_i.
T(I) = t_i.
X = x.
AMU = Parameter of the repair time distribution.
CUMX = Cumulative downtime.
P = Proportion of the time the system is down.
GAMMA (I) = Process generator for T(I).

FIGURE 7.13
Flow Chart for Example 7.13

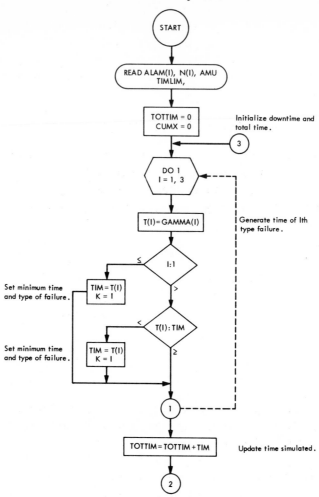

TIM = Time until next failure.
TIMLIM = Time limit (1,600 hours).

The results of one year's simulation are given below. The total number of hours simulated was 1,600.98. The total number of hours of operating time during the simulated period was 1,581.71, and the system was down for 19.27 hours, or 1.2 per cent of the simulated period.

FIGURE 7.13 *(continued)*

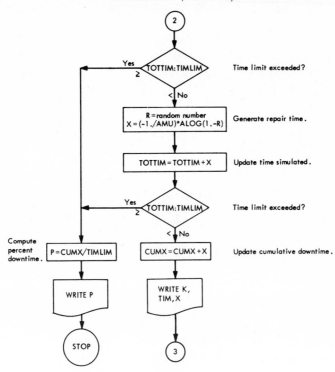

Example 7.14 — A Quality Control Problem

Let us develop a simulator for the problem given in example 5.9. The reader will recall that from each week's production of 10,000 units a random sample of size N was drawn and inspected. If the number of defective units found in the sample exceeded the acceptance number, c, the lot was rejected and scrapped at a cost of $2.50 per unit. If the lot was accepted, it was sent to an assembly line. Each defective unit reaching the assembly line resulted in a brief shutdown of the line at a cost of $25 per shutdown, which includes scrapping the item causing the shutdown. The cost of inspecting one unit is $2.50, and inspection includes a destructive test. Therefore, each unit inspected is destroyed.

The probability that a lot will be accepted or rejected is dependent upon the proportion of defective units, P, contained in the lot. From example 5.9 the density function of the proportion defective is

$$f_P P(p) = 19(1 - p)^{18}, \qquad 0 \le p \le 1$$

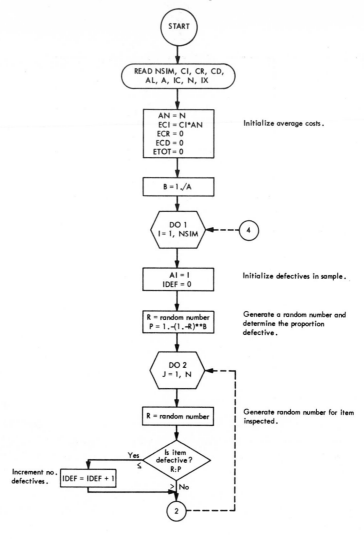

FIGURE 7.14
Flow Chart of Example 7.14

The purpose of the simulator we will develop is to determine the average total cost per lot of the quality control system proposed when $N = 5$ and $c = 0$. The simulator must recognize the existence of three costs. For each lot inspected a cost of $\$2.50\ N$ is incurred. If the lot is rejected, it is scrapped at a cost of $\$2\ (10{,}000\text{-}N)$. If a defective lot is accepted and passed on to the assembly line, a cost of $\$25\ (10{,}000\text{--}N)p$ results.

FIGURE 7.14 *(continued)*

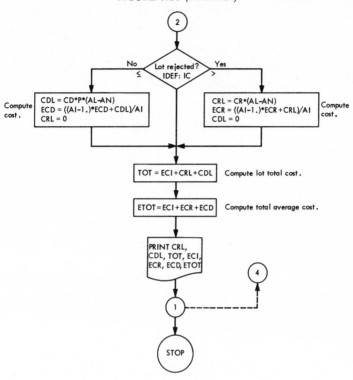

For each lot simulated we must determine the proportion defective for that lot. The process generator for P is derived as follows where r is a uniformly distributed random number.

$$r = \int_0^P 19(1-x)^{18}\, dx$$

Let $y = 1 - x$

$$r = \int_{1-p}^1 19y^{18}\, dy$$
$$= 1 - (1-p)^{19}$$

Therefore

$$p = 1 - (1-r)^{1/19}$$

Having generated the proportion defective for the lot, we start drawing our sample of five units. The probability that any randomly selected item is defective is p. Therefore to inspect the first item selected, we generate a random number, r, and compare it with p. If $r \leqslant p$, the item is defective. If $r > p$, the item is not defective. We then repeat this sampling procedure until five items have been inspected. If the total number of defective items found in the sample of five exceeds zero, the lot is rejected. If the lot is rejected the total cost is the inspection cost plus the cost of scrapping the lot. If the lot is accepted the total cost is the cost of inspection plus the cost of defective items reaching the assembly line.

The following variables will be used in the simulator, the program for which is given in flow chart in Figure 7.14.

NSIM = Number of lots simulated.
CI = Unit inspection cost.
CR = Unit rejection cost.
CD = Unit cost of defective item which reaches the assembly line.
AL = Lot size.
A = Parameter of the distribution of proportion defective (19).
IC = Acceptance number.
N = Sample size.
R = Random number.
P = Proportion defective.
IDEF = Number of defective found in sample of size N.
ECI = Average inspection cost per lot.
ECR = Average rejection cost per lot.
ECD = Average cost of defective items reaching the assembly line per lot.
ETOT = Average total cost per lot.
CRL = Cost of individual lot rejection.
CDL = Cost of individual lot acceptance.
TOT = Total cost of individual lot.

The results of 14,500 lot simulations are presented in Table 7.16. for every 1,000th simulation, starting with the 500th. In this table the cost of acceptance is the cost of defective units reaching the assembly line. Through equation (5.59) we obtain the following expected values. As we would expect the simulated average costs are

E (inspection cost/lot)	= $12.50
E (rejection cost/lot)	= $4,164.58
E (acceptance cost/lot)	= $7,912.71
E (total cost/lot)	= $12,089.79

TABLE 7.16
Simulation of the Quality Control System in Example 7.14

Simulation Number	Proportion Defective	Inspection Cost	Rejection Cost	Acceptance Cost	Total Cost	Average Inspection Cost	Average Rejection Cost	Average Acceptance Cost	Average Total Cost
500	0.0987	$12.50	$ 0.00	$24,651.52	$24,664.02	$12.50	$4,077.95	$8,372.12	$12,462.57
1500	0.0174	12.50	0.00	4,351.60	4,364.10	12.50	4,437.74	7,958.23	12,408.47
2500	0.0341	12.50	0.00	8,529.31	8,541.81	12.50	4,125.87	7,966.70	12,105.07
3500	0.0168	12.50	0.00	4,194.41	4,206.91	12.50	4,134.98	8,022.45	12,169.93
4500	0.0480	12.50	0.00	11,991.71	12,004.21	12.50	4,196.84	7,994.26	12,203.60
5500	0.0918	12.50	0.00	22,948.72	22,961.22	12.50	4,230.46	7,997.21	12,240.17
6500	0.0014	12.50	0.00	351.24	363.74	12.50	4,240.77	7,974.99	12,228.26
7500	0.0114	12.50	0.00	2,859.57	2,872.07	12.50	4,266.99	7,921.53	12,201.02
8500	0.0517	12.50	0.00	12,916.88	12,929.38	12.50	4,211.78	7,986.50	12,210.78
9500	0.0095	12.50	19,990.00	0.00	20,002.50	12.50	4,168.18	8,012.26	12,193.94
10500	0.0291	12.50	0.00	7,282.04	7,294.54	12.50	4,172.85	8,023.59	12,208.94
11500	0.0097	12.50	0.00	2,431.95	2,444.45	12.50	4,194.10	7,990.34	12,196.94
12500	0.0367	12.50	0.00	9,158.90	9,171.40	12.50	4,191.15	7,984.74	12,188.39
13500	0.0138	12.50	0.00	3,437.17	3,449.67	12.50	4,204.92	7,946.39	12,163.81
14500	0.0038	12.50	0.00	940.63	953.13	12.50	4,182.33	7,971.87	12,166.70

quite close to the corresponding mathematically derived expected costs. As the length of the simulation is increased we would expect the simulated results to approach those which were derived mathematically. Therefore, if the accuracy of estimation of given parameters or variables is questioned when the simulation is terminated, we could continue the simulation from the initial termination point until satisfactory results are obtained.

Example 7.15 – An Integration Problem

In this example we will demonstrate how simulation can be used to evaluate the integral of a function over finite limits where the function is single valued and finite over the range of integration. Suppose we wish to integrate $f_X(x)$ from a to b where $a < b$. We first enclose the integral in a rectangle of length $b - a$ and width equal to the maximum value of $f_X(x)$ over the range a to b as shown in Figure 7.15. We know that the total area enclosed by the rectangle is $(b - a)$ $[\max_{a,b} f_X(x)]$. Now we generate a random value, c, between a and b and a random value, d, between 0 and $\max_{a,b} f_X(x)$ and record whether

FIGURE 7.15

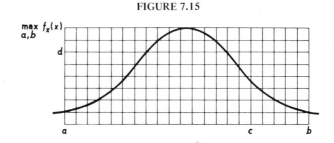

d is greater than or less than $f_X(c)$. Repeating this process N times we record the number of times, n, that $d < f_X(c)$. The area, A, under $f_X(x)$ between a and b is given by

$$A = \frac{n}{N}(b - a)\left[\max_{a,b} f_X(x)\right] \qquad (7.95)$$

To illustrate this procedure we will integrate the standard normal density function between -1 and $+1$ using the following program where

A,B = Limits of integration.
IDIV = Number of printouts of the area under the curve between A and B.

NSIM = Total number of simulations.

FMAX = Maximum value of the function integrated.

REC = Rectangular area enclosing the function.

AN = Number of points under the curve.

FX = Functional value.

MSIM = Number of simulations between successive printouts.

P = Area.

IX = Initial random number.

RANDU (IX,IY) = Random number generator given in Chapter 6.

```
      READ (5,1)A,B,IDIV,NSIM,IX
      WRITE(6,4)
      WRITE(6,1) A,B,IDIV,NSIM,IX
      FMAX=1./2.50662827
      REC=(B-A)*FMAX
      AN=0
      MSIM=NSIM/IDIV
      DO 30   I=1,IDIV
      DO 20   J=1,MSIM
      R1=RANDU(IX,IY)
      R2=RANDU(IX,IY)
      C=R1*(B-A)+A
      D=R2*FMAX
      AA=-(C**2)/2.
      FX=FMAX*EXP(AA)
      IF(D.GT.FX) GO TO 20
      AN=AN+1.
20    CONTINUE
      TOT=I*MSIM
      P=(AN/TOT)*REC
30    WRITE(6,5)TOT,P
      STOP
1     FORMAT(1X2F10.3,3I6)
4     FORMAT(1H1)
5     FORMAT(1X20HNO. OF SIMULATIONS =F12.2,2X6HAREA =F12.6)
      END
```

TABLE 7.17
Example of Integration by Simulation

Simulation Number	Area P	Percentage Error
1,000 . . . . . . 0.6847		0.0028
2,000 . . . . . . 0.6850		0.0034
3,000 . . . . . . 0.6838		0.0016
4,000 . . . . . . 0.6794		0.0048
5,000 . . . . . . 0.6795		0.0047
6,000 . . . . . . 0.6810		0.0025
7,000 . . . . . . 0.6818		0.0013
8,000 . . . . . . 0.6808		0.0028
9,000 . . . . . . 0.6810		0.0025
10,000 . . . . . . 0.6818		0.0013

The results of 10,000 simulations are shown in Table 7.17. In this table the percentage error is given by

$$\left| \frac{P - 0.6827}{0.6827} \right|$$

where 0.6827 is the true area under the standard normal distribution between -1 and $+1$.

Example 7.16 – A Production Ordering Problem

A manufacturer produces one of its products in lots of 300. Production schedules are made up 10 days in advance. For each unit of product manufactured one unit of a particular raw material is required. The required raw materials are purchased from a supplier, and the order for these raw materials must be placed within the 10-day period preceding the scheduled startup of production. The order can be placed on any one of these 10 days. If the order is placed too late, production will be delayed at a cost of $50,000 per year of delay. If, however, the order is placed too soon, the raw materials will have to be held in inventory until production begins, resulting in a cost of $50 per unit per year. The distribution of lead time in years, is gamma with $\lambda = 200$ and $n = 4$. The manufacturer wishes to determine when orders for raw materials should be placed.

The order point, t_1, is the point in time at which the order is placed and is measured in years until production is scheduled to start. Let t_2 be the time taken for receipt of the order. If $t_1 > t_2$, the order of 300 units of raw material must be carried in inventory for $t_1 - t_2$ years. If $t_1 < t_2$, production is delayed by $t_2 - t_1$ years. Therefore the cost of placing an order t_1 years before production begins, $C_0(t_1)$, can be expressed by

$$C_0(t_1) = 15,000(t_1 - t_2), \qquad t_1 > t_2$$
$$= 50,000(t_2 - t_1), \qquad t_1 \leq t_2$$

We will assume that t_1 is a discrete variable which can take on the values $1/365, 2/365, \ldots, 10/365$; although t_2 will be presumed to be continuous. To simulate this problem we must generate a gamma random variable, t_2, with parameters $\lambda = 200$ and $n = 4$, compare it with t_1, and assign the appropriate value of $C_0(t_1)$. The accompanying FORTRAN program can be used to simulate this problem.

```
          READ(5,1)   QMEAN,TLAM,TIM,CI,CDELAY,N,NSIM,IX
          WRITE(6,4)
          WRITE(6,1)   QMEAN,TLAM,TIM,CI,CDELAY,N,NSIM
          TIM=0
          DO 80 KK=1,10
          TIM=TIM+.003333
          WRITE(6,2)   TIM
          EQ=0
          ECARRY=0
          EDELAY=0
          ECLP=0
          ECI=0
          DO 70 J=1,NSIM
          AJ=J
          Q=QMEAN
   20     TLEAD=0
          DO 30 I=1,N
          R=RANDU(IX,IY)
   30     TLEAD=TLEAD-(1./TLAM)*ALOG(1.-R)
          IF(TIM.GT.TLEAD) GO TO 50
          TDELAY=TLEAD-TIM
          TCARRY=0
          GO TO 60
   50     TDELAY=0
          TCARRY=TIM-TLEAD
   60     COSTI=CI*Q*TCARRY
          CLP=CDELAY*TDELAY
          EDELAY=(EDELAY*(AJ-1.)+TDELAY)/AJ
          ECARRY=(ECARRY*(AJ-1.)+TCARRY)/AJ
          ECI=(ECI*(AJ-1.)+COSTI)/AJ
          ECLP=(ECLP*(AJ-1.)+CLP)/AJ
          EQ=(EQ*(AJ-1.)+Q)/AJ
          ETO=ECI+ECLP
   70     CONTINUE
          K=NSIM
   80     WRITE(6,3)K,Q,TDELAY,TCARRY,COSTI,CLP,EQ,EDELAY,ECARRY,ECI,ECLP,ET
          10
          STOP
   1      FORMAT(1X5F12.4,3I5)
   2      FORMAT(1X4HTIM=F12.6)
   3      FORMAT(1X2HJ=I5,2X2HQ=F12.1,2X7HTDELAY=E14.8,2X7HTCARRY=E14.8,2X6H
          1COSTI=E14.8,2X4HCLP=E14.8/1X3HEQ=E14.8,2X7HEDELAY=E14.8,2X7HECARRY
          2=E14.8,2X4HECI=E14.8,2X5HECLP=E14.8,2X5HETOT=E14.8//)
   4      FORMAT(1H1)
          END
```

The variables used in this program are defined as follows:

QMEAN = Order quantity (300).

TLAM = λ(200).

CI = Inventory carrying cost per unit per year ($\$50$).

CDELAY = Cost of production delay per year ($\$50,000$).

N = n (4).

NSIM = Number of simulations.

K = Order point (in days).

T = t_1.

TLEAD = t_2.

RANDU = Random number generator.

TDELAY = Number of years by which production is delayed.

TCARRY = Number of years for which Q units will be carried in inventory before production begins.

COSTI = Cost of carrying inventory.

CDP = Cost of delayed production.

EDELAY = Average production delay.

ECARRY = Average time for which Q units remain in inventory before production begins.

ECI = Average inventory cost.

ECDP = Average cost of delayed production.

ETOT = Average total cost.

For each of the 10 possible order points, K, 100 orders were simulated with the results shown in Table 7.18. Based upon the results of 100 orders simulated we would conclude that orders should be placed with the supplier eight days prior to production startup.

TABLE 7.18
100 Orders Simulated

Order Point (Days)	Average Inventory Cost per Order	Average Cost of Production Delay per Order	Average Total Cost per Order
1 . . . . $	0.00	$927.78	$927.78
2	1.92	700.39	702.31
3	2.56	500.30	502.86
4	9.90	369.96	379.86
5	29.72	263.80	293.52
6	58.01	203.61	261.62
7	104.76	114.35	219.11
8	118.10	78.60	196.70
9	204.84	39.11	243.95
10	193.91	41.07	234.98

One might question whether the simulation of 100 orders is sufficient to produce a reliable decision as to the optimal ordering policy. The pertinence of this query is underlined by the results obtained when the effect of each ordering policy is examined on the basis of the simulation of 300 orders (Table 7.19). In this case we would be led to the conclusion that the order point should be six days prior to production, contradicting the results obtained when only 100 orders were simulated. Which is the correct conclusion? To resolve this dilemma we might choose to simulate still more orders. Let us examine the results of the simulation of 500 orders under each ordering policy. In this case eight days would seem to be the best order point as seen in Table 7.20.

TABLE 7.19
300 Orders Simulated

Order Point Days	Average Inventory Cost per Order	Average Cost of Production Delay per Order	Average Total Cost per Order
1 . . . . $ 0.22		$871.07	$871.29
2 . . . . 0.36		665.72	666.08
3 . . . . 6.33		478.56	484.89
4 . . . . 17.66		374.15	391.81
5 . . . . 34.89		311.47	346.36
6 . . . . 52.01		156.97	208.98
7 . . . . 93.44		119.88	213.32
8 . . . . 130.72		95.60	226.32
9 . . . . 186.19		51.28	237.47
10 . . . . 221.70		43.73	265.43

Since the reliability of a simulation tends to increase as the length of the simulation is increased, we would probably accept the results given in Table 7.20 as the most reliable of the three and use eight days as our order point. One might also argue that it does not make much difference when we order as long as the order is placed between six and eight days prior to production since ordering anywhere within this period is likely to put us within $70 of the optimal average cost per order. A third alternative would be to increase the number of simulations still further.

TABLE 7.20
500 Orders Simulated

Order Point Days	Average Inventory Cost per Order	Average Cost of Production Delay per Order	Average Total Cost per Order
1 . . . . $ 0.13		$854.00	$854.13
2 . . . . 0.98		646.79	647.77
3 . . . . 6.55		528.77	535.32
4 . . . . 14.87		357.05	371.92
5 . . . . 35.34		273.15	308.49
6 . . . . 59.96		187.92	247.88
7 . . . . 87.93		127.22	215.15
8 . . . . 124.67		75.92	200.59
9 . . . . 163.87		53.97	217.84
10 . . . . 211.28		45.26	256.54

With reference to this particular problem, a case might be made for any of the above arguments. However, each of the arguments begs a question basic to the analysis of any problem by simulation. If we are to obtain reliable results from a simulation experiment we must have some criterion through which we can determine when to terminate the analysis. We will defer discussion of such criteria until Chapter 11. As we shall attempt to point out, derivation of objective criteria upon which reliable decisions can be based is one of the most perplexing problems facing the experimental analyst.

PROBLEMS

1. Develop a process generator for X corresponding to each of the following probability density functions:

a) $f_X(x) = \begin{cases} 1/2e^x, & -\infty < x < 0 \\ 1/2e^{-x}, & 0 < x < \infty \end{cases}$

b) $f_X(x) = 1/4xe^{-x/2}, \qquad 0 < x < \infty$

c) $f_X(x) = 12x^2(1 - x), \qquad 0 < x < 1$

2. Given the following cumulative distribution functions, develop the corresponding process generators:

a) $F_X(x) = \begin{cases} 0, & x < -2 \\ 1/2 - x^2/8, & -2 < x < 0 \\ 1/2 + x^2/8, & 0 < x < 2 \\ 1, & x > 2 \end{cases}$

b) $F_X(x) = (1/\pi)\tan^{-1}(x - 1), \qquad -\infty < x < \infty$

c) $F_X(x) = \dfrac{x(x + 1)(2x + 1)}{n(n + 1)(2n + 1)}, \qquad x = 1, 2, 3, \ldots, n$

3. Given the following density function for X, develop the corresponding process generator:

$$f_X(x) = (a + 1)(1 - x)^a, \qquad 0 < x < 1$$

4. Develop a process generator for the negative binomial random variable.

5. Pareto's distribution is defined by the density function

$$f_X(x) = ab^a 1/x^{a+1}, \qquad b \leq x < \infty, \quad a > 0, b > 0$$

Derive a process generator for the random variable defined by this distribution.

6. Derive a process generator for X if the density function of X is given by

$$f_X(x) = 1/a^2 xe^{-1/2(x/a)^2}, \qquad 0 < x < \infty$$

7. Develop process generators for the following probability density functions:

$$a) \ f_X(x) = \begin{cases} 1/6, & 0 < x \le 2 \\ 1/3, & 2 < x \le 3 \\ 1/12, & 3 < x \le 7 \end{cases}$$

$$b) \ f_X(x) = \begin{cases} x/100, & 0 < x \le 10 \\ \dfrac{20 - x}{100} & 10 < x \le 20 \end{cases}$$

$$c) \ f_X(x) = \begin{cases} 30x - 3, & 0.1 < x \le 0.2 \\ \dfrac{13 - 2x}{3} & 0.2 < x \le 0.5 \\ 2(1 - x), & 0.5 < x \le 1 \end{cases}$$

8. Develop a process generator which will produce random variables having the probability mass function given by

$$p_X(x) = \frac{p(1 - p)^{x-1}}{1 - (1 - p)^n}, \qquad x = 1, 2, 3, \ldots, n$$

9. Develop process generators for each of the random variables defined by the following probability mass functions:

$$a) \ p_X(x) = \frac{3n + 1}{n(3x - 2)(3x + 1)}, \qquad x = 1, 2, 3, \ldots, n$$

$$b) \ p_X(x) = \frac{1}{1,333,300}(2x - 1)^2, \qquad x = 1, 2, 3, \ldots, 100$$

$$c) \ p_X(x) = \begin{cases} \dfrac{3x^2}{n(n + 1)(2n + 1)}, & x = 1, 2, 3, \ldots, n \\ \dfrac{x}{n(3n + 1)}, & x = n + 1, n + 2, n + 3, \ldots, 2n \end{cases}$$

10. Automobiles are washed at a particular car wash in three stages. The distribution of time taken in the first stage, preliminary cleaning, is normal with a mean of three minutes and standard deviation of 0.2 minutes. The time spent in the second stage, washing, is exponentially distributed with a mean of eight minutes. The distribution of drying time, the final stage, is uniform between three and eight minutes. Develop a process generator for the total time in the system. Compute the average total time in the car wash (excluding waiting time) on the basis of 5,000 times generated by this process generator. Compare this average with the expected average.

11. The distribution time between the arrival of successive orders at a warehouse is exponential with a mean of one day. The distribution of the number of units requested of each order is geometric with $p = 0.5$. Develop a process generator which will produce the random variable which represents the

total number of units demanded per eight-hour day. Generate 100 days' demand and compute the average daily demand.

12. Each day a man leaves his home, A, and goes to work at G. As indicated in the diagram below, the routes he may take are

$$1\text{-}3\text{-}7, \quad 1\text{-}4\text{-}8, \quad 2\text{-}5\text{-}8, \quad 2\text{-}6\text{-}9$$

The value, p, for each route is the probability that

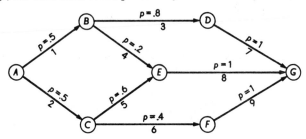

he takes that route. That is, if he arrives at point C, the probability that he takes route 5 is 0.6 and the probability he takes 6 is 0.4. The distribution of the time spent on each route is normal with parameters given below:

Route 1 — mean = 20 min., standard deviation = 1 min.
Route 2 — mean = 15 min., standard deviation = 2 min.
Route 3 — mean = 5 min., standard deviation = 0.5 min.
Route 4 — mean = 7 min., standard deviation = 1 min.
Route 5 — mean = 6 min., standard deviation = 1.5 min.
Route 6 — mean = 10 min., standard deviation = 2 min.
Route 7 — mean = 4 min., standard deviation = 0.6 min.
Route 8 — mean = 5 min., standard deviation = 0.8 min.
Route 9 — mean = 3 min., standard deviation = 0.25 min.

Develop a process generator which will produce the random variable representing the total time in transit between A and G. Simulate 500 such trips and compute the average trip time. How does this average compare with the expected average trip time of 28.2 min?

13. Derive a process generator for the beta random variable, the density function of which is given by

$$f_X(x) = \frac{(a+b+1)!}{a!\,b!}\, x^a (1-x)^b, \qquad 0 < x < 1$$

where a and b are integers

a) $a > 0, \qquad b = 0$

b) $a = 0, \qquad b > 0$

c) $a > 0, \qquad b > 0$

$$\frac{(x - 6,000)^2}{80,0000}$$

14. The distribution of daily production for a particular item is given by

$$f_X(x) = \frac{1}{200\sqrt{2\pi}} e^{-\frac{(x-6,000)^2}{80,000}}, \qquad 0 < x < \infty$$

Each day a certain portion, p, of the total production is scrapped. That is, if the percentage of scrap is $p100$ percent and x is the day's production, the total scrap is px. Net production, y, is then $y = x - px$. The density function of the proportion scrap is given by

$$g_P(p) = 99(1 - p)^{98}, \qquad 0 < p < 1$$

Develop a process generator for net daily production, Y; Generate 400 days' net production. Compute the mean and variance of Y. Using either the Kolmogorov-Smirnov or chi-square tests, determine whether the distribution of net daily production can be assumed to be normal. Let $\alpha = 0.05$.

15. The distribution of time until failure, T, for a particular machine is defined by

$$f_T(t) = 0.25e^{-0.25t}, \qquad 0 < t < \infty$$

where time until failure is measured in weeks. When the machine fails, a repairman immediately begins repairs on the machine. The distribution of repair time, S, in days, is defined by

$$f_S(s) = 4e^{-4s}, \qquad 0 < s < \infty$$

Develop a simulator to estimate the average downtime per week in days. Assume 365 days per year and a 24-hour working day. Simulate three years of operation, and compute the average downtime per week.

16. Simulate the system given in example 5.3 when the maintenance crew size is three. Continue the simulation until the average annual cost of maintaining the system is within 1 percent of the expected value, $28,613.

17. Simulate 10 years of operation of the system described in example 5.5 when the maintenance crew size is 15. Compute the average annual total cost of the system, the average number of failures per year, and the average downtime per failure.

18. Simulate the system discussed in example 5.7 when $n = 3$ and $T = 0.05$ years. Simulate 30 years of operation and compute the average annual total cost of the maintenance system.

19. Determine the average total cost per lot for the quality control system in example 5.11 by simulation when $n = 5$ and $c = 4$. Also determine the average cost per lot for rejection and acceptance. Based upon the results of 10,000 simulated lots, determine the probability distribution of total cost per lot.

20. For the problem given in example 5.14, determine the probability of lot rejection because of short-shots and because of cracks on the basis of 10,000 simulated lots.

21. A building contains 1,000 light bulbs. The frequency distribution of time until failure, in days, is given below.

TABLE 7.21

Time Until Failure (Days)	Frequency of Time Until Failure
0.00– 2.00	43
2.01– 4.00	84
4.01– 6.00	135
6.01– 8.00	102
8.01–10.00	88
10.01–12.00	61
12.01–14.00	33
14.01–16.00	18
16.01–18.00	9
18.01–20.00	4
20.01–22.00	1
22.01–24.00	0

The building manager wishes to determine the best policy for replacing burned-out bulbs. One such policy is to replace them as they burn out, which will cost $1 per replacement. Another possibility is to replace all bulbs every ith week in addition to replacing any which fail during the weeks between bulk replacement. The cost of replacing all bulbs at one time is $0.20 per bulb. By simulation determine the average cost of replacement per week for the following cases:

a) Replacement upon failure only.

b) Replacement upon failure in addition to quantity replacement every week.

c) Replacement upon failure in addition to quantity replacement every two weeks.

d) Replacement upon failure in addition to quantity replacement every three weeks.

e) Replacement upon failure in addition to quantity replacement every four weeks.

For each of the five cases simulate a one-year period and determine the least costly of the five cases. Use equation (7.84) to generate the time until bulb failure.

22. The following quality control system has been developed to control a particular dimension. A sample of size 50 is selected from a lot of 1,000 units. The dimension of each unit in the sample is measured and the mean dimensions for the sample $\bar{x}$, is calculated where,

$$\bar{x} = \frac{1}{50} \sum_{i=1}^{50} x_i$$

and x_i is the dimension of the ith unit in the sample. If $\bar{x}$ lies between 4.804 and 5.196, the lot is accepted. Otherwise the lot is rejected. The desired dimension is five. The distribution of the dimension for each unit in the lot is normal with mean m and standard deviation 0.7. The distribution of the lot mean, m, is normal with mean 5 and standard deviation 0.1 By simulating the inspection of 1,000 lots, determine the probability of rejecting a lot.

(Hint: To simulate this inspection plan, the value of m for the lot must first be generated. Based upon m and the lot standard deviation, 0.7, the dimension of each unit inspected is then generated.)

23. A particle moves on the following circle. The particle starts at zero. At any point on the circle, the particle will take one step which may be to either adjacent point on the circle. The probability that the particle moves clockwise or

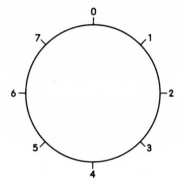

counterclockwise at any point is 0.5. By simulation determine the probability distribution of the number of steps until the particle returns to 0 and the expected number of steps until the particle returns to zero.

24. An electronic detection device is composed of three components, 1, 2, and 3, such that if any single component fails, the device fails. The mean and standard deviation of component life are given below. The distribution of time

TABLE 7.22

Component	Mean life (m_i)	Standard deviation of life (σ)
1. . . . . . .1.2 years.		0.10 years.
2. . . . . . .1.4 years.		0.15 years.
3. . . . . . .1.1 years.		0.10 years.

until failure for each component is normal with mean and standard deviation as given above. This detection device is to function for one year. The probability that it will survive for this period is the probability that each of the three components lasts for at least one year or

$$P \text{ (survival for one year)} = \prod_{i=1}^{3} \int_{1}^{\infty} \frac{1}{\sigma\sqrt{2\pi}} \exp\left[-\frac{(x_i - m_i)^2}{2\sigma^2}\right] dx_i$$

$$= (0.9772)(0.9961)(0.8413)$$

$$= 0.8189$$

A reliability of 0.8189 is not considered high enough. To increase the reliability of the device, stand-by components can be added which will take over upon failure of the original component, thereby extending the life of the equipment. The life distribution of each stand-by component is exponential with mean given in Table 7.23. Any number of stand-by units can be added but at the additional cost indicated in the table. For example, the mean life of the third component can be increased by 0.08 years by adding two stand-by units which would cost $0.40 over the present cost. By simulation, determine the number and arrangement of stand-by components which will bring the system reliability to 0.98.

TABLE 7.23

Component	Mean Life of Standby	Cost/Standby Unit Added
1. . . . . .0.05 years		$0.20
2. . . . . .0.07 years		0.30
3. . . . . .0.04 years		0.20

25. The distribution of demand for parking space in a particular downtown area has been found to be Poisson with mean 200 per eight-hour day. A parking lot is to be located in this area which is to have a 100-car capacity. The cost of operating and maintaining the lot is estimated to be $9,000 per year. The price of a parking space on the lot is to be $0.25 no matter how long the space is occupied. The distribution of the time a car spends on the lot is exponential with mean two hours. The parking lot is to remain open eight hours each day, 365 days per year. By simulation determine the annual profit which can be expected from this parking lot.

26. A training program has been developed for a certain class of jobs by the company. There are three phases to the training program, A, B, and C. Upon completion of each phase of the program the trainee takes a test. If he passes the test, he moves on to the next phase. If he fails the test, he must repeat that phase of the program and retake the test. This procedure continues until he finally passes the tests for all three phases. p_i is the probability that he fails the test for the ith phase on the first attempt. p_i^n is the probability that he fails the test on the nth try. Each phase of instruction requires one week before the test for that phase may be taken. The duration of the instruction period remains the same no matter how many times a trainee repeats the phase. Let $p_1 = 0.4$, $p_2 = 0.5$, and $p_3 = 0.2$.

Simulate the time taken, in weeks, for a trainee to complete the training program. Calculate the average time taken to complete each phase of the

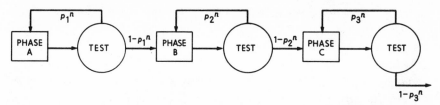

program and the average total time taken to complete the entire program. Also determine the distribution of time taken to complete the training program.

27. A computer center operates 24 hours per day requiring three computer operators per eight hour shift. Each operator is paid at a rate of $4 per hour. If an operator cannot work his shift, he must either be replaced on that shift or the machine he operates is shut down for that shift at a cost of $100 per hour. To provide insurance against the possibility of loss of machine time, it has been proposed that several of the operators be put "on call" during those shifts on which they are not working. The proposal calls for paying operators "on call" at a rate of $0.50 per hour for remaining available. Each operator is paid time and one half for all work over eight hours per day. The probability that an operator can work his shift is 0.95. The probability that an operator "on call" can be reached when neeeded is 0.90. By simulation, determine the number of "on call" operators to minimize the total cost of keeping the computers running. Assume that an operator "on call" is paid $0.50 per hour whether he is called or not.

REFERENCES

Chorafas, D. N. *Systems and Simulation.* New York: Academic Press, 1965.

Freeman, H. *Introduction to Statistical Inference.* Reading, Mass.: Addison-Wesley Publishing Co., Inc., 1963.

Hadley, G. *Introduction to Probability and Statistical Decision Theory.* San Francisco: Holden-Day, Inc., 1967.

Hogg, R. V. and Craig, A. T. *Introduction to Mathematical Statistics.* New York: The MacMillan Co., 1959.

McMillan, C. and Gonzolez, R. F. *Systems Analysis.* Homewood, Ill.: Richard D. Irwin, Inc., 1965.

Mize, J. H. and Cox, J. G. *Essentials of Simulation.* Englewood Cliffs, N.J.: Prentice-Hall, Inc., 1968.

Naylor, T. H., Balintfy, J. L., Burdick, D. S., and Chu, K. *Computer Simulation Techniques.* New York: John Wiley & Sons, Inc., 1966.

Parzen, E. *Modern Probability Theory and Its Applications.* New York: John Wiley & Sons, Inc., 1960.

———. *Stochastic Processes.* San Francisco: Holden-Day, Inc., 1962.

Siegel, S. *Nonparametric Statistics.* New York: McGraw-Hill Book Co., Inc., 1956.

Tocher, K. D. *The Art of Simulation.* London: The English Universities Press Ltd., 1963.

Wadsworth, G. P. and Bryan, J. G. *Introduction to Probability and Random Variables.* New York: McGraw-Hill Book Co., Inc., 1960.

Weiss, L. *Statistical Decision Theory.* New York: McGraw-Hill Book Co., Inc., 1961.

Wilks, S. S. *Mathematical Statistics.* New York: John Wiley & Sons, Inc., 1962.

CHAPTER
8

SIMULATION OF QUEUEING SYSTEMS

In Chapter 3 we investigated the mathematical aspects of some elementary queueing systems. In this chapter we present the basic concepts of simulation as applied to queueing systems. We will investigate the method of approach to this class of problems and then illustrate how some of the systems discussed in Chapter 3 can be analyzed via simulation techniques.

THE SINGLE CHANNEL SYSTEM

We will begin our study of simulation of queueing systems by investigating the single channel Poisson queueing system presented in Chapter 3. Remember that we were able to develop a closed form solution for the steady state conditions in this system. We will now construct a simulation model of this system and discuss some of the aspects we must consider when we design a simulation model. Then we will change some of the conditions of the system to show how simulation can be used for more advanced systems analysis. Figure 8.1 illustrates the system in which units arrive at the service facility demanding service. If the service facility or channel is empty, the unit enters the facility and is serviced. If a unit is already in the service channel, the arriving unit must take its place in the waiting line and wait its turn for service. Service takes place on a first-come first-serve basis. The distribution of time between successive arrivals to the system is assumed to be exponential, and the distribution of time to serve a unit will also be assumed to be exponential. Remember that we developed an interesting relationship regarding the exponential distribution, namely, that if time between successive events is exponentially distributed, then the distribution of the number of events occurring in any time interval follows a Poisson distribution. This concept of looking at the interevent time distribution will prove helpful in the simulation of queueing systems.

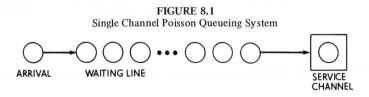

FIGURE 8.1
Single Channel Poisson Queueing System

ARRIVAL   WAITING LINE   SERVICE
                                                          CHANNEL

The single channel queueing system is manifested a great deal in our everyday lives. Any time we go to the movies we generally enter a single channel system to purchase our tickets. An automatic car washing system is another single channel system. Still another is the line of students at a registration desk or the line of students waiting to see a course advisor.

So now we must consider how to go about building a computer simulation model of this simple system. We should first consider what our objective is in studying this system. The formulation of objectives is not an easy task, and it is not within the scope of this text to teach the student how they should be formulated. However, this aspect is important and should not be overlooked. Let us say simply that we wish to examine the following aspects of the single channel queueing system:

1. The average time a unit spends in the system and the frequency distribution of this time.
2. The average utilization of the service facility.
3. The average number of units in the system as well as its frequency distribution.
4. The average amount of time a unit spends in the queue and the frequency distribution of it.

In this light we could say that the objective of the simulation program is to provide information regarding the operation of a single channel Poisson queueing system. We will assume, for now, that this is sufficient to allow us to proceed to construction of our computer model.

Now let us turn our attention to the actual model we will build for the computer solution of our single channel queueing system. We are faced with a system in which units arrive randomly to some service facility. We must be able to "cause" this to happen in our computer model. Further, these units must be serviced by the facility on a first-come first-serve basis. Hence some units will probably be forced to wait in a queue until their turn comes for service. We will look at the system from the standpoint of "next event" analysis. In this manner we can start by looking at our system at some arbitrary point in time and attempt to find out what is going to happen. The question, then, is what could happen? In this simple system there are only two possibilities: a unit could enter the system and the service facility could finish service on a unit. In this manner we have further simplified our analysis because all we now need do is to decide what must be done in the eventuality that one or the other of these events occur. Let us look at he diagram in Figure 8.2 to see what the simulator must accomplish when the second event occurs. Remember that we are concerned with the status of the service facility upon completion of a service.

FIGURE 8.2
Flow Diagram of Service Facility upon Service Completion

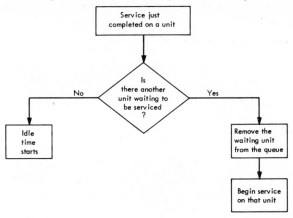

Looking at Figure 8.2, we can see that the service facility has only two states. That is, the service facility is either busy (service on the next waiting unit begins immediately) or idle (no unit is waiting for service.)

Now let us look at what occurs when a unit enters the system to be serviced (Figure 8.3). Looking at figure 8.3, we see that a unit entering the system is also in only one of two possible states: the unit is either in the waiting line or its is being serviced.

FIGURE 8.3
Flow Diagram of Unit Entering System

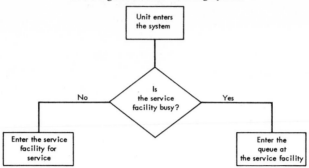

Continuing this idea of next-event analysis, we now investigate how the entire system can be modeled. The system includes the units in the queue, the unit being serviced, and the service facility itself. We will see that the idea of "states" of a given unit or the service facility can be incorporated into our model. Figure 8.4 shows a decision grid for a unit just entering the system. It shows what conditions might exist and the outcome for the unit when the given states do exist. The criterion here is whether the unit will enter the queue or whether it will proceed immediately into the service channel, implying a queue of length zero.

FIGURE 8.4
Decision Grid for Unit Status After Entry to System

Events upon System Entry by a Unit				Outcomes to the Unit	
Facility		Queue			
Busy	Idle	Not Empty	Empty	Enter Queue	Enter Service
X			X	X	
X		X		X	
	X		X		X

Figure 8.4 shows that when a unit enters the system it will go immediately to the service channel only when the service channel is idle and there are no other units in the queue ahead of it.

Examining a similar grid for the service facility, we would be interested in what conditions must exist for the service facility to either be busy or idle after it completes service on a given unit. Figure 8.5 illustrates this. Here we see that the facility will be busy after it completes service on a given unit only when the queue is not empty.

FIGURE 8.5
Decision Grid For Facility Stakes after Service

States		Outcomes	
Queue Not Empty	Queue Empty	Facility Busy	Facility Idle
X		X	
	X		X

Hence we have shown two methods of analysis to determine what might happen next in the system under given conditions. The next question we face is how we can cause these events to occur in simulated time. For this discussion we must concern ourselves with the idea of maintaining "clocks" for the purpose of "keeping an eye" on what must happen next in our model. In effect what we do in a computer model is to transform real time. Sometimes the transformation is of a compressive nature, such as when we simulate months of factory operation in minutes of computer time; sometimes the transformation is of an expansive nature, such as when we simulate the atomic reactions of a few nanoseconds (billionth of one second) in minutes or hours. In most queueing systems we deal with time as the random variable. In the next chapter we will show how other variables may be random in nature when the time increment is fixed, such as demand per day in an inventory system. However, we are now concerned with events which occur randomly in time. The question is how we can use this idea of next-event analysis to our advantage in building a computer model. Fortunately we have some advantage over the real world analyst in that we can know beforehand what is going to happen next. When a man begins to wash one car in a car wash, he does not know exactly how long it will take him. Similarly the girl selling tickets at a movie theatre does not know when the next person is going to walk up to buy a ticket. We could study both cases and arrive at some time distributions, but essentially in the real world, events are rarely deterministic. However, in a computer model we know when the next arrival is going to occur, and we know how long a given service will take simply because we can "generate" these times in our computer model.

Assume that we have two next-event clocks which run backwards from any given time to zero. One clock (t_1) will contain the time until the next arrival to the system occurs; the other clock (t_2) will contain the time until service is completed on the unit in the service channel. The actual time values placed into these clocks initially will be generated because we know both the distribution of interarrival time as well as the distribution of service time. Hence when a unit arrives at the system all we need do is generate an interarrival time for the next arrival and place this value in the proper clock. Similarly when a given unit enters the service channel, we will generate its service time from the distribution of service time as reflected in our process generator and place this value in the proper clock. Finally we will place a "master clock" (MCT) in our model to keep an overall record of the total elapsed simulated time. It is assumed that all clocks will operate with the same basic time unit.

To illustrate the use of these three clocks, consider the following example as summarized in Table 8.1. Our simulation starts at time zero, at which the system is empty. Since there is nothing in the service channel, a service cannot take place until the first unit arrives and enters the channel. Therefore the first event which takes place in our simulation is the arrival of a unit, and we must generate the time at which this arrival occurs. Let this time be two clock units (minutes, hours, days, etc.). We enter a "2" in the arrival clock, meaning that the arrival will occur two units of time from the present master clock time (0). Each time one of our clocks is adjusted we ask ourselves the question, "Do I know what the next event occurring in the simulation will be and when it will occur?" At this point we are looking into the future from master clock time zero, and we know that the next event that will occur is an arrival and that it will occur at master clock time "2". We therefore move the master clock forward and enter the unit into service. Having adjusted the clock, we ask ourselves when the next event will occur and what that event will be. At master clock time "2" we do not know whether or not service on the unit in the channel will be completed before the next arrival occurs. To determine what the next event will be, we must generate the service time of the unit which just entered the channel and the time until the next arrival occurs. Let the service and arrival times be five and three respectively. We enter these values in our arrival and service clocks at master clock time "2". The next event which takes place in our simulation is an arrival which will occur at master clock time "5". Therefore we adjust all clocks by three units. The master clock is advanced to "5" and the service clock is reduced to "2" since three units of service time will have been completed when the arrival occurred at master clock time "5". Since the service channel is busy, the arrival takes his place in the queue. Again, "what is the next event which occurs and when does it take place?" We cannot determine this until we know the time until the next arrival. Let this time be one unit. We enter this value in the arrival clock at master clock time "5" and observe that this arrival is the next simulated event which occurs. Thus we advance the master clock by one unit, reduce the service clock by one unit, and enter the arriving unit in the queue, bringing the queue length to two. Let the time until the next arrival be four units of time, indicating that the next event which occurs is completion of service on the unit presently in the service channel at master clock time "7". We advance the master clock to "7", reduce the arrival clock to "3", remove the unit from the service channel, and enter the first unit in the queue into the service channel, reducing the queue length to one. To determine the next event we generate a service time for the unit which just entered the channel. Let this service time be two units. We enter this value in the service clock at master clock time "7". Completion of service is the next event which occurs, taking place at master clock time "9". We advance the master clock by two units, reduce the arrival clock by the same amount, remove the unit presently in the service channel from the service channel, enter the waiting unit into the service channel, and reduce the queue length to zero. Again, to determine the next event we must generate the service time for the unit which just entered the channel. We would continue this manipulation of the three clocks until the system had been simulated for the period of time required for our analysis.

TABLE 8.1
Clocks in Simple Queueing Example

Master Clock	Arrival Clock t_1	Service Clock t_2	Units in Service	Units in Queue
0. 2	0	0	0
2. 3	5	1	0
5. 1	2	1	1
6. 4	1	1	2
7. 3	2	1	1
9. 1		1	0

One convenient method for constructing a computer model for this queueing system is to design two basic matrices. The first matrix we will call the "unit matrix". It contains the pertinent information about each unit in our system. The other matrix we will call our "next-event matrix," and it will contain essentially the clocks t_1 and t_2. Finally we will keep a master clock T to accumulate total elapsed simulated time.

Let us look at the entries we will place in our unit matrix (UM). Figure 8.6 shows this matrix in conceptual form.

FIGURE 8.6
Unit Matrix (UM)

	1	2	j 3	4	•	•	•	M
	Unit Number	MCT of Initial System Entry	Present State	MCT of Entry into Present State				
1								
2								
3								
4								
•								
•								
•								
N								

The entries in this matrix are defined as follows. Each horizontal vector $UM_{ij}(j = 1, \ldots, M)$ is called a unit vector. There is one vector in the UM for each unit in the system. The entries for each unit corresponding to j columns contain all the pertinent information about the ith unit, $i = 1, 2, \ldots, N$. The utility of some entries will not be fully realized until the rest of the model is described. The j columns are described as follows:

1. Unit number – This is a sequential number assigned for the purpose of identification to a unit generated by the simulator and entered into the queueing system.
2. MCT of initial system entry – This contains the master clock time recorded when the unit entered the system. Note that a unit enters the system when it arrives at the queue. Obviously, if queue length is zero the unit proceeds directly into the service facility.

3. Present state − This is an indicator identifying the present state of a unit which is still in the system. For our example the unit can be in two states, *i.e.*, $UM_{i,3}$ = 1 or 2, for the unit is either in the queue (1) or being serviced (2).

4. MCT of entry to present state − This contains the master clock time recorded when the unit entered the state indicated in $UM_{i,3}$. When $UM_{i,3}$ = 1 the $UM_{i,4} = UM_{i,2}$. This is because as we defined it, the unit entered the queue at the same time it entered the system. However, when $UM_{i,3}$ = 2 then $UM_{i,4}$ and $UM_{i,2}$ are not necessarily equal, but $UM_{i,4}$ = MCT of entry into the service facility.

As the figure shows, several more columns may be added to the UM. The use of additional columns will be illustrated later.

To illustrate the use of the unit matrix, let us construct the unit matrix for the example described in Table 8.1. The information summarized is for the units which are in the queueing system at six master clock units of time of the simulation. The unit matrix for these units is given in Table 8.2. At the point in time we are considering, the first three arrivals are still in the system. Therefore, information on all three is carried in Table 8.2. The first arrival entered the system at MCT = 2. At the present time it is in state 2 (in the service channel), and it entered its present state at MCT = 2. The second arrival entered the system at MCT = 5 and is presently in the queue (state 1) having entered its present state at MCT = 5. The third unit entered the system at MCT = 6, is presently in the queue, and entered the queue at MCT = 6.

TABLE 8.2
Example Unit Matrix at MCT = 6

Unit Number	MCT of Initial System Entry	Present State	MCT of Entry into Present State
1	2	2	2
2	5	1	5
3	6	1	6

If we look at the unit matrix at MCT = 7, we find that only the second and third arrivals are entered, because the first arrival has been serviced and has left the system. At MCT = 7 we have the unit matrix given in Table 8.3.

TABLE 8.3
Example Unit Matrix at MCT = 7

Unit Number	MCT of Initial System Entry	Present State	MCT of Entry into Present State
2	5	2	7
3	6	1	6

Now let us look at the next events matrix (NEM). This is shown conceptually in Figure 8.7.

FIGURE 8.7
Next Events Matrix (NEM)

i \ j		1 System Entry Condition	2 Facility Clock
1	Time until Event Occurs		
2	Unit Number in Question		

The column entries for this matrix indicate the conditions regarding the clocks t_1 and t_2. The column "System Entry Condition" contains two entries. The first row is titled "Time until Event Occurs." This is t_1, as described earlier, or the time until the next unit enters the system. The row "Unit Number in Question" contains the unit number as entered in $UM_{i,1}$ for the unit which will enter the system in t_1 time units. The first row of the column "Facility Clock" contains the amount of time that the facility will be busy servicing the unit it presently contains. The second row designates the unit number as registered in $UM_{i,1}$ for the unit being serviced.

We will again refer to the example given in Table 8.1 to illustrate the use of the next event matrix (NEM). The NEM for MCT=2 is

TABLE 8.4
Example NEM at MCT = 2

		1 System Entry Condition	2 Facility Clock
1	Time until Event Occurs	3	5
2	Unit Number in Question	2	1

given in Table 8.4. At MCT=2, the next arrival will occur three units of time hence, and this arrival will be the second unit entering the system. The present service will be completed five units hence; this service being on the first arrival to the system.

TABLE 8.5
Example NEM at MCT = 6

		1	2
		System Entry Condition	Facility Clock
1	Time until Event Occurs	4	1
2	Unit Number in Question	4	1

The NEM for MCT = 6 is given in Table 8.5. The next unit to arrive is number 4 and it will arrive four units hence. The unit presently being serviced is number 1, and it will remain in service for one more time unit.

Now let us define several other variables useful in collecting information about the queueing system under study.

IUNIT − Counter to record the number of units presently in the system.

FBUSY − Variable used to accumulate the total amount of time the facility is busy.

TIME (I) − A vector for collecting the frequency distribution of the total time a unit spends in the system.

TOTTIM − A variable used to accumulate the total of unit-times in the system. It will be used to calculate an average time after the simulation is over.

NUMBER (I) − A vector for collecting the frequency distribution of the number of units in the system.

TQUEUE − Variable used to accumulate the total unit waiting time in the queue. This variable will be used to calculate the average waiting time in the queue.

QTIME (I) − A vector used to collect the frequency distribution of queue waiting times.

IBS − A "busy switch" for the facility. IBS = 0 implies the facility is presently idle. IBS = 1 implies facility is presently busy.

Now let us begin to put the pieces together. From the analyst's point of view it is very helpful to construct a flow chart of the simulation model as the model would work at some point in time.

For the present we will not concern ourselves with starting conditions or output format. We will attempt to design a flow chart which depicts the operation of the model at an arbitrary point in time. Afer the logic of this aspect of the simulation model has been solidified and hand-checked, we will turn our attention to starting conditions for the simulation and output information. Figure 8.8 illustrates the

FIGURE 8.8
Macro Flow Chart for Basic Simulator

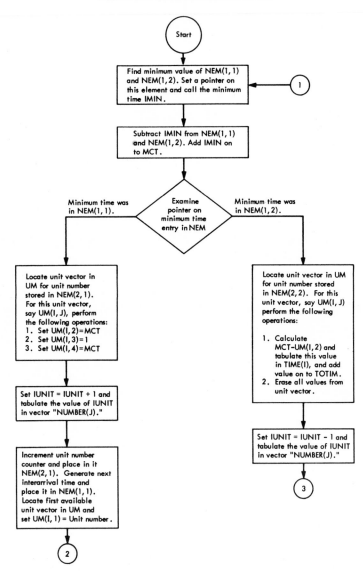

FIGURE 8.8 *(continued)*

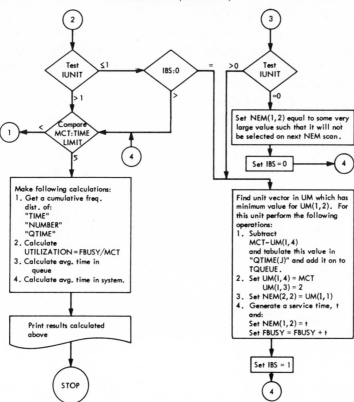

flow chart for the main body of our simulation model for this queueing system. Keep in mind that the method proposed herein is, for this basic system, somewhat inefficient, in that a great deal of array manipulation is necessary. However, for more complex queueing systems, this general approach will prove most helpful. The flow chart in Figure 8.8 depicts the several functions of the simulator which, in the actual program, would most probably be segmented into subroutines. In this particular model a "termination criterion" for our experiment has been selected to be an upper limit on the MCT value. This means that we allow the model to run for some specified amount of simulated time. A different termination criterion could just as easily have been employed, such as the total number of units through the system. For example, the analyst using the first termination criterion is in effect saying, "analyze this system for X hours of simulated time," whereas the analyst using the second criterion is saying "analyze the system until Y units have passed through it." The choice is based purely upon the objectives of the experiment. Further, any combination of the two could also be employed: the analyst might be saying, "analyze the system until either Y units have passed through it or until X units of simulated time have passed."

Now that the macro flow chart has been presented, several points should be discussed about the computer model before micro flow charts are constructed and program coding begins. These points will generally be directed to the model under present discussion. However, the concepts presented are applicable to any computer simulation model. The points are listed below for emphasis.

1. As a general rule the model should be constructed insofar as possible using integer arithmetic and integer variables. This is to reduce computer time. In most cases this can be accomplished without great difficulty. Floating point calculations at the end to summarize results can be effected without great difficulty. To say that integer arithmetic should be employed as much as possible in the computer simulation model is to concede, necessarily, loss of accuracy. In general, most computer languages allow enough places of accuracy in integer mode such that this should not be a problem. Later sections will discuss accuracy and statistical validation of the results of simulation runs in depth.

   In queueing models should be exercised when choosing the time unit for the simulation. Since the use of integer arithmetic is advocated, the programmer must remember that there are no places to the right of the decimal. Hence, excessive zeros may be generated. Thus, instead of using minutes as units you would select seconds.

2. Design of the program should incorporate to the fullest extent the concept of subprograms. Figure 8.8 can be looked upon as a functional description of the basic simulation model. Each function should be subdivided into a subprogram if possible. This has essentially three effects on the final model constructed. First, it makes the model easier to construct and much easier to debug. Second, it causes the model which is created to be much more flexible for extension and subsequent modification. Third, it causes the organization of the model to be, in general, much more efficient in execution.

3. The model developed here is rather inefficient for the simple single channel system. Employing the same concepts developed above to more sophisticated systems will yield more significant results.
4. Several arrays must, of necessity, be used in this model. In any compiler level computer language this array manipulation is costly in computer execution time. Great care should be exercised when developing the computer program so as to reduce or minimize array searches. These can be reduced in general by maintaining "pointers" for particular entries in arrays frequently used. Remember, the cost of the experiment and savings effected by results of simulation studies must also take into account the cost of computer time used in analyzing the system.

Several questions still remain unanswered with regard to our model. So far our discussion has dealt only with the formulation of the overall model. In order to solidify the next-event analysis concept and mechanics of the model before we go into the detailed aspects of program construction and analysis of results, consider Figure 8.9. In Figure 8.9 the system is presented as events on a time scale. In our model the master clock time value keeps track of the total amount of simulated time. We will view the time axis shown in Figure 8.9 as the MCT scale and observe what is actually occurring in the model.

FIGURE 8.9
Time Scale Representation of the Single Channel System

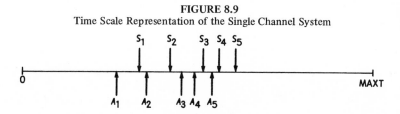

The arrows pointing upward to the time scale, which are designated as A_i, represent the points or instants in time (on the master clock) at which units enter the system. The arrows pointing downward to the time scale, designated as S_i, are the instants of time when services are completed. In general, the interarrival time of units to the system is given by $A_{i+1} - A_i$, and this is the value we generate and place in NEM(1,1). Further, we have inherently assumed that when a unit arrives to the system it proceeds immediately to the service facility if there are no units in the queue ahead of it. This says that service begins at A_i when the queue is empty. Hence the total time the ith unit spends in the system can be given by $S_i - A_i$. Thus, it becomes obvious that when there are units in the queue, the service time for the ith unit is given by $S_i - S_{i-1}$. If, however, there are no units in the system, the amount of idle time the facility will experience at any point between servicing the ith and $(i+1)$st unit is given by $A_{i+1} - S_i$. This result goes to zero, or negative, if there are units in the queue waiting to be serviced. The computer model will "cause" these arrows to be placed on the MCT scale and proceed from intersection to intersection on that scale, accumulating information as it goes out the scale. When an arrow is drawn which exceeds the limit of the scale, the simulation is complete.

To continue into the detailed development of the simulation model the following routines are needed:

1. A process generator which causes the various time values to be created.
2. A scan routine which finds the minimum NEM value, sets a pointer to it, and updates all clocks.
3. An arrival routine which updates the UM for new arrivals to the system and causes the NEM to be updated for interarrival times.
4. A service time routine which updates the UM for the amount of time a unit spends in the queue and in the system. It will also cause the process generator to update NEM for service time values.
5. A routine for tabulating values into frequency distributions.
6. A routine which performs summary calculations and outputs them.
7. A ' driver" routine which initiates the model and terminates it when the correct amount of time has been simulated.

The flow charts for these routines are presented in Figures 8.29 through 8.35 in the appendix at the end of this chapter.

One assumption will be employed in the construction of the "driver" routine for now. This assumption is that the model will begin at MCT = 0 and continue to its MAXT limit. We will soon see that this may not be statistically correct due to assumptions of steady-state conditions in the model. We shall later modify the routine accordingly.

FIGURE 8.10
Output from Single Channel Queueing Simulator

TIME UNIT USED IN THIS SIMULATION WAS SECONDS
INITIAL CONDITIONS FOR SINGLE CHANNEL POISSON QUEUEING SIMULATION
MEAN INTERARRIVAL TIME=   3000.00000 IN SECONDS
MEAN SERVICE TIME=   115.38461 IN SECONDS
INITIAL RANDOM NUMBER WAS   45555

SIMULATION PERIOD IN SECONDS = 8640000
ACTUAL SIMULATION PERIOD IN SECONDS = 8643761

FACILITY UTILIZATION FOR SIMULATED PERIOD =   .0374

DISTRIBUTION OF NUMBER OF UNITS IN SYSTEM
CLASS WIDTH ON FREQUENCY TABULATION IS   1 UNITS BEGINNING AT ZERO
CLASS NUMBER

	1	2	3	4	5	6	7	8	9	10
INDIVIDUAL COUNTS	5509	94	4	0	0	0	0	0	0	0
CUMULATIVE PERCENT	0.983	0.999	1.000	1.000	1.000	1.000	1.000	1.000	1.000	1.000

DISTRIBUTION OF TIME IN QUEUE

AVERAGE TIME IN QUEUE= 4.3042 SECONDS
CLASS WIDTH ON FREQUENCY TABULATION IS   3 UNITS BEGINNING AT ZERO
CLASS NUMBER

	1	2	3	4	5	6	7	8	9	10
INDIVIDUAL COUNTS	2714	0	1	0	4	1	2	1	2	79
CUMULATIVE PERCENT	0.968	0.968	0.968	0.968	0.970	0.970	0.971	0.971	0.972	1.000

DISTRIBUTION OF TOTAL TIME IN SYSTEM

AVERAGE TOTAL TIME IN SYSTEM= 119.5209 SECONDS
CLASS WIDTH ON FREQUENCY TABULATION IS   30 UNITS BEGINNING AT ZERO
CLASS NUMBER

	1	2	3	4	5	6	7	8	9	10
INDIVIDUAL COUNTS	614	489	399	305	227	171	120	95	98	285
CUMULATIVE PERCENT	0.219	0.394	0.536	0.645	0.726	0.787	0.829	0.863	0.898	1.000

Figure 8.36 in the chapter appendix shows the listing of a FORTRAN IV program for the single channel queueing system simulator described above. Figure 8.10 contains the output listing from the program. The simulation period for this run was selected to be one day of simulated time. The basic time unit for the run was chosen to be seconds. The output listing contains all necessary information to classify the run.

From Chapter 3 we see for the single channel Poisson system that the expected time in the queue, E(w), is as shown below,

$$E(w) = \frac{\lambda}{\mu^2 (1 - \lambda/\mu)}$$

$$= \frac{0.02}{(0.52)^2 (1 - 0.038)}$$

$$= 4.62 \text{ seconds}$$

This is compared to a simulated value of 4.30. Further, the expected total time in the system E(t), is

$$E(t) = E(w) + 1/\mu$$

$$= 4.62 + 115.38$$

$$= 120.00 \text{ seconds}$$

This is to be compared with a value of 119.52 obtained from the simulation run.

After Output – What Now?

The system has been described, a model for that system has been constructed and executed, and now output results are available from the computer run. Unfortunately, many analysts stop at this point and consider the analysis complete. However, a computer simulation model offers a unique method for studying and further analyzing any system. It again depends upon the basic objectives of any simulation study, whether or not further analysis should be undertaken after initial output has been achieved. However, consider the computer model in light of the analysis of any given system. If we were to design an experiment to study a real life system for the purpose of drawing conclusions or making inferences about some aspect of the system, once the data were collected we would be detached from the system, so to speak, and would proceed to analyze the data collected. For instance, say we were concerned with the average total time in the system for any given unit entering one of two single channel queueing systems in a plant. Assume for realism that the units here are parts entering a lathe operation where two particular lathes are to be studied. The general approach would be to design an experiment which could test a given hypothesis concerning the two time values. The number of observations to be taken would be calculated beforehand, based upon acceptable levels of significance in our test procedure. After collecting the samples and analyzing them we would probably draw some conclusions about the mean total time in the system for units in one operation as compared with units in the other operation. In actual practice the collection of data alone or design of the experiment can prove to be costly. Hence, if we wished to compare two other single channel systems the design procedure would necessarily be repeated and data collection would begin again. Further, to test hypotheses based upon systems not even in existance proves very costly. One method would be to construct physical prototypes and analyze these. This might involve confiscation of existing production facilities for modification and testing – thus removing them from a productive capacity.

Simulation analysis offers a powerful and usually cheaper alternative to the aforementioned approach. After the computer simulation model has been successfully constructed, it stands as a manifestation of the particular system and can be used for further analysis of that system as objectives demand. Thus, once the single channel model has been constructed it can be used to study any single channel system. Data collection might be needed to arrive at distributions for arrival or service processes, but in general this type of data collection can be effected cheaper. Further, the model can be used to study projected or proposed systems in which arrival and service time processes are determined by some less mathematical or more heuristic method.

Taken in this light the computer simulation model serves the same purpose as does the agriculturist's plots of ground, *i.e.*, an entity from which observations can be collected – not an end in itself. Therefore the same computer simulation model can be used many times to study the effects of different treatments or perturbations to the same general system. Paramount to accurate and statistically valid conclusions based upon any simulation analysis is a good, meaningful design of the experiment. In that the objectives of any given analysis must necessarily affect its experimental design, the analyst must be concerned with both the process being simulated and the statistical accuracy of the results. This results in two basic avenues of interrogation. One leads to conclusions about the system being studied, and the other leads to the statistical aspects of the experiment itself. The two are actually inseparable, for valid conclusions must be based upon a sound statistical foundation. Let's apply the above concepts to the analysis of our simple single channel system. The initial objectives of our study were presented earlier. These objectives would perhaps have been established when we were making an investigatory study of the system. Many useful simulation studies are of this nature; *i.e.,* the objective is to "get the feel" for the operation of a particular system.

Consider now a study of a particular single channel system in which more detailed information is desired. Below are listed some typical questions which might be posed regarding the operation of a single channel system. These questions could be raised regarding the process being studied.

1. Assuming a given service time distribution, how much could the mean arrival rate increase before the mean waiting time of a given unit is greater than some specified value?
2. What would be the effect on the system of an imposed limit on queue length?
3. How would a different queue discipline affect the mean waiting time of a unit; or what effect would priorities have?
4. What would be the effect on the system of a completely different interarrival or service time distribution, assuming the other were held constant?

These questions typify a more realistic situation to be analyzed but are not intended to be in any way exhaustive. However, to answer any of the questions posed above with confidence the statistical aspects of the study must be considered. Below are some questions which must be raised and answered regarding the statistical aspects of the study. These particular questions would not be unique to the study of our single channel system but are rather inherent in the design of almost any simulation experiment.

1. What particular tests should be applied to the random number generator to insure an acceptable sequence of pseudo-random numbers for the study?
2. If the system is to be studied under steady-state conditions, how can we determine when the model reaches a steady-state condition?
3. How long must the model run to give accurate results? What constitutes enough observations on the simulated process? How can replications of the experiment aid in the results and how can replications be effected in the model?

Chapters 6 and 11 concentrate upon many of the questions posed above, namely, aspects of the design of simulation experiments. But, in order to make the discussion of this system complete these questions have been included now so that the reader may be made aware of some of the far-reaching aspects of simulation studies. A brief discussion of these general questions is presented in the following paragraphs.

For the simple single channel system introduced in previous pages the analyst must consider several possible tests for the random number generator used in the simulation model. Since a period of one day was to be simulated in increments of seconds we would first make sure that the sequence required would not contain more than one cycle. The sequence should be tested for uniformity over the number of random numbers to be used. That is, if we expect to use a total of 200 random numbers for the run, then a sample of size 200 should be tested. Remember most random number generators exhibit desirable properties over the long run. It may turn out that the particular generator selected does not behave acceptably for a sample size of 200. We might further wish to generate two vectors of random numbers which represent, respectively, the values used for the service time process generator and the values used for the interarrival time process generator. We would then apply to each vector either the one-sample runs test or tests for autocorrelation, both within a vector as well as between vectors. If the sequences generated pass all tests, then the particular generator selected is acceptable. Note what might happen if the random number generator showed a high correlation between interarrival time random numbers and service time random numbers. How might this affect results?

How can we determine when the model reaches steady-state

conditions? Steady-state conditions for a particular model are based upon the parameters being measured. That is, when the mean and variance of a particular parameter stabilize to essentially constant values then that parameter is considered to be in a steady-state condition. This aspect of the analysis can prove to be very lengthy, for all salient parameters must be analyzed and the overall steady state of the model is achieved only when the mean and variance of each parameter stabilizes. Many simulation studies must of necessity not consider steady state. For example, if the operation of a barber shop were going to be studied for successive eight-hour periods, then steady-state analysis would not be important because the system reinitializes itself each eight hours. No people are left waiting overnight. In a situation like this it may well turn out that the system never reaches a steady-state condition.

In order to give accurate results the model must produce some minimum number of observations. The actual number of observations necessary is of course a function of the tests to be performed, the costs which might occur from making wrong decisions, and the nature of the system under study. Depending upon these considerations the model can be treated in several ways to insure enough observations. If the system being studied is such that it can be observed for a long period of simulated time with no loss of accuracy, then this is perhaps the simplest solution. For example, if we were studying a gasoline service station which operates 24 hours a day each day of the year then we could let the model simulate that operation until enough data on it has been collected. On the other hand, if the system being studied was the ticket booth at the theater which is only open for 30 minutes a day, possibly one day's operation would not yield enough information to satisfy the requirements of the number of observations. Obviously, we would not be correct in simulating this system for a period of any longer than 30 minutes of simulated time. In this case we would revert to simulating several days' operation of the ticket booth in order to satisfy these requirements. Remember from Chapter 6 that once the initial value of the random number generator is selected, the sequence of numbers produced is purely deterministic. By changing the initial random number we in effect determine a new sequence and, further, describe a new run. Replications on data obtained from a simulation model can be effected very simply by changing the initial random number supplied. If each initial random number to be used is selected, say, from a table of random numbers, then variation is introduced into the study.

Modifications of the Simulator

Now let us briefly turn our attention to some of the mechanics involved in changing the model. It should be obvious to the reader that for our simple system, different statistical processes may be introduced simply by changing the process generator program. Various queue disciplines can be introduced by including more elaborate coding into the service time routine. Limitations on queue size can be effected by placing a "counter" variable on the number in the queue and testing it against some maximum selected value whenever a unit is to be entered into the system. If the limit has been reached, "destroy" the unit to enter and proceed normally. Priorities for a given unit can be assigned in a Monte Carlo fashion, and the value for the unit priority can be entered as another element in the unit matrix. A change in the scan routine to investigate units in the unit matrix on the basis of the priority element can then be coded. If subprograms are used extensively in the construction of the computer simulation model, then these changes can be effected with relatively little difficulty.

If other characteristics of the jobs must be included in the simulation model, additional entries can be created in each unit vector of the unit matrix to contain these characteristics. One such characteristic mentioned above was job priority. In fact this concept can be extended to the point that the job is completely specified as soon as it is generated into the system. This can be done easily for our single channel model by including in each unit vector another element which represents the service time of the unit.

The necessary modifications to the service routine and arrival routine are minor, and the model would operate such as to generate all of the important characteristics of the job as soon as it entered the system. In many simulation experiments this is a very useful method and is extended to cause the model to actually be divided into two distinct phases, namely, a "job generator" and a "scheduler." These models are constructed such that an independent file of jobs is created. This technique might be particularly useful when evaluating the effect of various queue disciplines on the operation of a given single channel system. This removes any variability in the model due to a different set of jobs being generated. The problem of job variability arises by having a situation in the simulation model occur which causes the generated sequence of random numbers to be used for different determinations on successive runs even though the initial random number has not been changed. For instance, assume that on the first simulation run of an experiment requiring a total of 200 random numbers the first 10 numbers were used as follows: (a) interarrival time generation used the 1st, 3d, 4th, 6th, 7th, and 8th random numbers, (b) service time generation used the 2d, 5th, 9th, and 10th random numbers. Further suppose that the second run used a service time process generator which generated from a distribution with a much smaller mean service time. This time the first 10 random numbers were used as follows: (a) interarrival time generation used the 1st, 3d, 5th, 7th, 9th, and 10th, and (b) service time generation used the 2d, 4th, 6th, and 8th random numbers. What, in effect, has happened is that starting from the fourth random number the sequence of jobs passing through the system is arriving at a different time than the previous sequence of jobs on the initial run. Immediately a new source of variation is introduced which might not be detected as such. Hence, many simulation analysts prefer to generate a job file completely independent of the scheduling of the jobs.

The model presented herein for the simulation of queueing systems can be modified to include all necessary characteristics of the job when desired. However, the analyst must be sure that the same random numbers are used for the same determinations on successive runs if that is what is required. From run to run in the study this might require that random numbers be generated and not used to insure the proper sequence. One aspect to consider in the design of the computer model should be the maximum number of random numbers which will ever be needed to classify one job. The following example illustrates the concept of completely specifying a job by its salient characteristics as it enters the system.

Example 8.1

The computer center at *XYZ* Corporation consists of a batch processing computer in which jobs are presently processed on a first-come first-serve basis. In an attempt to improve overall service (by reducing average turnaround time for programs entering the center) the director of the facility decides to evaluate a queue priority rule based upon the expected total time for a given program. Highest priority in the queue is always given to the job whose maximum time estmate is the lowest of all jobs in the queue. Service for programs on the computer is nonpreemptive. The center operates on a 24-hour basis seven days a week. Further, the director wishes to study the system which will allow the inclusion of various characteristics for programs as part of each program description. The following is a list of program and system parameters the director wished to include in the model and had determined or assumed statistical distributions for:

1. Interarrival time of jobs to the computer center.
2. Computer time/program.
3. Number of source program cards/program.
4. Number of printed output lines/program.

The objective of the study is to compare the average turnaround time for a given job entering the system under the present queue discipline with the turnaround time for a job entering the system with the proposed queue discipline. We will assume that setup time between jobs under both systems is negligible.

Normally we would approach the study by deciding acceptable significance levels for the errors and then determine the number of observations we would need to take to insure these. For purposes of this discussion we will say that we wish to compare the two queue disciplines over a month of normal operation. This indicates that a steady-state condition must be reached in the model and then that information must be collected for a period of one month of simulated time.

Because the model will be used for other studies, we should design it to allow for all of the information to be contained about the programs in the model. In this light we should expand the unit matrix for the model to include all four items cited above. The unit matrix might then be depicted in Figure 8.11.

FIGURE 8.11
The Expanded Unit Matrix

1	2	3	4	5	6	7
Unit Number	MCT of Initial System Entry	Present State	MCT of Entry into Present State	Total Computer Time Required	Source Cards per Program	Output Print Lines per Program

The basic operation of both simulators is the same as that shown in Figure 8.8 with the following modifications:

1. For both queue disciplines the model would proceed by generating values for entries five, six, and seven in the unit vector for each program as it entered the simulated system.
2. The scan to find the next job for service for the model of the present system is exactly as that shown in Figure 8.8.
3. The scan to find the next job to be serviced for the proposed queue discipline would operate by scanning UM (I,5) and selecting for the next unit to service the program whose UM (I,5) is minimum.
4. In both cases the model would have to be modified to let NEM (1,2) = UM (I,5) for the job entering service.

With these modifications we would create two models to simulate the single channel system described. Notice that if the same initial random number is used for both simulation programs, the set of jobs generated as well as the interarrival times generated will be exactly the same. Therefore the only difference on results would be attributed to a difference in queue disciplines.

Note that the number of source cards for each program and output lines for each program would be generated and inserted into UM(I,6) and UM (I,7), respectively. If on these particular runs we did not need this information, we could either execute two "dummy" calls to the random number generator or actually include them and place the generated values in the UM entries. Later studies might include these entries, for instance when comparing different card readers with different reading rates to determine their relative effect on overall time.

Summary of the Single Channel System

This section has dealt primarily with both the broad and detailed aspects of simulation as applied to a single channel queueing system. The concept of next event analysis was introduced and applied to the investigation of the single single channel system and to the construction of the computer simulation model for that system. The basic computer model for the system was constructed and the FORTRAN IV computer program for the model discussed in detail. Finally we discussed some of the aspects concerning the results of our simulation and the broad aspects of analysis of those results.

Many times throughout the preceding pages the objectives of the particular simulation experiment were mentioned. Succeeding pages will be no different because one must constantly keep these in sight in any simulation experiment. It is not within the scope of this text to teach one how to form objectives. However, objectives must be established, and a means for quantifying them must be created before any analysis can come to fruition. Therefore the succeeding material attempts to illustrate how a given system can be modeled for a set of objectives. We hope the concepts were presented in sufficient detail to allow the reader to extend the simple model to include more information. In many industrial applications, the objective of a queueing analysis is to minimize the total cost of operation of the system. In this case the cost of units waiting at the facility is balanced against the cost of idle time on the facility. The results of the analysis determine the optimal mean service rate the facility should operate with, in order to minimize the total cost of the system. Later examples in this chapter will focus on inclusion of system cost information in analyses of queueing systems.

CHANNELS IN SERIES

We now turn our attention to simulation analysis of queueing systems containing multiple channels in series. Figure 8.12 illustrates this type of system—in which each unit arriving to the system must pass through each service channel.

FIGURE 8.12
Channels in Series

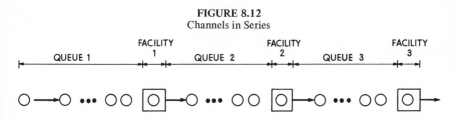

Let us define the queueing system to include N service channels or facilities and also N queues, one before each channel. The interarrival time distribution for units entering the system has λ as its mean, and service time for each channel is assumed to have mean $\mu_i (i = 1, 2, \ldots, N)$. We will not restrict ourselves to particular distributions here but rather will work with mean values and assume the distributions are either known or can be determined. Further we will say that each queue in the system will have a maximum permissible length, called $NQ_i (i = 1, 2, \ldots, N)$. A unit which attempts to enter the initial queue when it is full will be turned away from the system. A unit will leave any particular service channel only when the next queue is not full. If the next queue is full, the unit will remain in the service channel until it can enter the next queue, thus blocking the channel from further service. We will assume a first-come first-serve queue discipline at each queue. Note that the arrival process for units to each channel from 2 to N is governed by not only the arrival process to the initial facility but also by the service time distribution of each preceding facility.

In order to apply our next-event analysis concept to this system, let us look at what might happen to a particular unit at the point in time when it finished being serviced in the ith channel. Figure 8.13 shows a flow diagram of the possible outcomes. Further let us look at what might happen at the ith channel as it finishes service on a given unit. This is shown in Figure 8.14.

FIGURE 8.13
Flow Diagram of Unit Entering System

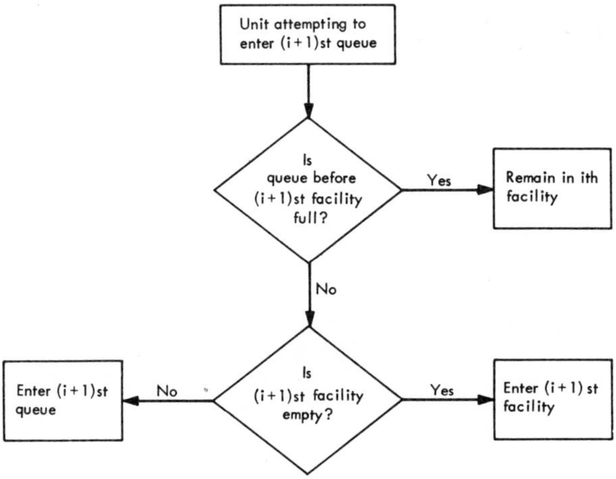

As in the single channel case the entities of the system are the units and the facilities or service channels. For each of the system entities, the above flow charts have illustrated the event-outcome decision process. Let us now build the decision grids for these entities as we did before. Figure 8.15 shows the decision grid for a unit which has just been serviced at the ith channel. Note the minor modification necessary to the logic when we are discussing a unit attempting to enter the first queue.

From the Figure 8.15 we will conclude that any given unit in the system is in one of three possible states: (a) blocked in a service

FIGURE 8.14

Flow Diagram of Service Completion on ith Channel

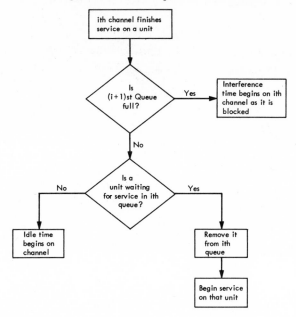

FIGURE 8.15

Decision Grid for Unit Attempting to Leave ith Service Channel

Events upon Attempting To Leave ith Service Channel						Outcomes to the Unit		
$(i+1)$st Channel Blocked	$(i+1)$st Queue Full	$(i+1)$st Queue Not Empty	$(i+1)$st Queue Empty	$(i+1)$st Channel Busy	$(i+1)$st Channel Idle	Remain in ith Channel	Enter $(i+1)$st Queue	Enter $(i+1)$st Channel
	X					X		
		X		X			X	
			X	X			X	
			X		X			X
X		X					X	
X			X				X	

channel, (*b*) being serviced in a service channel, or (*c*) waiting in queue. If we multiply this by N channels, the total number of possible states any given unit will pass through is $3N - 1$, for the unit cannot be blocked in the Nth channel.

Let us now look at the decision grid for the ith facility in the system at the completion of service on any given unit. Figure 8.16 illustrates the decision grid for a given facility. In this particular system there are three possible states any given facility (except the Nth facility) can be in: (a) blocked because of a full queue ahead of next facility, (b) busy in service on a given unit, (c) idle.

FIGURE 8.16
Decision Grid for ith Facility at the Completion of Service

Events at Completion of Service on a Given Unit				Outcomes to Facility		
$(i + 1)$st Queue Full	$(i + 1)$st Queue Not Full	ith Queue Not Empty	ith Queue Empty	Facility Blocked	Facility Idle	Facility Busy
X		X		X	X	
X			X	X	X	
	X	X				X
	X		X		X	

Now that we have described the possible states for the system entities let us proceed to build the computer model for this system. In order to effect any simulation run for a particular system of N facilities we would require at least the following information to describe the system:

1. Distribution of interarrival time to system.
2. Distribution of service time for each service channel.
3. Maximum queue length for each queue.

Depending upon the objectives of the experiment we may wish to measure any of the following response variables:

1. Utilization of facilities.
2. Mean total time through system.
3. Mean waiting time for a unit at each queue.
4. Mean facility interference time for each facility (interference time means the facility is blocked by a unit unable to enter next queue).

Let us define a particular system and build the computer simulation model for this system using the same concepts we employed to design the single channel model. Let us describe the following system which consists of three service channels in series. All service time distributions we will assume to be exponentially distributed with means μ_1, μ_2, μ_3, respectively. Service is nonpreemtive in the facility. Maximum queue lengths are given as NQ_1, NQ_2, NQ_3. The distribution of interarrival time for units entering the system is also exponential with mean λ.

The next event matrix for this system is very similar to that for the single channel system but more inclusive and obviously larger. This is shown in Figure 8.17

FIGURE 8.17
NEM for Three Facilities in Series

		1	2	3	4
		System Entry Condition	Minor Clock for Facility	Minor Clock for Facility	Minor Clock for Facility
			1	2	3
1	Time until Event Occurs				
2	Unit Number in Question				
3	Facility Status Indicator	Not Used			

The entries for the NEM are very similar to those for the single channel system. The row vector named "Facility Status Indicator" is included to provide information about each facility and will be defined as follows for any element in that vector, say $NEM_{3,J}$ (J=2,3,4). If

$NEM_{3,J}$ = 0, Facility J presently idle.
$NEM_{3,J}$ = 1, Facility J presently busy.
$NEM_{3,J}$ = 2, Facility J presently blocked.

When the facility is either blocked or busy, $NEM_{2,J}$ gives the unit number causing the action.

In addition the UM for this model is exactly as described in the section on the single channel system. However, as described above, each unit here may be in any one of $3N - 1$ or $3(3) - 1 = 8$ possible states after entry to the system. These possible states are listed below in Table 8.6.

TABLE 8.6
State Numbers and Descriptions

State Number	Description of State
1	In queue at facility 1
2	Being processed by facility 1
3	Blocked at facility 1
4	In queue at facility 2
5	Being processed by facility 2
6	Blocked at facility 2
7	In queue at facility 3
8	Being processed by facility 3

Figure 8.18 shows the UM for this system. Note that it also includes entries for processing times for any given unit on each of the three facilities. This is in keeping with the concepts presented previously regarding the generation of random numbers for a particular study.

FIGURE 8.18
UM for the Three Facility Case

	1	2	3	4	5	6	7
	Unit Number	MCT oᶜ Initial System Entry	Present State	MCT of Entry to Present State	Processing Time for Facility 1	Processing Time for Facility 2	Processing Time for Facility 3
Unit 1							
2							
⋮							

FIGURE 8.19
The QIM for the Three Facility Case

		Maximum Allowable Queue Length	Present No. of Units in Queue
	1	NQ_1	
Queue Number	2	NQ_2	
	3	NQ_3	

Finally, we will create one additional matrix called the Queue Information Matrix (QIM). This matrix will contain information

FIGURE 8.20
Macro Flow for Simulation Model of
Multiple Channels in Series

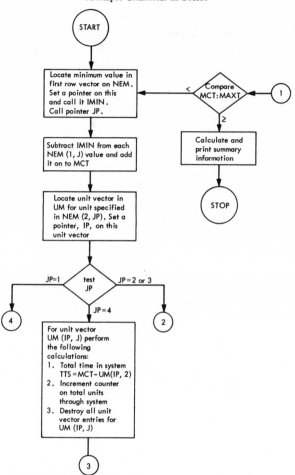

about the number of units presently in each queue as well as the maximum queue limits. A conceptual picture of this matrix is shown in Figure 8.19.

The overall operation of the simulation model for this case is very similar to the model presented in the earlier section of the chapter. A master clock is maintained to keep track of the cumulative amount of simulated time, whereas each minor clock in the NEM is maintained on a "time-to-event-completion" basis. Continual scans of the NEM clock values will dictate which event will happen next. This event is singled out, and the master clock is incremented by that

FIGURE 8.20 *(continued)*

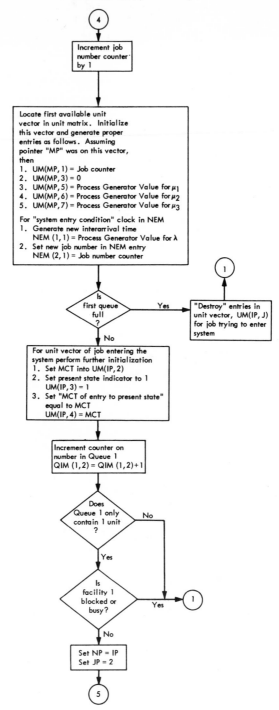

FIGURE 8.20 *(continued)*

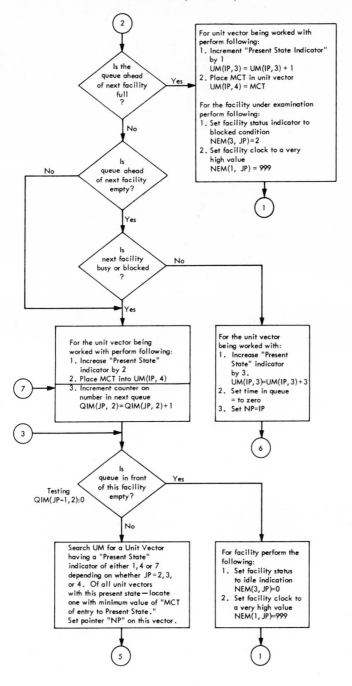

FIGURE 8.20 *(concluded)*

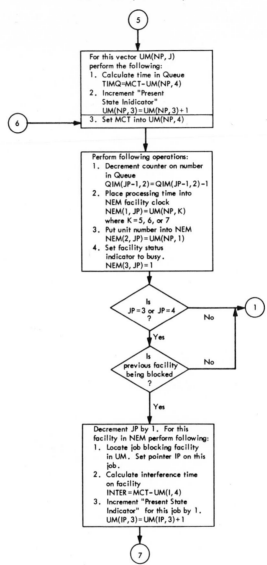

value. The model "causes" the event to occur and investigates the ramifications of the event upon the system. The macro flow chart for this simulation model is presented in Figure 8.20. The flow chart depicts the model as it would operate at some point in time. It is assumed that the various values needed have been previously read into the program.

The flow chart presented in Figure 8.20 contains no particular references about the information we should collect. It is general enough to be modified to collect the information needed on any given study with relative ease. Further, information on costs in the model can be included as desired.

After thorough examination of Figure 8.20 one can easily see how the model could be modified to include more channels. Although this simulation model is somewhat more complex than the previous model presented, the functions it performs are basically the same. The advantages of using subroutines when constructing these models becomes more apparent as the models become more complex.

The micro flow charts and computer programs for this model are not included in this section. The construction of these is left to the reader and has been included as a problem at the end of this chapter.

CHANNELS IN PARALLEL

Many physical systems of service facilities manifest themselves as queueing systems with multiple service channels in parallel. In this system, units arrive randomly and take their place in the waiting line if service cannot be obtained immediately. And, in this case there are two or more channels available for service. The system is illustrated in Figure 8.21.

The first unit in the waiting line enters the first service channel which becomes available. For purposes of discussion we will use the following definitions and terms. The system consists of N service

FIGURE 8.21
Channels in Parallel

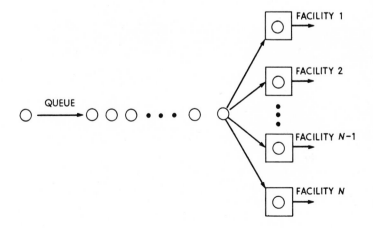

channels in parallel. The ith channel in the system operates with mean service rate μ_i. The queue before the N channels will have a maximum queue length of NQ. A unit which attempts to enter the queue when the queue is full will be turned away from the system. The system is defined here to include all of the units in the queue as well as the N service channels. Initially, let us assume a first-come first-serve queue discipline and a mean interarrival time of λ for units entering the system.

Let us investigate this system as usual, by employing our next-event analysis. As before, the entities of this system are considered to be the units and the service channels. We will begin by looking at the system at a point in time when the ith unit attempts to enter the system. Figure 8.22 shows a flow diagram of the possible outcomes to the unit in this event.

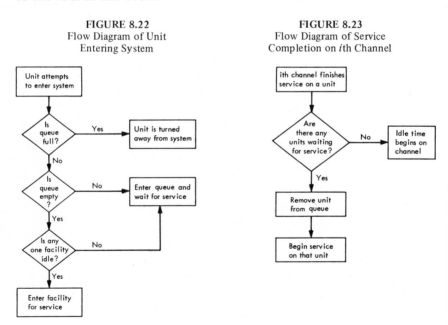

FIGURE 8.22
Flow Diagram of Unit
Entering System

FIGURE 8.23
Flow Diagram of Service
Completion on ith Channel

Now let us look at the ith channel at a point in time when it finishes servicing a unit. This is shown in Figure 8.23.

Notice the similarity between the operation shown in Figure 8.23 and the flow chart for the service channel in the single channel queueing system. In actuality, from the standpoint of the service facility, the systems are almost identical. The only difference here is that each channel in parallel must "compete" for units in the queue.

One could consider the single channel system to be a special case of this system, although this is not usually done.

Proceeding to construct decision grids for the event-outcome analysis for each of the system entities we see that for all practical purposes the decision grid for a given facility is the same as that shown in Figure 8.5. Further, the decision grid for units entering the system is also not too different from that shown in Figure 8.4. Figure 8.24 illustrates the decision grid for a unit attempting to enter the system. This figure illustrates that only when the queue is empty and at least one channel is idle will the unit enter service immediately upon system entry. If any other conditions exist, the unit will either leave the system or enter the queue to wait for service. If more than one channel is available when the unit is ready to enter service, the unit will enter the first available channel. This implies that no preference relationship exists between channels and the choice is rather a random one. In actuality, preferences may exist based upon perhaps service rates; *i.e.,* the unit would enter the channel with the shortest expected service time. However, for our present purposes we may ignore this effect.

FIGURE 8.24
Decision Grid for Unit Status Upon System Entry

Events upon System Entry by a Unit					Outcomes to the Unit		
Queue Full	Queue Not Full	Queue Empty	All N Channels Busy	At Least One Channel Idle	Enter Queue	Enter First Available Channel	Leave System
X							X
	X				X		
		X	X		X		
		X		X		X	

As always, we will construct a flow diagram for the overall simulator flow for this system. The operation of this simulator is very similar to that for the multiple series channels and is shown in Figure 8.25. For this flow chart the number of parallel channels is assumed to be three. From the previous discussion we can for convenience, assume that a particular unit can be in any one of four ($N + 1$) possible states. The first state is that of being in the queue;

the last N states dictate at which of the N channels the unit is being serviced. To be consistent with previous discussions regarding states of a unit we must realize that a given unit is only in one of two possible states while in the system: A given unit is either in the queue (state 1) or in the service channel (state 2). It is, however, much easier to program the simulator model under the assumption of $(N + 1)$ states. In this context we list the state numbers and their descriptions in Table 8.7.

TABLE 8.7
State Numbers and Descriptions

Unit State Number	Description of State
0	In queue
1	In service at channel 1
2	In service at channel 2
3	In service at channel 3

The states for any given channel are exactly as discussed for the single channel model; the facility is either busy (state 1) or idle (state 0). With this in mind the NEM for this model is exactly the same as that shown for the series model in Figure 8.17.

The unit matrix for this simulation model will be essentially the same as that for the series model shown in Figure 8.18. Note that in the unit matrix for this system there are three entries headed "processing time for facility 1, 2, or 3." In the parallel channel model the unit will enter only one of the three possible channels, and therefore the other two entries (for any given unit) will not be used. The reason for this is based upon the previous discussion regarding the generation of identical random sequences on successive runs of the model. Changes of distribution parameters might cause changes in the service facility selected for the jth unit entering the system on successive runs. By always generating the same sequence of random numbers, however, we still insure that we will remove that source of variation in the model. This is obviously a waste of computer storage. There is another method that may be employed to eliminate this problem which was not discussed previously but which may prove helpful. That is the creation of "separate" random number generators for each process being modeled. In this case each service time process would have its own random number generator as well as the arrival process generator. The detailed aspects of this method are left to the reader as food for thought.

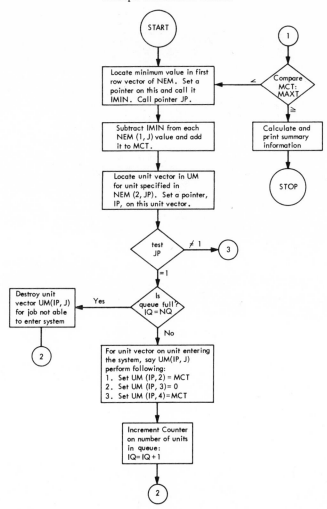

FIGURE 8.25
Macro Flow for Simulation Model of
Multiple Channels in Parallel

As in the model for the series channels system, no comments have been made about the information required. That is left to the reader and is dependent upon the particular application. The simulator model is constructed with enough generality and flexibility to allow inclusion of the proper routine at the user's discretion.

The scan routine for next event determination should operate in a manner which causes the facilities to take precedence over the arrivals in the event of NEM time ties. When two or more facilities

FIGURE 8.25 *(continued)*

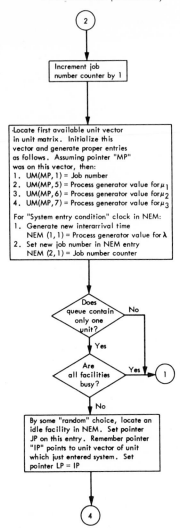

finish service at the same time, the choice should be a "random" one. The reasoning behind this is simply to reduce execution time. Little or no loss in generality arises by these rules.

The methodology employed here to simulate this parallel channel system is exactly the same as that used in each preceding case. Note how this model could be "collapsed" to the single channel system.

FIGURE 8.25 *(concluded)*

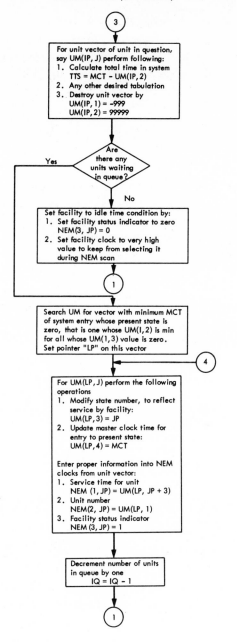

NETWORKS OF WAITING LINES

The preceding sections have discussed the aspects of simulation as applied to relatively simple systems. Further, each particular system was considered separately as an end in itself. Many industrial applications for simulation as applied to queueing systems involve networks of waiting lines. In this section the aspects of simulating these systems are discussed. Consider the following example of a system which contains a network of waiting lines:

Example 8.2

The *XYZ* Manufacturing Company is a job shop which produces special order machine tools. The facility consists of six lathes, one planer, one shaper, one abrasive polishing machine, two drill presses, and a small metal casting unit. For purposes of this discussion we will call each separate machine-type grouping a machine center. Hence there are essentially six different machine centers in the company. The company specializes in basically two different machine tools and manufactures each tool separately to order. No production exists to replenish inventory: All production is strictly based upon customer orders. Depending upon the machine tool being produced, one or all of the machine centers may be required; *i.e.*, some tools require processing on only the lathe while others must pass through all machine centers. In addition, the technological ordering of machine processing for all items is different. That is, one item may require the following sequence of machine centers:

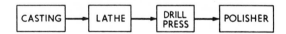

Another item might require a different sequence of operations as shown below:

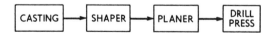

Hence, the entire job shop looks conceptually like a network of cross connected lines, perhaps as shown in Figure 8.26

Let us consider some of the detailed aspects of the job shop:

1. Distribution of time between orders for any given item is known or can be found.

FIGURE 8.26
Conceptual Picture of the Job Shop

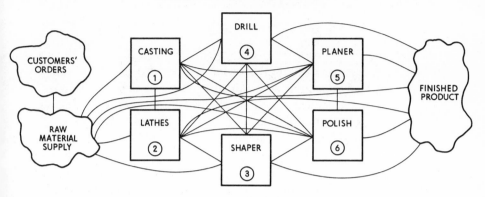

2. Technological order of required machine centers is known for each item.
3. Distribution of time for processing an item on each machine center is known.
4. Before any given machine center a queue of limited length can form.
5. At any machine center a queue discipline of first-come first-serve is employed.

In this example we might be interested in comparing the effect upon the average time a given item spends in the job shop under several conditions, *e.g.,* different queue disciplines, a change in technological ordering, equipment additions to specific machine centers, or increased demands. Note that this system also possesses characteristics, to some extent, of inventory systems. The example is a common one in the general problem area of production scheduling and sequencing. To further illustrate possible analyses, consider some of the different queue disciplines which could be investigated besides the first-come first-serve discipline. These are listed below:

1. Random ordering.
2. Priority based upon expected processing time at any machine center.
3. Priority based upon the dollar value of the job.
4. Priority based upon the number of remaining operations for an item.
5. Last-in first-out ordering.

The first important item for us to consider is that of constructing a computer model of the system. Let us discuss how we can adapt our previous models to incorporate the physical aspects of this job shop.

Notice that any given part to be manufactured proceeds through the job shop in a predetermined order. The part then "sees" the job shop as a queueing system with multiple channels in series because it proceeds in a sequential manner from machine center to machine center. Within a particular machine center the part might "see" a queueing system with multiple parallel channels. For example, the machine center containing the lathes may be set up such that any one of the six lathes could process the part. Expanding this concept, we shall see that the network of waiting lines actually consists of several series—and parallel—queueing systems. At any point in time the queue of jobs at a particular machine center may contain several different parts requested from several different orders.

How might the existing components of our computer models be expanded to deal with this system? First, we see that the NEM would be expanded to include column vector entries for the "System Entry Condition" portion of the NEM for each job. Further, a minor clock entry would be added in the form of a column vector in the NEM for each machine in the job shop. The expanded NEM might look conceptually like Figure 8.27.

Any given job may pass through one of several states. As mentioned above, the job passes through the machine shop in a predetermined manner. In this context it is helpful to simply number

FIGURE 8.27
The Expanded NEM

	System Entry Conditions				Job 10	Machine 1	Facility Minor Clocks	Machine 10	Machine 11
	Job 1	Job 2	Job 3						
Time Until Event Occurs									
Job Number in Question									
Facility Status Indicator									

TABLE 8.8
State Numbers and Descriptions

State Number	State Description
0	Not entered in system yet
1	Queued at machine center 1
2	Being processed by machine center 1
3	Queued at machine center 2
4	Being processed by machine center 2
5	Queued at machine center 3
6	Being processed by machine center 3
7	Queued at machine center 4
8	Being processed by machine center 4
9	Queued at machine center 5
10	Being processes by machine center 5
11	Queued at machine center 6
12	Being processed by machine center 6

each possible state that any job can be in within the entire system. In Table 8.8 is the state number and state description for the entire set of job state possibilities for this system.

If a particular unit is in state 7, that means that it is in the waiting line at machine center 4. That does not imply that it will continue into state 8; further it does not necessarily imply that it came from state 6. The state number, as used here indicates position of a job in the system. For a particular job the required sequence of operations might produce the following state numbers: 0–1–2–3–4–7–8–11–12. This indicates that the job in question would be processed as shown below:

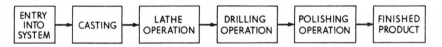

So, for each of our 10 job types we create a vector or ordered state numbers which defines the sequence of operations the job will undergo in passing through the shop.

Finally, let us discuss the modifications we must make to the UM in order to allow us to create the simulation model for this system. Now, we have a situation in which the unit matrix entries previously described can be fully exploited. You can see the utility of the subprogram concept in model construction, for if care is not exercised in construction of this model, it becomes hopelessly complex.

FIGURE 8.28

Correspondence between Working Matrices for Job Shop Simulator

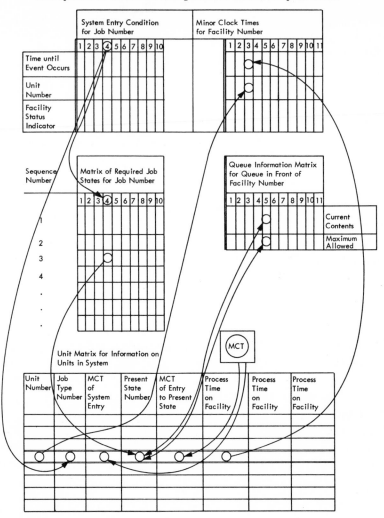

The important aspect to remember regarding jobs "created" into the system is that the job-type alone determines the sequence of required operations through the system. The various interarrival time distributions will determine the frequency of system entry by given job-types. Hence, each unit vector in the unit matrix must contain an additional entry indicating the type of job. As before, the unit vector should also contain the relatively standard entries for "MCT of

System Entry," "Present State," "MCT of Entry to Present State," and so forth. Figure 8.28 illustrates the relationship between the UM vectors, the NEM, the vectors of desired job states, and the queue information matrix. In Figure 8.28 we see that for a given job-type or job number the unit vector information comes from several sources. The job number entry is established upon entry to the system; the unit number entry is determined by a simple incrementation process which gives the nth job to enter the system a unit number of n. The MCT entries are obvious. The present state number is taken from the vector for the job-type in the "Matrix of Required Job States," and along with queue information the next "moves" can be established.

The overall simulator flow would proceed as usual in that the next event would be located from the NEM and the proper actions for that next event would be initiated and so forth. No flow chart is included for this model, but it should offer no great problems. Notice that the amount of matrix manipulation continues to increase as the system being modeled becomes more complex. The obvious extension to this train of thought is that as systems to be analyzed become more complex, the cost to perform the analysis increases. The computer models for some systems result in computer runs which are longer than the simulated time period. That is, a computer run may take an hour to simulate the operation of a system for a simulated period of one-half hour.

In the example just completed we investigated some of the aspects to be considered when constructing models for large-scale queueing systems. The case studied consisted of one particular job shop about which certain analyses were desired. Although we looked at only one particular example of a sophisticated system, we saw that the concepts developed previously could easily be applied to construct the computer model for this system. Keep in mind that the cost involved in constructing computer models and effecting analyses with these models can become very great. In a later chapter we shall investigate some computer languages which were created to reduce these costs. In many situations the cost of constructing the model represents the largest component of the total cost of analysis. By using simulation-oriented languages we can often reduce these construction costs a great deal. The choice of when to use or not to use the simulation languages available is not easy and must be based upon the objectives of the experiment.

SUMMARY OF SIMULATION OF QUEUEING SYSTEMS

In this chapter we have presented the basic concepts of simulation of queueing systems. In this section we will review the topics presented and discuss the aspects of modeling queueing systems.

All queueing systems consist of three basic entities, units to be serviced, a facility or facilities to effect the service, and a queue for units waiting to be serviced. Let us look at each of the entities and summarize the characteristics we might wish to include in a computer simulation model of these. Most of these characteristics have been discussed previously. The others are included for completeness and should not present great difficulty for inclusions into a particular model.

Units

The arrivals to a queueing system, called units or jobs, possess characteristics or affect the system in some way. In our discussion we employed unit vector entries in the unit matrix for each of the jobs in the system. Each unit vector contained elements for describing the various characteristics. These characteristics are listed below.

1. Arrival rate distribution or distribution of interarrival time. This is some stochastic process which governed the number of arrivals to the system.
2. Priority – this is some relative measure of a unit's worth to the system in comparison to all other units. It generally dictates how fast a unit will move through the system in relation to other units.
3. Impatience – this factor indicates how long a unit will remain in the system without being served. It can describe conditions about a unit called "balking" or "reneging" or "jockeying." Balking is the condition when a unit refuses to enter a queue because of its length. Reneging is a condition when the unit leaves the queue after waiting a certain period of time. Jockeying is the condition when the unit leaves one queue to enter another.

Another characteristic which we included (for simulation purposes only) as a description of a unit was facility service time. This is actually a function of the service channel and will be discussed there. We included it as descriptive information on units in the system to standardize the approach and to remove the effect of random number generation. One final aspect not previously discussed regarding arrivals is that of "bulk arrivals." Bulk arrivals can best be illustrated by the example of an elevator. The arrival to the system might be considered to be when the elevator stops at a floor. However, it contains several units. Previously we considered only arrivals of one unit. Another example of bulk arrivals is that of a box of parts arriving at a machine for processing.

Service Channel

The facility for serving the units in the system has several characteristics which we considered. These are listed below:

1. Serving process – this is the distribution of service time. It is considered to be a stochastic process whose variation is inherent to the facility. We generally tend to assign values for this to units as they arrive to the system.
2. Arrangement of channels – this dictates the configuration of the system. Channels are either arranged in series or parallel or some series-parallel combination.
3. Service discipline – this characteristic of the facility indicates whether or not it can be interrupted in service. Unit priorities go hand-in-hand with this aspect. Units of higher priority may demand that the facility stop its present process and service them. This is called preemptive processing. When no interruption can take place, it is called nonpreemptive processing.

Another aspect of servicing relates to bulk arrivals of units to the system. This is known as bulk service. Here the facility operates on batches of units at the same time.

Queue

The waiting line before service facilities offers the greatest area for investigation. The waiting line to the simulation model has the following characteristics:

1. Length – how many units can be in the line at the same time?
2. Queue discipline – this dictates the method of ordering of units in the queue. We generally think of this aspect as being queue dependent. Actually it is generally dependent upon the units in the queue. Seveal different possibilities for queue disciplines were presented in the job shop example in the

previous section. The simplest queue discipline is known as first-come first-serve.

Many investigations of queueing systems revolve around the question "what would happen if the queue discipline were . . . ." This aspect of queueing systems is; *i.e.,* the queue itself offers the best opportunity of study in an area under management control. That is, it is often much easier to effect a new queue discipline that it is to change a service rate process. Hence, many analyses are concerned with the investigation of various queue disciplines or "priority schemes."

Finally, the system as a whole has certain characteristics which cannot be included in the three entities. Among these are limitations on number of units in the system and operating periods. The restriction on number of units in the system is sometimes of great importance, for it represents a capacity constraint. The operating period of a system is that amount of time for which the system can operat continuously. Some systems can operate continuously for any length of time. In other systems this period might be limited to some maximum time.

The analysis of a particular queueing system involves synthesis of the characteristics described above. Sometimes all of these characteristics are present. At other times, only a few are considered. The system itself certainly dictates in large measure what characteristics exist. However, the objectives of a particular experiment or analysis might dictate that other characteristics be included. One other characteristic we might wish to include is cost information.

Finally, one must develop a sense of awareness to the problems of statistical validity of simulation models. This aspect will be presented in detail in later chapters. In this chapter we discussed some of the statistical aspects of steady-state considerations, pseudo-random number generators, and amount and quality of information to be collected. Certainly these must play a very important role in the simulation of any system. Although we did not discuss in any detail the formulation of objectives for analyses, this also affects our statistical consideration.

The simulation of queueing systems as presented here involved the concept of next-event analysis. Obviously, there are other ways to construct simulation models of queueing systems. The methods introduced here, however, provide a unified approach to analyses of this type. Any queueing system can be broken down into the component entities, and each entity can be analyzed using the decision grid approach.

PROBLEMS

1. For the single channel Poisson model shown in Figure 8.8 make the following modifications:

 a) Add a variable in the program which places a limit on queue length.
 b) Add two cost components, C_1 and C_2, which represent, respectively, the cost per unit time for a unit to wait in the system and the cost for each service.

Simulate the system with $\lambda = .04/min.$, $\mu = .05/min.$, $C_1 = \$5/hour$, $C_2 = \$100$, for a period of 10 days, and determine the average total cost per unit. Set queue limit at 100 units.

2. For the single channel model as modified in problem 1 above, make a further modification to change the queue discipline to give priority to the unit in the queue with shortest service time. Using the same values as for problem 1, compare the results of average total cost per unit.

3. A single channel Poisson system possesses the following characteristics:

 a) Distribution of arrivals is Poisson with $\lambda = 0.04/min.$
 b) Distribution of service time is exponential with $\mu = 0.05/min.$
 c) The mazimum number allowed in the queue at any one time is 200 units.
 d) No unit will stay in the queue more than one and one-half hours.
 e) First-come first serve queue discipline

Simulate the system for a period of 10 days, and compare results with those of Figure 8.10.

4. With the single channel system model presented in Figure 8.8 make the following runs: Set MAXT (the simulation period) at one, two, three, four, and five days. Compare results with those in Figure 8.10. Use the same initial random number in all cases. Plot the values of the mean waiting time and mean total time for these runs. When do you think the system reaches a steady state?

5. Arrivals to a single channel service facility come from a conveyor belt at the rate of one every four minutes. The service channel operates with exponential service rate, parameter μ. Find a value of μ which will minimize the chance of ever having a queue length greater than three. There is a cost of $\$1,000$ incurred to the system for each unit in the queue greater than three. The cost per day of the service facility is dependent upon the μ selected. This cost relationship is given by $C_s = 20,000 \mu$ where $C_s =$ cost per day. Determine the optimal value of μ which will minimize the total system cost/day based upon 30 days of eight-hour shifts.

(Note: You would have to assume that the total cost equation has only one minimum.)

6. Manufacturing facilities often experience a phenomenon known as "manufacturing progress," which causes the mean service rate to decrease over time. The function is usually based upon doubled production quantities; *i.e.*, the

service rate decreases by some constant amount with doubled production quantities. The formula for this function is given by: $y_i = y_0 \phi^d$ where y_i is the mean service rate for ith unit, y_0 is the mean service rate for first unit, ϕ is the slope parameter of the function, and d is manufacturing period. We assume $y_0 = 30$ minutes, ϕ is 0.9.

$$y_0 = 30$$
$$y_1 = 30(0.9)^1$$
$$y_2 = 30(0.9)^2$$
$$\vdots$$
$$y_5 = 30(0.9)^5$$

So, the first unit is served with a mean rate of 30 minutes, the second and third are served with a mean rate of 27 minutes; the fourth through seventh with a mean rate of 24.3 minutes, and so on. All service rates are assumed to be distributed exponentially with the proper parameter value μ. Simulate the system for a period of 10 days, assuming a Poisson arrival rate process with parameter $\lambda = 0.03333$. Compare this to a similar server which does not experience this manufacturing progress. Make conclusions about results. How many times was the production quantity doubled?

7. Modify the single channel model in Figure 8.8 such that information on mean facility idle time as well as the distribution of idle time can be collected. Assume a Poisson process for arrivals and exponential process for service. The values to be used for λ and μ are 0.04 and 0.05, respectively. Compare the idle time information on runs of 8,16,24,36,48, and 56 hours of simulated time.

8. For the single channel system described in problem 3 simulate the system for a period of 10 days after making the following modifications to the model. Instead of units leaving the system after a period of one and one-half hours in the queue, assume that the time to service these units (which have waited longer that one and one-half hours) increases by 10 per cent. How does this affect the expected total time in the system?

9. A single person operates a repair shop which fixes broken parts for the plant. The normal mode of operation is to allow parts to come in for the first half of the day and then refuse service for all arriving in the second half. The repairman then works until all parts which came in during the morning are repaired—even though he may have to work overtime. Normal work shift for the repairman is eight hours. Simulate this system for 30 working days, assuming a Poisson arrival process with parameter $\lambda = 0.08$ and an exponential service rate with $\mu = 0.10$. How many hours of overtime will the repairman work per day on the average? What is the minimum value of μ which will reduce overtime effectively to zero?

10. Write a FORTRAN program for the queueing system with multiple channels in series. Design the program to handle up to a maximum of 10

channels in series. With this model, simulate the following system which contains three series channels. Arrivals to the system follow a Poisson process with parameter $\lambda = 0.04$. The maximum queue lengths are $NQ_1 = 100$, $NQ_2 = 10$, $NQ_3 = 10$. The service facilities all operate with the exponential distribution for service process. The parameters are $\mu_1 = 0.06$, $\mu_2 = 0.06$, $\mu_3 = 0.09$.

Simulate the system until 200 units have passed completely through all channels. Change $NQ_2 = 5$ and $NQ_3 = 5$ and compare results with respect to distribution of interference times under the two systems.

11. A queueing system with four channels in series operates with the following characteristics:

a) Poisson arrivals, $\lambda = 0.04$
b) $\mu_1 = 0.05$
   $\mu_2 = 0.06$ (All distributions are exponential.)
   $\mu_3 = 0.05$
   $\mu_4 = 0.07$
c) $NQ_1 = 100$
   $NQ_2 = 10$
   $NQ_3 = 20$
   $NQ_4 = 30$

d) Only 50 per cent of the units enter facility 2. The other units go either to facility 3 or 4 with equal probability.

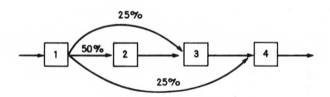

Analyze this system for a period of 30 days of simulated time. Notice the utilization of all service channels. What would happen if only 20 per cent of the units enter facility 2 and the others go with equal probability to facilities 3 and 4?

12. Write a FORTRAN program for the queueing system described in Figure 8.21, *i.e.*, the system with multiple channels in parallel. Design the program to handle up to 10 parallel channels. Simulate a system containing three channels in parallel, an unrestricted first-come first-serve queue, and a Poisson arrival process with $\lambda = 0.05$. Each service process is assumed to be exponential with $\mu_1 = 0.08$, $\mu_2 = 0.09$, and $\mu_3 = 0.12$. Simulate the system for a period of 20 days of simulated time. Compare results with the expected value as obtained in Chapter 3 for:

a) E (waiting time).
b) E (number of units in system).
c) Facility utilization.
d) E (queue length).

13. Assume that you are investigating the operation of a system containing two parallel channels. A queue can exist before each facility. Arrivals to the system will enter the first queue as long as there are less than 10 units in the queue. If there are 10 or more units in the first queue, units will proceed to the second queue. There is effectively no limit on the length of the second queue. Arrivals to the system follow the Poisson process with parameter $\lambda = 0.10$. The service times for both facilities are distributed exponentially with $\mu_1 = 0.08$ and $\mu = 0.09$.

Analyze the system for a period of two weeks of operation. The information desired for output is listed below:

a) Total number of units through system.
b) Total number of units serviced by the overflow channel.
c) Expected waiting time for
    (1) Any unit.
    (2) A unit at facility 1.
    (3) A unit at the overflow facility.
d) Frequency distribution of number in queue.
e) Facility utilization for both channels.

14. Consider the following single channel queueing system with Poisson arrivals. The system considered is an inventory system. An arrival to the system is a demand for one unit of product. If there is inventory on hand, the demand is filled immediately, service time being zero. If the system is out of stock, the service time for the demand is equal to the order lead time. When the simulator brings an arrival (demand) into the service channel, it checks the level of inventory. If the inventory level is greater than zero, a zero service time is generated for that demand, and the inventory level is reduced by one unit. If the inventory level is zero, an order is placed for Q units, an order lead time is generated, and the service time for the demand (arrival) just brought into the channel is set equal to the lead time. The inventory level is then raised to Q units. Through simulation, determine the average number of back orders (demands in the system). Attempt to interpret the results from the queueing simulator in the context of the inventory system. Let $\lambda = 100, Q = 34$, and lead time be constant at 0.08 years.

15. Modify the single channel queueing simulator given in this chapter to account for service failures. The service channel may fail only during those time periods when it is servicing a unit. When an arrival is brought into the channel, the service time for that unit is generated. In addition there is a probability p that the servicing mechanism will fail during the service period. Assume that the

time to repair the service mechanism when it fails is exponentially distributed with mean repair period 0.001 years. The program should calculate the number of failures during the simulation period, the total downtime, and the average downtime per failure. Assume that interarrival time is exponentially distributed with mean 0.002 years and that service time is exponentially distributed with mean 0.0015 years. Let $p = 0.05$.

APPENDIX: MICRO FLOW CHARTS AND PROGRAM LISTING FOR SINGLE CHANNEL QUEUEING SIMULATOR

FIGURE 8.29,
The Main Routine or "Driver"

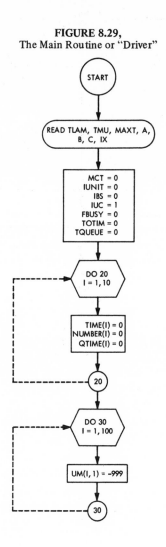

FIGURE 8.29 *(continued)*

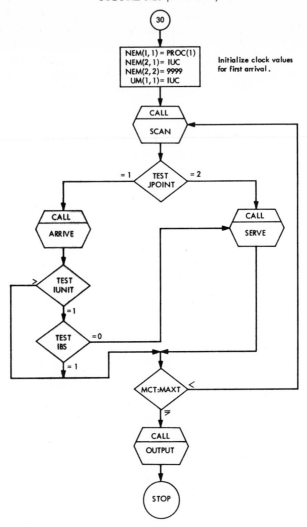

FIGURE 8.30
Scan Routine

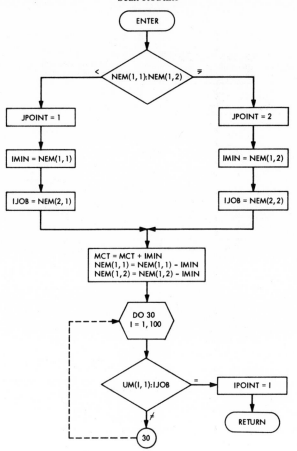

FIGURE 8.31
Arrival Routine

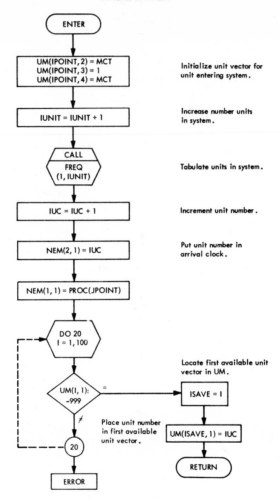

FIGURE 8.32
Service Routine

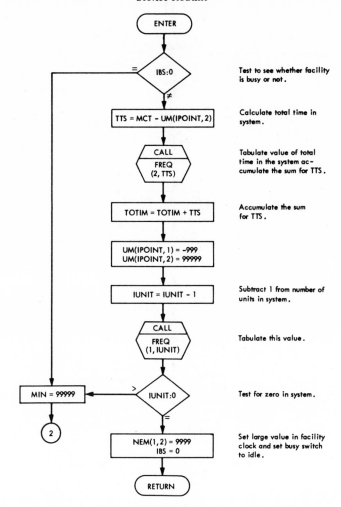

ENTER

IBS:0 — Test to see whether facility is busy or not.

TTS = MCT - UM(IPOINT, 2) — Calculate total time in system.

CALL
FREQ
(2, TTS) — Tabulate value of total time in the system ac-cumulate the sum for TTS.

TOTIM = TOTIM + TTS — Accumulate the sum for TTS.

UM(IPOINT, 1) = -999
UM(IPOINT, 2) = 99999

IUNIT = IUNIT - 1 — Subtract 1 from number of units in system.

CALL
FREQ
(1, IUNIT) — Tabulate this value.

MIN = 99999

IUNIT:0 — Test for zero in system.

2

NEM(1, 2) = 9999
IBS = 0 — Set large value in facility clock and set busy switch to idle.

RETURN

FIGURE 8.32 *(continued)*

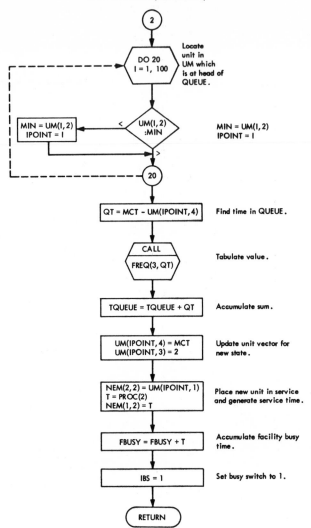

FIGURE 8.33
Process Generator for Arrivals and Services

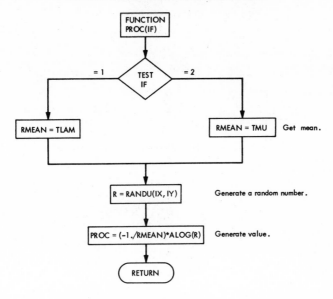

FIGURE 8.34
The Routine to Tabulate Frequency Distributions

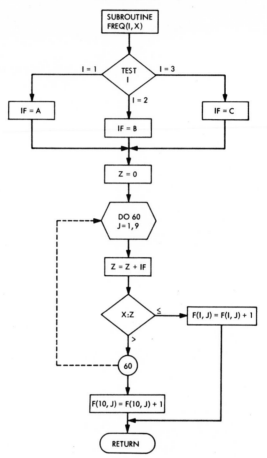

FIGURE 8.35
Output Routine

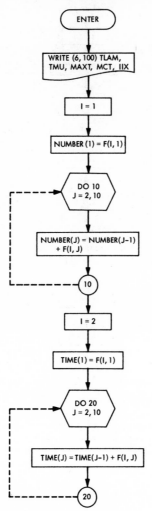

FIGURE 8.35 *(continued)*

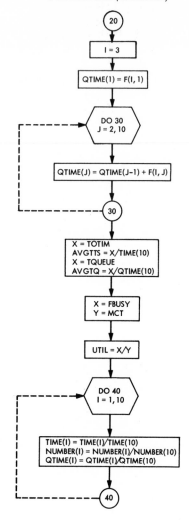

FIGURE 8.35 *(continued)*

FIGURE 8.35 *(continued)*

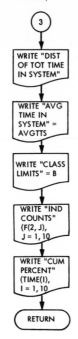

FIGURE 8.36A
Main Program

```
C      MAIN PROGRAM
C      PURPOSE - CONTROLS OVERALL OPERATION OF A
C      SINGLE CHANNEL POISSON QUEUEING SIMULATOR
C      AND PERFORMS FOLLOWING FUNCTIONS
C              1) READ IN VALUES TO INITIALIZE RUN
C              2) INITIALIZE ARRAYS AND PROGRAM VARIABLES
C              3) DRIVE OTHER ROUTINES
C              4) CONTROL SIMULATION RUN LENGTH
C
C      DESCRIPTION OF VARIABLES
C              TLAM-MEAN INTERARRIVAL TIME(IN PROGRAM TIME UNITS)
C              TMU-MEAN SERVICE TIME       (IN PROGRAM TIME UNITS)
C              A,B,C-CLASS WIDTHS FOR FREQ.DISTS.
C              MAXT-LIMIT ON AMOUNT OF SIMULATED TIME
C              IX-INITIAL RANDOM NUMBER
C              MCT-MASTER SIMULATION CLOCK
C              IUNIT-COUNTER ON NUMBER OF UNITS IN SYST.
C              IBS-BUSY SWITCH FOR FACILITY
C              TOTIM-USED TO ACCUMULATE TOTAL OF UNIT-TIMES
C                     FOR UNITS IN SYSTEM
C              TQUEUE-USED TO ACCUMULATE TOTAL OF UNIT-
C                     TIMES FOR UNITS IN QUEUE.
C              FBUSY-VARIABLE USED TO ACCUMULATE
C                     TOTAL AMOUNT OF BUSY TIME ON
C                     FACILITY
C              TIME-VECTOR FOR TABULATING FREQ.DIST.
C                     OF TOTAL TIME IN SYSTEM.
C              NUMBER-VECTOR FOR TABULATING FREQ.DIST.
C                     OF TOTAL NO. OF UNITS IN SYST.
C              QTIME-VECTOR FOR TABULATING FREQ.DIST.
C                     OF TIME IN QUEUE.
C              UM-UNIT MATRIX USED TO HOLD
C                     INFORMATION ABOUT UNITS IN SYSTEM.
C              NEM-NEXT EVENTS MATRIX CONTAINING
C                     CLOCKS ON ARRIVALS AND SERVICE.
C              MAXUM- A POINTER SET ON LAST ACTIVE UNIT VECTOR
C                     IN UM. USED TO MINIMIZE SEARCH TIME.
C              TIMUNT-TIME UNIT USED FOR SIMULATION
C              NOBIG-LARGEST INTEGER NUMBER POSSIBLE ON COMPUTER
C
C              OTHER ROUTINES USED
C         SCAN            SERVE           PROC
C         ARRIVE          OUTPUT
C
       DIMENSION NEM(2,2), UM(100,4),TIME(10)
       DIMENSION NUMBER(10),QTIME(10),F(3,10),TIMUNT(5)
       COMMON/BLOKA/NEM,UM,MCT,IPOINT,JPOINT,MAXUM,NOBIG
       COMMON/BLOKB/IUNIT,IUC
       COMMON/BLOKC/IBS,FBUSY,TOTIM,TQUEUE
       COMMON/BLOKD/TLAM,TMU,IX
       COMMON/BLOKE/ A,B,C,F
       COMMON/BLOKF/TIME,NUMBER,QTIME,MAXT,IIX
       COMMON/BLOKG/TIMUNT
C
       INTEGER UM,F,A,B,C,FBUSY,TOTIM,TQUEUE
       REAL NUMBER
C
```

FIGURE 8.36A *(continued)*

```
C       READ IN VALUES TO INITIALIZE RUN
C
        READ (5,100) TLAM,TMU,MAXT,A,B,C,IX
        READ(5,401) (TIMUNT(I),I=1,5)
C
C       INITIALIZE PROGRAM VARIABLES
        NOBIG=9999999
        MCT=0
        IUNIT=0
        IBS=0
        IUC=1
        FBUSY=0
        TOTIM=0
        TQUEUE=0
        MAXUM=1
        DO 20I=1,10
        TIME(I)=0.
        NUMBER(I)=0.
     20 QTIME(I)=0.
        IIX=IX
        DO 30 I=1,100
        UM(I,1)=-999
     30 UM(I,2)=NOBIG
        DO 40 I=1,3
        DO 40J=1,10
     40 F(I,J)=0
C
C       INITIALIZE SYSTEM BY SETTING NEM(1,1) EQUAL
C       TO FIRST INTERARRIVAL TIME FOR
C       JOB NUMBER 1,AND PLACE JOB IN UM.
C
        IIII=1
        NEM(1,1)=PROC(IIII)
        NEM(2,1) = IUC
        NEM(1,2)=NOBIG
        UM(1,1)= IUC
C
C       THE FOLLOWING SECTION OF CODING ACTUALLY
C       DRIVES THE SIMULATOR. THE SCAN ROUTINE
C       RETURNS A VALUE FOR JPOINT WHICH
C       TELLS WHETHER NEXT EVENT IS AN
C       ARRIVAL OR SERVICE.
C
     50 CALL SCAN
        GO TO (60,70), JPOINT
     60 CALL ARRIVE
C       IF THERE IS ONLY ONE UNIT IN SYSTEM
C       AFTER ARRIVAL AND THE FACILITY IS
C       IDLE, THEN UNIT JUST ARRIVED CAN
C       ENTER SERVICE IMMEDIATELY.
C
        IF(IUNIT.EQ.1.AND.IBS.EQ.0) GO TO 70
        GO TO 80
     70 CALL SERVE
     80 IF(MCT.LT.MAXT) GO TO 50
        CALL OUTPUT
        STOP
    100 FORMAT (2F6.0,5I5)

    401  FORMAT(5A5)
         END
```

FIGURE 8.36B
Subroutine Scan

```
      SUBROUTINE SCAN
C
C     PURPOSE - TO EXAMINE MINOR CLOCK
C     VALUES TO DETERMINE WHAT EVENT WILL
C     HAPPEN NEXT IN TIME IN THE SINGLE
C     CHANNEL QUEUEING SIMULATOR. FURTHER
C     IT INCREMENTS THE MASTER CLOCK BY
C     THE VALUE OF NEXT EVENT TIME,
C     AND LOCATES THE JOB IN THE
C     UNIT MATRIX WHICH HAS CAUSED
C     THE NEXT EVENT TO HAPPEN. TWO
C     POSSIBLE NEXT EVENTS MAY HAPPEN,
C     NAMELY THE ARRIVAL OF A UNIT TO
C     THE SYSTEM OR THE COMPLETION
C     OF A SERVICE.
C
C     DESCRIPTION OF VARIABLES
C             NEM-THE NEXT EVENTS MATRIX WHICH
C             CONTAINS MINOR CLOCKS FOR NEXT
C             EVENTS AS FOLLOWS
C                   NEM(1,1)-TIME TILL NEXT ARRIVAL.
C                   NEM(2,1)-JOB NUMBER OF NEXT ARRIVAL.
C                   NEM(1,2)-TIME TILL SERVICE COMPLETION
C                   NEM(2,2)-JOB NUMBER OF UNIT IN SERVICE
C             JPOINT-POINTER TO NEM TELLING WHICH
C                   CLOCK HAD MINIMUM TIME.
C             IMIN-MINIMUM TIME TILL NEXT EVENT
C             IJOB-JOB NUMBER FOR JOB CONCERNED
C                   WITH NEXT EVENT.
C             JPOINT-POINTER TO NEM TELLING WHICH
C                   CLOCK HAD MINIMUM TIME.
C             IMIN-MINIMUM TIME TILL NEXT EVENT
C             IJOB-JOB NUMBER FOR JOB CONCERNED
C                   WITH NEXT EVENT.
C             IPOINT-POINTER TO UM FOR UNIT VECTOR
C                   OF JOB IN QUESTION.
      DIMENSION NEM(2,2),UM(100,4)
      COMMON/BLOKA/NEM,UM,MCT,IPOINT,JPOINT,MAXUM,NOBIG
      INTEGER UM
C
C     COMPARING TWO CLOCK VALUES TO FIND
C     NEXT EVENT. NEM(1,1).LT.NEM(1,2)
C     IMPLIES THAT ARRIVAL TO SYSTEM WILL
C     OCCUR NEXT IN TIME. IF NEM(1,1).EQ.
C     NEM(1,2) THIS IMPLIES THAT ARRIVAL
C     AND SERVICE WILL HAPPEN SIMULTANEOUSLY
C     AND SIMULATOR WILL HANDLE SERVICE
C     FIRST, BEFORE ARRIVAL. THIS WILL NOT
C     AFFECT RESULTS.
C
      IF (NEM(1,1).GE.NEM(1,2))GO TO 10
      JPOINT=1
      IMIN = NEM(1,1)
      IJOB = NEM(2,1)
      GO TO 20
   10 JPOINT = 2
      IMIN=NEM(1,2)
      IJOB = NEM(2,2)
C     MODIFYING CLOCK VALUES BY TIME TILL
C     NEXT EVENT. INCREASE MCT AND DECREASE
C     BOTH MINOR CLOCKS.
   20 MCT=MCT+IMIN
      NEM(1,1)=NEM(1,1)-IMIN
      NEM(1,2)=NEM(1,2)-IMIN
C     FIND JOB IN QUESTION IN UM.
      DO 30 I=1,MAXUM
      IF(UM(I,1).EQ.IJOB) GO TO 40
   30 CONTINUE
   40 IPOINT=I
      RETURN
      END
```

FIGURE 8.36C
Subroutine Arrive

```
      SUBROUTINE ARRIVE
C     PURPOSE - CALLED WHEN NEXT EVENT WAS
C     ARRIVAL TO SYSTEM, THIS ROUTINE EFFECTS
C     ARRIVAL BY INITIALIZING ENTRIES IN
C     THE PROPER UNIT VECTOR OF UM FOR
C     JOB OR UNIT ENTERING SYSTEM.IT THEN
C     GENERATES NEXT INTERARRIVAL TIME
C     VALUE AND PLACES THIS YN NEM
C     CLOCK AS WELL AS NEW JOB NUMBER.
C     IT ALSO CREATES A UNIT VECTOR FOR
C     THIS JOB ABOUT TO ENTER SYSTEM.
C
C     DESCRIPTION OF VARIABLES
C          UM - UNIT MATRIX CONTAINING INFO.
C                 ABOUT EACH JOB IN SYSTEM.
C                 FOR ANY UNIT VECTOR (FOR ANY
C                 GIVEN UNIT IN THE SYSTEM)
C                 THE ENTRIES ARE
C                 UM(I,1) - UNIT OK JOB NUMBER
C                 UM(I,2) - MCT OF INITIAL SYSTEM ENTRY
C                 UM(I,3) - UNIT STATUS
C                     =1 MEANS UNIT IN QUEUE
C                     =2 MEANS UNIT IN SERVICE
C                 UM(I,4) = MCT OF ENTRY TO PRESENT STATE
C          IUNIT - COUNTER ON NUMBER OF UNITS IN SYST.
C          IUC - UNIT COUNTER-A SEQUENTIAL
C                 NUMBER ASSIGNED EACH UNIT ENTERING
C                 THE SYSTEM-CALLED JOB NUMBER.
C          NEM- NEXT EVENTS MATRIX
C          ISAVE - POINTER TO UM FOR FIRST
C                 AVAILABLE UNIT VECTOR.
C          IPOINT - POINTER TO VECTOR IN UM FOR ENTERING JOB.
C          MAXUM - POINTER TO LAST ACTIVE UM ENTRY
C     OTHER ROUTINES USED
C          FREQ     PROC
C
      DIMENSION NEM(2,2),UM(100,4),F(3,10)
      COMMON/BLOKA/NEM,UM,MCT,IPOINT,JPOINT,MAXUM,NOBIG
      COMMON/BLOKB/IUNIT,IUC
      COMMON/BLOKD/TLAM,TMU,IX
      COMMON/BLOKE/A,B,C,F
      INTEGER UM,A,B,C,F
C
C          INITIALIZE UNIT VECTOR FOR UNIT JUST
C          ENTERING SYSTEM. IPOINT POINTS TO
C          PROPER VECTOR IN UM.
C
      UM(IPOINT,2)=MCT
      UM(IPOINT,3)=1
      UM(IPOINT,4)=MCT
C
C     INCREMENT NO. OF UNITS IN SYSTEM AND
C     TABULATE THE VALUE
C
      IUNIT = IUNIT+1
      IIII=1
      CALL FREQ(IIII,IUNIT)
C
```

FIGURE 8.36C *(continued)*

```
C       INCREMENT UNIT COUNTER, PLACE PRESENT
C       UNIT NUMBER IN NEM ARRIVAL CLOCK AND
C       GENERATE INTERARRIVAL TIME FOR THIS
C       UNIT INNEM CLOCK.
C
        IUC=IUC+1
        NEM(2,1)=IUC
        NEM(1,1)=PROC(JPOINT)
C
C       LOCATE FIRST AVAILABLE UNIT VECTOR
C       IN UM AND ENTER UNIT NUMBER IN
C       UM(I,1) FOR UNIT IN NEM ARRIVAL
C       CLOCK.
C
        DO 20 I=1,100
        IF(UM(I,1).EQ.-999) GO TO 30
     20 CONTINUE
C       A NORMAL EXIT FROM ABOVE DO LOOP
C       CONSTITUTES AN ERROR. THIS INDICATES
C       UM IS FULL AND MUST BE INCREASED
C       IN SIZE FOR SIMULATION OF PARTICULAR
C       SYSTEM
        WRITE (6,100)
        CALL EXIT
     30 ISAVE=I
C       SETTING POINTER ISAVE ON AVAILABLE UNIT VECTOR.
C       IF FIRST AVAILABLE UV IS BELOW PRESENT VALUE
C       OF MAXUM--SET MAXUM DOWN TO NEW VALUE.
        IF(MAXUM.LT.ISAVE) MAXUM=ISAVE
        UM(ISAVE,1)=IUC
        RETURN
    100 FORMAT(1X14HERROR--UM FULL)
        END
C
```

FIGURE 8.36D
Subroutine Serve

```
      SUBROUTINE SERVE
C     PURPOSE-CALLED EITHER WHEN NEXT EVENT
C     WAS SERVICE COMPLETION,OR WHEN ARRIVAL
C     OCCURRED WHEN FACILITY WAS IDLE.THIS
C     ROUTINE AFFECTS SERVICE COMPLETION AND
C     CAUSES COLLECTION OF PERTINENT INFO.
C     IT FURTHER INITIATES NEXT SERVICE
C     IF A UNIT IS WAITING IN QUEUE. FOR UNIT
C     ENTERING SERVICE IT GENERATES SERVICE
C     TIME AND MODIFIES UNIT VECTOR ENTRIES.
C     FOR UNIT COMPLETING SERVICE IT CANCELS
C     ENTRIES IN UNIT VECTOR. QUEUE
C     DISCIPLINE ASSUMED IS FIRST-COME FIRST
C     SERVE.
C     DESCRIPTION OF VARIABLES
C          IBS - FACILITY BUSY SWITCH
C                    =0 MEANS FACILITY PRESENTLY IDLE
C                    =1 MEANS FACILITY PRESENTLY BUSY
C          TTS - VARIABLE USED TO CALCULATE TOTAL
C                    TIME IN SYSTEM FOR GIVEN UNIT.
C          MCT - MASTER CLOCK TIME
C          UM - UNIT MATRIX DEFINED ELSEWHERE
C          TOTIM - VARIABLE USED TO ACCUMULATE
C                    TOTAL TIME IN SYSTEM FOR ALL
C                    UNITS WHICH HAVE PASSED THRU.
C          IUNIT - COUNTER ON UNITS IN SYSTEM.
C          NEM- NEXT EVENTS MATRIX
C          IPOINT - POINTER TO UM VECTOR IN
C                    QUESTION.
C          QT - VARIABLE USED TO CALCULATE TIME
C                    IN QUEUE FOR ANY GIVEN UNIT.
C          TQUEUE - VARIABLE USED TO ACCUMULATE
C                    TOTAL TIME IN QUEUE FOR ALL
C                    UNITS PASSING THROUGH.
C          FBUSY - VARIABLE USED TO COLLECT
C                    TOTAL AMOUNT OF TIME FACILITY
C                    IS BUSY.
C          T - DUMMY VARIABLE.
C
C     OTHER ROUTINES USED
C          FREQ    PROC
C
      DIMENSION NEM(2,2),UM(100,4),F(3,10)
      COMMON/BLOKA/NEM,UM,MCT,IPOINT,JPOINT,MAXUM,NOBIG
      COMMON/BLOKB/IUNIT,IUC
      COMMON/BLOKC/IBS,FBUSY,TOTIM,TQUEUE
      COMMON/BLOKD/TLAM,TMU,IX
      COMMON/BLOKE/A,B,C,F
      INTEGER UM,F,FBUSY,TOTIM,TQUEUE,A,B,C,QT,T
      INTEGER TTS
C
C     TEST TO SEE WHETHER FACILITY BUSY
      IF(IBS.EQ.0) GO TO 10
C
C     CALCULATE TOTAL TIME IN SYSTEM, TABULATE
C     THE VALUE, AND ACCUMULATE IT IN TOTIM.
C
      TTS=MCT-UM(IPOINT,2)
```

FIGURE 8.36D *(continued)*

```
      IIII=2
      CALL FREQ(IIII,TTS)
      TOTIM = TOTIM + TTS
C
C     DESTROY UNIT VECTOR FOR UNIT JUST FINISHED
C     SERVICE.
C
      UM(IPOINT,1)=-999
      UM(IPOINT,2)=NOBIG
C
C     SUBTRACT ONE FROM NO OF UNITS IN
C     SYSTEM AND TABULATE VALUE.
C
      IUNIT =IUNIT-1
      IIII=1
      CALL FREQ(IIII,IUNIT)
C
C     IF ZERO UNITS IN SYSTEM SET FACILITY
C     BUSY SWITCH TO ZERO AND NEM CLOCK
C     TO A VERY LARGE TIME VALUE. IF
C     UNITS IN SYSTEM, LOOK FOR UNIT IN
C     UM WHICH IS AT HEAD OF QUEUE.
C
      IF(IUNIT.GT.0) GO TO 10
      NEM(1,2)= NOBIG
      IBS=0
      RETURN
   10 MIN=NOBIG
      DO 20 I=1,MAXUM
      IF(UM(I,2).GT.MIN) GO TO 20
      MIN=UM(I,2)
      IPOINT = I
   20 CONTINUE
C
C     FOR UNIT LEAVING QUEUE, FIND TIME IN
C     TQUEUE. TABULATE TIME AND ACCUMULATE
C     IT IN TQUEUE.
C
      QT=MCT-UM(IPOINT,4)
      IIII=3
      CALL FREQ(IIII,QT)
      TQUEUE = TQUEUE + QT
C
C     UPDATE UNIT VECTOR FOR UNIT ENTERING
C     SERVICE. PLACE UNIT NO IN NEM SERVICE
C     CLOCK VECTOR AND GENERATE A SERVICE
C     TIME.
C
      UM(IPOINT,4)=MCT
      UM(IPOINT,3)=2
      NEM(2,2)=UM(IPOINT,1)
      T=PROC(2)
      NEM(1,2)=T
C
C     ACCUMULATE FACILITY BUSY TIME AND
C     SET FACILITY BUSY SWITCH TO 1.
C
      FBUSY=FBUSY+T

      IBS=1
      RETURN
      END
```

FIGURE 8.36E
Function Process

```
      FUNCTION PROC (IF)
C     PURPOSE - TO GENERATE EXPONENTIALLY
C     DISTRIBUTED RANDOM VARIABLES FOR
C     EITHER INTERARRIVAL TIME OR SERVICE
C     TIME
C
C     USAGE      N= PROC (IF)
C
C     DESCRIPTION OF VARIABLES
C          IF-INDICATOR TELLING WHICH MEAN
C              TO USE IN GENERATION.
C          =1-USE MEAN INTERARRIVAL TIME
C          =2-USE MEAN SERVICE TIME
C          RMEAN - VALUE USED AS MEAN IN CALCULATION
C          TLAM - MEAN INTERARRIVAL TIME
C          TMU - MEAN SERVICE TIME
C          R - DUMMY VARIABLE USED TO GET RN.
C          IX - INITIAL RN. SUPPLIED
C     REMARKS - A RANDOM NUMBER GENERATOR
C     OF THE MULTIPLICATIVE CONGRUENTIAL
C     TYPE IS IMBEDDED IN THE ROUTINE.
C
      COMMON/BLOKD/TLAM,TMU,IX
C
C     THE FOLLOWING SECTION GENERATES A
C     UNIFORMLY DIST. RN.
C     MULTIPLIER IS 5**5
      IY=IX*03125
      IF(IY.)10,20,20
   10 IY=IY+ 2**35
   20 YFL=IY
      R=YFL*2.0**(-35)
      IX=IY
C     THE FOLLOWING SECTION GENERATES
C     THE EXPONENTIAL VARIABLE.
      GO TO (30,40),IF
   30 RMEAN = TLAM
      GO TO 50
   40 RMEAN = TMU
   50 PROC=(-1.0/RMEAN)*ALOG(R)
      RETURN
      END
```

FIGURE 8.36F
Subroutine Frequency

```
      SUBROUTINE FREQ (I,X)
C     PURPOSE - TO TABULATE FREQUENCY DISTS.
C     FOR THREE VARIABLES.
C     USAGE - CALL FREQ (I,X)
C
C     DESCRIPTION OF VARIABLES
C          I - INDICATOR FOR DISTRIBUTION
C          =1 - UNITS IN SYSTEM
C          =2 - TOTAL TIME IN SYSTEM
C          =3 - TIME IN QUEUE.
C          X - VALUE TO BE TABULATED
C          A,B,C - CLASS WIDTHS USED FOR DIFFERENT
C                 DISTRIBUTIONS.
C          F(I,J) - MATRIX USED TO COLLECT FREQ.
C                 COUNTS.I=1,2,AND 3 CORRESPOND
C                 TO I AS DEFINED ABOVE.
C          IF,Z,J - WORKING DUMMY VARIABLES.
C
      DIMENSION F(3,10)
      COMMON/BLOKE/A,B,C,F
      INTEGER A,B,C,F,Z,X
C
C     TEST TO DETERMINE WHICH DIST.
C
      GO TO (10,20,30),I
   10 IF=A
      GO TO 40
   20 IF = B
      GO TO 40
   30 IF = C
   40 Z = 0
C
C     TABULATING THE VALUE - F(I,10) IS USED
C     AS OVERFLOW.
C
      DO 60 J=1,9
      Z=Z+IF
      IF (X.GT.Z) GO TO 60
      F(I,J)=F(I,J)+1
      GO TO 70
   60 CONTINUE
      F(I,10)=F(I,10)+1
   70 RETURN
      END
C
```

FIGURE 8.36G
Subroutine Output

```
      SUBROUTINE OUTPUT
C     PURPOSE - MAKE FINAL CALCULATIONS FOR
C     SUMMARY STATISTICS AND PRINT RESULTANT
C     INFORMATION OUT AT THE END OF SIMULATION
C     RUN.
C
C     DESCRIPTION OF VARIABLES
C          ALL MAJOR VARIABLES USED HAVE
C     PREVIOUSLY BEEN DEFINED. OTHERS WILL
C     BE DEFINED AS NEEDED.
C
      DIMENSION NEM(2,2),UM(100,4),TIME(10),NUMBER(10)
      DIMENSION QTIME(10),F(3,10) ,TIMUNT(5)
      COMMON/BLOKA/NEM,UM,MCT,IPOINT,JPOINT,MAXUM,NOBIG
      COMMON/BLOKC/IBS,FBUSY,TOTIM,TQUEUE
      COMMON/BLOKD/TLAM,TMU,IX
      COMMON/BLOKE/A,B,C,F
      COMMON/BLOKF/TIME,NUMBER,QTIME,MAXT,IIX
      COMMON/BLOKG/TIMUNT
      INTEGER UM,F,A,B,C,FBUSY,TOTIM,TQUEUE
      REAL NUMBER
C
C     OUTPUTTING INFO. ON PROGRAM CONDITIONS
      TLAM=1./TLAM
      TMU=1./TMU
      WRITE(6,1055)
      WRITE(6,1001)(TIMUNT(I),I=1,5)
      WRITE(6,1000)TLAM,(TIMUNT(I),I=1,5),TMU,(TIMUNT(I),I=1,5),IXX
      WRITE(6,1005)MAXT,(TIMUNT(I),I=1,5),MCT
C     OBTAINING CUMULATIVE DISTRIBUTIONS FOR
C     ALL FREQUENCY COUNTS. FIRST FOR NUMBER
C     IN THE SYSTEM
C
      NUMBER(1)=F(1,1)
      DO 10 J=2,10
      X1=F(1,J)
   10 NUMBER(J)=NUMBER(J-1)+X1
C
C     NOW FOR TOTAL TIME IN SYSTEM
C
      TIME(1)=F(2,1)
      DO 20 J=2,10
      X2=F(2,J)
   20 TIME(J)=TIME(J-1)+X2
C
C     FINALLY FOR TIME IN QUEUE
C
      QTIME(1)=F(3,1)
      DO 30 J=2,10
      X3=F(3,J)
   30 QTIME(J)=QTIME(J-1)+X3
C
C     CALCULATION OF AVG. TOTAL TIME IN SYST.
C     AND AVG. TIME IN Q AND FACILITY UTILIZATION
      X=TOTIM
      AVGTTS=X/TIME(10)
      X=TQUEUE
      AVGTQ=X/QTIME(10)
```

FIGURE 8.36G *(continued)*

```
      X=FBUSY
      Y=MCT
      UTIL = X/Y
C
C     CALCULATION OF CUMULATIVE PERCENTAGES
C
      DO 40 I=1,10
      TIME(I) = TIME(I)/TIME(10)
      QTIME(I)=QTIME(I)/QTIME(10)
   40 NUMBER(I)=NUMBER (I) /NUMBER(10)
C
C     OUTPUTTING INFO. ON FACILITY UTILIZATION.
C
      WRITE (6,1010) UTIL
C
C     OUTPUTTING ALL DISTRIBUTION INFO.
C
      WRITE(6,1015)
      WRITE(6,1020) A
      WRITE(6,1025) (F(1,J),J=1,10)
      WRITE(6,1030) (NUMBER(I),I=1,10)
      WRITE(6,1035)
      WRITE(6,1040) AVGTQ,(TIMUNT(I),I=1,5)
      WRITE(6,1020) C
      WRITE(6,1025) (F(3,J),J=1,10)
      WRITE(6,1030) (QTIME(I),I=1,10)
      WRITE(6,1045)
      WRITE(6,1050) AVGTTS,(TIMUNT(I),I=1,5)
      WRITE(6,1020) B
      WRITE(6,1025) (F(2,J),J=1,10)
      WRITE(6,1030) (TIME(I),I=1,10)
      RETURN
 1000 FORMAT(1X64HINITIAL CONDITIONS FOR SINGLE CHANNEL POISSON QUEUEING
     1 SIMULATOR/25H MEAN INTERARRIVAL TIME= ,F15.5,4H IN ,5A5,/1X19HMEA
     2N SERVICE TIME= ,F15.5,4H IN ,5A5,/1X26HINITIAL RANDOM NUMBER WAS
     3,I5/)
 1001 FORMAT(1H ,38HTIME UNIT USED IN THIS SIMULATION WAS ,5A5)
 1005 FORMAT(1X21HSIMULATION PERIOD IN ,5A5,1H=,I10,/1H ,28HACTUAL SIMUL
     1ATION PERIOD IN ,5A5,1H=,I10,//)
 1010 FORMAT(1X43HFACILITY UTILIZATION FOR SIMULATED PERIOD= ,F8.4,//)
 1015 FORMAT(1X41HDISTRIBUTION OF NUMBER OF UNITS IN SYSTEM//)
 1020 FORMAT(1X39HCLASS WIDTH ON FREQUENCY TABULATION IS ,I6,24H UNITS B
     1EGINNING AT ZERO,/20X12HCLASS NUMBER/27X1H19X1H29X1H39X1H49X1H59X1
     2H69X1H79X1H89X1H99X2H10,/)
 1025 FORMAT(1X17HINDIVIDUAL COUNTS,2X,10(4X I6))
 1030 FORMAT(1X18HCUMULATIVE PERCENT,1X,10(4XF6.3)//)
 1035 FORMAT(1X29HDISTRIBUTION OF TIME IN QUEUE//)
 1040 FORMAT(1X23HAVERAGE TIME IN QUEUE= ,F9.4,5A5/)
 1045 FORMAT(1X36HDISTRIBUTION OF TOTAL TIME IN SYSTEM//)
 1050 FORMAT(1X30HAVERAGE TOTAL TIME IN SYSTEM= ,F9.4,5A5)
 1055 FORMAT(1H1)
      END
```

CHAPTER
9

SIMULATION OF INVENTORY SYSTEMS

In this chapter we shall construct a general simulation model which can be employed in the analysis of either reorder point or periodic review inventory systems. The next-event concept developed in the previous chapter will again be employed in the construction of the simulation model. We shall discuss the events which can occur and then investigate their outcomes with regard to both types of systems. Next we shall combine the concepts of the two systems into one "parameterized" simulation model which is capable of simulating either system.

Three features of the general inventory simulation model will be distinctly different from the queueing simulation model. First, all time values will be maintained as real variables in the simulation program. Second, the time values in the equivalent next event matrix will be maintained in terms of the master simulation clock instead of the time until next event method, i.e., minor clock entries will contain cumulative time values instead of interevent time values. Finally, an option will be included in the next event matrix which will allow the analyst to update pertinent statistics, print out operating information, or both at incremental time values. These modifications have been made purposely to provide further insight into the mechanics of constructing computer simulation models.

The reader is advised to review Chapter 4 for a discussion of the pertinent costs and the features of these two inventory systems. The simulation model developed here is a generalization of the inventory models considered in Chapter 4.

EVENTS TO CONSIDER IN INVENTORY SIMULATION

For the purposes of our development we shall define five distinct events which may occur in time in a general inventory simulation. These events are listed below:

1. The demand for items in inventory.
2. The receipt of an order.
3. The review of the inventory position to determine whether or not an order for additional stock should be placed.
4. The summarizing (and/or the output) of information regarding the status of the system at the point in time.
5. The end of the simulation run.

Notice that the last two events listed above are "model-oriented" items and do not have particular significance in a real world inventory system. The reader will see that by defining events in this fashion we will be able to construct a general simulation program which will handle both the reorder point model as well as the periodic review model. We shall define the measure of effectiveness for both systems as the total system cost per year. Included in the total system cost are the annual cost of carrying inventory, the annual cost of stock-outs, and the annual cost of reviewing the system and placing orders for inventory replenishment. Decisions regarding when and how much to order are based upon inventory position. The decision variables are generally considered to be when to place an order and how much to order. The objective of the simulation model will be to obtain a value for the measure of effectiveness based upon specified values of the decision variables. We will accomplish this by allowing the model to simulate a desired period of operation. Let us now begin to characterize the overall simulation process. Figure 9.1 illustrates a time scale over which the inventory simulation will operate. Let us say for purposes of discussion that we wish to simulate three years of operation of this inventory system; *i.e.*, $T = 3$ years. Further let us say that we wish a

FIGURE 9.1
Time Scale for Events during Inventory Simulation

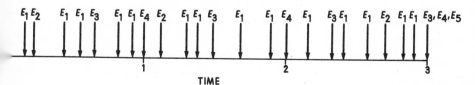

TIME

summary of statistical information at the end of each year's operation. This is shown on the scale by the arrows labeled E_4. Note that the point $T = 3$ on the scale is also labeled E_5, indicating the occurrence of event 5, namely, the end of the simulation run. All arrows labeled E_1 represent the points in time when demands occurred. In this particular case the distance between two successive E_1 arrows is not a constant. Further note that the arrows labeled E_3 represent the points in time when the inventory position is reviewed for the purpose of deciding whether or not to place an order. This particular figure illustrates a periodic review system. A reorder point system would differ only in that each point on the scale marked with an E_1 arrow would have a coincident E_3 arrow, *i.e.,* the inventory position would be reviewed each time a demand occurred. The points on the scale labeled with E_2 arrows represent those points in time when an order was received. If lead time is zero, the E_2 arrows would be coincident with the E_3 arrows.

As in the queueing simulator, the function of our inventory simulator will be to "place" the arrows on the scale and, as arrows are encountered, record the ramifications to the system caused by the particular event. By recording all time values in master clock time units rather than relative time units (as we did in the queueing simulator) we can, in effect, place the E_5 arrow on the scale at the beginning of the run by reading the value in. Further note that the distance between successive E_4 arrows can also be a parameter which can be read in. The simulator should function in such a fashion that whenever a given event occurs, the point in time at which the next similar event occurs is recorded on the scale. The method for arriving at the distance between two similar arrows will be dependent upon the nature of the model simulated. Also, when event 3 occurs we can determine generally both when the next event 3 will occur as well as when the corresponding event 2 will occur. That is to say, when a review occurs we can determine when the next review will occur (in a periodic review model) as well as when the order will be received if one was placed at that review time.

By reviewing the general inventory system in the above manner we can begin to discuss specific ramifications to particular events based upon the models we will work with. Note that as we cause the simulator to proceed from point to point on the time scale we must continually update the information we are collecting pertinent to costs. In particular as we move a distance Δt on the time scale, where Δt is the time between two events which change the status of the inventory system, we must modify the values for unit-years of inventory on hand as well as unit-years of back orders (if this is a back order example). This is accomplished by multiplying Δt by the inventory level and by the number of back orders if a stock-out results in a back order. The inventory and back order levels by which Δt is multiplied are those which existed when the period Δt commenced.

Let us now look at some of the desirable features we would like to include in our simulation model. These features are based upon characteristics of the events within the simulation.

CHARACTERISTICS OF A DEMAND

A request to the inventory system for items in inventory constitutes a demand. The characteristics of the demand pattern may be discussed independently, without regard to the type of inventory system being simulated. We make the assumption that the demand pattern is independent of the way the inventory system is managed. This is somewhat misleading because a poor system which does not satisfy demand will, in the long run, cause that demand to diminish. However, it is a common assumption and one we shall not violate.

We wish to be able to simulate systems with all types of varying demand patterns. The demand pattern is specified by the time between successive demands as well as the number of units requested per demand. It would be helpful if we considered the inclusion of parameters in our simulation model which would allow us to specify both of these characteristics. We also wish to allow for both constant or randomly distributed times between successive demands. By providing for constant interdemand times we are able to model systems in which demand is recorded as, say, demand per day or demand per month. We would then be able to simulate the operation of the system on a day-by-day or month-by-month basis. We also wish to allow for a constant or randomly distributed number of units being requested per demand. This can be accomplished again through the extensive use of subprograms.

CHARACTERISTICS OF AN ORDER

We previously listed the receipt of an order as an event to consider in the general inventory simulation model. Let us discuss what features regarding orders we would like to include in our model. The first such feature is the time between placement of an order and the receipt of that order, *i.e.,* the lead time. Generally we wish to allow for both constant and randomly distributed lead time values. Several orders might be outstanding at one time. Further, orders might also cross. An example of crossing orders is illustrated in Figure 9.2. Notice that although the kth order was placed after the jth order, it was received before the jth order. In reality this situation often exists. Note also that at time t there are three orders outstanding. It should be obvious that if lead time values are constant, orders cannot cross. It is well to remember that policies dictating when to order are based upon inventory position; so this crossing of orders should not affect the decision to place an order.

FIGURE 9.2
Crossing of Orders

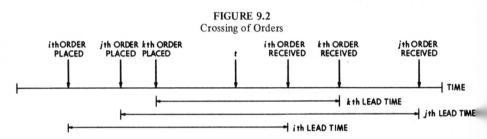

The number of units ordered is also of great importance. The value of this quantity, called the order quantity, is treated as a decision variable. We shall discuss the order quantity in greater detail when we consider the reorder point model and periodic review model in detail. Finally, we must consider that cost associated with placing the order. As in Chapter 4, we will consider this cost to be independent of the number of units ordered.

CHARACTERISTICS OF A REVIEW

In the periodic review model the status of inventory is reviewed at fixed intervals. Where a reorder point model is used, it is implied that the system is continuously reviewed. Actually, a review is necessary only when an event occurs which may cause inventory position to fall to or below the reorder point. Since a demand represents the only event which may cause such an adjustment in inventory position, a review of the system may be considered to be coincident with a demand when the reorder point model is used. It is possible then to consider the reorder point model as a special case of the periodic review model. Strictly speaking, the reorder point model is really a transactions recording system in which each event is recorded as it occurs and is brought to the attention of those responsible for reviewing the system and placing orders. Hence, we would need to consider both cases, *i.e.*, when inventory position is reviewed at each demand and when inventory position is reviewed at fixed intervals. In a periodic review model, the time between reviews is a decision variable and would be read into the program.

In the periodic review model the magnitude of the review cost will to some extent influence the time between reviews. As the cost of a review decreases, one would expect the optimal time between successive reviews to decrease. In fact, as this cost approaches zero, the optimal period between reviews will also approach zero—yielding, in effect, a transactions recording system. The cost of a review is not usually considered in a reorder point model, since this cost will not influence the optimal operating policy within this model class. However, if the reorder point policy is to be compared with a periodic review policy, then the cost of a review should be included in both models.

DESCRIPTION OF THE PROGRAM

In previous sections the discussion was centered about considerations for constructing a simulation model for each of the two inventory systems. In this section a general inventory simulation program will be presented. This program is capable of simulating either the reorder point or the periodic review inventory systems with lost sales or back orders. In addition, the order quantity may be a constant or may vary from one order to another. The program is constructed about the next-event concept and employs the five events discussed previously. The model consists of one main program and 10 separate subprograms. The main program is responsible for input of data, driving the simulation, and printing intermediate operating information. The subprograms are listed below with a brief description of their function.

1. SUBROUTINE NEXT – This subroutine determines which event will occur next in the simulation. This is similar to SUBROUTINE SCAN in the queueing simulator.
2. SUBROUTINE UPDATE – This subroutine accumulates both the unit-years of inventory and the unit-years of back orders (if a back order case).

3. SUBROUTINE REVIEW — When called, this subroutine will review the inventory position to determine whether or not an order should be placed. If an order should be placed, it calculates the order quantity and schedules the receipt of the order as a later event. It further increases the inventory position by the order quantity.

4. SUBROUTINE UNOUT — This routine updates the system after a demand occurs, determining whether the demand is met, back ordered, or lost.

5. SUBROUTINE UNIN — This routine handles the system after an order is received.

6. FUNCTION ORDER — This function generates the values for lead time.

7. FUNCTION DEMAND — This subprogram generates the time until the next demand.

8. FUNCTION UNITS — This subprogram generates the number of units requested at a given demand.

9. SUBROUTINE SIG — This routine computes the mean and the standard deviation of the mean of six separate quantities: unit-years of inventory; unit-years of stock-outs; number of stock-outs; number of orders; number of reviews; and total system cost.

10. FUNCTION RANDU — Generates uniformly distributed random numbers.

Although the program employs the next-event concept to perform operations, a next-event matrix as such is not created. Rather, separate variables are used to store the time values for the five events defined in the simulation. The five variables are listed below:

DE — Master clock time of the next demand.

OD(I) — A vector containing master clock times for the receipt of outstanding orders. OD(MIN) represents the master clock time for the receipt of the next order.

TREV — The master clock time at which the next review of the inventory position will take place.

TIMST — The master clock time at which the next statistcal update and/or printout will occur.

TIMLIM — The master clock time for the end of the simulation run

Before proceeding further into the development of the model it would be helpful to illustrate the manner in which the lead times are handled by the program. The vector OD is used to store the time values for receipt of all orders outstanding. Each time an order is placed, the receipt time is calculated and placed in the vector OD. The vector is then searched for the minimum value of OD(I). A pointer called MIN is set at this element. Then, at any time, OD(MIN) is the time of receipt of the next order. Figure 9.3A illustrates this vector. The variable NOUT counts the number of orders outstanding at any point in time. According to Figure 9.3A there are five orders outstanding (NOUT=5) and the next order received is order number 3 (MIN = 3). At time 11 the third order is received, placed in inventory, and is then destroyed. At that point the vector OD is rearranged as shown in Figure 9.3B. At time 11 there are four orders outstanding (NOUT = 4) the next order received is the second (MIN = 2) and will be received at time 17.

FIGURE 9.3
A – The vector OD before time 11.
(NOUT = 5, MIN = 3)
B – The vector OD after time 11.
(NOUT = 4, MIN = 2)

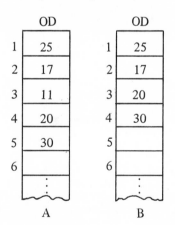

SUBROUTINE REVIEW performs the function of calculating receipt times, placing them in OD, and determining the value of MIN. In Figure 9.3B the vector OD is shown after the time 11 when OD(MIN), MIN = 3, was received. The element OD(MIN) is removed, and OD is compressed by moving all other time values up. The vector is then searched again to determine the new value of MIN. These functions are performed by SUBROUTINE UNIN. In correspondence with the vector OD is a vector AIOQ which contains the number of units to be received. Hence, when an order is received,

AIOQ(MIN) contains the number of units in that order. So the event OD(MIN) contains the time of receipt of the next order and AIOQ(MIN) contains the number of units received on that order.

We referred above to master clock time values. Unlike the queueing simulator presented in Chapter 8, this simulator works with accumulated time values for all events. To illustrate this, consider Table 9.1. In this table are the accumulated time values for a simulation run of 20 time units. The column headed "TIM1' indicates the "present time" or the equivalent to MCT in the queueing simulator. The process generators used still generate interevent time. However, the time used for scheduling events is that interevent time plus the value of TIM1. For instance, the time generated between the first and second demands was four time units. Those four time units added to the value of TIM1 give the next value of DE as seven.

TABLE 9.1
Example of Time Flow in Inventory Simulator

EVENT	TIM1	DE	OD(MIN)	TREV	TIMST	TIMLIM
1 3	(3)	****	4	10	20
2 4	7	****	(4)	10	20
3 7	(7)	****	8	10	20
4 8	9	****	(8)	10	20
5 9	(9)	14	12	10	20
6 10	13	14	12	(10)	20
7 12	13	14	(12)	20	20
8 13	(13)	14	16	20	20
9 14	15	(14)	16	20	20
10. 15	(15)	****	16	20	20
11. 16	18	****	(16)	20	20
12. 18	(18)	****	20	20	20
13. 20	22	****	(20)	20	20
14. 20	22	****	24	(20)	20
15. 20	22	****	24	30	(20)

**** Represents an extremly large value.

Looking at the column headed "TREV," we can see that this is a periodic review system with a time between reviews of four time units. The model was also set to update all statistics every 10 time units.

Notice that the time for receipt of an order [OD(MIN)] was initially set very high to avoid being selected by the next-event routine. During the fourth event, which was a review, a decision to order was made and the time for the receipt of that order was generated and placed in ariable OD(MIN). Once the order was received (EVENT 9), that variable was again set to a very high value.

It should be obvious now how this simulation model differs from the queueing simulator. It is very helpful to place the statistical update and/or printout option as an event in the list of events. Now, output can be effected at any point in time during the operation of the simulator. This option is very helpful in debugging the program.

Figure 9.4 shows the macro flow chart for the overall operation of the simulation program. Micro flow charts will not be included for the routines of this simulation program. The subroutines are described individually in the body of the chapter and shown in figures 9.5 through 9.15.

The listing of the main program is shown in Figure 9.34 in the appendix at the end of this chapter. The program is set to handle several sets of problems. The number of problem sets is read into variable NSIM. Further, each problem may be simulated several times to replicate the experiment. The variable ITER specifies this value. The sequence of statements after statement number 70 are valid only for the particular subprograms DEMAND, ORDER, and UNITS included in the program. If these subprograms are changed, then these statements have no meaning. The initial values of inventory level and inventory position are set arbitrarily at the sum of the reorder point plus order quantity, although almost any values could be used. The major variables are defined at the beginning of the program.

The program is set to accumulate information relevant to both the entire simulation run as well as the time period between successive printouts. The variables pertinent to the entire simulation run are labeled, beginning with the word "EXPECTED."

Notice that the section of the program between statement number 180 and statement number 290 constitutes the major portion of the simulator. The section of coding between statement number 250 and statement number 290 performs the updating function for the cost and statistical information. If desired (IPRINT=1), an output of the information can be made whenever the information is updated. The section of coding prior to statement 180 performs the initializing functions for the simulator.

As before in the queueing simulator, the main driver portion of this simulation model is very simple. This simplicity is achieved by the use of subprograms which provide for compartmentalized logic. The outcome(s) to each event is handled by a separate subprogram and the ramifications to the system are recorded in a common data

FIGURE 9.4
Macro Flow Chart of General Inventory Simulator

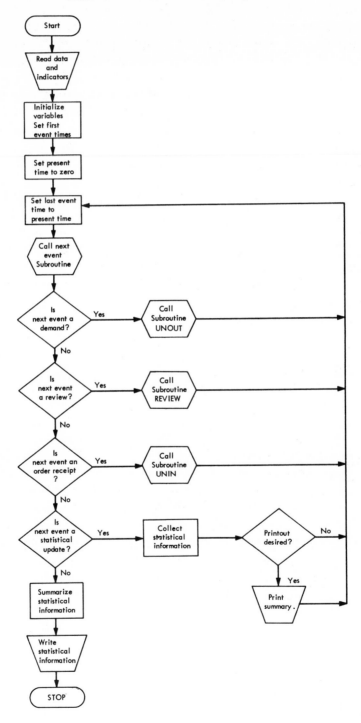

base. Although not as efficient in execution as a program with no subprograms, this program has the advantage in that it could be designed, coded, and debugged in much shorter time span. The section of coding (from statement 250 on) could easily have been placed into a separate subprogram.

SUBROUTINE NEXT is shown in Figure 9.5. The purpose of this routine is to determine the next event and to update the system to that next-event time. The five event times are stored in vector EM, and then EM is sorted to find the minimum value. The pointer NEVENT is set at a value from one to five, reflecting what the next event is to be. The present time variable (TIM1) is advanced to the next-event time, and then the system is updated to that event time by a call to subroutine UPDATE.

FIGURE 9.5
SUBROUTINE NEXT

```
      SUBROUTINE NEXT
C     PURPOSE - TO DETERMINE NEXT EVENT
      DIMENSION OD(100),EM(5),AIOQ(100)
      COMMON/BLOKA/NOUT,AIOQ,MIN
      COMMON/BLOKB/TIM1,TIMLIM,TIME,TIMST,OD,DE,TREV,NEVENT
      EM(1)=DE
      EM(2)=OD(MIN)
      EM(3)=TREV
      EM(4)=TIMST
      EM(5)=TIMLIM
      AMIN=EM(1)
      NEVENT=1
      DO 20 I=2,5
      IF(AMIN.LE.EM(I)) GO TO 20
      AMIN=EM(I)
      NEVENT=I
20    CONTINUE
      TIM1=AMIN
      CALL UPDATE
      RETURN
      END
```

FIGURE 9.6
SUBROUTINE UPDATE

```
      SUBROUTINE UPDATE
C     PURPOSE - TO ACCUMULATE BOTH UNIT-YEARS OF INVENTORY AND UNIT-
C               YEARS OF BACKORDERS(IF NECESSARY)
      DIMENSION OD(100)
      COMMON/BLOKB/TIM1,TIMLIM,TIME,TIMST,OD,DE,TREV,NEVENT
      COMMON/BLOKE/AIUY,AIL,LOST,BUY,ANBO
      XXX=TIM1-TIME
      AIUY=AIUY+AIL*XXX
      IF(LOST.LE.0) BUY=BUY+ANBO*XXX
      RETURN
      END
```

In SUBROUTINE UPDATE (Figure 9.6) the values for both unit-years of inventory on hand and unit-years of back orders (if a back order case) are accumulated. The subroutine is always called before the inventory level or number of back orders is adjusted, based upon the next event.

FIGURE 9.7
Method of SUBROUTINE UPDATE

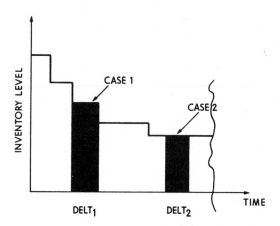

The effect of this is shown in Figure 9.7. for two cases. In Case 1 the last event occurred at the time stored in variable TIME. Then the inventory level was stored in variable AIL. The event which occurred at TIM1 in Case 1 was a demand which reduced the inventory level. The accumulated number of unit-years of inventory should be based on the value of AIL at time equal TIME. Hence, UPDATE in effect computes the shaded area shown. In Case 2 no event occurred to change the inventory level. However, time is advanced and the accumulation must still occur before proceeding to that time value.

SUBROUTINE UNOUT, shown in Figure 9.8 is called when the next event is a demand. It performs the function of adjusting inventory level and, if necessary, inventory position based upon the magnitude of the demand. If a reorder point model is being simulated, the routine sets the value of TREV (time of next review) equal to TIM1 (present time) so that a review will be forced as the next event. It then increments the counter on the number of demands (ANS), generates the time for the next demand (DE), generates the value for number of units requested at this demand (ANUD), and accumulates the total number of units demanded (TNUD).

If the inventory level is greater than the number of units demanded, then both the inventory level and inventory position are reduced by the amount ANUD. If the number of units being demanded exceeds the inventory level, the inventory position is reduced by an amount equal to the amount on hand. The variables ANBO and CNBO are employed to record the current number of stock-outs and accumulated number of stock-outs, respectively, when demand exceeds inventory level.

FIGURE 9.8
SUBROUTINE UNOUT

```
      SUBROUTINE UNOUT
C     PURPOSE - TO HANDLE SITUATION WHEN UNITS LEAVE SYSTEM. UPDATES
C               SYSTEM AFTER DEMAND OCCURS
      DIMENSION OD(100)
      COMMON/BLOKB/TIM1,TIMLIM,TIME,TIMST,OD,DE,TREV,NEVENT
      COMMON/BLOKC/AIP,PERREV
      COMMON/BLOKE/AIUY,AIL,LOST,BUY,ANBO
      COMMON/BLOKF/ANS,ANUD,CNBO,TNUD
      COMMON/BLOKG/A,B,G,H
      COMMON/BLOKI/IX
      IF(PERREV)10,10,20
10    TREV=TIM1
20    ANS=ANS+1.
      DE=TIM1+DEMAND(A,B,IX)
      ANUD=UNITS(G,H,IX)
      TNUD=TNUD+ANUD
      IF(LOST.EQ.0.OR.AIL.GE.ANUD) GO TO 50
      AIP=AIP-AIL
      GO TO 60
50    AIP=AIP-ANUD
      IF(AIL-ANUD)60,60,70
60    CNBO=CNBO+ANUD-AIL
      ANBO=ANBO+ANUD-AIL
      AIL=0
      GO TO 80
70    AIL=AIL-ANUD
80    RETURN
      END
```

SUBROUTINE REVIEW, when called, performs the review operation on the inventory position. This routine is shown in Figure 9.9. If the inventory position is greater than the reorder point, no ordering action is taken and the time for the next review is calculated and the routine returns. When an order must be placed, the receipt time for that order is calculated and placed in the vector OD. The variable NOUT which counts the number of orders outstanding is incremented by one as well as the counter on the number of orders placed ANORD. The order quantity is calculated based upon the value of variable DEC. If DEC=0, the order quantity is set equal to AIQ. If DEC = 1, the order quantity is set to be ALEVEL − AIP, which reflects an "order-up-to" policy. The receipt time of this order is compared with the minimum receipt time value. If it is less, then the pointer MIN is set to NOUT.

The outcomes to the system when an order is received are taken care of in SUBROUTINE UNIN, as shown in Figure 9.10. Remember

FIGURE 9.9
SUBROUTINE REVIEW

```
      SUBROUTINE REVIEW
C     PURPOSE - TO REVIEW INVENTORY POSITION TO DETERMINE WHETHER OR
C               NOT AN ORDER SHOULD BE PLACED
      DIMENSION OD(100),AIOQ(100)
      COMMON/BLOKA/NOUT,AIOQ,MIN
      COMMON/BLOKB/TIM1,TIMLIM,TIME,TIMST,OD,DE,TREV,NEVENT
      COMMON/BLOKC/AIP,PERREV
      COMMON/BLOKD/AIR,ANORD,DEC,ALEVEL,REV,REVTIM,AIQ
      COMMON/BLOKH/C,D
      COMMON/BLOKI/IX
      IF(AIP-AIR)10,10,70
10    NOUT=NOUT+1
      TL=ORDER(C,D,IX)
      OD(NOUT)=TL+TIM1
      ANORD=ANORD+1.
      IF(DEC)20,20,30
20    AIOQ(NOUT)=AIQ
      GO TO 40
30    AIOQ(NOUT)=ALEVEL-AIP
40    AIP=AIP+AIOQ(NOUT)
      IF(OD(NOUT).LT.OD(MIN)) MIN=NOUT
70    REV=REV+1.
      IF(PERREV)80,80,90
80    TREV=10.**30
      GO TO 100
90    TREV=TIM1+REVTIM
100   RETURN
      END
```

from previous discussions that only the inventory level is modified upon the receipt of an order. The inventory position is modified at the time when the order is placed. If a lost sales case is being simulated, the inventory level is simply increased by the amount of the order quantity AIOQ(MIN). In the back order case all unfilled orders are satisfied first. If the number of items back ordered is greater than the quantity received, the inventory level is not raised. If all back orders can be filled, the inventory level is raised by the difference between the order quantity and the number of back ordered units.

After the inventory level is adjusted, the vector OD is compressed and then sorted to determine the time for receipt of the next order. This particular operation has been discussed previously and illustrated in Figure 9.3.

Three function subprograms in the simulator are employed to generate the values for lead time, interdemand time, and number of units requested per demand. In FUNCTION ORDER, shown in Figure 9.11, the lead time values are generated. Based upon the values of the arguments supplied to it, the function can generate constant, exponential, or gamma lead time values.

FUNCTION DEMAND generates interdemand time values. This function is shown in Figure 9.12. It also is capable of generating time

FIGURE 9.10
SUBROUTINE UNIN

```
      SUBROUTINE UNIN
C     PURPOSE - UPDATES STATUS OF SYSTEM AFTER AN ORDER IS RECEIVED
      DIMENSION OD(100),AIOQ(100)
      COMMON/BLOKA/NOUT,AIOQ,MIN
      COMMON/BLOKB/TIM1,TIMLIM,TIME,TIMST,OD,DE,TREV,NEVENT
      COMMON/BLOKE/AIUY,AIL,LOST,BUY,ANBO
      IF(LOST)20,20,10
10    AIL=AIL+AIOQ(MIN)
      GO TO 50
20    IF(AIOQ(MIN)-ANBO)30,30,40
30    ANBO=ANBO-AIOQ(MIN)
      GO TO 50
40    AIL=AIL+AIOQ(MIN)-ANBO
      ANBO=0
50    IF(MIN-NOUT)60,80,80
60    NO=MIN+1
      DO 70 I=NO,NOUT
70    OD(I-1)=OD(I)
      GO TO 90
80    OD(NOUT)=10.**30
90    NOUT=NOUT-1
      MIN=1
      IF(NOUT)130,130,100
100   DO 120 I=1,NOUT
      IF(OD(I)-OD(MIN))110,110,120
110   MIN=I
120   CONTINUE
130   RETURN
      END
```

FIGURE 9.11
FUNCTION ORDER[*]

```
      FUNCTION ORDER(C,D,IX)
C     PURPOSE - GENERATE LEAD TIME
C     D=0, CONSTANT LEAD TIME    EQUAL TO C
C       =1, EXPONENTIAL LEAD TIME WITH PARAMETER C
C       =J, GAMMA LEAD TIME WITH PARAMETERS C AND J
      IF(D)30,30,10
10    ID=D
      ORDER=0
      DO 20 I=1,ID
      R=RANDU(IX,IY)
20    ORDER=ORDER-(1./C)*ALOG(1.-R)
      GO TO 40
30    ORDER=C
40    RETURN
      END
```

* Equation 7.10 represents a more efficient gamma process generator.

values which are constant, exponential, or gamma. It operates in exactly the same fashion as FUNCTION ORDER.

Figure 9.13 shows FUNCTION UNITS which generates the number of units requested per demand. The values of parameters G and H specify whether the number of units requested is constant or follows a geometric distribution.

SUBROUTINE SIG, as shown in Figure 9.14, computes the standard deviation of the mean of several quantities. Each time it is

FIGURE 9.12
FUNCTION DEMAND

```
     FUNCTION DEMAND(A,B,IX)
C    PURPOSE - GENERATE TIME TILL NEXT DEMAND
     DIMENSION OD(100)
     COMMON/BLOKB/TIM1,TIMLIM,TIME,TIMST,OD,DE,TREV,NEVENT
C    B=0, CONSTANT TIME BETWEEN SUCCESSIVE DEMANDS EQUAL TO 1./A
C      =1, EXPONENTIAL TIME BETWEEN SUCCESSIVE DEMANDS WITH PARAMETER A
C      =J, GAMMA TIME BETWEEN SUCCESSIVE DEMANDS WITH PARAMETERS A AND J
     IF(B)30,30,10
  10 IB=B
     DEMAND=0
     DO 20 I=1,IB
     R=RANDU(IX,IY)
  20 DEMAND=DEMAND-(1./A)*ALOG(1.-R)
     GO TO 40
  30 DEMAND=1./A
  40 RETURN
     END
```

FIGURE 9.13
FUNCTION UNITS

```
     FUNCTION UNITS(G,H,IX)
C    PURPOSE - GENERATE NUMBER OF UNITS PER DEMAND
C    H=0, NUMBER OF UNITS DEMANDED PER DEMAND IS GEOMETRICALLY
C         DISTRIBUTED WITH PARAMETER G
C      =J, NUMBER OF UNITS DEMANDED PER DEMAND IS CONSTANT AND EQUALS J
     IF(H)10,10,50
  10 R=RANDU(IX,IY)
     TERM1=ALOG(1.-R)/ALOG(1.-G)
     TERM2=TERM1+1.
     UNITS=1.
  20 IF(UNITS-TERM1)40,30,30
  30 IF(UNITS-TERM2)60,40,40
  40 UNITS=UNITS+1.
     GO TO 20
  50 UNITS=H
  60 RETURN
     END
```

called with the variable PROC equal to zero, the subroutine accumulates sums and sums of squares. When the value of variable PROC is greater than zero, the routine calculates means and standard deviations.

Figure 9.15 shows the random number generator. It is a modification of the one shown in Figure 6.4.

Again the advantage of using extensive subprograms in constructing the simulation model should be obvious. The functions ORDER, DEMAND, and UNITS could all be changed at the analyst's desire to reflect any situation necessary. If great programming efficiency is desired, the subroutines can be incorporated into the main program after the program is debugged.

FIGURE 9.14
SUBROUTINE SIG

```
      SUBROUTINE SIG
C     PURPOSE - COMPUTES STD. DEVIATION OF MEAN OF
C           A) UNIT YEARS OF INVENTORY
C           B) UNIT YEARS OF STOCKOUTS
C           C) NO. OF STOCKOUTS
C           D) NO. OF ORDERS
C           E) NO. OF REVIEWS
C           F) TOTAL SYSTEM COST
      DIMENSION AMEAN(20),SSQ(20),AM(20),SQ(20)
      COMMON/BLOKJ/BIUY,BBUY,BNBO,BNORD,BREV,I1,III,PROC,AMEAN,SSQ,TOT
      COMMON/BLOKK/COUNT
      IF(PROC)10,10,70
10    AM(1)=BIUY
      AM(2)=BBUY
      AM(3)=BNBO
      AM(4)=BNORD
      AM(5)=BREV
      AM(6)=TOT
      COUNT=COUNT+1.
      DO 20 I=1,6
20    SQ(I)=AM(I)**2
      IF(I1*(III-1)30,30,50
30    DO 40 I=1,6
      SSQ(I)=SQ(I)
40    AMEAN(I)=AM(I)
      GO TO 90
50    DO 60 I=1,6
      SSQ(I)=SSQ(I)+SQ(I)
60    AMEAN(I)=AMEAN(I)+AM(I)
      GO TO 90
70    DO 80 I=1,6
      AMEAN(I)=AMEAN(I)/COUNT
      SSQ(I)=(SSQ(I)-COUNT*AMEAN(I)**2)/(COUNT-1.)
80    SSQ(I)=SQRT(SSQ(I)/COUNT)
90    RETURN
      END
```

FIGURE 9.15
FUNCTION RANDU

```
      FUNCTION RANDU(IX,IY)
      IY=IX*65539
      IF(IY)5,6,6
5     IY=IY+2147483647+1
6     YFL=IY
      RANDU=YFL*0.4656613E-9

      IX=IY
      RETURN
      END
```

OUTPUT FROM THE GENERAL INVENTORY SIMULATION PROGRAM

In this section we shall characterize the types of output which can be expected from the general inventory simulation program. It is important to remember that the flexibility of this program is achieved through extensive use of input parameters which describe the system to be simulated. In this context we are able to simulate a large variety of different systems.

As the first example, consider a reorder point model with back orders which is to be simulated for a period of five years. We will say that we wish for statistics to be compiled and a summary of operating information printed on a year-by-year basis. Further, the system has the following characteristics:

1. Mean annual demand is 100 units/year distributed Poisson, one at a time.
2. Lead time is constant at 0.08 years.
3. Reorder point is 8 units.
4. Order quantity is 34 units.
5. Order cost is $100.
6. Carrying cost is $20/unit year.
7. Stock-out costs C_ℓ = $10, C_b = $15.
8. Review cost is considered to be zero.

Only one replication of the experiment is desired. That is, only one run of length five years is conducted. Based upon this description, the input data can be coded. The program operates such that it initially prints the input parameters so they can be validated. This part of the output is shown in Figure 9.16. The program then begins simulation of the system.

In that compilation of statistics and printouts are desired each year, the program prints five separate tables, one for each year. These are shown in Figure 9.17A through E. Each of these figures summarizes the information during the last year's operation as well as the cumulative information for the operation to that point. For instance, in Figure 9.17B, the column headed "PER TIME PERIOD" contains information pertinent only to the operation of the system during the second year of operation. The column headed "EXPECT-ED PER YEAR" contains information based upon two years of operation. In this column the output of the information is always on a per year basis, whereas the information in the first column is based upon the value of DELT. It simply summarizes the information applicable to the last DELT time units. In this example the value of DELT is one; so it summarizes the last year's information.

The last type of output provided by the program is shown in Figure 9.20. In this section the information collected by SUB-

FIGURE 9.16

Simulator Output of
Input Parameters for
Reorder Point Model

```
NSIM=     1
STAT=  1.
IPRINT=     1
AIR= 0.8000000E 01
AIQ= 0.3400000E 02
REVTIM= 0.0000000E 00
CI= 0.2000000E 02
CO= 0.1000000E 03
CB1= 0.1000000E 02
CB2= 0.1500000E 02
CP= 0.0000000E 00
TIMLIM= 0.5000000E 01
DEC= 0.0000000E 00
ALEVEL= 0.0000000E 00
DELT= 0.1000000E 01
LOST=     0
PERREV= 0.0000000E 00
ITER=     1
A= 0.1000000E 03
B= 0.1000000E 01
C= 0.7999998E-01
D= 0.0000000E 00
G= 0.0000000E 00
H= 0.1000000E 01
```

FIGURE 9.17A
Operating Information for First Year (Reorder Point Model)

```
REORDER POINT MODEL
BACKORDERS
MEAN ANNUAL DEMAND =0.10000000E 03 UNITS
MEAN LEAD TIME =0.79999980E-01 YEARS


III=    1 I1=    1 TIME=0.10000000E 01
```

	PER TIME PERIOD	EXPECTED PER YEAR
NUMBER OF REVIEWS	0.11500000E 03	0.11500000E 03
UNIT YRS OF INVENTORY	0.18109170E 02	0.18109170E 02
UNIT YRS OF STOCKOUTS	0.66436640E-01	0.66436640E-01
NUMBER OF STOCKOUTS	0.80000000E 01	0.80000000E 01
NUMBER OF ORDERS	0.30000000E 01	0.30000000E 01
INVENTORY CARRYING COST	0.36218330E 03	0.36218330E 03
STOCKOUT COST (TIME*QUANTITY)	0.66436640E 00	0.66436640E 00
STOCKOUT COST (QUANTITY)	0.12000000E 03	0.12000000E 03
ORDERING COST	0.30000000E 03	0.30000000E 03
REVIEW COST	0.00000000E 00	0.00000000E 00
TOTAL COST	0.78284760E 03	0.78284760E 03

```
NO OF DEMANDS RECEIVED = 0.11500000E 03
TOTAL UNITS DEMANDED = 0.11500000E 03
AVERAGE UNITS PER DEMAND = 0.10000000E 01
```

ROUTINE SIG is printed. This includes the mean and standard deviation of the mean of several quantities. The mean total annual cost of $717.07 is based upon five years of operation. Compare this with the cost obtained in example 4.11. It should be noted that the statistics computed in SUBROUTINE SIG are on a per DELT time

FIGURE 9.17B

Operating Information for Second Year (Reorder Point Model)

```
III=    1  I1=    2   TIME=0.20000000E 01
```

	PER TIME PERIOD	EXPECTED PER YEAR
NUMBER OF REVIEWS	0.10300000E 03	0.10900000E 03
UNIT YRS OF INVENTORY	0.18323360E 02	0.18216260E 02
UNIT YRS OF STOCKOUTS	0.63627240E-01	0.65031940E-01
NUMBER OF STOCKOUTS	0.40000000E 01	0.60000000E 01
NUMBER OF ORDERS	0.30000000E 01	0.30000000E 01
INVENTORY CARRYING COST	0.36646720E 03	0.36432510E 03
STOCKOUT COST (TIME*QUANTITY)	0.63627240E 00	0.65031940E 00
STOCKOUT COST (QUANTITY)	0.60000000E 02	0.90000000E 02
ORDERING COST	0.30000000E 03	0.30000000E 03
REVIEW COST	0.00000000E 00	0.00000000E 00
TOTAL COST	0.72710350E 03	0.75497530E 03

```
NO OF DEMANDS RECEIVED = 0.21800000E 03
TOTAL UNITS DEMANDED = 0.21800000E 03
AVERAGE UNITS PER DEMAND = 0.10000000E 01
```

FIGURE 9.17C

Operating Information for Third Year (Reorder Point Model)

```
III=    1  I1=    3   TIME=0.30000000E 01
```

	PER TIME PERIOD	EXPECTED PER YEAR
NUMBER OF REVIEWS	0.10800000E 03	0.10866660E 03
UNIT YRS OF INVENTORY	0.17975080E 02	0.18135860E 02
UNIT YRS OF STOCKOUTS	0.28835290E-01	0.52966390E-01
NUMBER OF STOCKOUTS	0.20000000E 01	0.46666660E 01
NUMBER OF ORDERS	0.30000000E 01	0.30000000E 01
INVENTORY CARRYING COST	0.35950140E 03	0.36271720E 03
STOCKOUT COST (TIME*QUANTITY)	0.28835290E 00	0.52966390E 00
STOCKOUT COST (QUANTITY)	0.30000000E 02	0.69999980E 02
ORDERING COST	0.30000000E 03	0.30000000E 03
REVIEW COST	0.00000000E 00	0.00000000E 00
TOTAL COST	0.68978970E 03	0.73324650E 03

```
NO OF DEMANDS RECEIVED = 0.32600000E 03
TOTAL UNITS DEMANDED = 0.32600000E 03
AVERAGE UNITS PER DEMAND = 0.10000000E 01
```

FIGURE 9.17D

Operating Information for Fourth Year (Reorder Point Model)

```
III=    1  I1=    4   TIME=0.40000000E 01
```

	PER TIME PERIOD	EXPECTED PER YEAR
NUMBER OF REVIEWS	0.82000240E 02	0.10200000E 03
UNIT YRS OF INVENTORY	0.17917200E 02	0.18081190E 02
UNIT YRS OF STOCKOUTS	0.11241970E-01	0.42535270E-01
NUMBER OF STOCKOUTS	0.10000010E 01	0.37500000E 01
NUMBER OF ORDERS	0.30000000E 01	0.30000000E 01
INVENTORY CARRYING COST	0.35834390E 03	0.36162370E 03
STOCKOUT COST (TIME*QUANTITY)	0.11241970E 00	0.42535270E 00
STOCKOUT COST (QUANTITY)	0.15000020E 02	0.56250000E 02
ORDERING COST	0.30000000E 03	0.30000000E 03
REVIEW COST	0.00000000E 00	0.00000000E 00
TOTAL COST	0.67345620E 03	0.71829900E 03

```
NO OF DEMANDS RECEIVED = 0.40800000E 03
TOTAL UNITS DEMANDED = 0.40800000E 03
AVERAGE UNITS PER DEMAND = 0.10000000E 01
```

FIGURE 9.17E
Operating Information for Fifth Year (Reorder Point Model)

III=   1 I1=   5 TIME=0.50000000E 01

	PER TIME PERIOD	EXPECTED PER YEAR
NUMBER OF REVIEWS	0.10200000E 03	0.10200000E 03
UNIT YRS OF INVENTORY	0.17587600E 02	0.17982460E 02
UNIT YRS OF STOCKOUTS	0.40819160E-01	0.42192050E-01
NUMBER OF STOCKOUTS	0.40000000E 01	0.37999990E 01
NUMBER OF ORDERS	0.30000000E 01	0.30000000E 01
INVENTORY CARRYING COST	0.35175190E 03	0.35964910E 03
STOCKOUT COST (TIME*QUANTITY)	0.40819160E 00	0.42192040E 00
STOCKOUT COST (QUANTITY)	0.60000000E 02	0.56999980E 02
ORDERING COST	0.30000000E 03	0.30000000E 03
REVIEW COST	0.00000000E 00	0.00000000E 00
TOTAL COST	0.71215990E 03	0.71707080E 03

NO OF DEMANDS RECEIVED = 0.51000000E 03
TOTAL UNITS DEMANDED = 0.51000000E 03
AVERAGE UNITS PER DEMAND = 0.10000000E 01

FIGURE 9.18
Output on Mean and Standard Deviation of the
Mean of Several Quantities (Reorder Point Model)

UNIT YRS INVENTORY	MEAN=0.17982480E 02	STD DEV=0.12098020E 00
UNIT YRS STOCKOUTS	MEAN=0.42192060E-01	STD DEV=0.10453360E-01
NUMBER OF STOCKOUTS	MEAN=0.37999990E 01	STD DEV=0.11999990E 01
NUMBER OF ORDERS	MEAN=0.30000000E 01	STD DEV=0.00000000E 00
NUMBER OF REVIEWS	MEAN=0.10200000E 03	STD DEV=0.55045420E 01
TOTAL COST	MEAN=0.71707120E 03	STD DEV=0.18837440E 02

basis. For example, if DELT had been one month, then the means computed would be per month rather than per year. Next, note the standard deviation of the mean total cost. This is relatively high, but it could be reduced through longer simulation runs or through replications. Compare the mean values for the other quantities in Figure 9.18 with those same quantities as summarized in the second column of Figure 9.17E. These values were computed separately and in some cases may differ slightly due to internal round-off.

The second illustration of sample output is the five-year simulation of a periodic review model with back orders. We desire to collect and output information again on a year-by-year basis. In this illustration the following conditions hold:

1. Mean annual demand is Poisson distributed with 200 units being demanded one at a time per year.
2. Lead time is zero.
3. An order-up-to policy is employed which states that every time a review takes place, an order should be placed to bring the inventory position up to 42 units.
4. Time between successive reviews is 0.20 years.

5. Order cost is $200.
6. Carrying cost is $20/unit year of inventory.
7. Stock-out costs C_β = $10, C_b = $50.
8. Review cost is $60 per review.

The initial output of parameters is shown in Figure 9.19. Note that the value for AIQ(92) has no significance because an order-up-to

FIGURE 9.19
Printout of Parameters for
Periodic Review Model

```
NSIM=    1
STAT=  1.
IPRINT=     1
AIR= 0.4100000E 02
AIQ= 0.9200000E 02
REVTIM= 0.2000000E 00
CI= 0.2000000E 02
CO= 0.2000000E 03
CB1= 0.1000000E 02
CB2= 0.5000000E 02
CP= 0.6000000E 02
TIMLIM= 0.5000000E 01
DEC= 0.1000000E 01
ALEVEL= 0.4200000E 02
DELT= 0.1000000E 01
LOST=    0
PERREV= 0.1000000E 01
ITER=    1
A= 0.2000000E 03
B= 0.1000000E 01
C= 0.0000000E 00
D= 0.0000000E 00
G= 0.0000000E 00
H= 0.1000000E 01
```

FIGURE 9.20A
Operating Information for First Year (Periodic Review Model)

```
PERIODIC REVIEW MODEL
BACKORDERS
MEAN ANNUAL DEMAND =0.20000000E 03 UNITS
MEAN LEAD TIME =0.00000000E 00 YEARS


III=    1  I1=    1  TIME=0.10000000E 01
```

	PER TIME PERIOD	EXPECTED PER YEAR
NUMBER OF REVIEWS	0.50000000E 01	0.50000000E 01
UNIT YRS OF INVENTORY	0.46428340E 02	0.46428340E 02
UNIT YRS OF STOCKOUTS	0.74706070E-02	0.74706070E-02
NUMBER OF STOCKOUTS	0.20000000E 01	0.20000000E 01
NUMBER OF ORDERS	0.30000000E 01	0.30000000E 01
INVENTORY CARRYING COST	0.92856680E 03	0.92856680E 03
STOCKOUT COST (TIME*QUANTITY)	0.74706070E-01	0.74706070E-01
STOCKOUT COST (QUANTITY)	0.10000000E 03	0.10000000E 03
ORDERING COST	0.60000000E 03	0.60000000E 03
REVIEW COST	0.30000000E 03	0.30000000E 03
TOTAL COST	0.19286410E 04	0.19286410E 04

```
NO OF DEMANDS RECEIVED = 0.21800000E 03
TOTAL UNITS DEMANDED = 0.21800000E 03
AVERAGE UNITS PER DEMAND = 0.10000000E 01
```

FIGURE 9.20B
Operating Information for Second Year (Periodic Review Model)

```
III=    1  I1=    2   TIME=0.20000000E 01
```

	PER TIME PERIOD	EXPECTED PER YEAR
NUMBER OF REVIEWS	0.50000000E 01	0.50000000E 01
UNIT YRS OF INVENTORY	0.21864020E 02	0.34146170E 02
UNIT YRS OF STOCKOUTS	0.92552180E-01	0.50011390E-01
NUMBER OF STOCKOUTS	0.90000000E 01	0.55000000E 01
NUMBER OF ORDERS	0.50000000E 01	0.40000000E 01
INVENTORY CARRYING COST	0.43728050E 03	0.68292350E 03
STOCKOUT COST (TIME*QUANTITY)	0.92552180E 00	0.50011390E 00
STOCKOUT COST (QUANTITY)	0.45000000E 03	0.27500000E 03
ORDERING COST	0.10000000E 04	0.80000000E 03
REVIEW COST	0.30000000E 03	0.30000000E 03
TOTAL COST	0.21882050E 04	0.20584230E 04

```
NO OF DEMANDS RECEIVED = 0.40800000E 03
TOTAL UNITS DEMANDED = 0.40800000E 03
AVERAGE UNITS PER DEMAND = 0.10000000E 01
```

FIGURE 9.20C
Operating Information for Third Year (Periodic Review Model)

```
III=    1  I1=    3   TIME=0.30000000E 01
```

	PER TIME PERIOD	EXPECTED PER YEAR
NUMBER OF REVIEWS	0.50000000E 01	0.50000000E 01
UNIT YRS OF INVENTORY	0.23597380E 02	0.30629910E 02
UNIT YRS OF STOCKOUTS	0.63676830E-01	0.54566530E-01
NUMBER OF STOCKOUTS	0.50000000E 01	0.53333330E 01
NUMBER OF ORDERS	0.50000000E 01	0.43333330E 01
INVENTORY CARRYING COST	0.47194750E 03	0.61259810E 03
STOCKOUT COST (TIME*QUANTITY)	0.63676830E 00	0.54566530E 00
STOCKOUT COST (QUANTITY)	0.25000000E 03	0.26666650E 03
ORDERING COST	0.10000000E 04	0.86666650E 03
REVIEW COST	0.30000000E 03	0.30000000E 03
TOTAL COST	0.20225840E 04	0.20464760E 04

```
NO OF DEMANDS RECEIVED = 0.59300000E 03
TOTAL UNITS DEMANDED = 0.59300000E 03
AVERAGE UNITS PER DEMAND = 0.10000000E 01
```

FIGURE 9.20D
Operating Information for Fourth Year (Periodic Review Model)

```
III=    1  I1=    4   TIME=0.40000000E 01
```

	PER TIME PERIOD	EXPECTED PER YEAR
NUMBER OF REVIEWS	0.50000000E 01	0.50000000E 01
UNIT YRS OF INVENTORY	0.21979490E 02	0.28467300E 02
UNIT YRS OF STOCKOUTS	0.42778680E 00	0.14787160E 00
NUMBER OF STOCKOUTS	0.18000000E 02	0.85000000E 01
NUMBER OF ORDERS	0.50000000E 01	0.45000000E 01
INVENTORY CARRYING COST	0.43958980E 03	0.56934590E 03
STOCKOUT COST (TIME*QUANTITY)	0.42778680E 01	0.14787150E 01
STOCKOUT COST (QUANTITY)	0.90000000E 03	0.42500000F 03
ORDERING COST	0.10000000E 04	0.90000000E 03
REVIEW COST	0.30000000E 03	0.30000000E 03
TOTAL COST	0.26438670E 04	0.21958240E 04

```
NO OF DEMANDS RECEIVED = 0.79600000E 03
TOTAL UNITS DEMANDED = 0.79600000E 03
AVERAGE UNITS PER DEMAND = 0.10000000E 01
```

FIGURE 9.20E
Operating Information for Fifth Year (Periodic Review Model)

```
III=    1  II=    5  TIME=0.50000000E 01
```

	PER TIME PERIOD	EXPECTED PER YEAR
NUMBER OF REVIEWS	0.50000000E 01	0.50000000E 01
UNIT YRS OF INVENTORY	0.21742240E 02	0.27122280E 02
UNIT YRS OF STOCKOUTS	0.46035430E 00	0.21036810E 00
NUMBER OF STOCKOUTS	0.16000000E 02	0.10000000E 02
NUMBER OF ORDERS	0.50000000E 01	0.45999990E 01
INVENTORY CARRYING COST	0.43484490E 03	0.54244550E 03
STOCKOUT COST (TIME*QUANTITY)	0.46035430E 01	0.21036810E 01
STOCKOUT COST (QUANTITY)	0.80000000E 03	0.50000000E 03
ORDERING COST	0.10000000E 04	0.91999970E 03
REVIEW COST	0.30000000E 03	0.30000000E 03
TOTAL COST	0.25394480E 04	0.22645480E 04

```
NO OF DEMANDS RECEIVED = 0.10030000E 04
TOTAL UNITS DEMANDED = 0.10030000E 04
AVERAGE UNITS PER DEMAND = 0.10000000E 01
```

policy has been selected. This can be seen because variable DEC is one. The value of ITER of one indicates only one replication is desired, as in the previous example. Further, note that the value of AIR, the reorder point, is set to be ALEVEL − 1. This causes an order to be placed every time the inventory position reaches ALEVEL−1 as it should be.

In Figure 9.20A through 9.20E the year-by-year summary output is shown. The time base for the calculation and printing of statistics is one year. Finally, Figure 9.21 illustrates the printout on means and standard deviations for the various quantities. Appendix B illustrates sample output for five-year simulations of the lost sales case for both periodic review and reorder point models. This is included to provide examples for both cases.

FIGURE 9.21
Output on Mean and Standard Deviation of Mean (Periodic Review Model)

UNIT YRS INVENTORY	MEAN=0.27122290E 02	STD DEV=0.48383380E 01
UNIT YRS STOCKOUTS	MEAN=0.21036810E 00	STD DEV=0.96522090E-01
NUMBER OF STOCKOUTS	MEAN=0.10000000E 02	STD DEV=0.30822060E 01
NUMBER OF ORDERS	MEAN=0.45999990E 01	STD DEV=0.40000350E 00
NUMBER OF REVIEWS	MEAN=0.50000000E 01	STD DEV=0.00000000E 00
TOTAL COST	MEAN=0.22645470E 04	STD DEV=0.14083460E 03

Example 9.1

A company has used a reorder point model to maintain final product inventory on one of its products. The reorder point and order quantity are 400 and 3,100 units, respectively. Demand is Poisson distributed with parameter 2,000. Each demand consists of a request for 12 units of product. If a customer requests 12 units and there are only x units in inventory ($x < 12$), the x units on hand are sold and the remaining $12 - x$ sales are lost. Lead time is constant at 0.02 years. Pertinent cost information is as follows: $C_I = \$2$, $C_o = \$10$, and $C = \$5$.

A directive was issued recently by top management to the effect that the number of lost sales per month should be kept below 5 percent of average monthly demand for all products. How well does the inventory system described above satisfy management's restriction on lost sales?

To analyze this problem we will simulate the current inventory policy for a period of 10 years (TIMLIM = 10). Since management is interested in the rate of incidence of lost sales per month, we will call for a printout (IPRINT = 1) every month (DELT = 0.0833). We will also call for a statistical update at these intervals to calculate the mean lost sales per month and the standard deviation of the mean. The input data for this problem is as follows:

NSIM=1
STAT=1.0
IPRINT=1
AIR=400.0
AIQ=3100.0
REVTIM=0.0 (any value could be read in here since this variable is
    not used)
CI=2.0
CO=10.0
CB1=0.0 (any value)
CB2=5.0
CP=0.0
A=2,000.0
B=1.0
C=.02
D=0.0
G=0.0
H=12.0
TIMLIM=10.0
DEC=0.0
DELT=.0833
ALEVEL=0.0 (any value)
PERREV = 0.0
IX= any five-digit random number
ITER=1
LOST=1

A frequency distribution of monthly lost sales is given in Figure 9.22. Average demand per month for this product is 2,000 units. Therefore management's directive would place an upper limit of 100 on the number of lost sales which might be incurred in any month. However, using the inventory policy described above, the system experienced simulated lost sales in excess of 100 in 35 of the 120 months analyzed, or slightly more than 29 percent of the time. Based upon this analysis one would conclude that the inventory policy must be modified if the limit on lost sales is to be met with regularity.

It should be noted that the mean number of lost sales per month for this system was only 55.27. The problem is then caused by high variability. This result illustrates the problems that may arise when one attempts to judge the adequacy of a system from expected values or averages alone.

FIGURE 9.22
Histogram of Lost Sales per Month

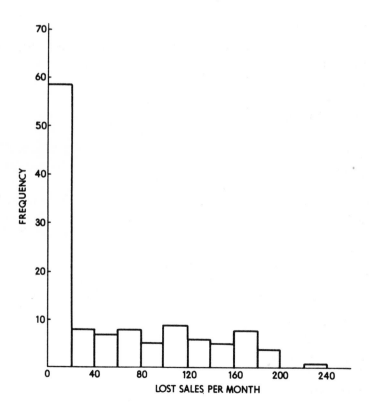

COMMENTS ON SIMULATOR ACCURACY AND VALIDATION

Although the next chapter will cover the topic of simulator validation in some detail, it is wise to keep this aspect in mind at all times. In this section we shall attempt to point out in a general fashion some considerations of this topic.

In this simulation model real variables were employed for the majority of data storage. In a binary computer the effect of round-off error might become critical as the number of calculations increases. Double precision variables should be avoided if possible because of the increase in execution time. However, some corrective measures might be needed. One general rule to be followed is to use the minimum number of calculations possible in the determination of any given value. In this particular model the values for mean unit-years of inventory as shown in figures 9.20E and 9.21 differed in the seventh decimal place. In longer runs the discrepancy often appeared in the fourth decimal place. At any rate it is wise to keep round-off error in mind.

Another topic worthy of consideration again is the generation and use of random numbers. In particular, what tests should be applied to the sequence of pseudo-random numbers generated for the inventory simulator? Random numbers are used in the inventory simulator for determining interdemand time values, units per demand, and lead time values. Which relationships should be investigated? How would one collect the information?

In the previous chapter a similar discussion appeared. In that chapter we noted that it is often desirable to insure that the ith random number generated is always used in the same determination. In the queueing simulator we illustrated how this could be insured, namely, by generating all the characteristics of a job immediately as it entered the system. In this regard we illustrated the manner in which the unit matrix could be expanded to contain all of one job's characteristics in a unit vector. Is this a desirable feature to consider for the inventory simulator? If it is desirable, how could the program be modified to provide this feature? At this time it might prove helpful to review Chapter 6 in order to decide what the undesirable features of a pseudo-random sequence would be for this simulator. We shall not attempt to point these out at this time. The problem shall remain as food for thought.

Finally, let us consider again the topic of the transient state. What is the transient state for this simulator? How can we get an idea of when the simulator becomes stable? In Chapter 6 we introduced the concept of the transient state in a simulator and alluded to possible techniques for determining this. It is widely accepted that simulation models do, in fact, experience transience. However, techniques for determining the period of transience center about one common theme: Allow the model to run until you are absolutely sure you are out of the transient state. Another common rule is that if a simulation period of 30 years is good, then a simulation period of 40 years is better, and so on. Again, an answer to this question must be predicated upon the objectives of the experiment, since extensive simulation can lead to a point of diminishing returns.

Unfortunately we shall not be able to provide a solution to these problems. However, by keeping the reader aware of them we hope to detour many of the pitfalls open to the layman. It is not within the scope of this text to discuss the theoretical aspects of this topic. However, a simple plot of the simulator estimates for the effectiveness function over time can provide a great deal of insight into this problem.

INVENTORY SIMULATION — ALLIED TOPICS

The inventory simulator developed in this chapter is certainly applicable to a wide range of cases. However, several other allied topics should be discussed in order to provide the reader at least with an introduction.

The first such topic we shall consider in regard to inventory systems is that of constraints. Previously we assumed that the optimum value of the objective function could, in fact, be obtained under normal operating conditions. What happens when a policy that causes the warehouse to overflow is dictated? In other words, how could one rationalize an operating policy which says, for example, that the average on-hand inventory level is equal to the storage capacity of the warehouse? Under this condition, the on-hand inventory would, at times, exceed the capacity of the storage facility. This is not a rational policy! Another constraint of a similar nature might occur when upper management places a limit on the dollars to be invested in inventory at any point in time.

These constraints, when binding, may serve to restrict the operating policy from ever being purely optimal. They do, however, introduce more realistic inventory systems to one's mind and are in general not difficult to work with through simulation. Problems involving a warehouse constraint are included in the exercises at the end of the chapter.

Multiple item inventories are also very prevalent. For instance, it is not uncommon to see a manufacturing plant carry as many as 20,000 separate items in inventory. If no restrictions are prevalent, the multiple item inventory system is essentially several single item inventory systems and can be treated as such. If, however, a constraint is introduced over the entire system, the individual inventory systems become highly interactive. When, for example, a warehouse restriction is introduced, then each separate item must, in effect, compete for storage space.

In this chapter as well as Chapter 4 the item cost was not considered. In all cases this cost was assumed to be constant and hence there was no need to include it in the model. However, in many inventory systems the item cost is a variable which is a function of the number of units procured at any time. There are essentially two types of these quantity discounts: the first type is termed "all-units" discount and the second is known as "increment-al" quantity discount.

The all-units discount schedule is characterized as follows: There are quantities $q_1, q_2, q_3, \ldots, q_n$ with $q_0 = 0$, $q_{n+1} = \infty$, and $q_j < q_{j+1}$. If a given quantity Q is procured, $q_j \leqslant Q < q_{j+1}$, the price paid for each of the Q units is UC_j, $UC_{j+1} < UC_j$. The total cost for procurement of the entire Q units is $Q(UC_j)$. This is termed an all-units schedule because the discount applies to all units procured.

In the incremental discount schedule a unit cost UC_1 is charged for units $1, \ldots, q_1$; the unit cost of UC_2 is charged for units $q_1 + 1, \ldots, q_2$, etc. The total cost for procurement of Q units, $q_j \leqslant Q \leqslant q_{j+1}$, is given as

$$\sum_{k=1}^{j} UC_k q_k + UC_{j+1}(Q - q_j) \tag{9.1}$$

In this schedule we could calculate the average cost per unit as a function of Q as

$$AC = \frac{TC(Q)}{Q} \tag{9.2}$$

The reader is asked to simulate systems under each of these schedules in the exercises.

These quantity discounts are not difficult to deal with in a simulation program. The reader is asked to solve an all-units schedule case in problem 17 at the end of the chapter and an incremental schedule case in problem 18. These discounts also serve to shift the optimal policy away from the "fixed unit cost" policy optimal. In what direction would you expect the shift to be?

In most real world inventory systems the mean demand per year is not constant, as we have assumed in this chapter. Indeed, even within the year the demand rate changes. This brings up the topic of treating demand as a function of time. For example, the demand rate for tire chains is certainly different in January than it is in June. If we fail to take this function into account during the analysis of a given system and derive a policy we think to be optimal we shall cause the total system cost to be increased greatly. The reason for this should be obvious. In addition to this seasonality factor there is often a trend in the demand from year to year. For example, the demand over the past five years for plastic bottles has increased markedly each year. If we fail to take this trend into account and use the overall mean, we shall again derive a policy which is grossly inadequate. This discussion alludes to the fact that if demand is a function of time, then the operating policy must also be a function of time. Economic forecasting techniques have been developed which will predict future demand based upon the past demand. It is not within the scope of this text to discuss these forecasting techniques. Rather, this section is intended to make the reader aware of this aspect of demand. Problems 16 and 19 at the end of the chapter are included to illustrate the aspect of time dependent demand. The effect of time dependent demand upon a static inventory system is illustrated in the following example:

Example 9.2

A reorder point system has been proposed for maintaining the inventory of a particular product. The policy dictates a reorder point of four units and an order quantity of 31. The cost of placing an order for inventory replenishment is $30, and the inventory carrying cost is $50/unit-year of inventory on hand. Stock-outs result in lost sales at a cost of $70 each. Order lead time is 0.0083 years and is assumed to be constant. The proposed policy is based upon the demand rate in the previous year, which was 250 units and Poisson distributed. Although management realizes that the demand rate is likely to increase in the future, it is argued that this policy will prove to be adequate for at least five years.

Suppose the demand rate increases continuously at the rate of $50t$, where t is time in years, measured from the end of the last year. The distribution of demand is assumed to remain Poisson. Therefore, the parameter of the demand distribution, λ, at any point in time, t, is given by

$$\lambda = 250 + 50t \qquad (9.3)$$

Let us investigate the adequacy of the proposed policy under these conditions. To accomplish this we shall simulate the proposed system for a period of five years. We will examine the year-by-year change in the number of lost sales incurred, orders placed, total cost of the inventory system, and the components of total cost.

To improve the year-by-year estimates, the five-year simulation run will be repeated five times. It should be noted that a five-year simulation is not the same as simulation of one year five times in this case. Similarly, one 10-year simulation is not the same as two five-year simulations. Therefore, to obtain five replications of each year we need to simulate for a period of five years five times, starting each simulation at time zero. To do this we must insure that we begin each simulation with a new random number. This aspect of simulation was discussed in the previous chapter.

The results of the simulation are summarized in figures 9.23 and 9.24. In these figures each point represents an average of five simulations for that year. Comparing figures 9.23A and 9.23B we see that as the average demand per year increases so does the average number of lost sales incurred per year as well as the number of orders placed per year. This result is to be expected. As the annual demand rate increases, the average time between successive demands decreases.

If the lead time and the reorder point remain constant as the time between successive demands decreases, one could only anticipate more stock-outs. Two factors contribute to this result. First, as the time between successive demands decreases, the expected time required for the inventory level to fall from the reorder point to zero is reduced, thus increasing the length of the stock-out period. Second, the increased demand rate per unit stock-out period will cause more lost sales to occur in that interval of time. An increased demand rate causes inventory level and inventory position to decline more rapidly, thus causing inventory position to reach the reorder point with increased frequency.

As shown in Figure 9.24 the year-by-year cost of operation increases over time, or as demand increases. This does not necessarily mean that the proposed policy is inadequate. In fact, this policy may be optimal for all five years. However, since the cost of operation did

FIGURE 9.23

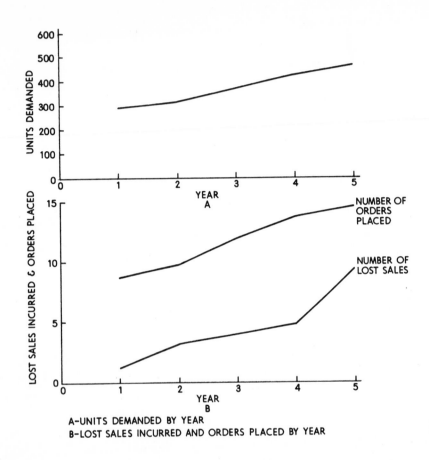

A–UNITS DEMANDED BY YEAR
B–LOST SALES INCURRED AND ORDERS PLACED BY YEAR

increase rather substantially between the first and fifth years, the assumption that the proposed policy continues to be optimal should be investigated further. Thus, the effect of time dependent demand was to increase the total cost of operating the system. To accomplish the simulation in this example FUNCTION DEMAND was modified as shown in Figure 9.25.

It is worth noting that the system discussed in the previous example is in a transient state for the entire duration of the simulation. In general, replication of a simulation of a system in a transient state requires reinitialization of the simulation at each replication. When dealing with systems in the steady state, replication can be effected either by reinitializing at each replication or by continuing the simulation for a longer period of time.

FIGURE 9.24
Lost Sales Cost, Carrying Cost, Ordering Cost, and Total Cost by Year

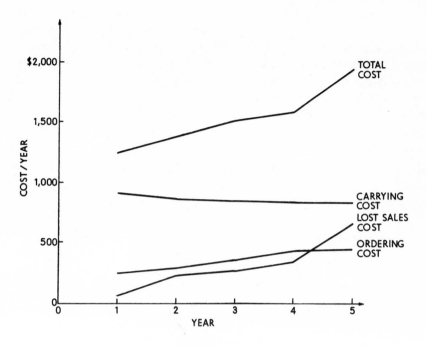

FIGURE 9.25
Modified Function Demand

```
      FUNCTION DEMAND(A,B,IX)
C     PURPOSE - GENERATE TIME TILL NEXT DEMAND
      DIMENSION OD(100)
      COMMON/BLOKB/TIM1,TIMLIM,TIME,TIMST,OD,DE,TREV,NEVENT
C     B=0, CONSTANT TIME BETWEEN SUCCESSIVE DEMANDS EQUAL TO 1./A
C       =1, EXPONENTIAL TIME BETWEEN SUCCESSIVE DEMANDS WITH PARAMETER A
C       =J, GAMMA TIME BETWEEN SUCCESSIVE DEMANDS WITH PARAMETERS A AND J
      A=250.+50.*TIM1
      IF(B)30,30,10
10    IB=B
      DEMAND=0
      DO 20 I=1,IB
      R=RANDU(IX,IY)
20    DEMAND=DEMAND-(1./A)*ALOG(1.-R)
      GO TO 40
30    DEMAND=1./A
40    RETURN
      END
```

INVENTORIES IN SERIES

In a manufacturing context one cannot ordinarily analyze a given inventory system without considering its effect on other inventory systems and production facilities with which it interacts. For example, consider the production-inventory facility described in Figure 9.26. The ordering policy used for any one of the five inventories will affect the operation of each of the remaining four inventories as well as the operation of the production lines. To illustrate, suppose that demand for the product manufactured by this production system increases and results in a reevaluation of the operating policy for finished goods inventory, which in turn results in a decrease in the time between successive reviews. Treating an order placed from the finished goods inventory as a production order, the number of production setups per year will increase, producing an increased demand on the in-process raw materials inventories, which in turn increases the demand on the initial raw materials inventory. Since the demand rate increases for all inventories, it is reasonable to suspect that the initial operating policies are no longer optimal.

FIGURE 9.26
Production-Inventory System

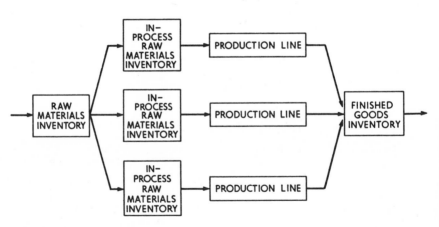

To illustrate some of the considerations pertinent to the simulation of a production facility, consider a single series of inventories such as shown in Figure 9.27. Two successive inventories may or may not be connected by a production line. Assume that a series of n inventories is to be simulated. An order placed by the $(i + 1)$st inventory results in a demand to the ith inventory. If the entire demand cannot be satisfied by the ith inventory, the unsatisfied portion is either back ordered or lost. If a stock-out results in a lost sale, the unfilled portion of the demand is placed with an outside source. The source of this supply is the inventory I_1 and is

FIGURE 9.27
Inventories in Series

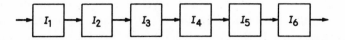

considered to carry an inexhaustable supply of all of the products demanded by the n inventories under study. Therefore, the series of inventories analyzed is $I_2, I_3, \ldots, I_{n+1}$. I_1 *is also considered the* primary source of supply to I_2. The final product inventory is I_{n+1}, and customer demands are filled from I_{n+1}. To generate these demands, a second outside inventory, I_{n+2}, is established. Therefore

I_1 = Source of supply of all demand which is not taken care of by $I_2, I_3, \ldots, I_{n+1}$.

I_2 = Raw materials inventory.

$I_3, I_4, \ldots, I_n$ = In-process inventories.

I_{n+1} = Final product inventory.

I_{n+2} = Inventory which generates demand for the final product.

In many respects, simulation of this series of inventories is similar to that for a single inventory. The mechanics for calculating unit-years of inventory, inventory level, unit-years of stock-outs, the number of stock-outs, and the number of outstanding orders used for a single inventory may also be applied to each of the serial inventories. However, a new methodology must be adopted to calculate the time until the next demand and the time until an order is received. The reader will recall that each time a demand was received by the inventory the next demand was immediately generated. Demand to I_{n+1} can be treated in a similar fashion since the mechanism through which customer demands are generated is assumed to be unknown and therefore considered random. However, the mechanism generating demand to I_i, $1 < i \leqslant n$ is known and is controlled by the ordering policy for I_{i+1}, although this mechanism may include a random component. Since an order from I_{i+1} results in a demand to I_i, the time at which that demand is received by I_i is generated at the time the order from I_{i+1} is issued.

In a single inventory, the time at which an order is received is generated when the order is placed and also applies to any order filled by I_1. However, the order receipt time for the remaining $n-1$ inventories can be more explicitly defined. Suppose an order is placed by I_{i+1}, $1 < i \leqslant n$. The time at which this order is received cannot be evaluated until the status of I_i is determined. If the stock level of I_i is sufficient to fill the order when it is received as a demand, the time at which the filled order is received by I_{i+1} can be calculated. However, if the stock level of I_i is zero, the order from I_{i+1} must either be back ordered or placed with I_1 when stock-outs result in lost sales. If the order is back ordered, the time at which the filled order is received by I_{i+1} cannot be determined until I_i is replenished. If a stock-out produces a lost sale, the order is placed with I_1 and the demand to I_i is destroyed. If the order placed with I_i can be partially filled, the initial order is divided into two separate orders. The first order is for a quantity equal to the number of units currently contained in I_i, and the time at which this order is received by I_{i+1} can be generated immediately. The second order is for a quantity equal to the difference between the original order quantity and the inventory level of I_i. The second order is then treated as a back order or a lost sale and is handled in the manner already discussed.

Since demand for final product originates outside of the system studied, we will assume that the mechanism generating demand to the system is understood in a probabilistic sense only, as in a single inventory. Therefore orders must be placed by I_{n+2}, according to the assumed distribution of customer demand. For example, suppose that customer demand is Poisson distributed, and units are demanded one at a time. To accomplish this an ordering policy must be established for I_{n+2} which will place orders in a Poisson fashion where the order quantity is one unit. This result can be achieved by using a periodic review inventory system for I_{n+2}, where the time between successive reviews is considered an exponential random variable. If an order is placed at each review, demand to I_{n+1} will have the desired distribution. In a periodic review model an order is placed if inventory position is less than or equal to the reorder point, r. To guarantee that an order will be placed at each review, the initial inventory level for I_{n+2} is set equal to zero and a reorder point of infinity is assumed. However, since an infinite value for r cannot be accepted by a computer, the value assigned to r should be large enough to insure that inventory position for I_{n+2} will not reach r in the course of the simulation.

In the system considered here an inventory may be reviewed each time a demand is received, at constant intervals of time, or at random intervals of time. A separate function subprogram has been developed to calculate the time until the next review. When the inventory under consideration is I_{n+2}, the time until the next review is generated at random. For any other inventory the time until the next review is dependent upon whether a periodic review of reorder point system is used. Where a periodic review system is used, the time between successive reviews is assumed constant. A simulator for a system of inventories in series is given in the chapter appendix along with a description of its operation.

Example 9.3

Simulate the manufacturing-sales system shown in Figure 9.28. Customer demand is met at the retail outlet (5) and is Poisson-distributed with mean 100 demands per year. Each customer demand results in a request for five units of product and an unfilled customer demand results in a lost sale. Orders for replenishment of the retail outlet inventory are filled by the warehouse (4). Orders from the warehouse are filled from the final products inventory (3) at the manufacturing plant. Orders from the final product inventory result in a production setup, and one unit of raw material (2) is required for each unit of final product manufactured. The time lag between the placement of an order from 5 until its reception is 0.001 years. The time required for the warehouse to fill an order and deliver it to the retail outlet is 0.01 years if the warehouse inventory level is greater than zero. The time lag between the placement of an order by the warehouse and its receipt by the final product inventory is 0.003 years, and 0.001 years are required to fill and deliver the order. An order from the final product inventory results in a production order, and the lag between the placement of the order and the startup of production is 0.01 years, which includes the setup time. The time to produce the order and place it in the final product inventory is 0.02 years. Units are not placed in the final product inventory as they are produced; but are held until the entire lot is manufactured. Orders

FIGURE 9.28
Manufacturing-Sales System

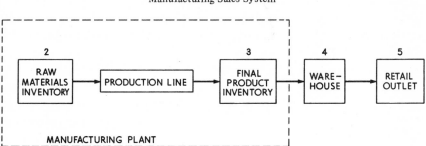

for raw materials are placed with an outside supplier, and lead time on these orders is a constant of 0.08 years.

Reorder point systems are used for all inventories, except the warehouse which uses a periodic review system with an order up to R policy where review time is 0.10 years and R is 70. The input data for this simulation is shown in Table 9.2 (page 449). Since the system studied consists of four inventories, INV=6. A summary of operating information is to be given after each event and after every 0.30 years of operation. Therefore IPRINT =1 and DELT=0.30. The period to be simulated is to be three years, TIMLIM = 3.0.

The function subprograms used to generate the time for a demand to reach inventory I and the time for an order to be filled and delivered to I from J are given in Figures 9.29 and 9.30. For this simulation FUNCTION UNITS(G,H,IX,I) is not used. However, since it is referenced in SUBROUTINE REVIEW, it must be included in the simulator.

FIGURE 9.29
FUNCTION DEMAND

```
FUNCTION DEMAND(A,B,IX,I)
DIMENSION ANS(7),TNUD(7),CNBO(7)
DIMENSION A(7),B(7)
COMMON/BLOKF/ANS,TNUD,CNBO,INV
DEMAND=A(I)
2 RETURN
END
```

FIGURE 9.30
FUNCTION ORDER

```
FUNCTION ORDER(C,D,IX,I,J)
DIMENSION C(7),D(7)
ORDER=C(I)
RETURN
END
```

In Table 9.2 several entries are left blank. Any blank entry indicates that either the corresponding variable is not used in the simulation or that it is defined somewhere in the body of the program. For example, C(1) is not defined in Table 9.2. C(I) in this simulation is used to define the time required to fill an order from I and deliver it to I. However, since REVTIM(1) = $10^{**}20$, a review of the first inventory will never take place. Therefore, C(1) would never be used even if it were assigned a value. Similarly, values for REVTIM(1) and AIR(6) need not be defined as part of the information read by the main program since they are assigned values further along in the program.

FIGURE 9.31A

Summary Printout for Example 9.3 (Order Receipt for Inventory 5)

```
TIM1= 0.3034260E-01    IND= 3
IMIN= 5    JMIN= 4    KMIN= 1

        AIUY            BUY            AIP            AIL            REV           IDEM      ANS
  1  0.0000000E 00  0.0000000E 00  0.9999998E 20  0.9999998E 20  0.0000000E 00    0   0.0000000E 00
  2  0.0000000E 00  0.0000000E 00  0.1400000E 03  0.1400000E 03  0.0000000E 00    0   0.0000000E 00
  3  0.0000000E 00  0.0000000E 00  0.2000000E 02  0.2000000E 02  0.0000000E 00    0   0.0000000E 00
  4  0.1423982E 01  0.0000000E 00  0.5000000E 02  0.5000000E 02  0.0000000E 00    0   0.1000000E 01
  5  0.4946113E 00  0.0000000E 00  0.3000000E 02  0.3000000E 02  0.4000000E 01        0.4000000E 01
  6  0.0000000E 00  0.0000000E 00  0.2000000E 02  0.0000000E 00  0.4000000E 01    0   0.0000000E 00

        TNUD            CNBO           ANBO      NOUTK1  NOUT1   ANDROK1        ANDRD1
  1  0.0000000E 00  0.0000000E 00  0.0000000E 00    0      0   0.0000000E 00  0.0000000E 00
  2  0.0000000E 00  0.0000000E 00  0.0000000E 00    0      0   0.0000000E 00  0.0000000E 00
  3  0.0000000E 00  0.0000000E 00  0.0000000E 00    0      0   0.0000000E 00  0.0000000E 00
  4  0.2000000E 02  0.0000000E 00  0.0000000E 00    0      0   0.0000000E 00  0.0000000E 00
  5  0.2000000E 02  0.0000000E 00  0.0000000E 00    4      4   0.1000000E 01  0.0000000E 00
  6  0.0000000E 00  0.0000000E 00  0.0000000E 00           4   0.4000000E 01  0.0000000E 00

        TIME            TREV
  1  0.0000000E 00  0.9999998E 20
  2  0.0000000E 00  0.9999999E 30
  3  0.0000000E 00  0.9999999E 30
  4  0.2034260E-01  0.1000000E 00
  5  0.3034260E-01  0.9999998E 20
  6  0.1934261E-01  0.3528970E-01

  I  J         DE            OD           DEQ       AIOQ
  I  J  K
  6  5  1                 0.1000000E 02           0.5000000E 01
  6  5  2                 0.1000552E 02           0.5000000E 01
  6  5  3                 0.1001338E 02           0.5000000E 01
  6  5  4                 0.1001934E 02           0.5000000E 01
```

FIGURE 9.31B

Summary Printout for Example 9.3 (Review of Inventory 6)

```
TIM1= 0.3528970E-01   IND= 1
IMIN= 6   JMIN= 0   KMIN= 0

       AIUY            BUY             AIP             AIL             REV             IDEM        ANS
  1  0.0000000E 00   0.0000000E 00   0.9999998E 20   0.9999998E 20   0.0000000E 00     0      0.0000000E 00
  2  0.0000000E 00   0.0000000E 00   0.1400000E 03   0.1400000E 03   0.0000000E 00     0      0.0000000E 00
  3  0.0000000E 00   0.0000000E 00   0.2000000E 02   0.2000000E 02   0.0000000E 00     0      0.0000000E 00
  4  0.1423982E 01   0.0000000E 00   0.5000000E 02   0.5000000E 02   0.4000000E 01     0      0.1000000E 01
  5  0.4946113E 01   0.0000000E 00   0.3000000E 02   0.3000000E 02   0.5000000E 01     0      0.4000000E 01
  6  0.0000000E 00   0.0000000E 00   0.2500000E 02   0.0000000E 00                            0.0000000E 00

       TNUD            CNBQ            ANBQ          NOUTK1  NOUT1    ANORDK1          ANORD1
  1  0.0000000E 00   0.0000000E 00   0.0000000E 00    0      0    0.0000000E 00   0.0000000E 00
  2  0.0000000E 00   0.0000000E 00   0.0000000E 00    0      0    0.0000000E 00   0.0000000E 00
  3  0.2000000E 02   0.0000000E 00   0.0000000E 00    0      0    0.0000000E 00   0.0000000E 00
  4  0.2000000E 02   0.0000000E 00   0.0000000E 00    0      0    0.1000000E 01   0.1000000E 01
  5  0.0000000E 00   0.0000000E 00   0.0000000E 00    0      5    0.5000000E 01   0.5000000E 01

       TIME            TREV
  I
  1  0.0000000E 00   0.9999998E 20
  2  0.0000000E 00   0.9999999E 30
  3  0.2034260E-01   0.9999999E 30
  4  0.3034260E-01   0.9999998E 20
  5  0.3528970E-01   0.4870215E-01
  6

       DE              DEQ
  I  J
  5  5  0.3528970E-01   0.5000000E 01

       OD              AIOQ
  I  J  K
  6  5  1  0.1000000E 02   0.5000000E 01
  6  5  2  0.1000552E 02   0.5000000E 01
  6  5  3  0.1001338E 02   0.5000000E 01
  6  5  4  0.1001934E 02   0.5000000E 01
  6  5  5  0.9999999E 30   0.5000000E 01
```

FIGURE 9.31C
Summary Printout for Example 9.3 (Demand to Inventory 5)

```
TIM1= 0.3528970E-01   IND= 2
IMIN= 5  JMIN= 5  KMIN= 0
```

	AIUY	BUY	AIP	AIL	REV	IDEM	ANS
1	0.0000000E 00	0.0000000E 00	0.9999998E 20	0.9999998E 20	0.0000000E 00	0	0.0000000E 00
2	0.0000000E 00	0.0000000E 00	0.1400000E 03	0.1400000E 03	0.0000000E 00	0	0.0000000E 00
3	0.0000000E 00	0.0000000E 00	0.2000000E 02	0.2000000E 02	0.0000000E 00	0	0.0000000E 00
4	0.1423982E 01	0.0000000E 00	0.5000000E 02	0.5000000E 02	0.0000000E 00	0	0.1000000E 01
5	0.6430242E 00	0.0000000E 00	0.2500000E 02	0.2500000E 02	0.4000000E 01	2	0.5000000E 01
6	0.0000000E 00	0.0000000E 00	0.2500000E 02	0.0000000E 00	0.5000000E 01	0	0.0000000E 00

I	TNUD	CNBO	ANBO	NOUTK1	NOUT1	ANDRDK1	ANDRD1
1	0.0000000E 00	0.0000000E 00	0.0000000E 00	0	0	0.0000000E 00	0.0000000E 00
2	0.0000000E 00	0.0000000E 00	0.0000000E 00	0	0	0.0000000E 00	0.0000000E 00
3	0.0000000E 00	0.0000000E 00	0.0000000E 00	0	0	0.0000000E 00	0.0000000E 00
4	0.2000000E 02	0.0000000E 00	0.0000000E 00	0	0	0.0000000E 00	0.0000000E 00
5	0.2500000E 02	0.0000000E 00	0.0000000E 00	0	0	0.1000000E 01	0.0000000E 00
6	0.0000000E 00	0.0000000E 00	0.0000000E 00	5	0	0.5000000E 01	0.0000000E 00

I	TIME	TREV
1	0.0000000E 00	0.9999998E 20
2	0.0000000E 00	0.9999999E 30
3	0.0000000E 00	0.9999999E 30
4	0.2034260E-01	0.1000000E 00
5	0.3528970E-01	0.3528970E-01
6	0.3528970E-01	0.4870215E-01

I	J	K	DE	OD	AIOQ	DEQ
6	5	1		0.1000000E 02	0.5000000E 01	
6	5	2		0.1000552E 02	0.5000000E 01	
6	5	3		0.1001338E 02	0.5000000E 01	
6	5	4		0.1001934E 02	0.5000000E 01	
6	5	5		0.1003529E 02	0.5000000E 01	

FIGURE 9.31D
Summary Printout for Example 9.3 (Review of Inventory 5)

```
TIM1= 0.3528970E-01   IND= 1
IMIN= 5   JMIN= 0   KMIN= 1

        AIUY            BUY                    AIP             AIL              REV           IDEM          ANS
  1  0.0000000E 00  0.0000000E 00      0.9999998E 20   0.9999998E 20     0.0000000E 00      0     0.0000000E 00
  2  0.0000000E 00  0.0000000E 00      0.1400000E 03   0.1400000E 03     0.0000000E 00      0     0.0000000E 00
  3  0.0000000E 00  0.0000000E 00      0.2000000E 02   0.2000000E 02     0.0000000E 00      0     0.0000000E 00
  4  0.1423982E 01  0.0000000E 00      0.5000000E 02   0.5000000E 02     0.0000000E 00      0     0.1000000E 01
  5  0.6430242E 00  0.0000000E 00      0.2500000E 02   0.2500000E 02     0.5000000E 01      0     0.5000000E 01
  6  0.0000000E 00  0.0000000E 00      0.2500000E 02   0.0000000E 00     0.5000000E 01            0.0000000E 00

        TNUD            CNBO           ANBO          NDUTK1  NDUT1      ANDROK1          ANDRD1
  1  0.0000000E 00  0.0000000E 00  0.0000000E 00      0       0     0.0000000E 00   0.0000000E 00
  2  0.0000000E 00  0.0000000E 00  0.0000000E 00      0       0     0.0000000E 00   0.0000000E 00
  3  0.2000000E 02  0.0000000E 00  0.0000000E 00      0       0     0.0000000E 00   0.0000000E 00
  4  0.2500000E 02  0.0000000E 00  0.0000000E 00      0       0     0.1000000E 01   0.0000000E 00
  5  0.2500000E 02  0.0000000E 00  0.0000000E 00      5       0     0.5000000E 01   0.0000000E 00
  6  0.0000000E 00  0.0000000E 00  0.0000000E 00

            TIME              TREV
  I
  1      0.0000000E 00    0.9999998E 20
  2      0.0000000E 00    0.9999999E 30
  3      0.2034260E-01    0.9999999E 30
  4      0.3528970E-01    0.1000000E 00
  5      0.3528970E-01    0.9999998E 20
                          0.4870215E-01
                              DEQ
          DE      OD          AIDQ
  I  J  K
  6  5  1   0.1000000E 02   0.5000000E 01
  6  5  2   0.1000552E 02   0.5000000E 01
  6  5  3   0.1001338E 02   0.5000000E 01
  6  5  4   0.1001934E 02   0.5000000E 01
  6  5  5   0.1003529E 02   0.5000000E 01
```

FIGURE 9.32
Summary Printout at TIM1 = 0.30 for Example 9.3

TIM1= 0.3000000E 00   IND= 4

I	AIUY	BUY	AIP	AIL	REV	IDEM	ANS
1	0.2999997E 20	0.0000000E 00	0.9999998E 20	0.9999998E 20	0.0000000E 00	0	0.1000000E 01
2	0.2825998E 02	0.0000000E 00	0.1200000E 03	0.1200000E 03	0.1200000E 02	0	0.1200000E 02
3	0.4800000E 01	0.2399998E 01	0.2000000E 02	0.2000000E 02	0.1200000E 02	0	0.2000000E 01
4	0.1119241E 02	0.1088393E 00	0.3000000E 02	0.3000000E 02	0.2000000E 02	5	0.8000000E 01
5	0.4874511E 01	0.0000000E 00	0.3000000E 02	0.3000000E 02	0.3500000E 02	0	0.3500000E 02
6	0.0000000E 00	0.1750000E 02	0.1750000E 03	0.0000000E 00			0.0000000E 00

I	TNUD	CNBO	ANBO	TIME	TREV	NOUTK1	NOUT1	ANDROK1	ANDRD1
1	0.1000000E 03	0.0000000E 00	0.0000000E 00	0.3000000E 00	0.9999998E 20	0	0	0.0000000E 00	0.0000000E 00
2	0.1200000E 03	0.0000000E 00	0.0000000E 00	0.3000000E 00	0.9999998E 20	0	0	0.1000000E 01	0.1000000E 01
3	0.1200000E 03	0.8000000E 02	0.0000000E 00	0.3000000E 00	0.9999998E 20	0	0	0.1200000E 02	0.0000000E 00
4	0.1600000E 03	0.1000000E 00	0.0000000E 00	0.3000000E 00	0.3000001E 00	0	0	0.1000000E 02	0.0000000E 00
5	0.1750000E 03	0.1500000E 02	0.1500000E 02	0.3000000E 00	0.9999998E 20	0	0	0.9000000E 01	0.0000000E 00
6	0.0000000E 00	0.0000000E 00	0.0000000E 00	0.3000000E 00	0.3102519E 00	32	8	0.3500000E 02	0.8000000E 01

DE   DEQ

I	J	K	DD	AIDQ
6	6	3	0.1011353E 02	0.5000000E 01
6	1	6	0.1018203E 02	0.5000000E 01
6	1	8	0.1026978E 02	0.5000000E 01
6	1	1	0.1000000E 00	0.5000000E 01
6	5	2	0.1000552E 02	0.5000000E 01
6	5	3	0.1001338E 02	0.5000000E 01
6	5	4	0.1001936E 02	0.5000000E 01
6	5	5	0.1003529E 02	0.5000000E 01
6	5	6	0.1004870E 02	0.5000000E 01
6	5	7	0.1005168E 02	0.5000000E 01
6	5	8	0.1007463E 02	0.5000000E 01
6	5	9	0.1007543E 02	0.5000000E 01
6	5	10	0.1008002E 02	0.5000000E 01
6	5	11	0.1008735E 02	0.5000000E 01
6	5	12	0.1010340E 02	0.5000000E 01
6	5	13	0.1010469E 02	0.5000000E 01
6	5	14	0.1011233E 02	0.5000000E 01
6	5	15	0.1013448E 02	0.5000000E 01
6	5	16	0.1013719E 02	0.5000000E 01
6	5	17	0.1014480E 02	0.5000000E 01
6	5	18	0.1014542E 02	0.5000000E 01
6	5	19	0.1015372E 02	0.5000000E 01
6	5	20	0.1017249E 02	0.5000000E 01
6	5	21	0.1017252E 02	0.5000000E 01
6	5	22	0.1017760E 02	0.5000000E 01
6	5	23	0.1019033E 02	0.5000000E 01
6	5	24	0.1019212E 02	0.5000000E 01
6	5	25	0.1021583E 02	0.5000000E 01
6	5	26	0.1024999E 02	0.5000000E 01
6	5	27	0.1026027E 02	0.5000000E 01
6	5	28	0.1026191E 02	0.5000000E 01
6	5	29	0.1026322E 02	0.5000000E 01
6	5	30	0.1026797E 02	0.5000000E 01
6	5	31	0.1027867E 02	0.5000000E 01
6	5	32	0.1027910E 02	0.5000000E 01

FIGURE 9.33
Simultaneous Fluctuation of Net Inventory and Inventory Position for Inventories
2,3,4 and 5

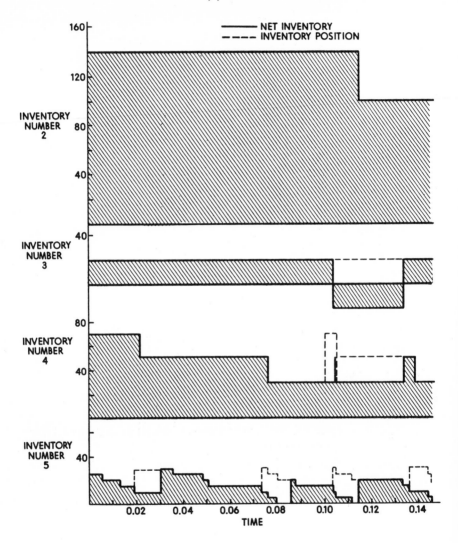

The reader will note that C(6) has been given the value 10 years. Since the period simulated is only 3 years, the sixth inventory will never be replenished. However, it should be remembered that inventory 6 is a dummy inventory used only to generate customer demands, and we are not interested in its status at any point in the course of the simulation. Therefore if C(6)>TIMLIM, the simulator will not waste time replenishing this inventory.

TABLE 9.2
Input Data for Example 9.3

I	1	2	3	4	5	6
Inventory System	Periodic Review	Reorder Point	Reorder Point	Periodic Review	Reorder Point	Periodic Review
AIR(I)		40.00	10.00	69.00	10.00	
AIQ(I)		100.00	10.00		20.00	5.00
ALEVEL(I)				70.00		
REVTIM(I)				0.100		
PERREV(I)	1.00	0.00	0.00	1.00	0.00	1.00
DEC(I)	0.00	0.00	0.00	1.00	0.00	0.00
NDOWN(I)	6	1	2	3	4	5
NUP(I)	2	3	4	5	6	1
LOST(I)		0	0	0	1	1
A(I)		0.010	0.003	0.001	0.000	100.000
B(I)						
C(I)		0.080	0.020	0.001	0.010	10,000
D(I)						
G(I)						
H(I)						

Summary printouts for all events taking place between 0.030 years and 0.040 years are given in Figures 9.31A to 9.31D (pages 443–446). The summary printout at 0.30 years is given in Figure 9.32. The simultaneous fluctuation of net inventory and inventory position for the four inventories studied is shown graphically in Figure 9.33.

SUMMARY

In this chapter the next event concept has been extended to the simulation analysis of inventory systems. By employing this concept and defining five separate events to consider, a general inventory simulation was constructed. The events for inventory simulation were defined as:

1. The demand for an item or items.
2. The review of inventory.
3. The receipt of an order.
4. The updating of statistics.
5. The end of the simulation run.

The fourth and fifth events were defined as being "model oriented." The fourth event was included to provide time based statistical and operational information regarding the operation of the system.

Simulation analysis of inventory systems provides a feasible alternative for the derivation of rational operating policies. Indeed, for many inventory models which cannot be solved analytically, simulation is the only alternative.

PROBLEMS

1. Simulate the problem given in example 4.11 under each of the following demand conditions and compare the average annual costs:

   a) Demand is Poisson distributed with a mean of 50 demnds per year. At each demand two units are requested.

   b) Demand is Poisson distributed with a mean of 25 demands per year. At each demand four units are requested.

   c) Demand is Poisson distributed with a mean of 50 demands per year. The number of units requested per demand is geometrically distributed with parameter $p = 0.5$.

   d) Demand is Poisson distributed with a mean of 25 demands per year. The number of units requested per demand is geometrically distributed with parameter $p = 0.25$.

Simulate each of the four conditions for 100 years using the optimal operating doctrine derived in example 4.12.

2. Simulate the problem in example 4.11 under the optimal operating doctrine for each of the following lead time distributions:

   a) Exponential lead time with $\lambda = 12.5$.

   b) Gamma lead time with $\lambda = 25, n = 2$.

   c) Gamma lead time with $\lambda = 125, n = 10$.

For each case let TIMLIM = 100. Under which condition is the annual cost of operation closest to that for a constant lead time of 0.08 years. Can you explain why?

3. A periodic review inventory system with lost sales is to be simulated for various demand conditions. Lead time is zero, and units are demanded one at a time. Each review costs $60 and each order placed costs $100. A lost sale costs $10, and the inventory carrying charge is $20 per unit-year. The period between successive reviews is 0.5 years, and the number of units on each order is that quantity sufficient to bring inventory position to 42 units. The demand conditions to be simulated are as follows (Simulate each condition for a period of 100 years):

   a) The time between successive demands is 0.005 and constant.

   b) The time between successive demands is exponentially distributed with $\lambda = 200$.

   c) The time between successive demands is gamma distributed with $\lambda = 1000$, $n = 5$.

   d) The time between successive demands is gamma distributed with $\lambda = 5000$, $n = 25$.

Explain the effect of variation in demand distribution on the annual cost of operation.

4. Simulate the following reorder point inventory system in which stock-outs result in lost sales, lead time is constant, and units are demanded one at a time:

Demand — Poisson with a mean demand of 30,000 units per year.

Lead time = 0.008 years.

$r = 400$.

$Q = 3,100$.

$C_I = \$50$.

$C_o = \$300$.

$C_L = \$70$.

The simulation period is to be one year.

5. Simulate the problem described in example 4.11 with the following modification. Instead of reviewing the status of inventory at each demand, inventory is reviewed every 0.01 years. If, at a review, inventory position is at or below eight, an order is placed for 34 units. The cost of a review may be considered to be zero. Simulate for a period of 50 years and compare the annual cost of this system with that in example 4.12.

6. Consider the problem described in example 4.13. Suppose that lead time is not, in fact, constant but is normally distributed with a mean of 0.0083 years and standard deviation of 0.0020 years. Assuming the optimal operating policy given in example 4.14 ($r=4$, $Q=61$), how much is the estimated annual cost of operation ($\$3,158.57$) in error due to the assumption that lead time is constant?.

7. Consider the problem given in example 4.12. The optimal system resulted in a review period of 0.449 years and an R of 92 units. The production manager questions the ability of his personnel to stick to the review period of 0.449 years. Although it is unlikely that a review will be conducted early, the review may be conducted as much as a week late. In particular, the time to the next review is estimated to be uniformly distributed between 0.449 and 0.468 years. Through simulation, estimate the effect of this variation on the cost of the proposed optimal system.

8. The generalized inventory simulator presented in this chapter assumes that stock-outs result in either back orders or lost sales but not both. Modify the simulator such that $100p$ percent of the stock-outs result in lost sales while the remaining $100(1-p)$ percent result in back orders.

9. For the problem described in example 4.11, suppose that available storage space was limited to 36 units. Any time the inventory level exceeds 36 units, a cost of $5 is incurred for each unit placed in storage in excess of 36. Using a reorder point of 8 units and an order quantity of 34 units, estimate the annual cost of operating the system through simulation.

10. Simulate the system given in problem 9 when each unit in inventory in excess of 36 is stored at a cost of $40 per unit-year plus a handling cost of $2 per

unit. Note that unit-years of inventory must now be calculated for units stored at $20 per unit-year and for units stored at $40 per unit-year. Is this method of handling excess inventory preferable to that described in problem 9?

11. In problem 9 assume that an inventory of more than 32 units cannot be handled. If an order is received which raises the inventory level above 32 units, those units in excess of 32 are returned to the supplier at a cost of $2 per unit returned. Is this system of dealing with excess inventory more effective on an annual cost basis than that described in problem 9?

12. A directive from top management has been issued which indicates that the company's annual investment in inventory for a particular product should be kept below $1,000. For this product a reorder point system is now in use. Each stock-out results in lost sale at a cost of $70. The inventory carrying charge is $60 per unit-year, and orders are placed at a cost of $300. Demand is Poisson distributed with a mean rate of 300 units per year. Units are demanded one at a time. Lead time is 0.008 years and is constant. The reorder point is 4 units, and the reorder quantity is 31 units. By simulating this system for 200 years, determine the probability that the annual inventory carrying cost will exceed $1,000.

13. Simulate the system in problem 4 with the following change. The mean annual demand is 30,000 units, but the demand rate during the first half of the year is higher than that for the second. Demand during the first half of the year is Poisson distributed with a mean of 20,000 units. During the second half of the year the demand is Poisson distributed with mean 10,000 units. How does this variation in the demand rate affect the annual cost of operating the inventory system? What components of the average total annual cost change? Explain these changes.

14. Make the necessary modifications to the general inventory simulation program so that a multiple item inventory system may be simulated. Include the following parameters in the model:

w_i — The space required for storage of a single item of the ith type (expressed in cubic units).

W — The total storage capacity in cubic units.

When the receipt of an order causes the total storage capacity to be exceeded, the excess units contained in that order are returned to the supplier at a cost Cw_i/unit.

15. A large chain food store purchases Q loaves of bread from a bakery each day on a modified consignment basis. The bakery will take back up to dQ unsold loaves, where $0 < d < 1$, at the end of the day. The purchase price of the bread is $0.22 per loaf and the selling price is $0.25 per loaf. The inventory carrying cost of a loaf of bread is negligible as is the cost of placing an order and reviewing inventory. Daily demand to the food store for bread is Poisson distributed with parameter λ. The number of loaves requested per demand is geometrically

distributed with parameter p. Unfilled demand results in a lost sale at a cost of $0.04 per loaf, which includes lost profit and lost goodwill. Lead time may be considered to be zero. Any loaves unsold at the end of the day in excess of dQ are discarded and cost the market $0.22 each. Develop a simulator for this inventory system. If $d = 0.10$, $\lambda = 200$, and $p = 0.50$, find the optimal value of Q.

16. The demand in any month for a particular detergent at a local supermarket is a function of both the previous month's demand as well as the number of lost sales in the previous month. In particular, the demand rate in the ith month, λ_i, is expressed by

$$\lambda_i = \lambda_{i-1} + q\lambda_{i-1} - ps_{i-1}$$

where q and p are positive constants, and units are demanded one at a time. The demand rate in the $(i - 1)$st month is λ_{i-1}, and s_{i-1} is the number of lost sales incurred in the $(i - 1)$st month. Presently the status of inventory is reviewed twice a month at equal intervals at a cost of $1 per review.

The quantity ordered is such that inventory position is raised to 312 units. It costs $5 to place an order. Each lost sale costs $0.75, and the inventory carrying cost is $0.50/unit-year. Lead time is constant at one week. Monthly demand is Poisson distributed with parameter λ_i. Assume that $p = 0.05$ and $q = 0.01$. Last month's demand was 400 units and there were 20 lost sales. Modify the simulation program presented in the chapter to handle this situation an; analyze the current problem. Attempt to improve the policy.

17. Given the problem of example 4.11, suppose that the following discount schedule was submitted by the supplier:

$1 \leqslant Q \leqslant 35$	Unit Cost = $80
$36 \leqslant Q \leqslant 105$	Unit Cost = $75
$106 \leqslant Q \leqslant 245$	Unit Cost = $73
$246 \leqslant Q$	Unit Cost = $70

Keeping the reorder point at eight units, simulate the system for

$Q = 34$
$Q = 36$
$Q = 106$
$Q = 246$

Does this analysis indicate that the present policy ($r = 8$, $Q = 34$) should be changed?

18. Carry out the analysis suggested in problem 17 when the quantity discount schedule is as follows: The first 35 units on an order cost $80/unit. The 36th to the 105th unit on an order costs $75/unit. The 106th to the 245th unit on an order costs $73/unit. All units in excess of 245 cost $70 each.

19. An appliance dealer experienced the following demand for air conditioners during the past year.

Month	Demand
January	0
February	1
March	2
April	10
May	25
June	40
July	70
August	85
September	50
October	3
November	4
December	2
Total	292

Monthly demand from May through September is expected to increase at a rate of about 10 percent per year for the next five years. Demand in the remaining months is not expected to change. Order lead time is a constant of two weeks. The present inventory policy calls for the placement of an order for 25 air conditioning units whenever inventory position falls to 6 units. The inventory carrying charge is $90 per unit-year. Stock-outs result in lost sales at a cost of $300 each. The ordering cost is $25.

a) Simulate five years of operation and assess the adequacy of this inventory policy.

b) Attempt to develop separate policies for in-season and out-of-season demand which will reduce the cost of operation for the first year.

20. The inventory system described in problem 4 is to be simulated with the following modification: When an order is received, it is subjected to an incoming inspection by the quality control department. If the lot is rejected upon this inspection, it is returned to the supplier and another order is placed with the supplier for a quantity equal to that rejected. If the order is accepted, it is placed in inventory. The inspection procedure consists of selecting five units from the receipt lot and accepting the lot if no defective units are found. If one or more defective units are detected, the lot is rejected. The density function of proportion defective, P, is given by

$$f_P(p) = 21(1 - p)^{20}, \quad 0 < p < 1$$

Develop a subroutine which will carry out the inspection procedure, place a new order when necessary, and update all necessary counters. Simulate the system for 100 years, and compare the annual cost of this system with that where no inspection is carried out. Ignore all quality control costs. Assume inspection is non-destructive.

21. Simulate the system described in problem 20 when the cost of quality

control is considered. The cost of inspecting one unit is $4. The cost of rejecting a lot is the cost of placing a new order and is to be distinguished from orders placed from inventory. Each accepted defective unit costs $2. Simulate the system for 100 years. The simulator should calculate and distinguish between the annual cost of operating the inventory system and the annual cost of quality control.

22. A hospital blood bank operates in the following manner: Whenever the inventory position of blood falls to r units, an order is placed for Q units. Lead time for such orders is exponentially distributed with a mean of 12 hours. The number of persons requiring blood is Poisson distributed with a mean of eight persons per day. The number of units of blood required per person is geometrically distributed with $p=0.80$. If a person requires blood which cannot be supplied from the blood bank, an emergency order can be delivered within one-half hour. In addition to those units received through normal and emergency ordering procedures, the hospital receives blood through donations. Each blood donor contributes one unit. The number of blood donors per day is Poisson distributed with a mean of five per day.

The inventory system is to operate in a manner such that the probability that 10 or more emergency orders are placed per year is less than 0.05. Either modify one of the simulators in this chapter to fit this problem or develop your own simulator for this problem. Find values of r and Q such that the above criterion for operation is satisfied.

23. Modify the simulator developed in problem 22 to account for deterioration of blood during storage. In particular, blood donated directly to the hospital has a life of 30 days, after which it cannot be used. Blood obtained through normal and emergency orders has a life of 21 days. Find the values of r and Q which satisfy the criterion given in problem 22.

24. In the generalized inventory simulator given in this chapter, the initial program included the following subroutine for adjusting the status of the inventory system after each demand (SUBROUTINE UNOUT) instead of the one given in this chapter.

```
      SUBROUTINE UNOUT
      DIMENSION OD(100)
      COMMON/BLOKB/TIM1,TIMLIM,TIME,TIMST,OD,DE,TREV,NEVENT
      COMMON/BLOKC/AIP,PERREV
      COMMON/BLOKE/AIUY,AIL,LOST,BUY,ANBO
      COMMON/BLOKF/ANS,ANUD,CNBO,TNUD
      COMMON/BLOKG/A,B,G,H
      COMMON/BLOKI/IX
      IF(PERREV)1,1,2
    1 TREV=TIM1
    2 ANS=ANS+1
```

```
   DE=TIM1+DEMAND(A,B,IX)
   CALL UPDATE
   ANUD=UNITS(G,H,IX)
   AIP=AIP−ANUD
   IF(LOST) 3,3,4
 4 IF(AIP) 5,5,3
 5 AIP=0
 3 TNUD=TNUD+ANUD
   IF(AIL−ANUD) 6,6,7
 6 CNBO=CNBO+ANUD−AIL
   ANBO=ANBO+ANUD−AIL
   AIL=0
   GO TO 8
 7 AIL=AIL−ANUD
 8 RETURN
   END
```

What problem or problems would you expect this subroutine to cause?

25. In SUBROUTINE REVIEW (I) of the sequential inventory simulator, explain the significance of the logical IF statement following statement 20. Note that a corresponding statement does not appear in SUBROUTINE REVIEW of the single system simulator. What effect does omission of this statement have with regard to the intended function of a reorder point model?

26. Consider the following production system: Customer demand for final product is Poisson distributed with a mean of 300 units per year. Units are demanded one at a time, and an unfilled demand results in a lost sale. To maintain the final product inventory a reorder point model is used with reorder point 10 units and order quantity 20 units. An order placed from the final product inventory results in a production order for 20 units. The time between the issue of the order and the startup of production is 0.0015 years, and 0.001 years are required to produce one unit of final product. The entire order is manufactured before any units are placed in inventory. The time required to get the finished order from the production line to the final product inventory is 0.0005 years. Production starts upon receipt of the production order as long as the inventory level of raw materials is not zero. If the raw materials inventory is empty, production must wait until it is replenished. One unit of raw material is required for each unit of final product manufactured. If the level of the raw materials inventory is such that a full order cannot be manufactured, that portion which can be manufactured is produced and placed in the final product inventory. The unfilled portion of the order is back ordered and manufactured at a later date as a separate order. A periodic review system is used to maintain the raw materials inventory. The period between successive reviews is 0.10 years, and the quantity ordered at a review is that quantity which will bring inventory position up to 100 units. Orders for raw materials are placed with an outside

supplier, and lead time is a constant of 0.06 years. Simulate this system for a period of three years using the sequential inventory simulator given in this chapter.

27. Modify the sequential inventory simulator developed in this chapter to calculate the inventory carrying cost, the stock-out cost, the ordering cost, the review cost for each inventory studied, and the total cost of maintaining the entire system of inventories. The ordering cost is to apply to all orders produced, including split orders.

28. Using the program developed in problem 27, estimate the annual cost of the inventory system described in problem 26 given the following cost information:

Cost Classification	Final Product Inventory	Raw Materials Inventory
Carrying cost/unit-year	$160	|$30
Stock-out cost/unit-year		100
Stock-out cost/unit	50	30
Ordering cost	60	40
Review cost	10	10

Simulate the system for three years.

29. In the production system described in problem 26 assume that the minimum production quantity is 20 units. That is, the manufacturing process is not set up for production unless at least 20 units of raw materials are available. Include an option in the sequential inventory simulator to allow for this possibility.

30. Simulate the production inventory system shown below given the following information:

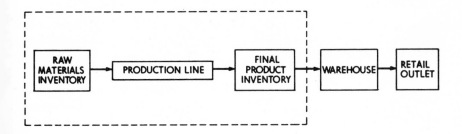

		Inventory Information		
	Retail Outlet	*Warehouse*	*Final Product*	*Raw Materials*
Stock outs	Lost sale	Back order	Back order	Back order
Ordering policy	Reorder point	Periodic review order up to R	Reorder point	Periodic review up to R
Reorder point	10 units	79 units	0 units	199 units
Order quantity	40 units		80 units	
Time between reviews		0.10 years		0.30
R		80 units		200

Retail demand is Poisson distributed, one unit per demand with mean demand rate of 500 units per year. The time taken for an order to reach the warehouse from the retail outlet may be considered negligible since it requires only a telephone call. The time taken for an order to reach the retail outlet once it has been received by the warehouse is 0.009 years. The time taken for an order to reach the final product inventory from the warehouse is 0.003 years; an additional 0.02 years is required for the order to be completely or partially filled and transported to the warehouse. The time taken for a production order issued from the final product inventory to reach the production line is negligible, but it takes 0.0003 years to set up the production line and another 0.0001 years to manufacture one unit of final product. Orders for replenishment of the raw materials inventory are placed with an outside supplier. Lead time on these orders is exponentially distributed with a mean of 0.04 years. Simulate this system for five years.

31. Develop a statistical routine for the sequential inventory simulator similar to SUBROUTINE SIG in the single inventory simulator.

32. A retailer may place orders for inventory replenishment of one of his products with one of three warehouses. Retail demand is Poisson distributed with mean rate μ per year and units are demanded one at a time. The three warehouses serve other retailers in addition to the one considered here. When the retailer is ready to place an order, he calls warehouse number 1 to see if it can fill the order. If the first warehouse cannot fill the order, he tries the second and finally the third if necessary. The probability that the ith warehouse will be able to fill the retailer's order for k units is given by

$$P(k \text{ units on hand at } i\text{th warehouse}) = \left|1 - \sum_{x=0}^{k} \frac{\lambda_i^x}{x!} e^{-\lambda_i}\right|, \quad i = 1, 2, 3$$

Partial orders are not filled. If a warehouse cannot fill the order, the retailer is informed of when that warehouse will be able to fill the order. The density function of the time until the order can be filled by the ith warehouse is exponential with parameter ϕ_i. If the order cannot be filled immediately by any of the three warehouses, the retailer places the order with that warehouse with the shortest estimated back order time. Delivery time on an order placed with the ith warehouse is constant and equal to T_i. Therefore lead time for an order placed with the ith warehouse is T_i plus the time taken to fill the order. Develop a simulator for the retailer's inventory system.

APPENDIX: SINGLE INVENTORY SIMULATOR AND SEQUENTIAL INVENTORY SIMULATOR

Single Inventory Simulator—Program Listing and Main Program

FIGURE 9.34
Main Program for Single Inventory Simulator

```
C      NSIM=NUMBER OF PROBLEMS OR CONDITIONS SIMULATED
C      PERREV=0, REORDER POINT MODEL
C             =1, PERIODIC REVIEW MODEL
C      IX=INITIAL RANDOM NUMBER
C      AIR=REORDER POINT-IF INVENTORY POSITION IS AT OR BELOW THIS LEVEL
C          AT THE TIME OF A REVIEW AN ORDER IS PLACED. (IN A PERIODIC
C          REVIEW CASE AIR SHOULD=ALEVEL-1.  THIS WILL FORCE A REVIEW
C          EVERY TIME A DEMAND OCCURS.)
C      AIQ=ORDER QUANTITY IF THE SAME NUMBER OF UNITS ARE TO BE INCLUDED
C          IN EACH ORDER
C      ALEVEL=LEVEL TO WHICH INVENTORY POSITION IS TO BE BROUGHT IF THE
C             ORDER POLICY IS SUCH THAT INVENTORY POSITION IS TO BE
C             BROUGHT TO A SPECIFIED LEVEL EACH TIME AN ORDER IS PLACED
C      DEC=0, IF THE ORDER QUANTITY IS AIQ
C          =1,   IF INVENTORY POSITION IS TO BE BROUGHT TO A SPECIFIED
C                LEVEL WITH EACH ORDER
C      LOST=0, BACKORDER MODEL
C            1, LOST SALES MODEL
C      TIMLIM=DURATION OF EACH SIMULATION (DAYS, MONTHS, YEARS, ETC.)
C      REVTIM=TIME BETWEEN SUCCESSIVE REVIEWS
C      TL=LEAD TIME
C      TREV=TIME OF THE NEXT REVIEW
C      TIM1=TIME AT WHICH THE PRESENT EVENT OCCURS (SAME AS MCT IN
C           QUEUEING SIMULATOR)
C      TIME=TIME AT WHICH THE LAST EVENT OCCURRED
C      OD(K)=TIME AT WHICH THE KTH ORDER WILL BE RECEIVED
C      DE=TIME AT WHICH THE NEXT DEMAND WILL OCCUR
C      DELT=TIME BETWEEN SUCCESSIVE UPDATES OF STATISTICS
C      TIMST=TIME OF NEXT UPDATE OF STATISTICS
C      AIL=CURRENT INVENTORY LEVEL
C      AIP=CURRENT INVENTORY POSITION
C      ANBO=CURRENT NUMBER OF STOCKOUTS (BACKORDERS OR LOST SALES)
C      NOUT=NUMBER OF OUTSTANDING ORDERS
C      AIOQ(K)=NUMBER OF UNITS TO BE INCLUDED IN THE KTH ORDER
C      ANUD=NUMBER OF UNITS REQUESTED AT AN INDIVIDUAL DEMAND
C      AIUY= ACCUMULATED UNIT-YEARS OF INVENTORY
C      BUY=ACCUMULATED UNIT-YEARS OF BACKORDERS
C      CNBO=ACCUMULATED NUMBER OF STOCKOUTS (BACKORDERS OR LOST SALES)
C      ANS=ACCUMULATED NUMBER OF DEMANDS
C      REV=ACCUMULATED NUMBER OF REVIEWS
C      ANORD=ACCUMULATED NUMBER OF ORDERS
C      TNUD=ACCUMULATED NUMBER OF UNITS DEMANDED (WILL BE GREATER THAN
C           ANS IF UNITS ARE NOT DEMANDED ONE AT A TIME)
```

FIGURE 9.34 *(continued)*

```
C       BREV=NUMBER OF REVIEWS DURING THE TIME BETWEEN SUCCESSIVE
C            STATISTICAL UPDATES
C       BIUY=UNIT-YEARS OF INVENTORY ACCUMULATED SINCE THE LAST
C            STATISTICAL UPDATE AT DELT TIME UNITS AGO
C       BBUY=UNIT-YEARS OF BACKORDERS ACCUMULATED SINCE THE LAST
C            STATISTICAL UPDATE AT DELT TIME UNITS AGO
C       BNBO=NUMBER OF STOCKOUTS ACCUMULATED SINCE THE LAST STAT
C            UPDATE AT DELT TIME UNITS AGO
C       BNORD=NUMBER OF ORDERS PLACED SINCE THE LAST STAT UPDATE AT DELT
C            TIME UNITS AGO
C       EREV=EXPECTED OR AVERAGE NUMBER OF REVIEWS PER UNIT OF TIME
C       ENUD=EXPECTED NUMBER OF UNITS REQUESTED PER DEMAND
C       EUY=EXPECTED UNIT-YEARS OF INVENTORY PER TIME UNIT
C       EBUY=EXPECTED UNIT-YEARS OF BACKORDERS PER TIME UNIT
C       I1=PRINTOUT NUMBER WITHIN REPLICATION
C       EBO=EXPECTED NUMBER OF BACKORDERS PER TIME UNIT
C       EO=EXPECTED NUMBER OF ORDERS PER TIME UNIT
C       CI=INVENTORY CARRYING COST PER UNIT-YEAR
C       CO=COST OF PLACING AN ORDER
C       CB1=BACKORDER COST PER UNIT-YEAR (FUNCTION OF TIME AND THE NUMBER
C            OF BACKORDERS)
C            =0 FOR MODEL WITH LOST SALES
C       CB2=COST PER STOCKOUT (FUNCTION OF THE NUMBER OF STOCKOUTS ONLY)
C            =SPECIFIED VALUE FOR MODEL WITH BACKORDERS
C       CP=COST PER REVIEW
C       CINV(I,J)=INVENTORY CARRYING COST DURING THE JTH TIME PERIOD OF
C                 LENGTH DELT WITHIN THE ITH SIMULATION
C       CBUY(I,J)=TIME DEPENDENT COST OF BACKORDERS DURING THE JTH TIME
C                 PERIOD OF LENGTH DELT WITHIN THE ITH SIMULATION
C       CBO(I,J)=QUANTITY COST OF STOCKOUTS DURING THE JTH TIME PERIOD OF
C                LENGTH DELT WITHIN THE ITH SIMULATION
C       COR(I,J)=COST OF ORDERS PLACED DURING THE JTH TIME PERIOD OF
C                LENGTH DELT WITHIN THE ITH SIMULATION
C       CREV(I,J)=COST OF REVIEWS DURING THE JTH TIME PERIOD OF LENGTH
C                 DELT WITHIN THE ITH SIMULATION
C       TOT=TOTAL COST INCURRED DURING THE JTH TIME PERIOD OF LENGTH DELT
C            WITHIN THE ITH SIMULATION
C       ECREV=EXPECTED OR AVERAGE REVIEW COST PER TIME UNIT
C       ECI=EXPECTED OR AVERAGE INVENTORY CARRYING COST PER TIME UNIT
C       ECBUY=EXPECTED OR AVERAGE TIME DEPENDENT COST OF BACKORDERS PER
C            TIME UNIT
C       ECBO=EXPECTED OR AVERAGE QUANTITY DEPENDENT COST OF STOCKOUTS PER
C            TIME UNIT
C       ECO=EXPECTED OR AVERAGE COST OF ORDERING PER TIME UNIT
C       ETOT=EXPECTED OR AVERAGE TOTAL COST PER TIME UNIT
C       A,B=PARAMETERS OF THE DEMAND DISTRIBUTION
C       C,D=PARAMETERS OF THE LEAD TIME DISTRIBUTION
C       G,H=PARAMETERS OF THE DISTRIBUTION OF THE NUMBER OF UNITS INCLUDED
C            IN THE DEMAND
C       ITER=NUMBER OF SIMULATIONS EACH OF DURATION TIMLIM
C       IPRINT=1, SUMMARY OF ACCUMULATED INFORMATION PRINTED OUT EVERY
C            DELT TIME UNITS
C            0,SUMMARY OF ACCUMULATED INFORMATION NOT PRINTED OUT EVERY
C            DELT TIME UNITS
C       STAT=0, OVERALL MEAN AND STANDARD DEVIATION ARE NOT COMPUTED
C            1, OVERALL MEAN AND STANDARD DEVIATION ARE COMPUTED
        DIMENSION STD(20),AMEAN(20),SSQ(20)
        DIMENSION AIOQ(100),OD(100),CINV(10,200),CBUY(10,200),CBO(10,200)
        DIMENSION COR(10,200),CREV(10,200)
        COMMON/BLOKA/NOUT,AIOQ,MIN
        COMMON/BLOKB/TIM1,TIMLIM,TIME,TIMST,OD,DE,TREV,NEVENT
        COMMON/BLOKC/AIP,PERREV
        COMMON/BLOKD/AIR,ANORD,DEC,ALEVEL,REV,REVTIM,AIQ
        COMMON/BLOKE/AIUY,AIL,LOST,BUY,ANBO
        COMMON/BLOKF/ANS,ANUD,CNBO,TNUD
        COMMON/BLOKG/A,B,G,H
        COMMON/BLOKH/C,D
        COMMON/BLOKI/IX
```

FIGURE 9.34 *(continued)*

```
        COMMON/BLOKJ/BIUY,BBUY,BNBO,BNORD,BREV,I1,III,PROC,AMEAN,SSQ,TOT
        COMMON/BLOKK/COUNT
        COMMON /BLOKL/RF
        READ(5,9000) NSIM, STAT,IPRINT
10      DO 310 NS=1,NSIM
        WRITE(6,9010)
        READ(5,9020)AIR,AIQ,REVTIM,CI,CO,CB1,CB2,CP
        READ(5,9020)A,B,C,D,G,H,TIMLIM,DEC
        READ(5,9030)DELT,ALEVEL,PERREV,IX,ITER,LOST
        WRITE(6,9200)NSIM,STAT,IPRINT
        WRITE(6,9210)AIR,AIQ,REVTIM,CI,CO,CB1,CB2,CP
        WRITE(6,9220)TIMLIM,DEC,ALEVEL,DELT,LOST,PERREV,ITER
        WRITE(6,9230)A,B,C,D,G,H
        WRITE(6,9010)
20      IF(PERREV)40,40,30
30      WRITE(6,9070)
        GO TO 50
40      WRITE(6,9080)
50      IF(LOST)60,60,70
60      WRITE(6,9090)
        GO TO 80
70      WRITE(6,9100)
C       BEGIN
C       THE FOLLOWING TWELVE STATEMENTS HOLD FOR THE PROBABILITY
C          DISTRIBUTIONS DEFINED IN SUBROUTINES DEMAND, ORDER, AND UNITS
C       ONLY
80      IF(H)100,100,90
90      ANDEM=A*H/B
        GO TO 110
100     ANDEM=A*(1./G)/B
110     WRITE(6,9110)ANDEM
        IF(D)120,120,130
120     TILEAD=C
        GO TO 140
130     TILEAD=D/C
140     WRITE(6,9120)TILEAD
C       END
        COUNT=0
        DO 290 III=1,ITER
        AIUY=0
        TL=0
        CNBO=0
        ANS=0
        ANBO=0
        REV=0
        BREV=0
        EREV=0
        ENUD=0
        EUY=0
        EBUY=0
        EBO=0
        EO=0
        BUY=0
        ANORD=0
        AIL=AIR+AIQ
        AIP=AIL
        TIMST=DELT
        IF(PERREV)150,150,160
150     TREV=10.**30
        GO TO 170
160     TREV=REVTIM
170     TIM1=0
        OD(1)=10.**30
        DE=DEMAND(A,B,IX)
        NOUT=0
        MIN=1
        TNUD=0
        I1=0
```

FIGURE 9.34 *(continued)*

```
180    TIME=TIM1
       CALL NEXT
       GO TO(230,240,210,250,290),NEVENT
210    CALL REVIEW
       GO TO 180
230    CALL UNOUT
       GO TO 180
240    CALL UNIN
       GO TO 180
250    XXX=TIM1-DELT
       I1=I1+1
       BIUY=AIUY-EUY*XXX
       BBUY=BUY-EBUY*XXX
       BNBO=CNBO-EBO*XXX
       BNORD=ANORD-EO*XXX
       BREV=REV-EREV*XXX
       CINV(III,I1)=CI*BIUY
       CBUY(III,I1)=CB1*BBUY
       CBO(III,I1)=CB2*BNBO
       COR(III,I1)=CO*BNORD
       CREV(III,I1)=CP*BREV
       TOT=CINV(III,I1)+CBUY(III,I1)+CBO(III,I1)+COR(III,I1)+CREV(III,I1)
       IF(STAT)280,280,270
270    PROC=0.
       CALL SIG
280    TIMST=TIM1+DELT
       EUY=AIUY/TIM1
       EBUY=BUY/TIM1
       EREV=REV/TIM1
       EBO=CNBO/TIM1
       EO=ANORD/TIM1
       ENUD=TNUD/ANS
       ECREV=EREV*CP
       ECI=CI*EUY
       ECBUY=CB1*EBUY
       ECBO=CB2*EBO
       ECO=CO*EO
       ETOT=ECI+ECO+ECBUY+ECBO+ECREV
       IF(IPRINT.LE.0.) GO TO 180
       WRITE(6,9130)III,I1,TIM1
       WRITE(6,9140)
       WRITE(6,9150)BREV,EREV
       WRITE(6,9160)BIUY,FUY,BBUY,EBUY,BNBO,EBO,BNORD,EO,CINV(III,I1),
      1ECI,CBUY(III,I1),ECBUY,CBO(III,I1),ECBO,COR(III,I1),ECO
       WRITE(6,9170)CREV(III,I1),ECREV,TOT,ETOT
       WRITE(6,9180)ANS,TNUD,ENUD
       WRITE(6,9010)
       GO TO 180
290    PROC=1
       IF(STAT)310,310,300
300    CALL SIG
       WRITE(6,9190)(AMEAN(I),SSQ(I),I=1,6)
310    CONTINUE
       RETURN
9000   FORMAT(1X15,F10.2,I5)
9010   FORMAT(1H1)
9020   FORMAT(8F10.0)
9030   FORMAT(3F10.0,3I5)
9070   FORMAT(1X21HPERIODIC REVIEW MODEL)
9080   FORMAT(1X19HREORDER POINT MODEL)
9090   FORMAT(1X10HBACKORDERS)
9100   FORMAT(1X10HLOST SALES)
9110   FORMAT(1X20HMEAN ANNUAL DEMAND =E14.8,1X5HUNITS)
9120   FORMAT(1X16HMEAN LEAD TIME =E14.8,1X5HYEARS)
9130   FORMAT(////1X4HIII=I5,1X3HI1=I5,2X5HTIME=E14.8//)
9140   FORMAT(30X36HPER TIME PERIOD    EXPECTED PER YEAR)
9150   FORMAT(1X17HNUMBER OF REVIEWS,14XE14.8,6XE14.8)
9160   FORMAT(1X21HUNIT YRS OF INVENTORY,10XE14.8,6XE14.8/1X22HUNIT YRS O
```

FIGURE 9.34 *(concluded)*

```
      1F STOCKOUTS  ,9XE14.8,6XE14.8/1X20HNUMBER OF STOCKOUTS ,11XE14.8,6X
      2E14.8/1X16HNUMBER OF ORDERS,15XE14.8,6XE14.8/1X23HINVENTORY CARRYI
      3NG COST,8XE14.8,6XE14.8/1X30HSTOCKOUT COST (TIME*QUANTITY) ,1XE14.
      48,6XE14.8/1X25HSTOCKOUT COST (QUANTITY) ,6XE14.8,6XE14.8/1X13HORDE
      5RING COST,18XE14.8,6XE14.8)
 9170 FORMAT(1X11HREVIEW COST,20XE14.8,6XE14.8/1X10HTOTAL COST,21XE14.8,
      16XE14.8)
 9180 FORMAT(1X25HNO OF DEMANDS RECEIVED = E14.8/1X23HTOTAL UNITS DEMAND
      1ED = E14.8/1X27HAVERAGE UNITS PER DEMAND = E14.8)
 9190 FORMAT(1X26HUNIT YRS INVENTORY   MEAN=E14.8,3X8HSTD DEV=E14.8/1X26
      1HUNIT YRS STOCKOUTS   MEAN=E14.8,3X8HSTD DEV=E14.8/1X26HNUMBER OF
      2STOCKOUTS  MEAN=E14.8,3X8HSTD DEV=E14.8/1X26HNUMBER OF ORDERS
      3MEAN=E14.8,3X8HSTD DEV=E14.8/1X26HNUMBER OF REVIEWS   MEAN=E14.8,
      43X8HSTD DEV=E14.8/1X26HTOTAL COST         MEAN=E14.8,3X8HSTD DEV
      5=E14.8)
 9200 FORMAT(1X5HNSIM=I5/1X5HSTAT=F4.0/1X7HIPRINT=I5)
 9210 FORMAT(1X4HAIR=E14.7/1X4HAIQ=E14.7/1X7HREVTIM=E14.7/1X3HCI=E14.7/1
      1X3HCO=E14.7/1X4HCB1=E14.7/1X4HCB2=E14.7/1X3HCP=E14.7)
 9220 FORMAT(1X7HTIMLIM=E14.7/1X4HDEC=E14.7/1X7HALEVEL=E14.7/1X5HDELT=E1
      14.7/1X5HLOST=I5/1X7HPERREV=E14.7/1X5HITER=I5)
 9230 FORMAT(1X2HA=E14.7/1X2HB=E14.7/1X2HC=E14.7/1X2HD=E14.7/1X2HG=E14.7
      1/1X2HH=E14.7)
      END
```

Sequential Inventory Simulator--Program Listing and Description

The main program reads all input information, establishes the initial conditions for the simulation, determines the next event, prints out cumulative operating information every DELT time units (IPRINT = 0) or after every event (IPRINT = 1), and terminates the simulation when TIM1 ≥ TIMLIM. The operating information calculated in this program does not include the component operating costs or the total cost of operation. However, these costs can be calculated in a manner similar to that used in the single system simulator. The reader will note that many of the variables used in this program are the same as those used in the single inventory simulator with the addition of subscripts where necessary.

The simulation is initiated by generating a demand to I_{n+1}. This is accomplished by generating the time of the first review of I_{n+2}. To determine the next event and the time of its occurrence, TIM1, the simulator examines each inventory comparing TIM1 with TREV(I), DE(I,K), and OD(I,J,K), where TREV(I) is the time of the next review of the Ith inventory, DE(I,K) is the time at which the Kth demand to the Ith inventory occurs, and OD(I,J,K) is the time at which the Kth order from the Ith inventory to the Jth inventory occurs. For OD(I,J,K) J is equal to 1 or NDOWN(I). Following the above analysis for all inventories, TIM1 is compared with TIMPR and then TIMLIM. The main program is shown in Figure 9.35.

FIGURE 9.35

Main program for the Simulation of a System of Sequential Inventories

```
C     IX=RANDOM NUMBER
C     INV=TOTAL NUMBER OF INVENTORIES, INCLUDING THE INVENTORY WHICH
C          FILLS ORDERS PLACED WITH AN OUTSIDE SUPPLIER AND THE INVENTORY
C          WHICH PLACES CUSTOMER DEMANDS ON THE SYSTEM
C          =NUMBER OF INVENTORIES STUDIED + 2
C     IPRINT=1, CUMULATIVE OPERATING SUMMARY PRINTED OUT AFTER EACH
C               EVENT
C            =0, CUMULATIVE OPERATING SUMMARY NOT PRINTED OUT AFTER EACH
C               EVENT
C     IND=1, NEXT EVENT IS A REVIEW
C        =2, NEXT EVENT IS A DEMAND
C        =3, NEXT EVENT IS AN ORDER RECEIPT
C        =4, NEXT EVENT IS A PRINT OUT
C     PERREV(I)=0,REORDER POINT MODEL USED FOR INVENTORY I
C              =1,PERIODIC REVIEW MODEL USED FOR INVENTORY I
C     NDOWN(I)=INVENTORY RECEIVING ORDERS FROM INVENTORY I
C     NUP(I)=INVENTORY RECEIVING ORDERS FILLED BY INVENTORY I
C     DEC(I)=0., ORDER QUANTITY IS A CONSTANT FOR INVENTORY I
C           =1., ORDER QUANTITY IS BASED UPON AN ORDER UP TO R POLICY
C               FOR INVENTORY I
C     LOST(I)=0, STOCKOUTS FOR INVENTORY I RESULT IN BACKORDERS
C            =1, STOCKOUTS FOR INVENTORY I RESULT IN LOST SALES
C     A(I),B(I)=PARAMETERS OF THE DISTRIBUTION OF TIME FOR A DEMAND TO
C               REACH INVENTORY I FROM I+1, I LESS THAN INV
C              =PARAMETERS OF THE DISTRIBUTION OF TIME BETWEEN
C               SUCCESSIVE REVIEWS FOR INVENTORY I, I=INV
C     C(I),D(I)=PARAMETERS OF THE DISTRIBUTION OF TIME FOR A FILLED
C               ORDER TO REACH INVENTORY I
C     G(I),H(I)=PARAMETERS OF THE DISTRIBUTION OF THE NUMBER OF UNITS
C               PER DEMAND FOR INVENTORY I
C     AIP(I)=INVENTORY POSITION FOR INVENTORY I
C     AIR(I)=REORDER POINT FOR INVENTORY I, DEC(I)=0.
C           =ALEVEL(I)-1., DEC(I)=1.
C     AIQ(I)=REORDER QUANTITY, DEC(I)=0.
C           =ALEVEL(I)-AIP(I), DEC(I)=1.
C     ALEVEL(I)=LEVEL TO WHICH INVENTORY POSITION FOR INVENTORY I IS
C               BROUGHT AT EACH REVIEW , WHERE AN ORDER UP TO R POLICY
C               IS USED, DEC(I)=1.
C     REVTIM(I)=TIME BETWEEN SUCCESSIVE REVIEWS OF INVENTORY I, WHERE
C               REVIEW TIME IS A CONSTANT
C     AIL(I)=INVENTORY LEVEL FOR INVENTORY I
C     IDEM(I)=CURRENT NUMBER OF DEMANDS RECEIVED BUT NOT YET FILLED BY
C             INVENTORY I
C     ANBO(I)=CURRENT NUMBER OF STOCKOUTS FOR INVENTORY I
C     NOUT(I,J)=NUMBER OF ORDERS OUTSTANDING FROM INVENTORY I TO
C               TO INVENTORY J
C     ANORD(I,J)=CUMULATIVE NUMBER OF ORDERS PLACED FROM INVENTORY I TO
C                INVENTORY J
C     REV(I)=CUMULATIVE NUMBER OF REVIEWS OF INVENTORY I
C     ANS(I)=CUMULATIVE NUMBER OF DEMANDS RECEIVED BY INVENTORY I
C     TNUD(I)=CUMULATIVE NUMBER OF UNITS DEMANDED OF INVENTORY I
C     CNBO(I)=CUMULATIVE NUMBER OF STOCKOUTS FOR INVENTORY I
C     AIUY(I)=CUMULATIVE UNIT-YEARS OF INVENTORY FOR INVENTORY I
C     BUY(I)=CUMULATIVE UNIT-YEARS OF STOCKOUTS FOR INVENTORY I
C     TIM1=TIME AT WHICH THE NEXT EVENT TAKES PLACE
C     TIMPR=TIME OF THE NEXT PRINT OUT
C     DELT=TIME PERIOD BETWEEN THE PRINT OUT OF SUCCESSIVE CUMULATIVE
C          OPERATING SUMMARIES
C     TREV(I)=TIME OF THE NEXT REVIEW OF INVENTORY I
C     DE(I,K)=TIME OF KTH DEMAND TO INVENTORY I
C     DEQ(I,J)=NUMBER OF UNITS REQUESTED ON THE KTH DEMAND TO INVENTORY
C              I
C     OD(I,J,K)=TIME KTH ORDER FROM INVENTORY I TO INVENTORY J IS
C               RECEIVED BY INVENTORY I
C     AIOQ(I,J,K)=NUMBER OF UNITS REQUESTED ON THE KTH ORDER FROM
C                 INVENTORY I TO INVENTORY J
C     TIMLIM=TOTAL NUMBER OF YEARS TO BE SIMULATED
```

FIGURE 9.35 – (*continued*)

```
C      TIME(I)=TIME OF THE LAST UPDATE OF INVENTORY I
       DIMENSION DE(7,90)
       DIMENSION PERREV(7),A(7),B(7),G(7),H(7),AIP(7),TREV(7)
       DIMENSION NOUT(7,7),DEQ(7,90),AIOQ(7,7,90),OD(7,7,90),C(7),D(7)
       DIMENSION NDOWN(7),ANORD(7,7)
       DIMENSION AIR(7),AIQ(7),REVTIM(7),ALEVEL(7),DEC(7),REV(7)
       DIMENSION NUP(7),AIL(7),IDEM(7),ANBO(7)
       DIMENSION ANS(7),TNUD(7),CNBO(7)
       DIMENSION AIUY(7),BUY(7),TIME(7),LOST(7)
       COMMON/BLOKA/NOUT,DE,DEQ,AIOQ,OD,C,D,IX
       COMMON/BLOKB/PERREV,A,B,G,H,AIP,TREV
       COMMON/BLOKD/AIR,AIQ,REVTIM,ALEVEL,DEC,REV,ANORD,NDOWN
       COMMON/BLOKE/NUP,AIL,IDEM,ANBO
       COMMON/BLOKF/ANS,TNUD,CNBO,INV
       COMMON/BLOKH/AIUY,BUY,TIME,LOST,TIM1
       READ(5,9000) INV,IX,IPRINT,TIMLIM,DELT
       WRITE(6,9150) INV,IPRINT,TIMLIM,DELT
       TIMPR=DELT
       WRITE(6,9200)
       IND=0
       DO 10 I=1,INV
       READ(5,9010)AIR(I),AIQ(I),REVTIM(I),PERREV(I),DEC(I),ALEVEL(I)
       WRITE(6,9160) I,AIR(I),I,AIQ(I),I,ALEVEL(I)
       WRITE(6,9170) I,REVTIM(I),I,PERREV(I),I,DEC(I)
       READ(5,9020) NDOWN(I),NUP(I),LOST(I)
       WRITE(6,9180) I,NDOWN(I),I,NUP(I),I,LOST(I)
       READ(5,9010) A(I),B(I),C(I),D(I),G(I),H(I)
       WRITE(6,9190) I,A(I),I,B(I),I,C(I),I,D(I),I,G(I),I,H(I)
       AIUY(I)=0
       BUY(I)=0
       IF(I.NE.1)GO TO 10
       REVTIM(I)=10.**20
       AIP(I)=10.**20
       GO TO 30
10     IF(I.NE.INV)GO TO 20
       AIR(I)=10.**20
       AIP(I)=0
       GO TO 30
20     AIP(I)=AIR(I)+AIQ(I)
30     AIL(I)=AIP(I)
       REV(I)=0
       IDEM(I)=0
       ANS(I)=0
       TNUD(I)=0
       CNBO(I)=0
       ANBO(I)=0
       K1=NDOWN(I)
       NOUT(I,K1)=0
       NOUT(I,1)=0
       ANORD(I,K1)=0
       ANORD(I,1)=0
       TIME(I)=0
       IF(PERREV(I).EQ.0.) GO TO 40
       TREV(I)=REVTIM(I)
       GO TO 50
40     TREV(I)=10.**30
50     DO 60 J=1,90
       DE(I,J)=10.**30
       DEQ(I,J)=0
       DO 60 K=1,INV
       AIOQ(I,K,J)=0
60     OD(I,K,J)=10.**30
       WRITE(6,9200)
       TREV(INV)=0
70     IF(IPRINT.EQ.0) GO TO 140
80     WRITE(6,9040)
       DO 90 I=1,INV
       WRITE(6,9050) I,AIUY(I),BUY(I),AIP(I),AIL(I),REV(I),IDEM(I),ANS(I)
```

FIGURE 9.35 – (*continued*)

```
90     CONTINUE
       WRITE(6,9060)
       DO 100 I=1,INV
       K11=NDOWN(I)
       WRITE(6,9070)I,TNUD(I),CNBO(I),ANBO(I),NOUT(I,K11),NOUT(I,1),
      1ANORD(I,K11),ANORD(I,1)
100    CONTINUE
       WRITE(6,9080)
       DO 110 I=1,INV
       WRITE(6,9090) I,TIME(I),TREV(I)
110    CONTINUE
       WRITE(6,9110)
       DO 120 I=1,INV
       DO 120 J=1,90
       IF(DEQ(I,J).EQ.0.) GO TO 120
       WRITE(6,9120) I,J,DE(I,J),DEQ(I,J)
120    CONTINUE
       WRITE(6,9130)
       DO 130 I=1,INV
       DO 130 J=1,INV
       DO 130 K=1,90
       IF(AIOQ(I,J,K).EQ.0.) GO TO 130
       WRITE(6,9140) I,J,K,OD(I,J,K),AIOQ(I,J,K)
130    CONTINUE
       WRITE(6,9200)
140    TIM1=10.**30
       IMIN=0
       JMIN=0
       KMIN=0
       DO 210 I=1,INV
       IF(TIM1.LE.TREV(I)) GO TO 150
       IND=1
       IMIN=I
       TIM1=TREV(I)
150    K1=NUP(I)
       K2=NDOWN(I)
       IF(NOUT(K1,I).LE.0) GO TO 170
       J=NOUT(K1,I)
       DO 160 K3=1,J
       IF(TIM1.LE.DE(I,K3)) GO TO 160
       IND=2
       IMIN=I
       JMIN=K3
       TIM1=DE(I,K3)
160    CONTINUE
170    IF(NOUT(I,1).LE.0) GO TO 190
       K=NOUT(I,1)
       DO 180 K3=1,K
       IF(TIM1.LE.OD(I,1,K3)) GO TO 180
       IND=3
       IMIN=I
       JMIN=1
       KMIN=K3
       TIM1=OD(I,1,K3)
180    CONTINUE
190    IF(NOUT(I,K2).LE.0) GO TO 210
       K=NOUT(I,K2)
       DO 200 K3=1,K
       IF(TIM1.LE.OD(I,K2,K3)) GO TO 200
       IND=3
       IMIN=I
       JMIN=K2
       KMIN=K3
       TIM1=OD(I,K2,K3)
200    CONTINUE
210    CONTINUE
       IF(TIM1.LE.TIMPR) GO TO 220
       IND=4
```

FIGURE 9.35 – (*concluded*)

```
      TIM1=TIMPR
220   IF(TIM1.GT.TIMLIM) GO TO 290
      IF((IPRINT.EQ.0) GO TO 230
      WRITE(6,9030) TIM1,IND
      WRITE(6,9100) IMIN,JMIN,KMIN
230   GO TO (260,270,280,240),IND
240   TIMPR=TIMPR+DELT
      DO 250 I=1,INV
      CALL UPDATE(I)
250   CONTINUE
      WRITE(6,9030) TIM1,IND
      GO TO 80
260   CALL REVIEW(IMIN)
      GO TO 70
270   CALL UNOUT(IMIN,JMIN)
      GO TO 70
280   CALL UNIN(IMIN,JMIN,KMIN)
      GO TO 70
290   CALL EXIT
9000  FORMAT(1X3I5,2F10.2)
9010  FORMAT(1X6F10.2)
9020  FORMAT(1X3I5)
9030  FORMAT(1X5HTIM1=E14.7,2X4HIND=I5)
9040  FORMAT(15X4HAIUY,12X4HBUY ,12X4HAIP ,12X4HAIL ,12X4HREV ,12X4HIDEM
     1,12X4HANS )
9050  FORMAT(6XI4,2XE14.7,2XE14.7,2XE14.7,2XE14.7,2XE14.7,7XI5,6XE14.7)
9060  FORMAT(12X4HTNUD,12X4HCNBO,12X4HANBO,7X6HNOUTK1,3X5HNOUT1,5X8HANOR
     1DK1 ,8X8HANORD1   )
9070  FORMAT(1XI4,2XE14.7,2XE14.7,2XE14.7,2XI6,2XI6,2XE14.7,2XE14.7)
9080  FORMAT(3X1HI,           21X4HTIME,12X4HTREV)
9090  FORMAT(1XI5,14XE14.7,2XE14.7)
9100  FORMAT(1X5HIMIN=I5,2X5HJMIN=I5,2X5HKMIN=I5)
9110  FORMAT(3X1HI ,5X1HJ,9X4H DE ,12X4H DEQ)
9120  FORMAT(1XI5,1XI5,2XE14.7,2XE14.7)
9130  FORMAT(3X1HI ,5X1HJ,5X1HK,9X4H OD ,12X4HAIOQ)
9140  FORMAT(1XI5,1XI5,1XI5,2XE14.7,2XE14.7)
9150  FORMAT(1X4HINV=I5,2X7HIPRINT=I3,2X7HTIMLIM=F10.2,2X5HDELT=F10.2)
9160  FORMAT(1X4HAIR(I3,2H)=F10.2,2X4HAIQ(I3,2H)=F10.2,2X7HALEVEL(I3,2H)
     1=F10.2)
9170  FORMAT(1X7HREVTIM(I3,2H)=F10.2,2X7HPERREV(I3,2H)=F10.2,2X4HDEC(I3,
     12H)=F10.2)
9180  FORMAT(1X6HNDOWN(I3,2H)=I5,2X4HNUP(I3,2H)=I5,2X5HLOST(I3,2H)=I5)
9190  FORMAT(1X2HA(I3,2H)=F10.4,2X2HB(I3,2H)=F10.2,2X2HC(I3,2H)=F10.4,2X
     12HD(I3,2H)=F10.2,2X2HG(I3,2H)=F10.4,2X2HH(I3,2H)=F10.2)
9200  FORMAT(1H1)
      END
```

If the next event is a review (IND=1), SUBROUTINE REVIEW, shown in Figure 9.36, is called, where IMIN is the inventory reviewed and is carried as *I* in the subroutine. The first step in the review of inventory *I* is to update the unit-years of inventory and the unit-years of stock-outs for that inventory, and this is accomplished by calling SUBROUTINE UPDATE, which is shown in Figure 9.37 where *I* is the inventory updated. If AIP(I)≤AIR(I), an order is placed to inventory NDOWN(I), then the current number NOUT(I,J) and cumulative number ANORD(I,J) of orders from *I* to *J*[J= NDOWN(I)] is increased by one. The order quantity may or may not be a random variable. If the value of AIQ(I) read in by the main program is negative, the order quantity is a random variable defined by UNITS(G,H,IX,I). If AIQ(I)≥0, the quantity ordered is either a constant, AIQ(I) [DEC(I) = 0], or a variable quantity equal to ALEVEL(I) - AIP(I) [DEC(I) = 1]. The order quantity in either case is defined by AIOQ(I,J,K) where K is the number of orders currently outstanding from I to J. After increasing inventory position by AIOQ(I,J,K), the time at which the order for AIOQ(I,J,K) units reaches inventory J is generated, DE(J,K). The corresponding demand quantity, DEQ(J,K), is equal to AIOQ(I,J,K). Finally the number of reviews, REV(I), is increased by one, and the time of the next review of the Ith inventory is generated. Explanation of the logical IF statement following statement number 20 is left as an exercise for the reader. If AIP(I)>AIR(I), the number of reviews is increased by one, the time of the next review is calculated, and control of the simulation is returned to the main program.

FIGURE 9.36
Subroutine Used for the Review of Any Inventory

```
       SUBROUTINE REVIEW(I)
       DIMENSION NOUT(7,7),DEQ(7,90),AIOQ(7,7,90),OD(7,7,90),C(7),D(7)
       DIMENSION DE(7,90)
       DIMENSION PERREV(7),A(7),B(7),G(7),H(7),AIP(7),TREV(7)
       DIMENSION AIR(7),AIQ(7),REVTIM(7),ALEVEL(7),DEC(7),REV(7)
       DIMENSION AIUY(7),BUY(7),TIME(7),LOST(7)
       DIMENSION NDOWN(7),ANORD(7,7)
       DIMENSION ANS(7),TNUD(7),CNBO(7)
       COMMON/BLOKA/NOUT,DE,DEQ,AIOQ,OD,C,D,IX
       COMMON/BLOKB/PERREV,A,B,G,H,AIP,TREV
       COMMON/BLOKD/AIR,AIQ,REVTIM,ALEVEL,DEC,REV,ANORD,NDOWN
       COMMON/BLOKF/ANS,TNUD,CNBO,INV
       COMMON/BLOKH/AIUY,BUY,TIME,LOST,TIM1
       CALL UPDATE(I)
       IF(AIP(I).GT.AIR(I)) GO TO 60
10     J=NDOWN(I)
       NOUT(I,J)=NOUT(I,J)+1
       ANORD(I,J)=ANORD(I,J)+1.
       K=NOUT(I,J)
       IF(AIQ(I).LT.0.) GO TO 40
       IF(DEC(I))20,20,30
20     AIOQ(I,J,K)=AIQ(I)
       GO TO 50
30     AIOQ(I,J,K)=ALEVEL(I)-AIP(I)
       GO TO 50
40     AIOQ(I,J,K)=UNITS(G,H,IX,I)
50     AIP(I)=AIP(I)+AIOQ(I,J,K)
       DE(J,K)=TIM1+DEMAND(A,B,IX,J)
       DEQ(J,K)=AIOQ(I,J,K)
60     REV(I)=REV(I)+1.
       IF(PERREV(I).EQ.0.AND.AIP(I).LE.AIR(I)) GO TO 10
       TREV(I)=TIMREV(PERREV,REVTIM,I,A,B,IX,INV)+TIM1
       RETURN
       END
```

If demand KMIN to inventory IMIN is the next event occurring in the simulation, SUBROUTINE UNOUT is called where I=IMIN and K=KMIN. SUBROUTINE UNOUT is shown in Figure 9.38. After updating unit-years of inventory and stock-outs, the inventory

FIGURE 9.37
Subroutine Used to Update Unit-Years of
Inventory and Unit-Years of Stockouts

```
SUBROUTINE UPDATE(I)
DIMENSION AIUY(7),BUY(7),TIME(7),LOST(7)
DIMENSION NUP(7),AIL(7),IDEM(7),ANBO(7)
COMMON/BLOKE/NUP,AIL,IDEM,ANBO
COMMON/BLOKH/AIUY,BUY,TIME,LOST,TIM1
DD=TIM1-TIME(I)
AIUY(I)=AIUY(I)+AIL(I)*DD
TIME(I)=TIM1
IF(LOST(I).GT.0)RETURN
BUY(I)=BUY(I)+ANBO(I)*DD
RETURN
END
```

placing the Kth demand upon the Ith inventory is defined, J=NUP(I), and the number of unfilled demands upon I, IDEM(I), is increased by one, and the cumulative number of demands and units demanded are increased by one and DEQ(I,K), respectively. If a reorder point model is used for the Ith inventory, TREV(I)=TIM1. If on-hand inventory exceeds DEQ(I,K), thefollowing steps are executed:

1. Inventory position is reduced by DEQ(I,K).
2. The time at which the quantity DEQ(I,K) reaches inventory J is calculated and given by OD(J,I,K).
3. DE(I,K) is destroyed.
4. The on-hand inventory level is reduced by DEQ(I,K).
5. DEQ(I,K) is destroyed.
6. The number of unfilled demands upon I is reduced by one.
7. Control of the simulation returns to the main program.

If AIL(I)<DEQ(I,K) and unfilled demand results in a lost sale, the following operatins are performed:

1. Inventory position is reducedby AIL(I) where AIL(I) is the portion of the demand filled.
2. The portion of the demand which cannot be filled is placed as an order from J to 1, and the current and cumulative number of orders from J to 1 are increased by 1. The order quantity associated with this order is AIOQ(J,1,K1) and is equal to the original demand quantity, DEQ(I,K), minus the inventory level. Since this order is placed with inventory 1, the time at which this order reaches J is generated and is defined by OD(J,1,K1).
3. If AIL(I)>0, the time at which the filled portion of the order reaches J is calculated and is given by OD(J,I,K). If AIL(I)=0, the current number of orders outstanding from J to I is reduced by one, as is the number of unfilled demands upon J.

FIGURE 9.38

Subroutine Used to Adjust Each Inventory When a Demand Occurs

```
       SUBROUTINE UNOUT(I,K)
       DIMENSION NOUT(7,7),DEQ(7,90),AIOQ(7,7,90),OD(7,7,90),C(7),D(7)
       DIMENSION DE(7,90)
       DIMENSION PERREV(7),A(7),B(7),G(7),H(7),AIP(7),TREV(7)
       DIMENSION NUP(7),AIL(7),IDEM(7),ANBO(7)
       DIMENSION ANS(7),TNUD(7),CNBO(7)
       DIMENSION AIUY(7),BUY(7),TIME(7),LOST(7)
       DIMENSION AIR(7),AIQ(7),REVTIM(7),ALEVEL(7),DEC(7),REV(7)
       DIMENSION NDOWN(7),ANORD(7,7)
       COMMON/BLOKA/NOUT,DE,DEQ,AIOQ,OD,C,D,IX
       COMMON/BLOKB/PERREV,A,B,G,H,AIP,TREV
       COMMON/BLOKD/AIR,AIQ,REVTIM,ALEVEL,DEC,REV,ANORD,NDOWN
       COMMON/BLOKE/NUP,AIL,IDEM,ANBO
       COMMON/BLOKF/ANS,TNUD,CNBO,INV
       COMMON/BLOKH/AIUY,BUY,TIME,LOST,TIM1
       CALL UPDATE(I)
       J=NUP(I)
       IDEM(I)=IDEM(I)+1
       ANS(I)=ANS(I)+1.
       TNUD(I)=TNUD(I)+DEQ(I,K)
       IF(PERREV(I).GT.0.) GO TO 10
       TREV(I)=TIM1
10     IF(AIL(I)-DEQ(I,K))20,20,90
20     IF(LOST(I).GT.0) GO TO 40
       AIP(I)=AIP(I)-DEQ(I,K)
       IF(AIL(I).EQ.0.) GO TO 30
       NOUT(J,I)=NOUT(J,I)+1
       ANORD(J,I)=ANORD(J,I)+1.
       K1=NOUT(J,I)
       AIOQ(J,I,K1)=DEQ(I,K)-AIL(I)
       DEQ(I,K1)=AIOQ(J,I,K1)
       GO TO 50
30     ZZ=DEQ(I,K)
       GO TO 80
40     AIP(I)=AIP(I)-AIL(I)
       NOUT(J,1)=NOUT(J,1)+1
       ANORD(J,1)=ANORD(J,1)+1.
       K1=NOUT(J,1)
       AIOQ(J,1,K1)=DEQ(I,K)-AIL(I)
       I1=1
       OD(J,1,K1)=TIM1+ORDER(C,D,IX,J,I1)
       IF(AIL(I).EQ.0.) GO TO 60
50     OD(J,I,K)=TIM1+ORDER(C,D,IX,J,I)
       GO TO 70
60     NOUT(J,I)=NOUT(J,I)-1
       IDEM(I)=IDEM(I)-1
70     ZZ=DEQ(I,K)-AIL(I)
       DEQ(I,K)=0
       AIOQ(J,I,K)=AIL(I)
80     ANBO(I)=ANBO(I)+ZZ
       CNBO(I)=CNBO(I)+ZZ
       DE(I,K)=10.**30
       AIL(I)=0
       GO TO 100
90     AIP(I)=AIP(I)-DEQ(I,K)
       OD(J,I,K)=TIM1+ORDER(C,D,IX,J,I)
       DE(I,K)=10.**30
       AIL(I)=AIL(I)-DEQ(I,K)
       DEQ(I,K)=0
       IDEM(I)=IDEM(I)-1
100    RETURN
       END
```

4. For either AIL(I)>0 or AIL(I)=0, AIOQ(J,I,K)=AIL(I); the current and cumulative number of stock-outs are increased; DEQ(I,K) and DE(I,K) are destroyed; AIL(I) is reduced to zero; and control of the simulation is returned to the main program.

If AIL(I)<DEQ(I,K) and unfilled demand is back ordered, the status of the system is modified as follows:

1. Inventory position is reduced by DEQ(I,K).
2. If AIL(I)>0, part of the demand is filled and part is back ordered. The back ordered portion results in an additional order from J to I. The number of units on this order is given by DEQ(I,K) − AIL(I) and also represents the associated demand quantity upon I. The time at which the filled portion of the demand is received by J is calculatd and defined by OD(J,I,K). The corresponding order quantity, AIOQ(J,I,K), is AIL(I). The number of units back ordered is defined by ZZ, and DEQ(I,K) is destroyed. If AIL(I) = 0, the number of units back ordered is DEQ(I,K) and is not destroyed until a later time at which it is filled.
3. For AIL(I)>0 or AIL(I)=0, the current and cumulative number of back orders are increased; DE(I,K) is destroyed; AIL(I) is reduced to zero; and control of the simulation is returned to the main program.

When the next event occurring in the simulation is the arrival of a filled order (IND=3), the main program executes a call to SUBROUTINE UNIN (IMIN,JMIN,KMIN), shown in Figure 9.39, which in turn immediately calls UPDATE. When an order containing AIOQ(I,J,K) units is received by the *I*th inventory, an attempt is made to fill as many back orders as possible. No back orders exist if stock-outs result in lost sales, LOST(I)=1, or if IDEM(I)=0. Let J1 be the inventory placing demands upon I, J1=NUP(I), and NOUT(J1,I) be the number of orders currently outstanding from J1 to I. If LOST(I)=0 and IDEM(I)>0, the following steps are executed:

FIGURE 9.39
Subroutine Used to Adjust Each Inventory Upon Receipt of a Filled Order

```
SUBROUTINE UNIN(I,J,K)
DIMENSION NOUT(7,7),DEQ(7,90),AIOQ(7,7,90),OD(7,7,90),C(7),D(7)
DIMENSION DE(7,90)
DIMENSION NUP(7),AIL(7),IDEM(7),ANBO(7)
DIMENSION AIUY(7),BUY(7),TIME(7),LOST(7)
DIMENSION AIR(7),AIQ(7),REVTIM(7),ALEVEL(7),DEC(7),REV(7)
DIMENSION NDOWN(7),ANORD(7,7)
```

FIGURE 9.39 *(continued)*

```
COMMON/BLOKA/NOUT,DE,DEQ,AIOQ,OD,C,D,IX
COMMON/BLOKD/AIR,AIQ,REVTIM,ALEVEL,DEC,REV,ANORD,NDOWN
COMMON/BLOKE/NUP,AIL,IDEM,ANBO
COMMON/BLOKH/AIUY,BUY,TIME,LOST,TIM1
CALL UPDATE(I)
J1=NUP(I)
K1=NOUT(J1,I)
OD(I,J,K)=10.**30
K4=NOUT(I,J)
10    IF(LOST(I).GT.0.OR.IDEM(I).LE.0) GO TO 50
AK=10.**20
DO 40 K2=1,K1
IF(DE(I,K2).LT.AK.OR.DEQ(I,K2).EQ.0.) GO TO 40
IF(DEQ(I,K2).LE.AIOQ(I,J,K)) GO TO 20
NOUT(J1,I)=NOUT(J1,I)+1
ANORD(J1,I)=ANORD(J1,I)+1.
K3=NOUT(J1,I)
AIOQ(J1,I,K3)=DEQ(I,K2)-AIOQ(I,J,K)
DEQ(I,K3)=AIOQ(J1,I,K3)
AIOQ(J1,I,K2)=AIOQ(I,J,K)
ZZ=AIOQ(I,J,K)
GO TO 30
20    ZZ=DEQ(I,K2)
IDEM(I)=IDEM(I)-1
30    OD(J1,I,K2)=TIM1+ORDER(C,D,IX,J1,I)
AIOQ(I,J,K)=AIOQ(I,J,K)-ZZ
ANBO(I)=ANBO(I)-ZZ
DEQ(I,K2)=0
IF(AIOQ(I,J,K).LE.0.) GO TO 50
40    CONTINUE
50    AIL(I)=AIL(I)+AIOQ(I,J,K)
NOUT(I,J)=NOUT(I,J)-1
IF(NOUT(I,J).LE.0) GO TO 70
DO 60 K2=K,K4
K5=K2+1
AIOQ(I,J,K2)=AIOQ(I,J,K5)
OD(I,J,K2)=OD(I,J,K5)
IF(J.LE.1) GO TO 60
DE(J,K2)=DE(J,K5)
DEQ(J,K2)=DEQ(J,K5)
60    CONTINUE
70    AIOQ(I,J,K4)=0
OD(I,J,K4)=10.**30
DEQ(J,K4)=0
DE(J,K4)=10.**30
RETURN
END
```

1. Determine which of the NOUT(J1,I) outstanding orders have been received by I but not filled. That is, for the K2th order, if $DE(I,K2) > 10^{20}$ and $DEQ(I,K2) > 0$, the order has been received but not filled since $DE(I,K2) = 10^{30}$ as soon as the demand corresponding to the order in question is received. However, DEQ(I,K2) is not reduced to zero until the demand is filled.

2. If $DEQ(I,K2) > AIOQ(I,J,K)$, the order is broken into two parts and NOUT(J1,I) and ANORD(J1,I) are increased by one. The demand quantity which is not filled is equal to $DEQ(I,K2) - AIOQ(I,J,K)$, and the demand quantity which is filled is AIOQ(I,J,K). Finally the amount by which the current number

of back orders is to be reduced is calculated and given by ZZ=AIOQ(I,J,K).

3. If DEQ(I,K2)≤AIOQ(I,J,K), the number of unfilled demands, IDEM(I), is reduced by one and the amount by which the current number of back orders is to be reduced is calculated and defined as ZZ=DEQ(I,K2).

4. For DEQ(I,K2) greater than, equal to, or less than AIOQ (I,J,K), the time at which the order quantity AIOQ(J1,I,K2) is received by J1 is calculated and defined by OD(J1,I,K2). The order quantity AIOQ(I,J,K) is reduced by ZZ units—the number of units drawn from that order to fill back orders. The current number of back orders is reduced by ZZ, and DEQ(I,K2) is destroyed. If the order quantity AIOQ(I,J,K) has not been reduced to zero, another unfilled demand is examined by returning to step 1.

5. Steps 1 to 4 are repeated until either all of the units contained in AIOQ(I,J,K) have been used to make up back orders or until no back orders remain.

After taking care of as many back orders as possible, if any exist, AIL(I) is increased by AIOQ(I,J,K) for both the back order and lost sales cases, and the number of outstanding orders, NOUT(I,J), is reduced by one. The final step is to adjust the subscripts on all outstanding orders from and demands to I to account for the order which has been received and back ordered demands which have been filled. The purpose of this step is to minimize the number of unfilled demands evaluated in step 1 and the number of orders calculated in determining the next event in the main program.

The subprograms FUNCTION DEMAND, FUNCTION ORDER, and FUNCTION UNITS are not given here. However, the corresponding subprograms given in the single inventory system simulator may be modified to serve this purpose by noting that A,B,C,D,G, and H are subscripted variables. In FUNCTION ORDER I is the inventory placing the order and J is the inventory receiving that order as a demand and may assume the values NDOWN(I) or 1. Therefore the analyst is able to distinguish between the time taken for an order to travel from NDOWN(I) to I and from 1 to I. The reader should recognize that the time generated in ORDER is not necessarily the lead time. In general, Lead Time = DEMAND + Time delay in filling the demand + ORDER.

FUNCTION TIMREV is given in Figure 9.40. For I < INV, the time until the next review is dependent upon the values of PERREV(I) and REVTIM(I). For I = INV, the time of the next review is dependent upon the assumed distribution of time between successive customer demands to INV-1. The process generator used to generate the time between successive reviews replaces f(R,A,B) in Figure 9.40 where A and B are the parameters of the process generator. Since TIMREV is the total time between successive customer demands, DEMAND = 0 for I = INV-1.

FIGURE 9.40
FUNCTION TIMREV

```
FUNCTION TIMREV(PERREV,REVTIM,I,A,B,IX,INV)
DIMENSION PERREV(7),REVTIM(7),A(7),B(7)
IF(I.NE.INV)GO TO 10
R=RANDU(IX,IY)
TIMREV=(-1./A(I))*ALOG(1.-R)
GO TO 30
10    IF(PERREV(I).LE.0.)GO TO 20
TIMREV=REVTIM(I)
GO TO 30
20    TIMREV=10.**20
30    RETURN
END
```

Two printout options are available in this simulator. The analyst may obtain a printout of cumulative operating information after each event by setting IPRINT equal to unity. If IPRINT=0, printouts are obtained every DELT time units only. The time of the next printout is TIMPR and is an integer multiple of DELT. When the next event is such a printout, IND=4. The operating information summarized is the same whether output is obtained after every event or every DELT time units. Each time a summary of operating information is obtained, the values of AIUY(I), BUY(I), REV(I), ANS(I), TNUD(I), CNBO(I), ANORD(I,I-1), and ANORD(I,1) are printed out for each inventory. All of these variables are cumulative. Corresponding year-by-year values are not calculated. At each printout the current values of AIP(I), AIL(I), IDEM(I), ANBO(I), NOUT(I,I-1), NOUT(I,1), TIME(I), and TREV(I) are given for each inventory. For all I and K for which DEQ(I,K)>0, both DE(I,K) and DEQ(I,K) are included in the output summary, as are OD(I,J,K) and AIOQ(I,J,K) for all I, J, and K for which AIOQ(I,J,K) > 0.

REFERENCES

Brenner, Michael E.   "A Relation between Decision Making Penalty and Simulation Sample Size for Inventory Systems," *Journal of Operations Research*, Vol. 13 (May–June 1965), pp. 433–43.

Buffa, E. S.   *Production–Inventory Systems: Planning and Control.* Homewood, Ill.: Richard D. Irwin, Inc., 1968.

Collcutt, R. H. Banbury, J., Massey, R. G., and Ward, R. A.   "A Method of Fixing Desirable Stock Levels, and of Stock Control," *Operational Research Quarterly,* Vol 10 (June 1959), pp. 81–95.

Geisler, Murray A.   "Some Statistical Properties of Selected Inventory Models," The RAND Corporation (December 1961).

Geisler, Murray A.   "The Sizes of Simulation Samples Required to Compute Certain Inventory Characteristics with Stated Precision and Confidence," No. RM–3242–PR, The RAND Corporation, Santa Monica, California, October 1962.

Holt, C. C., Modigliani, F., Muth, J. F., and Simon, H. A.   *Planning Production, Inventories, and Work Force.* Englewood Cliffs, N. J.: Prentice-Hall, Inc., 1960.

Morse, P. M.   *Queues, Inventories, and Maintenance.* New York: John Wiley & Sons, Inc., 1958.

Naddor, E.   *Inventory Systems.* New York: John Wiley & Sons, Inc., 1966.

Prabhu, N. V.   *Queues and Inventories.* New York: John Wiley & Sons, Inc., 1965.

Rauner, R. M.   *Laboratory Evaluation of Supply and Procurement Policies.* ASTIA Document Number AD 156042, The RAND Corporation, July 1958.

Model Validation and Analysis of Results

CHAPTER
10

DATA INPUT AND SIMULATOR VALIDATION

If a simulator is to reasonably represent a real world system, then all those variables and parameters affecting the real world system must be taken into account in the simulator is such a way that their effect is accurately reflected. The analyst should recognize, and distinguish from one another, three categories of varaiables. First are the decision variables. These variables are characterized by the fact that their values are completely controlled by personnel within the system. The second class of variables we shall call primary random variables. Within this category are included all of those random variables which act in an independent manner. That is, their values cannot be predicted from a knowledge of the values of the other random variables in the system. With respect to inventory systems, demand and lead time fall into this category, while inventory position, although a random variable, is not a primary random variable because its value can be predicted at any point in time given a knowledge of the values of the other variables in the system. The third type of variable we shall call a secondary random variable. Secondary random variables include all of these variables whose values can be completely related to the values of other random variables, to the decision variables, and to the parameters of the system. Examples of secondary random variables are inventory position, inventory level, the number of units in a queue, the time a unit spends in a queue, the average cost of product rejection by a quality control plan.

A system parameter is a quantity which affects the performance of the system, can be predicted with certainty, but either cannot or will not be altered by those operating the system. It should be noted that as we have defined it, a parameter need not be a constant. To illustrate, consider the cost of placing a long-distance telephone call. The cost per minute is completely predictable but varies with time of day and day of the week.

The reader should note that a primary random variable is not necessarily an independent random variable. For example, the number of defective units found in a sample is dependent, in a statistical sense, upon the proportion of defective units in the lot from which the sample was selected, but is nonetheless considered a primary random variable. We classify such a random variable as primary because its value cannot be precisely determined by the lot proportion defective. Therefore, unless the value of a random variable can be completely determined by the values of other variables and parameters, it is a primary random variable. From the point of view of simulation, primary random variables are generated but secondary random variables are calculated.

At this point we will assume that, given that a variable is secondary random variable, we know how to calculate its value at any point in time. Usually it is not difficult to identify the decision variables in a system because these are the variables which can be controlled from within the system itself. Let us now turn our attention to the estimation of system parameters and determination of the distributions of the primary random variables.

Estimation of system parameters can be a perplexing problem. First of all, given that we know what parameters to estimate, we must determine how to estimate them. In some cases this is an easy task. For example, the current selling price of an item is not difficult to ascertain, and usually can be predicted rather reliably for the near future. Similarly, costs of production and transportation are often readily available. However, consider the problems involved in attempting to estimate the cost of a lost sale or the cost of a back order. Here we must estimate the cost of intangibles, such as lost goodwill which may be converted into the loss of business in the future. Mean annual product demand is an example of a system parameter which is very easy to determine in some cases but very difficult to determine in others. To a large extent the magnitude of this difficulty depends upon the type of records kept by the business. For example, a pharmacist may know that during the last month he sold 100 tubes of toothpaste and that sometime during that month he ran out, but he does not know when. Therefore he has a record of sales but not demand, which is more important from an inventory analysis viewpoint. On the other hand, a manufacturer may have on hand an explicit record of the time at which every demand was received for a period covering several years.

In the discussion which follows we will attempt, by example, to point out some useful methods for estimating system parameters. This treatment by no means exhausts all available methods for parameter estimation, and the reader should consult a text on mathematical statistics or statistical inference for a more sophisticated treatment.

PROBABILITY DISTRIBUTIONS AND PARAMETER ESTIMATION

In Chapter 7 we demonstrated that if we know the probability mass function or the density function of a random variable, we can derive a process generator for that random variable. Unless we use an empirical process generator, such as that given in equation (7.84), we will have to determine the distributional properties of each random variable to be included in the simulator. Three steps are involved in defining the distribution of a random variable. First we must make a guess regarding the general form of the distribution. For example, if we are dealing with a continuous random variable whose frequency distribution is roughly symmetrical, we might hypothesize that the random variable is either normal, gamma, or Laplace distributed. The second step is to estimate the parameters of the hypothesized distribution. If we have hypothesized a normal distribution, we would then have to estimate the mean and variance to completely specify which normal distribution we are concerned with. The last step is to determine whether or not the hypothesized distribution adequately represents the random variable in question. If we conclude that the hypothesized distribution is unreliable, we repeat this procedure, starting with a search for a new distribution.

Identifying the Distribution

With very few exceptions one cannot make a reasonable guess regarding the distribution of a random variable unitil data has been collected which can be used as a guide. The collected data are usually summarized in a frequency distribution. With discrete random

TABLE 10.1
Frequency Distributions of Weekly Demand and Order Lead Time

Demand per Week	Frequency	Lead Time, t Years	Frequency
0.	1	$0.000 \leqslant t \leqslant 0.005$	5
1.	2	$0.005 < t \leqslant 0.010$	21
2.	4	$0.010 < t \leqslant 0.015$	24
3.	7	$0.015 < t \leqslant 0.020$	10
4.	.11	$0.020 < t \leqslant 0.025$	13
5.	.15	$0.025 < t \leqslant 0.030$	9
6.	.17	$0.030 < t \leqslant 0.035$	9
7.	.16	$0.035 < t \leqslant 0.040$	3
8.	.12	$0.040 < t \leqslant 0.045$	2
9.	8	$0.045 < t \leqslant 0.050$	1
10.	3	$0.050 < t \leqslant 0.055$	2
11.	2	$0.055 < t \leqslant 0.060$	1
12.	1		
13.	1		
	Total, 100		Total, 100

FIGURE 10.1
Relative Frequency Distribution of Demand, x

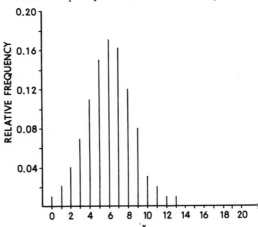

variables we will usually record the frequency with which each individual value of the random variable occurs. If the random variable is continuous, we break the range of values of the variable into intervals and record the frequency which occurs within each interval. For example, in Table 10.1 we present the frequency distributions of demand per week and lead time per order.

Plotting the relative frequency distribution of the random variable

FIGURE 10.2
Relative Frequency Distribution of Lead Time, *t*

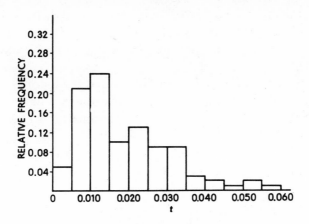

FIGURE 10.3
Normal Distributions with Mean Zero

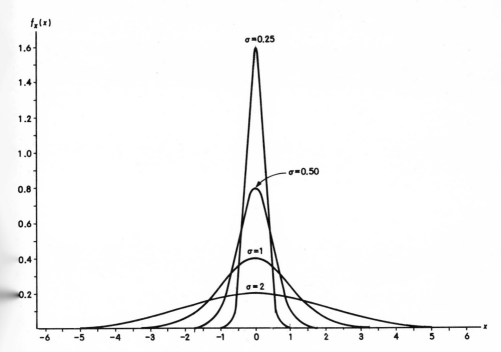

under study is often helpful in determining its probability mass
function or density function. The relative frequency in each interval
is the observed frequency count in each interval divided by the total
frequency count. Once the analyst has obtained a graph of the

relative frequency distribution, selection of the appropriate probability distribution becomes a matter of judgment and experience. Comparing Figures 10.1 and 10.2 with Figures 10.3, 10.4, 10.8, and 10.9, we might guess that weekly demand is either Poisson, binomially, or even normally distributed and that lead time may be gamma distributed.

It is not always necessary to describe a discrete random variable by the probability mass function of a discrete variable. For example, the normal distribution can be used as an approximation to the binomial when n is large and p is close to 0.5. Similarly, as the parameter of the Poisson distribution increases the normal distribution becomes an excellent approximation to the Poisson.

FIGURE 10.4
Gamma Density Function
$\lambda = 1$

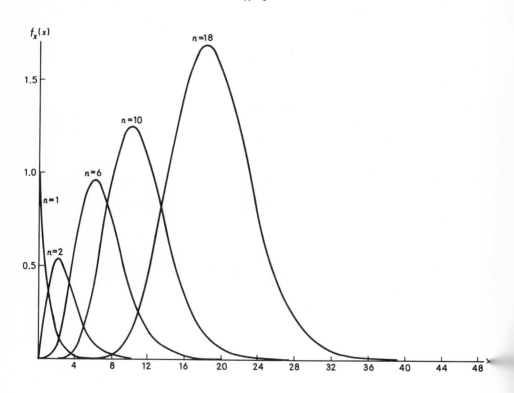

FIGURE 10.5

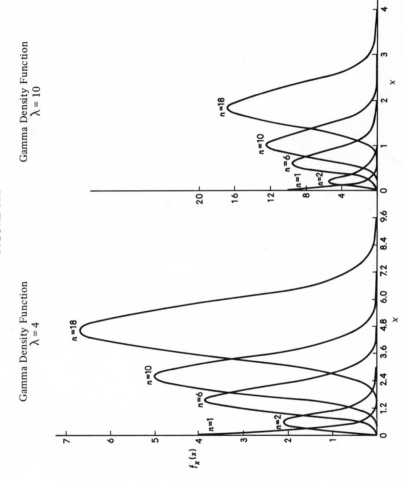

Gamma Density Function
λ = 4

Gamma Density Function
λ = 10

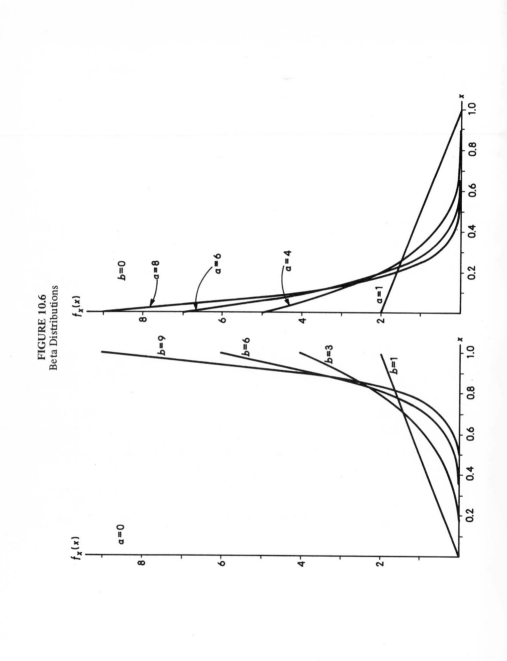

FIGURE 10.6
Beta Distributions

FIGURE 10.7
Beta Distributions

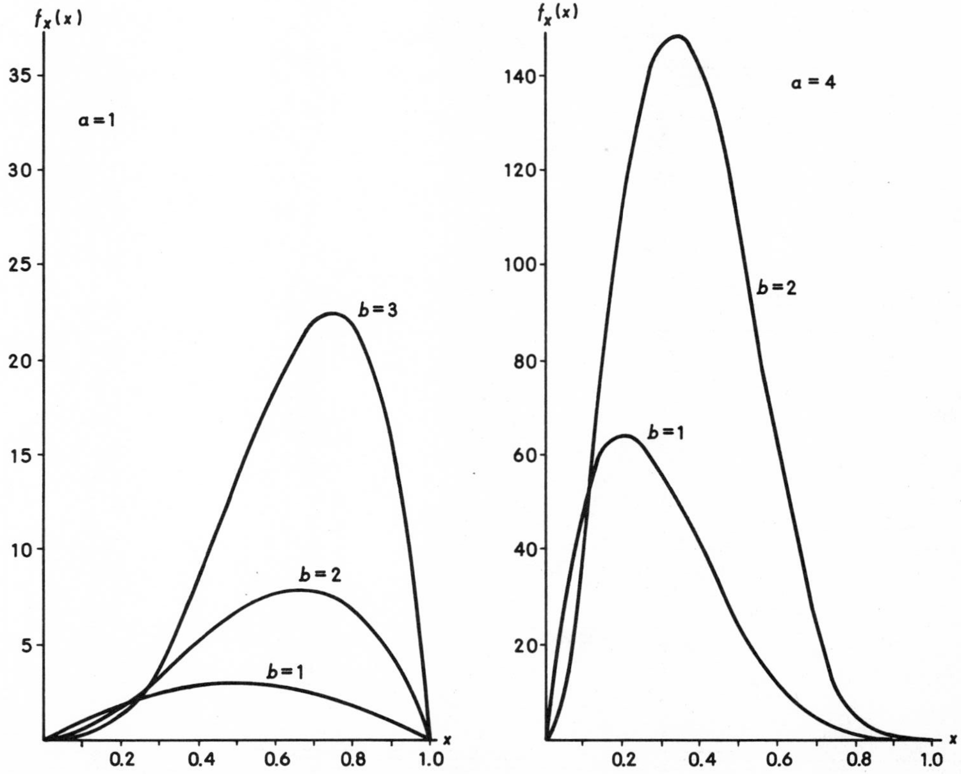

FIGURE 10.8
Binomial Distributions

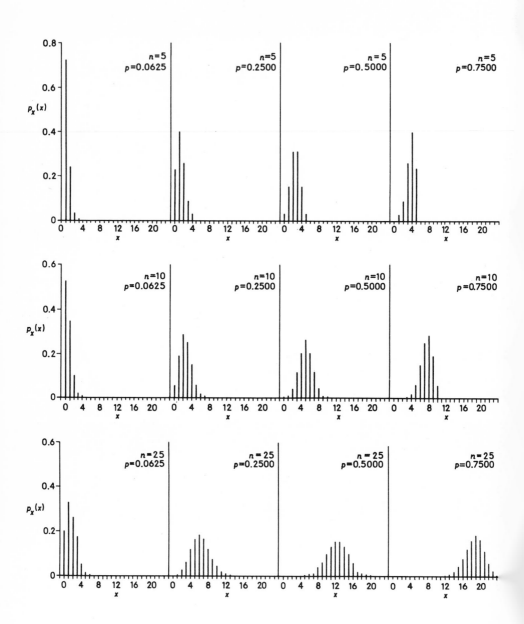

FIGURE 10.9
Poisson Distributions

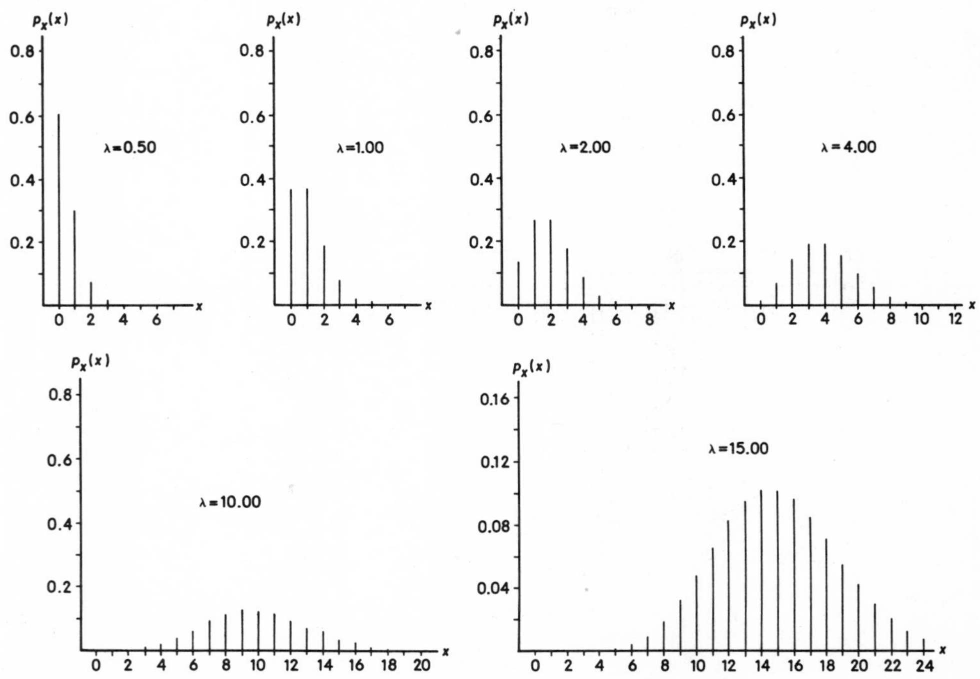

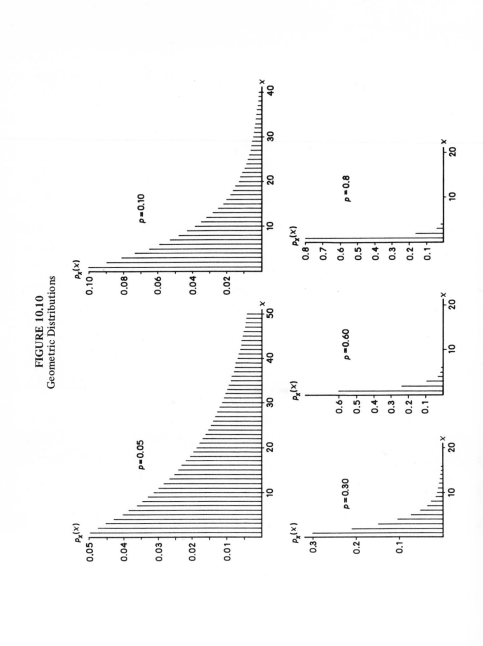

FIGURE 10.10
Geometric Distributions

Estimation of Distribution Parameters

Once the analyst has identified one or more distribution classes, gamma, normal, Poisson, geometric, etc., which he feels may adequately represent the variable he is studying, he must then determine the numerical values of the distribution parameters to reduce the distribution class to a specific distribution. When the hypothesized distribution is a function of two parameters, he can usually estimate these parameters from the sample mean and sample variance. For example, let us estimate the sample mean and sample variance for the distributions given in Table 10.1. To compute the sample mean and variance from a frequency distribution we use equations (10.1) and (10.2) where m_i is the midpoint of the ith class interval, f_i is the frequency in that inverval, and n is the number of intervals. The calculations for $\bar{x}$ and s^2 are summarized in Table 10.2.

TABLE 10.2

Calculations for the Mean and Variance of Demand and Lead Time

Demand				Lead Time			
Interval Midpoint m_i	Frequency f_i	$m_i f_i$	$m_i^2 f_i$	Interval Midpoint m_i	Frequency f_i	$m_i f_i$	$m_i^2 f_i$
0	1	0	0	0.0025	5	0.0125	0.00003125
1	2	2	2	0.0075	21	0.1575	0.00118125
2	4	8	16	0.0125	24	0.3000	0.00375000
3	7	21	63	0.0175	10	0.1750	0.00306250
4	11	44	176	0.0225	13	0.2925	0.00658125
5	15	75	375	0.0275	9	0.2475	0.00680625
6	17	102	612	0.0325	9	0.2925	0.00950625
7	16	112	784	0.0375	3	0.1125	0.00421875
8	12	96	778	0.0425	2	0.0850	0.00361250
9	8	72	648	0.0475	1	0.0475	0.00225625
10	3	30	300	0.0525	2	0.1050	0.00551250
11	2	22	242	0.0575	1	0.0575	0.00330625
12	1	12	144	Total	100	1.8850	0.04982500
13	1	13	169				
Total	100	609	4309				

$$\bar{x} = \frac{\sum\limits_{i=1}^{n} m_i f_i}{\sum\limits_{i=1}^{n} f_i} \qquad (10.1)$$

$$s^2 = \frac{\sum\limits_{i=1}^{n} m_i^2 f_i - n\bar{x}^2}{\sum\limits_{i=1}^{n} f_i - 1} \tag{10.2}$$

The sample mean and variance of demand are given by

$$\bar{x} = \frac{609}{100}$$

$$= 6.09$$

$$s^2 = \frac{4309 - 100(6.09)^2}{99}$$

$$= 6.06$$

By similar calculations the sample mean and variance of lead time are given by

$$\bar{x} = \frac{1.8850}{100}$$

$$= 0.01885$$

$$s^2 = \frac{0.049825 - 100(0.01885)^2}{99}$$

$$= 0.000144$$

We note that the sample mean and variance of weekly demand are nearly equal. This relationship between the mean and variance strengthens our hypothesis that the distribution of demand is Poisson. In the next section we will test the hypothesis that demand is Poisson distributed with $\lambda = 6.09$.

As we have indicated in the previous section, Figure 10.2 suggests that lead time might be gamma distributed. If the parameters of the gamma distribution are μ and n then

$$\text{mean} = \frac{n}{\mu} \tag{10.3}$$

$$\text{variance} = \frac{n}{\mu^2} \tag{10.4}$$

To estimate the values of μ and n, $\bar{x}$ is set equal to n/μ and s^2 is set equal to n/μ^2.

$$\frac{n}{\mu} = 0.01885$$

$$\frac{n}{\mu^2} = 0.000144$$

Solving for μ and n yields

$$\mu = 130.90$$
$$n = 2.47$$

In our discussion of the gamma distribution in Chapter 2 we pointed out that n does not have to be an integer and we might choose to use the values of μ and n given above. For simplicity in handling the gamma distribution we could restrict n to an integer value, either two or three, in which case we would have the following two solutions:

$$n = 2 \Rightarrow \mu = 106.10$$
$$n = 3 \Rightarrow \mu = 158.63$$

The method we have offered here for the estimation of distribution parameters relates the sample mean and variance to the theoretical mean and variance of the proposed distribution. This approach is adequate as long as there are only two parameters to be estimated and as long as the mean and variance of the hypothesized distribution are defined. If the distribution is a function of three or more parameters, we could compute the third, fourth, and so on sample moments about zero and relate these to the corresponding moments for the hypothesized probability distribution. We calculate the jth sample moment about zero, M_j, from a frequency distribution of observed data by

$$M_j = \frac{\sum_{i=1}^{n} f_i m_i^j}{\sum_{i=1}^{n} f_i} \tag{10.5}$$

where m_i, f_i, and n are as previously defined. If $f_x(x)$ is the density function that we are going to attempt to use to represent the random variable with which we are concerned, then the jth moment is given by (10.6)

$$E(x^j) = \int_x x^j f_x(x)\, dx \tag{10.6}$$

or for a discrete random variable

$$E(x^j) = \sum_x x^j p_X(x) \qquad (10.7)$$

Letting

$$M_3 = E(x^3) \qquad (10.8)$$

we have a third equation which, combined with the previous equations relating the sample and population mean and the sample and population variance, allows us to estimate three distribution parameters where necessary.

Testing the Probability Distribution

Having hypothesized that a random variable is characterized by a specific probability distribution, we are left with the task of determining whether this hypothesis, which at best is usually nothing more that an educated guess, is valid. To accomplish this we can compare the hypothesized distribution with that which was experimentally derived through application of either the Kolmogorov-Smirnov or the chi-square goodness-of-fit tests. We will illustrate this procedure by example. Suppose that demand per hour was recorded for 1,000 hours and summarized as in Table 10.3. The mean and variance of hourly demand are given by

$$\text{mean} = 0.455$$
$$\text{variance} = 0.418$$

Plotting the relative frequency distribution of hourly demand and comparing it with Figures 10.8 and 10.9, we might conclude that demand is either Poisson or binomially distributed. From Table 2.1 we have

Poisson:

$$\text{mean} = \lambda$$
$$\text{variance} = \lambda$$

Binomial:

$$\text{mean} = np$$
$$\text{variance} = np(1 - p)$$

According to our observation, the mean and variance of hourly demand are not equal, which might lead us to reject the Poisson as an

TABLE 10.3
Hourly Demand Distribution

Hourly Demand	Frequency
0	650
1	270
2	60
3	15
4	5
5	0
	1000

FIGURE 10.11
Relative Frequency Distribution of Demand

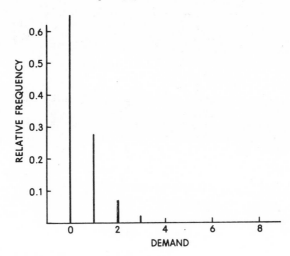

adequate representation of the demand distribution. However, since the sample mean and variance are so close, we will continue to consider the Poisson as a possibility and let λ equal the average of the sample mean and variance, or $\lambda = 0.437$.

For the binomial we have

$$np = 0.455$$
$$np(1 - p) = 0.418$$

Solving for n and p, we get

$$p = 0.08$$
$$n = 5.7$$

Since n must be an integer, we will try $n = 5$ ($p = 0.091$) and $n = 6$ ($p = 0.076$). Therefore we have narrowed our search for a probability distribution down to three possibilities:

$$\text{Poisson:} \quad \lambda = 0.437$$
$$\text{Binomial:} \quad n = 5, p = 0.091$$
$$\text{Binomial:} \quad n = 6, p = 0.076$$

The application here of the Kolmogorov-Smirnov test is identical to that in Chapter 6. The calculations for this test are summarized in Table 10.4.

TABLE 10.4
Kolmogorov–Smirnov Test for the Distribution of Demand

Demand Category	Observed Cumulative Distribution	Hypothesized Cumulative Distribution		
		Poisson	Binomial $n = 5$	Binomial $n = 6$
0	0.650	0.646	0.621	0.622
1	0.920	0.928	0.932	0.929
2	0.980	0.990	0.994	0.990
3	0.995	0.999	1.000	0.997
4	1.000	1.000	1.000	1.000
5 and above	1.000	1.000	1.000	1.000
D_{max}		0.010	0.029	0.028

Letting $\alpha = 0.05$, we have

$$D_{0.95} = \frac{1.36}{\sqrt{1,000}}$$

$$= 0.043$$

Since $D_{max} < D_{0.95}$ for all three distributions we might use any one of these distributions to describe demand. However, since the value of D_{max} is the least in the Poisson distribution, we would probably use the Poisson distribution to describe hourly demand.

The reader should not conclude from this example that probability distributions are always so easily determined. Often many man-hours are consumed in attempting to find a probability distribution which reliably describes the random variable under study. Such attempts frequently end without acceptable results. When the analyst finds that none of the distributions with which he is familiar fits the observed distribution, he may find that he can use the observed distribution itself. For the example just discussed this distribution would be specified by (10.9).

$$p_X(x) = \begin{cases} 0.650, & x = 0 \\ 0.270, & x = 1 \\ 0.060, & x = 2 \\ 0.015, & x = 3 \\ 0.005, & x = 4 \\ 0.000, & x \geq 5 \end{cases} \qquad (10.9)$$

The reader might wonder why such observed distributions are not always used; thus eliminating the need to search further for a probability distribution. Returning to our example, the reader will notice that adoption of the observed distribution would eliminate the possibility of five or more demands in any hour, as specified in equation (10.9). However, if we use the Poisson distribution a chance exists, although slight, that five or more demands will occur in any hour. In this case, unless there was reason to believe that more than four demands could not occur in any hour, we would probably use the Poisson distribution. In general, the observed distribution would be used only if the analyst felt that it reflected the variable's true range of variation.

To conclude our discussion of probability distributions, let us consider the case where the analyst finds that he cannot use the observed distribution for the purpose of process generation and that those theoretical distributions with which he is familiar are inappropriate. As an illustration of this situation consider the following example:

Example 10.1

A forester is involved in a simulation study in which he will have to generate the number of clear-cut areas per sale in national forests in the Appalachian region. To clarify the problem, when a logging company purchases timber in a national forest, it may purchase the timber in more than one area. That is, the sale may consist of all the trees in several separated areas. If the areas are to be clear-cut, the logger takes out all trees in each area as opposed to thinning, in which he would remove only a certain proportion of the trees in each area. The forester has gathered the data in Table 10.5.

If the forester uses an empirical distribution based upon the observed data, he will eliminate the possibility of generating four or six clear-cut areas per sale. On the other hand, let us assume that those theoretical distributions with which he is familiar fail to adequately describe the variability in this random variable. Then the

TABLE 10.5

Clear Cut Areas/Sale	Frequency
1	3
2	2
3	4
4	0
5	8
6	0
7	7
8	6
9	4
10	2

forester would be well advised to use the empirical process generator given in equation (7.84), and avoid further attempts at fitting a distribution. To assess the validity of this process generator he should compare the generated values with the observed values. The reader will note that through equation (7.84) a probability of occurrence of four and six areas per sale would be assigned and weighted by the observed frequencies for four and six and by the frequencies of occurrence of the remaining values. Therefore equation (7.84) will tend to smooth out the distribution function.

VALIDATING THE SIMULATOR

Implicit in our discussion of simulation has been the assumption that the simulator works, carrying out the necessary calculations in a valid manner. However, even the novice programmer knows that such an assumption is suspect at best. A computer simulation program may fail to attain its purpose either because of coding errors or errors in logic. Errors of the first type are detected with relative facility since they usually negate execution of the program. In user-oriented programming languages, these errors are usually accompanied by diagnostic "error messages" describing the nature of the error, thereby indicating the remedial action required.

Logical errors are more troublesome. In this context, a logical error occurs when the program functions but fails to obtain correct results. Normally such errors are detected by comparing computer output with hand calculations. However, the very purpose of simulation can rule out complete comparisons of this kind. As we have already pointed out, simulation is often used as an alternative to mathematical analysis. Having no mathematical model with which to compare simulated results, we must take one of several alternative courses of action. First, we might have the program print out each calculation which it performs and verify these calculations by hand. Obviously this is a tedious process, but it may be the only available alternative. This is frequently the case when simulating proposed systems, such as traffic flow on a proposed highway, the effect of changes in plant layout, the incremental profit derived from a change in airline scheduling, and so forth.

A second and less monotonous technique may be applied in the validation process when simulating an existing system. This consists of simulating present conditions and comparing the results with those obtained from observation of the physical system. Verification on this basis would imply only that the simulator reliably describes the functioning of the system under present conditions. However, this provides no guarantee that the simulator will prove as useful in predicting how the system will function under modified conditions. A primary candidate for the cause of such simulation failures is the simplifying assumption which works today but not tomorrow. The following examples will illustrate how such problems can arise.

Example 10.2

For several years a quality control department had been carrying out an inspection program which consisted of selecting eight units of product per hour from each production line. Each unit was inspected, and the number of defects recorded. The defects were of the attributes type, and their identification was largely a matter of subjective judgment on the part of the inspector. When an inspector found what he considered to be too many defective units, the source of the difficulty was investigated and the required corrective action taken on the production line. However, rejection of the lot manufactured during that hour we never called for and was considered outside the realm of responsibility of the quality control department.

In 1964 one of the company's customers initiated an incoming quality control program which called for return to the supplier of any production lots which failed to pass that inspection. The cost of return transportation was to be borne by the supplier. As a defense against the effect of the customer's inspection progam the quality control department was charged with the responsibility of developing and implementing an out-the-door inspection program to prevent the shipment of lots of inferior quality. Further, the quality control department was to be held responsible for any lots rejected by the customer.

Through simulation, a minimum cost sampling plan was developed. The distribution of proportion defective per lot was obtained from the data collected in previous years by the quality control department. It seemed reasonable to assume that the rate of occurrence of defectives would not increase in view of continuing efforts to improve product quality.

Soon after the inspection system was implemented it became apparent that the rate of lot rejections before shipment far exceeded that which had been anticipated. Evidently the rate of production of defective units had increased, contrary to expectations. However, further investigation proved that this was not true. The quality control inspectors, having been told that they were responsible for finding bad lots, did so with a vengeance. Therefore the problem was not a change in quality but a change in the attitude of the inspectors.

This example demonstrates what can happen when the analyst fails to recognize possible interactions between a system and its environment. Although such interactions are not at all unusual, they are difficult to foresee, and even when they are recognized their effect can be virtually impossible to measure. However, simple recognition that a problem of this nature may arise should serve as a warning to the analyst that flexibility should be a part of his proposed solution. In planning for unpredictable conditions it is always useful to allow for a testing period in which a "dry run" can be made to determine the adequacy of the proposed solution.

In the example just discussed the analyst failed to consider the full impact of the customer's inspection system in making the quality control department responsible for substandard product which reached the customer. Without realizing it, he was assuming that the customer's plan would have no effect on the inspectors. Let us now look at a case where the assumption is expressed rather than implicit.

Example 10.3

This example is an extension of example 10.2. The customer's quality control plan was actually designed to control three classes of defects: minor, major, and critical. A production lot received by the customer could be rejected on any one or more of these defects. In the simulation analysis discussed in the above example, it was found that customer rejections were likely only on critical defects. The analyst decided to drop inspection for minor and major defects out of the simulator, realizing significant savings in the time required for the simulation of the inspection systems which he investigated.

Eighteen months later the customer issued tightened quality standards for all three defect categories. Presuming that the customer's standard could still be met with respect to minor and major defects, the analyst used the same simulator, which considered only critical defects, to assess the effect of the tightened standards. The results of this investigation indicated that the proposed standards would be very difficult to meet with respect to critical defects. This situation might have drawn the attention of the quality control department to further consideration of the other two defect categories but, in fact, had the opposite effect. Realizing the significant effect which the change in standards would have regarding critical defects, the department concentrated its attention on resolving this problem while unwittingly pushing further consideration of major and minor defects into the background. Success was achieved in persuading the customer to relax his requirements in the critical category, and the standards for minor and major were accepted without much discussion. The result of the analyst's assumption was that major defects became troublesome, as did minor defects to a lesser extent.

Although some assumptions are unavoidable in all investigations of the type discussed in this book, it is wise to avoid those which are unnecessarily restrictive. Where assumptions must be made, they should be recorded explicitly. Conclusions drawn from the study should then be weighted according to the credibility of the assumptions included. Where time and budget permit, a sensitivity analysis is useful in assessing the effects of violations of the assumptions. For example, suppose that an inventory system had been proposed, based on the assumption that annual demand for coming year would be λ. To determine how sensitive the system is to error in the prediction of demand for the coming year, the analyst might test the inventory system, assuming an error in prediction of $\Delta\lambda$. The procedure for carrying out this test is as follows:

1. Simulate the proposed system, assuming demand $\lambda \pm \Delta\lambda$, and evaluate the resulting cost.
2. By simulation determine the optimal system design for demand $\lambda \pm \Delta\lambda$, and evaluate the resulting cost.
3. Compare the costs of the proposed and optimal systems when demand is $\lambda \pm \Delta\lambda$ to determine the loss incurred by adherence to the proposed system when demand changes by $\Delta\lambda$.

Since an appropriate mathematical model would usually take precedence over simulation as an analytic tool, we might assume that whenever simulation is used for this purpose no mathematical model is available which might be used to check the results of the simulator. However, this is only partially true. To illustrate this point suppose we are faced with the problem of analyzing a single channel queueing problem for which the time between successive arrivals has a Chi-square distribution and service time is F distributed. In all other respects the system resembles that described in Chapter 3. Although development of a mathematical model to represent this system would not be impossible, it would be difficult. Referring to the single server simulator developed in Chapter 8, we see that the overall functioning of the simulator is not dependent upon the distribution of interarrival time or service time, except that these variables must be generated in some manner. That is, we could replace the exponential process generators by whatever process generators seemed appropriate without altering the remainder of the program. To verify the logic of the program we need only to insert exponential interarrival time and service time process generators and compare the output of the simulator with that predicted by theory. If the simulator functions properly for these distributions, it should also function properly for other distributions, providing the associated process generators are reliable.

For the purpose of the logic check the most reliable comparisons result from comparing simulated and theoretical probability distributions instead of simply comparing parameter estimates with theoretical values. Consider the following frequency distribution of total time in the system generated by the single channel simulator developed in Chapter 8. The distribution is based upon 2,803 units through the system where the mean arrival rate, λ was 0.00033 per second and the mean service rate, μ, was 0.00867 per second. Based upon the discussion of single channel queueing systems in Chapter 3, total time in the system should be exponentially distributed with mean $1/(\mu - \lambda)$.

From equation (3.55), total time in the system, t, has the density function

$$f_T(t) = (\mu - \lambda)e^{-(\mu - \lambda)t} \tag{10.10}$$

and the cumulative distribution function is given by

$$F_T(t) = 1 - e^{-(\mu - \lambda)t} \tag{10.11}$$

TABLE 10.6
Frequency Distribution of Total Time in the
System for a Single Channel Queueing System
$(\lambda = .00033, \mu = .00867)$

Time Interval Seconds	Frequency	Cumulative Frequency
0–30	614	614
31–60	489	1103
61–90	399	1502
91–120	305	1807
121–150	227	2034
151–180	171	2205
181–210	120	2325
211–240	95	2420
241–270	98	2518
271–∞	285	2803

or in this case

$$F_T(t) = 1 - e^{-0.008345} \qquad (10.12)$$

Comparing the observed with the theoretical distributions of time in the system using the Kolmolgorov-Smirnov test for $\alpha = 0.10$ leads to the calculations given in Table 10.7.

TABLE 10.7

Kolmolgorov-Smirnov Test for the Comparison of the
Theoretical and Observed Distribution of Time in the System

Time Interval Seconds	Observed Relative Cumulative Distribution Function	Hypothesized Relative Cumulative Distribution Function-Equation (10.12)	$\lvert D \rvert$
0–30	0.219	0.221	0.002
31–60	0.393	0.393	0.000
61–90	0.535	0.528	0.007
91–120	0.644	0.632	0.012
121–150	0.725	0.713	0.012
151–180	0.786	0.777	0.009
181–210	0.829	0.826	0.003
211–240	0.863	0.865	0.002
241–270	0.898	0.895	0.003
271–∞	1.000	1.000	0.000

$D_{0.10} = \dfrac{1.22}{\sqrt{2,803}} = 0.023$

Since the maximum difference, 0.012, is less than $D_{0.10}$, we conclude that the simulator is functioning correctly with respect to the calculations necessary in computing total time in the system. A similar analysis should be conducted to verify the logic by which the distributions of time in the queue, the number of persons in the system, and so forth, are computed.

Frequently mathematical models describing systems which are modifications of that under study are available. However, these models may not provide probability distributions such as those discussed in the above queueing problem. For instance, suppose that a simulation model has been developed to study the behavior or a reorder point inventory system with lost sales, under various demand and lead time distributions. A mathematical model for this system was derived in Chapter 4 for constant lead time. From this model we could obtain the expected annual inventory carrying cost, ordering cost, and lost sales cost. However, the distribution of these annual costs are not given and will be presumed to be unavailable. Our check on the performance of the simulator will be its ability to estimate the three expected annual costs mentioned when the lead time is zero. Ten years of operation are simulated assuming a reorder point of 3 and an order quantity of 15. The remaining conditions under which the simulation was conducted are the same as those described in example 4.13. The results obtained from the simulation are given in Table 10.8. The expected costs given in this table were derived from equation (4.126).

Since 10 observations are included in each average, it is appropriate to assume that these averages are normally distributed. Based

TABLE 10.8

Ten Years Simulation of a Reorder Point Inventory Model with
Lost Sales, Constant Lead Time, Poisson Demand, $r = 3$ and $Q = 15$

Year	Inventory Carrying Cost	Ordering Cost	Lost Sales Cost	Total Cost
1	$427.00	$5,100.00	$490.00	$6,017.00
2	433.00	5,400.00	210.00	6,043.00
3	410.00	6,300.00	490.00	7,200.00
4	451.00	5,400.00	560.00	6,411.00
5	439.00	5,700.00	420.00	6,559.00
6	435.00	6,000.00	840.00	7,275.00
7	408.00	6,000.00	1,120.00	7,528.00
8	435.00	5,700.00	210.00	6,345.00
9	437.00	5,400.00	420.00	6,257.00
10	440.00	5,700.00	280.00	6,420.00
Average Cost	$431.50	$5,670.00	$504.00	$6,605.50
Expected Cost	$433.60	$5,836.00	$566.00	$6,835.00

on this assumption, the t test would be appropriate for the comparison of the estimated costs with the expected costs. The experimental t statistic is given by

$$t_{exp} = \frac{\bar{x} - \mu}{s/\sqrt{n}} \tag{10.13}$$

where n is the sample size (10), $\bar{x}$ is the average cost, μ is the corresponding expected cost, and s is the sample standard deviation and is defined as

$$s = \sqrt{\frac{\sum_{i=1}^{n} x_i^2 - n\bar{x}^2}{n - 1}} \tag{10.14}$$

with the result

$$s = \begin{cases} 13.32, & \text{Inventory carrying cost} \\ 357.63, & \text{Ordering cost} \\ 285.39, & \text{Lost sales cost} \end{cases}$$

Testing at $\alpha = 0.05$, $t_{0.975}$ (9) = 2.262 and $t_{0.025}$ (9) = −2.262. The experimental t values are as follows:

$$t_{exp} = \begin{cases} -0.356 & \text{Inventory carrying cost} \\ -1.459 & \text{Ordering cost} \\ -0.687 & \text{Lost sales cost} \end{cases}$$

Since $t_{0.025}$ (9) $< t_{exp} < t_{0.975}$ (9) in all three cases, we would conclude that the simulator is functioning properly as far as its ability to estimate these three costs is concerned. If the simulator works for zero lead time, it should also work for nonzero and stochastic lead times.

In the example just discussed, we assumed that if the simulator works for zero lead time, it will also function when lead time is not zero. Such an assumption would not have been warranted had we been dealing with a system where stock-outs result in back orders rather than in lost sales. As we mentioned in Chapter 4, orders may cross when lead time is stochastic and when stock-outs produce back orders. Since orders may cross, the ability of the simulator to handle such a contingency should be verified. The analyst could run the simulator until a case is encountered where two orders cross and check the simulator at that point. However, this procedure might require an extensive, and therefore expensive, run. Let us consider a more efficient approach.

Consider a periodic review inventory system with back orders where T is the time between successive reviews. Let t_n be the lead time at which the nth order was placed, and let Υ_n be the time of arrival of the nth order. One method of checking the mechanics of the simulator when orders cross is to generate orders in such a way that the first k are received in the reverse of the order in which they were placed. To accomplish this we define T large enough that it is virtually certain that an order will be placed at every review. If we define t_n as

$$t_n = \begin{cases} (2k - 2n + 1)T, & n \le k \\ kT, & n > k \end{cases} \qquad (10.15)$$

and

$$\Upsilon_b = t_n + nT \qquad (10.16)$$

then orders will arrive in the sequence shown in Table 10.9, guaranteeing that the first k orders placed will be received in reverse order and allowing the analyst to check the performance of the simulator when the orders cross:

TABLE 10.9

n	t_n	Υ_n
1 . . .	$(2k - 1)T$	$2kT$
2 . . .	$(2k - 3)T$	$(2k - 1)T$
3 . . .	$(2k - 5)T$	$(2k - 2)T$
4 . . .	$(2k - 7)T$	$(2k - 3)T$
$\vdots$	$\vdots$	$\vdots$
$k - 1$	$3T$	$(k - 2)T$
k	T	$(k + 1)T$
$k + 1$	kT	$(2k + 1)T$
$k + 2$	kT	$(2k + 2)T$

Although most systems are not so easily reduced to mathematical models, it is often possible to segment the system in such a way that each segment, perhaps in modified form, can be checked against an available mathematical model. However, when checking the performance of a simulator in parts, it is important to verify the linkage connecting each part. Finally, the analyst might choose to reduce all random variables to constants, or at least predictable values, and compare the simulated results with those derived from the corresponding deterministic model. Although conceptually simple, this method of validation may prove tedious, requiring the analyst to consider many alternative combinations of variable values to be sure that all possibilities are covered.

PROBLEMS

1. During the course of the development of a system for maintaining an adequate supply of photographic film, a photo supply dealer conducted a one-month study of demand for 620 film. The data collected during this period is as follows: Assume that film is demanded one roll at a time.

Day of the Month	Demand	Day of the Month	Demand
1	1	16	2
2	2	17	1
3	5	18	6
4	3	19	3
5	3	20	7
6	2	22	3
8	3	23	3
9	6	24	2
10	6	25	2
11	3	26	6
12	3	27	8
13	3	29	5
1ᶜ	4	30	8

Using the Chi-square goodness-of-fit test with $\alpha = 0.05$ to determine the distribution of demand, develop a process generator for the time between successive demands.

2. The following data was collected on order lead time (days) during the past three years:

Order No.	Lead Time	Order No.	Lead Time
1	3.8	21	3.8
2	3.7	22	4.5
3	2.9	23	3.1
4	3.6	24	4.7
5	3.0	25	5.1
6	5.6	26	5.4
7	3.3	27	5.8
8	3.9	28	5.4
9	5.0	29	4.4
10	4.7	30	3.9
11	3.3	31	6.4
12	2.9	32	3.1
13	5.5	33	4.5
14	3.3	34	4.7
15	4.3	35	4.8
16	4.7	36	3.2
17	3.3	37	4.9
18	3.9	38	3.0
19	4.2	39	4.8
20	4.4	40	4.5

Derive a process generator for lead time based upon this data.

3. Draw 300 consecutive telephone numbers out of your local telephone directory and record the last four digits. Using the Kolmogorov-Smirnov test with $\alpha = 0.10$, determine whether the numbers formed by the last four digits are uniformly distributed between 0 and 9999.

4. One thousand units were selected at random from each of 30 production lots which were also selected at random. The number of minor defects found in each sample is recorded below. Develop a process generator for lot proportion defective for minor defectives.

Lot No.	Defects	Lot No.	Defects
1	4	16	74
2	34	17	39
3	14	18	28
4	27	19	12
5	4	20	19
6	62	21	21
7	18	22	23
8	38	23	48
9	28	24	15
10	20	25	43
11	50	26	11
12	74	27	22
13	39	28	32
14	21	29	16
15	12	30	25

5. The XYZ Company plans to study its shipping practices through simulation. One of the products involved is shipped to customers by truck. However, more than one truckload may be shipped at a time. The following data has been recorded on the number of truckloads per shipment.

Truckloads/Shipments	Frequency
1	77
2	90
3	35
4	8
5	1

Develop a process generator for the number of trucks required per shipment.

6. One hundred defective units of product were examined to determine the distribution of the number of defects present per defective unit of product. The results are recorded below. Develop a process generator for this random variable.

Defects/Defective Unit	Frequency
1	82
2	12
3	5
4	1

7. The following program is said to generate chi-square random variables where N is the number of variables generated. Would you agree?

```
  READ1, N, IX
1 FORMAT(1X2I5)
  DO 2 I=1, N
  X = 0
  DO 3 J = 1, 10
  R = RANDU(IX,IY)
3 X = X + (-2)*ALOG(1.-R)
2 PRINT 4, X
4 FORMAT (1XF10.4)
  STOP
  END
```

8. If r_1 and r_2 are uniformly distributed random variables on the interval $(0,1)$, then the pairs of random variables X_1 and X_2 are said to have a unit normal distribution, where

$$X_1 = (-2 \ln r_1)^{1/2} \cos 2\pi r_2$$
$$X_2 = (-2 \ln r_1)^{1/2} \sin 2\pi r_2$$

Write a program to generate N pairs of these variables and test the hypothesis that they follow a unit normal distribution.

9. The following program is supposed to generate exponentially distributed random variables where A is the parameter of the exponential distribution and N is the number of variables generated. Generate 100 values and test the hypothesis that the variables are exponentially distributed.

```
  READ 1, A, N, IX
1 FORMAT (1XF10.4, 2I5)
  DO 2 I = 1, N
6 Q = RANDU(IX,IY)
  SUM = 0
  M = 1
5 SUM = SUM + RANDU (IX,IY)
  IF(SUM-Q) 3,3,4
3 M = M+1
  GO TO 5
4 M1 = M-2*(M/2)
  IF (M1)6,6,7
7 X = A*Q
2 PRINT 1,X
  STOP
  END
```

10. Would you accept the assertion that the following program generates

geometrically distributed random variables, X, where P is the parameter of the geometric distribution? N is the number of variables generated.

```
   READ 1,P,IX,N
1  FORMAT(1XF10.4,2I5)
   DO 2 I=1,N
   M=1
5  R=RANDU(IX,IY)
 · IF(R−P)3,3,4
4  M=M+1
   GO TO 5
3  X=M
2  PRINT 1,X
   STOP
   END
```

11. Let $Z_1, Z_2, \ldots, Z_n$ be normally and independently distributed random variables, each with mean 10 and variance unity. Show, by simulation, that X does not have a Chi-square distribution with n degrees of freedom, where

$$X = \sum_{i=1}^{n} Z_i^2$$

12. Let T be a t random variable with q degrees of freedom. Show, by simulation, that X has an F distribution with one, and q degrees of freedom where $X = T^2$.

13. Write a program to simulate the system discussed in example 5.3. Using the t test with $\alpha = 0.10$, compare the simulated avarage number of failures per year and the average downtime per year with values derived by the following:

$$E(\text{Number of failures per year}) = \frac{n\lambda u}{nu + \lambda}$$

$$E(\text{Downtime per year}) = \frac{\lambda}{nu + \lambda}$$

14. The quality control department has adopted a sampling plan for lots which are received from an outside supplier. Units are selected one at a time from the lot. If two defective items are found, the lot is rejected. If the number of defective items found after 10 inspections is zero or one, the lot is accepted. The lot proportion defective, P, is beta distributed with $a = 10$, $b = 0$. That is,

$$f_P(p) = (a + 1)(1 - p)^a, \qquad 0 < p < 1$$

The probability that X defective units will be contained in a sample of size 10, given a lot proportion defective p, is given by

$$p_X(x \mid 10, p) = \binom{10}{x} p^x (1 - p)^{10-x}, \qquad x = 0, 1, \ldots, 10$$

Each inspection costs $1.. The expected cost of inspection has been estimated to be $8.50 per lot inspected. By simulation determine whether or not this estimate can be accepted. Use the t test and let $\alpha = 0.05$.

15. In Chapter 4 in the discussion of reorder point inventory systems with back orders and stochastic demand, it was stated that the distribution of inventory position was uniform with density function

$$P_{r+j} = \frac{1}{Q}, \qquad j = 1, 2, \ldots, Q$$

when units are demanded one at a time. Assume the same system except that either one or two units may be requested per demand with equal probability. Let the number of demands per time period be Poisson distributed with mean annual rate of 400 units. The reordering policy will be such that an order is placed whenever inventory position reaches or falls below r. The reorder quantity is Q. Notice the j still assumes values between one and Q inclusive. However, when an order is placed, inventory position may be either $r + Q$ or $r + Q - 1$. If inventory position is at $r + 1$ and a demand for two units occurs, an order is placed for Q units, raising inventory position to $r + Q - 1$ instead of $r + Q$.

By simulation, determine whether the distribution of inventory position is still uniform. Use the Kolmogorov-Smirnov test with $\alpha = 0.10$.

16. Solve problem 15 for the case where the number of units requested per demand is geometrically distributed with $p = 0.2$.

17. A pulp mill occasionally purchases wood chips from a nearby logging firm. The chips have not been debarked when they are received at the pulp mill. The mill cannot use the chips until the bark content is reduced to or below 1 pei cent by weight. Upon their arrival at the mill, the chips contain 20 per cent bark by weight, and this percentage is relatively constant. The pulp mill is considering the purchase of a recently developed debarking process. The company which developed the debarking process claims that the bark content in the chips can be reduced below 1 per cent in two passes. The purchased chips are fed into the debarking process upon their arrival at the mill. If the process fails to bring the bark content down to or below 1 per cent, the entire shipment of chips is fed through the debarking process again. The chips are reprocessed over and over until the bark content falls below 1 per cent. Available information indicates that the proportion of bark removed per pass is uniformly distributed between 0.7 and 0.95. By simulation determine whether the manufacturer's claim is justified. Use a t test with $\alpha = 0.05$. Simulate 100 chip lots, recording the number of passes required per lot to reduce the bark content of the lot to 1 per cent or less.

18. Solve problem 17 where the initial bark content is a random variable which is exponentially distributed with mean bark content 0.20.

19. A manufacturer produces a particular plastic bottle at a rate of 200 per

hour. The probability, p, that a bottle is defective varies with density function given by

$$f_P(p) = 201 \ (1 - p)^{200}, 0 < p < 1$$

The quality control department assumes that the distribution of lot proportion defective is normal where a lot equals one hour's production. Simulate 100 hours production as follows:

1. For each bottle produced, generate the probability, p, that it is defective.
2. Generate a random number r and compare it to p to determine if the bottle is actually defective.
3. Repeat steps 1 and 2 for 100 hours, 200 bottles per hour, and record the hourly proportion defective.
4. Using the Chi-square test, $\alpha = 0.01$, determine whether the quality control department's assumption is valid.

20. The following simulator was developed for the problem given in example 5.9:

```
      READ 1, CI,CR,CD,AL,A,N,IC,NSIM,IX,ECI,ECR,ECD,ETOT,EP,MSIM
1     FORMAT(1X5F6.2,4I8/1X4F12.3,F10.6,I8)
      B=1./(A+1.)
      AN=N
      COSTI=CI*AN
      ECI=COSTI
      DO 2 I=1,NSIM
      IDEF=0
      R=RANDU(IX,IY)
      P=(1.-R)**B
      AI=I+MSIM
      DO 3 J=1,N
      R=RANDU(IX,IY)
      IF(R-P)6,6,3
6     IDEF=IDEF+1
3     CONTINUE
      IF(IDEF-IC) 7,7,8
7     COSTA = CD*(AL-AN)*P
      COSTR=0
      GO TO 4
8     COSTA = 0
      COSTR=CR*(AL-AN)
4     ECD=((AI-1.)*ECD+COSTA)/AI
      ECR = ((AI-1.)*ECR+COSTR)/AI
      COST=COSTI + COSTA + COSTR
      ETOT = ((AI-1.)*ETOT + COST)/AI
      EP=((AI-1.)*EP+P)/AI
```

```
    PRINT 5,I,COSTI,COSTA,COSTR,COST,ECI,ECD,ECR,ETOT,P.EP
5   FORMAT(1XI6,8F12.2,2F12.8)
2   CONTINUE
    STOP
    END
```

CI = Unit cost of inspection.

CR = Cost of each unit in a rejected lot.

CD = Cost of each defective unit in an accepted lot.

A   = Parameter of the beta distribution.

AL = Lot size.

N   = Sample size.

IC = Acceptance number.

ECI,ECR,ECD,ETOT = Cumulative average costs of inspection, rejection, acceptance, and total cost per lot.

P = Lot proportion defective.

EP = Cumulative average lot proportion defective.

NSIM = Number of lot inspections to be simulated.

IX = Initial random number.

MSIM = Previous number of lot inspections simulated. (The values of ECI, ECR,ECD,ETOT,EP read in are those resulting from the first MSIM lot simulations. If there is no prior simulation, these values are zero, as is MSIM.)

IDEF = Number of defective units found in a given inspection.

P = Lot proportion defective, beta distributed with parameters a and $b = 0$.

COSTI, COSTR, COSTA, COST = Cost of inspection, rejection, acceptance, and total cost for a given lot.

Given the information in example 5.9, determine whether this simulator provides results which correspond to those given by equation (5.59). In particular, using the t test, compare the expected costs of inspection, rejection, and acceptance given by the simulator and the mathematical model when $N = 149$ and $IC = 12$. If the simulator proves unreliable, find the source of the trouble in the simulator.

21. Write a simulation program for the problem discussed in example 5.14. However, assume that lot size is a random variable which is normally distributed with mean 100,000 units and standard deviation 10,000 units. Check the results of the simulator against those given in example 5.14 by initially generating constant lot sizes of 100,000. By comparing the simulated costs of inspection, rejection, and acceptance when lot size is normally distributed with the results in example 5.14, determine whether the mathematical model given in equation (5.82) is appropriate if L is defined as the mean lot size. That is, does the mean cost of the quality control system change for a given sampling plan, if lot size is considered a random variable rather than a constant? Does the variance of cost

per lot change? Use an F test to compare the variances of cost per lot when lot size is a constant and a normally distributed variable.

22. Write a simulation program to estimate the annual cost of the following quality control system. Lots of size L are inspected using a sampling plan with sample size N and acceptance number c. If the lot is rejected, it is 100 percent inspected at a cost of C_I per unit, and defective items are discarded at a cost C_R per unit. If it is accepted, it is shipped to a customer who also has an inspection plan. However, the customer does not inspect every lot. If he inspects the lot, he uses a sample of size M and an acceptance number of s. Submitted lots are inspected $100q$ percent of the time by the consumer. If the customer rejects the lot, it is returned to the supplier who pays the two-way cost of transportation, C_T per lot, and 100 percent inspects the lot to screen out defective items which are discarded as before at a cost C_R per unit. Lot proportion defective is beta distributed with $a = 100$, $b = 1$. Modify your simulator to check its performance against the model given in equation (5.67). What part or parts of the simulation does this modified version of the simulator fail to check?

23. A simulator has been developed to analyze the performance of a hospital blood bank. Whenever the number of units of blood on hand plus on order falls to or below r, an order is placed with the Red Cross for Q units. If a patient needs blood and there is an insufficient quantity on hand to supply his need, the remainder is obained from emergency donors, one unit from each donor. The blood back also receives blood from donors who come in at random and donate exactly one unit of blood. Lead time, the number of patients requiring blood, and the number of units required per patient are random variables. The simulator is to estimate the average annual unit-years of blood carried, the average annual number of emergency units required, the average number of units obtained from the Red Cross per year, and the average number of unsolicited units donated per year. What inventory system discussed in Chapter 4 most closely resembles the above blood bank inventory system, and how could this simulator be modified to check its results against that model?

24. A single channel queueing simulator has been developed which is similar to that given in Chapter 8 with two exceptions. The simulator deals with persons waiting at a department store counter for service. These people are not necessarily given service on a first-come first-serve basis. The following subroutine has been developed to select the next person for service:

```
SUBROUTINE NEXT (N,IX,J)
SUM = N*(N+1)/2
CUM = 0
R = RANDU(IX,IY)
DO 1 I=1, N
AN = N–I+1
CUM = CUM+AN/SUM
IF(R–CUM) 2,2,1
```

```
2  J = I
   GO TO 3
1  CONTINUE
3  RETURN
   END
```

In this subroutine

N = Number of people currently in the waiting line.

$$\text{Sum} = \sum_{i=1}^{N} i$$

I = Position of each person in the waiting line.

AN/SUM = Probability that the Ith person in the waiting line is serviced next (AN = N−I+1).

J = Position of the next person serviced.

Therefore if N = 5, SUM = 15 and

P(First person in the line is serviced next) = 5/15,

P(Second person in the line is serviced next) = 4/15,

and so forth.

If a customer in the waiting line finds that someone else farther back in the waiting line is given service before he (or she) is, he may become aggravated and leave the counter. The customer does not leave the line if the person serviced was in front of him. The simulator must record the number of customers lost for this reason. The probability that a customer leaves the counter is I/M where M is the number of persons waiting for service after a person has been selected for the next service and I is his position in the line.

How would you modify the simulator so that it could be checked against one of the models in Chapter 3? Determine a method for quickly checking the simulators ability to record lost customers and to adjust the positions of those customers waiting after lost customers have been accounted for.

25. In the problem described in example 4.11, the analyst would like to know the distribution of annual cost in addition to mean annual cost. Using the inventory simulator described in Chapter 9, simulate 400 years of operation calling for a printout every year (DELT = 1 and IPRINT = 1). Calculate a frequency distribution of annual cost and attempt to identify the density function of total annual cost.

26. Find the distribution of annual cost for the problem given in example 4.13, using the optimal operating policy derived in that example by simulating this policy for 400 years.

CHAPTER
11

DESIGN AND ANALYSIS OF
SIMULATION EXPERIMENTS

A simulator provides the systems analyst with a tool through which he can synthetically gather data describing the system under study. Similar data could be collected on the existing system. However, the number of conditions which could be studied and the volume of data obtained for each would normally be seriously limited. Although these limitations also apply to simulation, they are not nearly as restrictive. Therefore, given relative freedom in conducting the simulation experiment, the analyst must decide what conditions to simulate and how much time should be devoted to the simulation of each. The answers to these two questions constitute the design of the simulation experiment.

The design of the experiment depends upon the methodology to be used in analyzing the simulation results, which in turn depends upon the objectives of the simulation. For example, if the objective of the simulation is to estimate the total average annual cost of maintaining a specific inventory system, the form of the analysis would be different than it would be if the objective were to determine the operating policy which would minimize total annual cost. The former objective might be satisfied by constructing an appropriate confidence interval about the estimated average annual cost; the latter would require a search technique.

ESTIMATION THROUGH SIMULATION

In Chapter 10 we discussed the estimation of parameters of probability distributions. Basically we will pursue the same ideas here, expanding them to introduce the concept of estimator reliability. By the reliability of an estimate we mean the degree to which it accurately estimates the parameter of interest. For example, suppose it is known that daily consumption of gasoline by a fleet of trucks is normal with standard deviation 200 gallons, but the mean consumption, m, is not known. To estimate the mean, nine days are sampled at random, recording the consumption per day. Computing the sample mean, $\bar{x}_1$, indicates that an average of 10,060 gallons are consumed by the fleet per day. We might accept this estimate as the mean of the distribution. Suppose, however, we were to sample nine more days, again computing the sample mean, $\bar{x}_2$. We would probably find that $\bar{x}_1$ and $\bar{x}_2$ are not equal. Of course, this is due to the fact that $\bar{x}$ is a random variable. Combining the two samples, we obtain the estimate of m given by

$$\bar{x} = \frac{\bar{x}_1 + \bar{x}_2}{2} \tag{11.1}$$

Since $\bar{x}$ is based upon more information than either $\bar{x}_1$ or $\bar{x}_2$, we would expect $\bar{x}$ to be a more reliable estimate of m than either $\bar{x}_1$ or $\bar{x}_2$.

It can be shown that the sample mean, $\bar{x}$, is approximately normally distributed with mean m and variance σ^2/n for $n > 5$ where n is the sample size and σ^2 the variance of the population from which the sample was selected. The variance of the sample mean will hereafter be denoted by $\sigma^2_{\bar{x}}$. By definition of $\sigma^2_{\bar{x}}$ as n increases, $\sigma^2_{\bar{x}}$ decreases. Since $\sigma^2_{\bar{x}}$ measures the degree to which $\bar{x}$ is likely to vary from m as n is increased, we would expect $\bar{x}$ to approach m.

Since the reliability of $\bar{x}$, as an estimate of m, can be increased by increasing the sample size, the analyst must decide how reliable the estimate should be. Let us assume that the sample size must be large enough to provide reasonable assurance that $\bar{x}$ is with $\pm d$ of m. In mathematical terms

$$P(m - d \leq \bar{x} \leq m + d) = 1 - \alpha \tag{11.2}$$

where $0 < \alpha < 1$. Since $\bar{x}$ has an approximate normal distribution with mean m and variance $\sigma^2_{\bar{x}}$, $z = (x - m)/\sigma^2_{\bar{x}}$ has a unit normal distribution and

$$P(m - d \leq \bar{x} \leq m + d) = P\left(-\frac{d}{\sigma_{\bar{x}}} \leq z \leq \frac{d}{\sigma_{\bar{x}}}\right)$$

$$P(m-d \leq \bar{x} \leq m + d) = P\left(z \leq \frac{d}{\sigma_{\bar{x}}}\right) - P\left(z \leq -\frac{d}{\sigma_{\bar{x}}}\right)$$

$$= 2P\left(z \leq \frac{d}{\sigma_{\bar{x}}}\right) - 1 \tag{11.3}$$

From equation (11.2)

$$P\left(z \leq \frac{d}{\sigma_{\bar{x}}}\right) = 1 - \frac{\alpha}{2} \tag{11.4}$$

Let $z_{1-\alpha/2}$ be that value of the unit normal random variable such that

$$P(z \leq z_{1-\alpha/2}) = 1 - \frac{\alpha}{2}$$

Then

$$\sigma_{\bar{x}} = \frac{d}{z_{1-\alpha/2}} \tag{11.5}$$

and the required sample size, n, is determined by noting that $\sigma_{\bar{x}} = \sigma/\sqrt{n}$.

$$n = \left(\frac{\sigma z_{1-\alpha/2}}{d}\right)^2 \tag{11.6}$$

For the example already discussed, suppose that mean gasoline consumption was to be estimated within $\pm$ 100 gallons and $\alpha = 0.05$. The required sample size is

$$n = \frac{(40,000)(3.84)}{10,000}$$

$$= 15.36$$

Therefore, if daily consumption is recorded for 16 days, we would expect the resulting value of $\bar{x}$ to be within 100 gallons of the true mean.

Often the analyst is unable to determine the required sample size at the outset of the experiment. This would have been true in the previous example if σ^2 had not been known. Although these situations can present serious problems when experimenting with the physical system under study, the problem is not so troublesome when simulating the system since additional data can be generated with relative ease if it is required. For example, to determine the mean annual cost of a given inventory system we would simulate the system for n_1 years, compute the average annual cost, and assess the reliability of the estimate. If the estimator is judged to be inadequate, we could simulate for an additional n_1 years. This process would be repeated until an acceptable estimate of mean annual cost is found. The problem is then to select a method through which the reliability of the estimator can be determined by the simulator. For this purpose we will use confidence intervals.

For the truck fleet example discussed above, a 95 percent confidence interval for m is given by

$$L = \bar{x} - z_{0.975} \frac{\sigma}{\sqrt{n}} \qquad (11.7)$$

$$U = \bar{x} + z_{0.975} \frac{\sigma}{\sqrt{n}} \qquad (11.8)$$

where L and U are the lower and upper confidence limits, respectively. It is important that the reader understands the meaning of a confidence interval. Suppose a sample of size n is selected from a normal population with known variance, σ^2, but unknown mean, m. Applying equations (11.7) and (11.8), we get a 95 percent confidence interval for m. We now repeat the process 100 times, each time developing a 95 percent confidence interval. Of the 100 confidence intervals constructed, we would expect 95 to contain the true mean, m. Stated another way, the probability that the interval (L, U) will contain the true mean, m, is 0.95 before the sample is selected. However, once the sample is drawn and $\bar{x}$ is computed, the interval (L, U) either contains m or it does not. Returning to the truck fleet example, let us construct a 95 percent confidence interval for m, where

$$\sigma = 200$$
$$n_1 = 10$$
$$\bar{x}_1 = 10{,}060$$
$$z_{0.975} = 1.96$$

From equations (11.7) and (11.8)

$$L = \$9{,}929.34$$
$$U = \$10{,}190.66$$

As we have already pointed out, the interval (9,929.34, 10,190.66) may not contain m, although the method will generate intervals

TABLE 11.1

100 $(1 - \alpha)$% Confidence Intervals

Parameter Estimated	Qualifications	Confidence Limits	
		L	U
mean (m)	variance (σ^2) known	$\bar{x} - z_{1-\alpha/2} \dfrac{\sigma}{\sqrt{n}}$	$\bar{x} + z_{1-\alpha/2} \dfrac{\sigma}{\sqrt{n}}$
mean (m)	variance (σ^2) unknown	$\bar{x} - t_{1-\alpha/2}(n-1) \dfrac{s}{\sqrt{n}}$	$\bar{x} + t_{1-\alpha/2}(n-1) \dfrac{s}{\sqrt{n}}$
variance (σ^2)		$(n-1)s^2/\chi^2_{1-\alpha/2}(n-1)$	$(n-1)s^2/\chi^2_{\alpha/2}(n-1)$
Standard Deviation (σ)		$\sqrt{(n-1)s^2/\chi^2_{1-\alpha/2}(n-1)}$	$\sqrt{(n-1)s^2/\chi^2_{\alpha/2}(n-1)}$
Proportion (p)	k/n is the estimate of p where n is the sample size and m the number of events of interest occurring in the n observations	$\dfrac{k}{k + (n - k + 1)F_{1-\alpha/2}(r_1, r_2)}$ $r_1 = 2(n - k + 1)$ $r_2 = 2k$	$\dfrac{(k + 1)F_{1-\alpha/2}(r_1, r_2)}{n - k + (k + 1)F_{1-\alpha/2}(r_1, r_2)}$ $r_1 = 2(k + 1)$ $r_2 = 2(n - k)$

which do contain m 95 percent of the time. The formulas for confidence intervals for means, variances, and proportions are given in Table 11.1.

The width of a confidence interval is defined by $U - L$ and the level of confidence by $1 - \alpha$. By decreasing α we increase the chance that the interval (L,U) will contain the parameter estimated, that is, we increase the confidence that the interval contains the parameter of interest. Ideally we would like to obtain a narrow interval to which we can attribute a high degree of confidence. For example, suppose that a 99 percent confidence interval was developed for the mean annual cost of operating a given system and yielded the following limits:

$$L = \$10,862$$
$$U = \$10,864$$

Given the high degree of confidence and the narrowness of the interval we would be justified in believing that average annual cost has been rather precisely estimated. That is, it is reasonable to believe that the estimated mean annual cost, $10,863, is very close to the true mean annual cost. On the other hand, if the 99 percent confidence limits had been given by

$$L = \$5,862$$
$$U = \$15,864$$

we would question the reliability of the estimator due to the magnitude of the width of the interval.

Example 11.1

To illustrate the use of confidence interval estimation consider the simulation results given in Table 7.20, which indicates that the best ordering policy is to place orders eight days in advance of production. Suppose the analyst is satisfied that this is the optimal ordering policy but would like to improve the estimate of the average cost per order. Specifically, the mean cost per order is to be estimated within $\pm$ \$15 with 95 percent confidence. To accomplish this the assumed optimal policy is simulated, computing a 95 percent confidence interval for the mean every N simulations, until the width of the confidence interval, $U - L$, is less than \$30. Theoretically the t distribution should be used to compute this confidence interval. However, when the number of simulations used in computing the interval is 100 or more, the unit normal distribution can be used to approximate the t—the reliability of the approximation increasing as the number of simulations increases. Therefore, equations (11.7) and (11.8) can be used to determine the required confidence limits where σ is replaced by the sample standard deviation, s.

In this example confidence limits were computed after each 100 simulations, $N = 100$. The results of this analysis are summarized in Table 11.2. Based upon 1,000 simulated orders, the analyst would expect the average cost per order under the presumed optimal policy to be between 206.63 and 234.57, the best point estimate being $220.60.

TABLE 11.2
95% Confidence Intervals for the Mean

Simulations	$\bar{x}$	L	U	U–L
100	$197.63	$156.01	$239.24	$83.23
200	202.40	174.50	230.30	55.80
300	220.45	195.84	245.06	49.22
400	219.69	198.50	240.87	42.37
500	219.05	200.11	238.00	37.89
600	216.08	198.02	234.13	36.11
700	219.97	202.99	236.96	33.97
800	222.01	206.27	237.75	31.48
900	222.26	207.14	237.39	30.25
1000	220.60	206.63	234.57	27.94

In the preceding example we considered estimation of the average cost of a given ordering policy. However, in addition to the average cost per order the analyst might also be interested in the likely upper limit on the cost of an individual order. One method of accomplishing this is to find an upper limit on cost per order such that the cost of an order can be expected to fall below this limit $(1 - \alpha)100$ percent of the time. Many times such a limit is calculated assuming that the random variable of interest, in this case cost per order, is normally distributed. Where this assumption is valid, the required upper limit, U, is given by

$$U = \bar{x} + z_{1-\alpha}\sigma \qquad (11.9)$$

However, a question may be raised regarding the validity of the assumption or normality. A preferred method is to calculate the desired limit from the observed cumulative distribution function which can be obtained from the simulation. This procedure is illustrated in the following example.

Example 11.2

Find a limit on cost per order such that 95 percent of the orders placed under the policy described in example 11.1 can be expected to cost less than this limit.

To calculate this limit the cumulative distribution function of cost per order must be obtained during the simulation. In this example the simulator divided the range of cost into intervals of width $100 and recorded the number of simulated orders falling into each interval. The calculations are summarized in Table 11.3 From the

TABLE 11.3
Cumulative Distribution Function for Cost per Order

Interval (dollars)	*Frequency*	*Cumulative Frequency*	*Cumulative Distribution Function*
0– 99	240	240	0.240
100– 199	330	570	0.570
200– 299	270	840	0.840
300– 399	80	920	0.920
400– 499	15	935	0.935
500– 599	14	949	0.949
600– 699	10	959	0.959
700– 799	9	968	0.968
800– 899	7	975	0.975
900– 999	4	979	0.979
1,000–1,099	9	988	0.988
1,100–1,199	0	988	0.988
1,200–1,299	3	991	0.991
1,300–1,399	1	992	0.992
1,400–1,499	1	993	0.993
1,500–1,599	3	996	0.996
1,600–1,699	1	997	0.997
1,700–1,799	1	998	0.998
1,800–1,899	0	998	0.998
1,900–1,999	0	998	0.998
2,000–2,099	0	998	0.998
2,100–2,199	1	999	0.999
2,200–2,299	0	999	0.999
2,300–2,399	1	1,000	1.000

results given in Table 11.3, one would expect 95 percent of the orders placed to cost $600 or less. Therefore $600 is the 95 percent limit desired.

Let us suppose for a moment that the analyst had assumed that the distribution of cost per order was normal and had computed the 95 percent upper limit using equation (11.9). Based upon the 1,000 orders simulated, the best estimate of σ is $226.31 and of $\bar{x}$ is $220.60.

Therefore

$$U = 220.60 + (1.65)(226.31)$$
$$= 594.01$$

In this example the error resulting from the assumption of normality is slight. Even though equation (11.9) proved reliable here, the reader should be warned against using it indiscriminately.

OPTIMIZATION THROUGH SIMULATION

More often than not the purpose of a simulation analysis is to determine which of a series of alternatives will best serve the needs of the organization for which the simulation is conducted. When the number of alternatives under consideration is limited, investigation of each through simulation may be justified. However, situations frequently arise where the number of possible alternatives is so large that evaluation of each is economically infeasible. For example, an inventory simulator might be developed to determine that operating policy which will minimize the total cost of maintaining the inventory. Here the number of alternatives which might be investigated is at best large and is limitless from a theoretical point of view. Since the simulation of any individual alternative is likely to consume several seconds of computer time, simulation of each of the possible alternatives would prove impractical. When the analyst is faced with a problem of this nature, he must resort to a search technique through which he can investigate systematically selected alternatives in such a way that he will eventually be able to select the optimal, or at least a near optimal, alternative for implementation. If the search technique is to be practical, it should lead to selection of the optimal alternative in as few steps as possible. That is, the number of alternatives simulated in the course of the search should be minimized as far as possible without frustrating the ultimate goal of the search—finding optimal conditions.

A LIMITED NUMBER OF ALTERNATIVES

If the number of alternatives considered is limited to the extent that each can be evaluated through simulation, confidence intervals may be used to determine the optimal alternative. Suppose M alternatives are to be compared on the basis of a given measure of effectiveness. Let ϕ_i be the value of the measure of effectiveness for the ith alternative. The problem is then to select that alternative with the optimal value of ϕ_i, $i = 1,2, \ldots ,M$. For example, if ϕ_i is the mean annual cost of the ith alternative, then the most desirable alternative is that for which ϕ_i is a minimum. Let L_i and U_i be the lower and upper $(1 - \alpha)100$ percent confidence limits for ϕ_i, and let $\hat{\phi}_i$ be the statistic used to estimate ϕ_i. After K simulations of each alternative (K may be in years, events, etc.) the confidence interval (L_i, U_i) and $\hat{\phi}_i$ are computed for $i = 1,2, \ldots ,M$. The confidence interval for each alternative is then compared with that having the optimal value of $\hat{\phi}_i$. Let j be the alternative possessing the optimal measure of effectiveness after K simulations. If the problem involves maximization of ϕ_i over i, then any alternative, i, for which $U_i < L_j$ is eliminated from further consideration. The rationale underlying this decision is that if the upper confidence limit for ϕ_i is less than the lower confidence limit for ϕ_j, there is little chance that $\phi_i > \phi_j$. If the minimum value of ϕ_i is sought, then any alternative, i, for which $L_i > U_j$ is eliminated. If more than one alternative remains after the initial K simulations, the simulation is continued in an attempt to eliminate further alternatives.

Theoretically the procedure described above will eventually eliminate all but one alternative. However, the simulation period required to achieve this result may prove excessive. This situation is likely to arise when several alternatives are nearly equivalent. In problems of this type the analyst will find that a point of diminishing returns is reached in attempting to detect differences among such alternatives, and at such a point the search should be terminated.

A method which might be employed in this determination is to calculate the difference between the maximum upper confidence limit and the minimum lower confidence limit for the alternative which have not been eliminated. If this difference is less than some specified value, d, the search is discontinued. Otherwise the search is continued. For example, suppose $d = \$10$ and after K simulations, three alternatives remain under consideration where

$$L_1 = \$200.00 \qquad U_1 = \$205.00 \qquad \hat{\phi}_1 = \$202.50$$
$$L_2 = \$201.00 \qquad U_2 = \$208.00 \qquad \hat{\phi}_2 = \$204.50$$
$$L_3 = \$203.00 \qquad U_3 = \$209.00 \qquad \hat{\phi}_3 = \$206.00$$

According to the established search procedure none of the three alternatives can be eliminated at this point. However, since $U_3 - L_1 < d$, the search would be terminated. If the problem is one of minimization of ϕ_i, the first alternative would appear to be optimal, but the third would be selected if ϕ_i is to be maximized. In either case, any error resulting from selection of the wrong alternative will probably cost less than $9 ($U_3 - L_1$). Therefore, the value of d used as a termination criterion should reflect the error allowed as a result of selection of a nonoptimal alternative. The procedure outlined above can be summarized in the following steps:

1. Select the measure of effectiveness to be used in comparing the alternatives under consideration, ϕ_i, $i = 1, 2, \ldots, M$, and its estimator, $\hat{\phi}_i$, $i = 1, 2, \ldots, M$.
2. Select the level of confidence.
3. Define the error to be allowed as a result of selection of a nonoptimal alternative, d. ϕ_i and d should be measured in the same units.
4. Simulate each alternative, computing $\hat{\phi}_i$ and the confidence interval (L_i, U_i) every K simulation periods.
5. If the optimal alternative is j at any point in the simulation, eliminate any alternative i for which:
   a) $U_i < L_j$ if the problem is one of maximizaton.
   b) $L_i > U_j$ if the problem is one of minimization.
6. Terminate the search when only one alternative remains or when

$$\max_i U_i - \min_i L_i < d$$

7. If the search is terminated without finding a unique optimal, select the alternative having the optimal value of $\hat{\phi}_i$ at the point of termination.

Example 11.3

Find the optimal ordering policy for the production ordering example in Chapter 7.

In seeking the optimal ordering policy, 95 percent confidence intervals will be constructed for the mean cost per order for each alternative. These intervals will be computed after 100, 200, 300, . . . orders have been simulated until only one alternative remains or until

$$\max_i U_i - \min_i L_i < d.$$

Let $d = \$30$.

TABLE 11.4
Optimum Ordering Policy Search

Orders Simulated		1	2	3	4	5	6	7	8	9	10	Alternatives Eliminated	$\max_i U_i - \min_i L_i$
100	L_i	$748	$620	$441	$262	$204	$219	$177	$156	$197	$221	1,2,3,4	$204
	U_i	977	814	623	425	343	360	265	239	277	313		
200	L_i					297	241	203	175	193	216	5,6	96
	U_i					418	338	271	230	242	270		
300	L_i							200	196	203	226	none	70
	U_i							256	245	244	266		
400	L_i							205	199	207	228	none	62
	U_i							256	241	243	261		
500	L_i							207	200	213	229	none	58
	U_i							252	238	245	258		
600	L_i							203	198	219	232	none	60
	U_i							242	234	249	258		
700	L_i							200	203	218	234	none	57
	U_i							236	237	245	257		
800	L_i							199	206	221	235	10	48
	U_i							231	238	247	256		
....								...	...	...		...	...
1500	L_i							205	208	221		none	34
	U_i							230	230	239			
1700	L_i							208	208	220		none	29
	U_i							232	228	237			

Therefore, for this analysis

ϕ = Mean cost per order for the ith ordering policy
$K = 100$
$\alpha = 0.05$
$d = \$30$

and the objective of the analysis is to determine the value of i for which ϕ_i is minimized. For convenience the ith alternative will refer to a policy of ordering i days prior to production.

The search procedure for this problem is summarized in Table 11.4. After simulation of the first 100 orders for each alternative, the first four ordering policies were eliminated. The fifth and sixth alternatives were eliminated after 200 simulations. Elimination of the 10 ordering policy occurred after 800 simulations. The decision rule requiring that the search be terminated when

$$\max_{i} U_i - \min_{i} L_i < \$30$$

brought the search to an end before a unique optimum was obtained. For the three alternatives remaining under consideration upon termination

$$\hat{\phi}_7 = \$220.00$$
$$\hat{\phi}_8 = \$218.00$$
$$\hat{\phi}_9 = \$228.50$$

Therefore, placing orders eight days prior to production would be adopted as the optimal ordering policy since $\hat{\phi}_8$ is less than $\hat{\phi}_7$ and $\hat{\phi}_9$.

A LARGE NUMBER OF ALTERNATIVES

In many, if not most, practical simulation problems the analyst is faced with, the problem is in choosing one course of action from a number of alternatives which is so large that analysis of each is not possible. Theoretically, the analyst seeks the optimal alternative, fully realizing that with luck he may be able to come up with something reasonably close to the optimal. Since the number of possible alternatives is such that complete enumeration and analysis is infeasible, the optimal alternative must be sought through the analysis of only a small portion of the total possible. In other words, the analyst must have at his disposal a methodology through which he can eliminate most of the alternatives without ever investigating them.

Basically, optimum seeking or search techniques are founded upon the same procedural philosophy. One or more alternatives are selected for the initial investigation. Each alternative is evaluated in terms of the measure of effectiveness to be used to preferentially distinguish one alternative from another. The optimum seeking technique to be used is then applied to the initial set of alternatives. The result of this application is the next set of alternatives to be investigated. Each of the new set of alternatives is evaluated, and the search technique is reapplied yielding the third set of alternatives to be studied. This procedure is repeated until the search technique indicates that an optimum has been found.

To illustrate the manner in which a search technique functions, consider the problem of a mountain climber attempting to reach the summit of a mountain in the fog. Since he cannot visually determine which way to go, be must strike out in an arbitrarily given direction. The contour (isolines) of the mountain are shown in Figure 11.1 where the mountain climber is initially located at point A. He decides that he will climb a distance d north and assess his progress after reaching point B. If the altitude at B is greater than that at A, he will continue north. Otherwise, he will turn around and move south toward, and perhaps past, A until he reaches a point having altitude greater than A. He will continue to move north or south as long as his position is improved. When he can no longer improve his position in a north or south direction, he will move east in steps of length d as long as his position is improved. Again when his position ceases to improve in a east-west direction, he will move north or south. The climber's progression to the summit is shown in Figure 11.1.

Usually one does not expect a search technique to achieve precise optimal conditions, particularly when simulation is used to evaluate the alternatives studied. However, these techniques can prove useful in locating the region of the optimal solution. That is, an effective search technique is one which terminates at a point which results in near optimal conditions. Specifically the value of the measure of system effectiveness for the alternative suggested as optimal by the search technique should not differ greatly from that for the true optimal alternative.

The optimum-seeking techniques described here may be used in conjunction with either mathematical or simulation models. Search

FIGURE 11.1

Mountain Climber Attempting to Reach the Summit of a Mountain

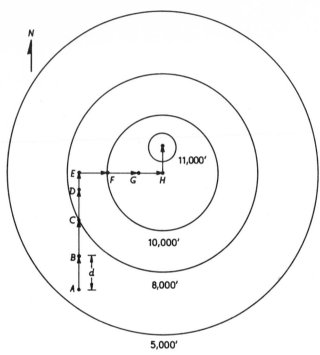

techniques will generally prove more effective when used with a mathematical model, since random variation, which can distort the search, is eliminated. However, the analyst can reduce this distortion introduced by simulation by increasing the number of times a given alternative is simulated, that is, by replicating the experiment.

Each of the search techniques presented in this chapter will be demonstrated by applying it to examples discussed in previous chapters. To demonstrate its effectiveness, each technique will be used to determine an optimal solution for a mathematical model for which the solution is already known. The technique will then be applied to determine the optimal solution for the same problem through simulation. It is hoped that this parallel presentation will give the reader some insight into the problems he will have to face in attempting to optimize a system through simulation. In Appendix C, computer programs are presented for both of the search techniques presented in this chapter.

Sectioning

Sectioning or the one-at-a-time method proposed by Friedman and Savage is one of the simplest optimum-seeking techniques available and may be applied to functions of any number of decision variables. Suppose $C(A_1, A_2, \ldots, A_n)$ is a cost function to be minimized, where $A_i, i = 1, 2, \ldots, n$, are the decision variables. Let a_i be a specific value of A_i. To apply the method of sectioning, the analyst fixes the values of the last $n - 1$ variables and varies the first until a minimum, or at least near minimum, is found. Let a_1° be the minimizing value of A_1 with associated cost $C(a_1^\circ, a_2, \ldots, a_n)$. The value of A_1 is now fixed at a_1°, and A_2 is varied until its optimal value is determined, a_2°. This procedure is repeated for all n decision variables. The entire process is repeated until values of the decision variables are found such that further change in any one of the variables will result in an increase in the value of the objective function.

The sectioning search may be effected in several ways. However, the initial step is always the same. All but one of the decision variables are given fixed values. Let these variables be $A_2, \ldots, A_n$ and let their initial values be $a_2, \ldots, a_n$. The initial value of the remaining variable, a_1, must now be set and the measure of effectiveness, $C(a_1, \ldots, a_n)$, evaluated. The initial search over A_1 usually involves changing A_1 in rather large increments. Let Δ_{ij} be the jth increment chosen for the ith decision variable and let m be the number of increments for each variable, $j = 1, 2, \ldots, m$. Choosing Δ_{11} relatively large allows the search to rapidly locate the general region of the optimum value of A_1, a_1^*, given the fixed values of the remaining variables. Let us arbitrarily assume that in searching over any decision variable, we first increase the value of the variable and if this does not prove fruitful we then decrease its value. Therefore, the first step in the search moves us to the point $(a_1 + \Delta_{11}, a_2, \ldots, a_n)$. If $C(a_1 + \Delta_{11}, a_2, \ldots, a_n) < C(a_1, \ldots, a_n)$, we must continue to increase A_1, next examining the measure of effectiveness at $(a_1 + 2\Delta_{11}, a_2, \ldots, a_n)$. This procedure is continued until a point $(a_1 + m\Delta_{11}, a_2, \ldots, a_n)$ is found such that $C(a_1 + m\Delta_{11}, a_2, \ldots, a_n) > C(a_1 + (m - 1)\Delta_{11}, a_2, \ldots, a_n)$. If the objective function is convex, a_1^* lies between $a_1 + (m - 2)\Delta_{11}$ and $a_1 + m\Delta_{11}$.

If $C(a_1 + \Delta_{11}, a_2 \cdots a_n) > C(a_1, \ldots, a_n)$, a further increase in A_1 would not be warranted if the objective function is convex. Therefore, the next point evaluated would be $(a_1 - \Delta_{11}, a_2, \ldots, a_n)$. If $C(a_1 - \Delta_{11}, a_2, \ldots, a_n) > C(a_1, \ldots, a_n)$, then $a_1 - \Delta_{11} < a_1^* < a_1$

$+ \Delta_{11}$. If $C(a_1 - \Delta_{11}, a_2, \ldots, a_n) < C(a_1, \ldots, a_n)$, A_1 is further reduced until a point $(a_1 - m\Delta_{11} a_2, \ldots, a_n)$ is found such that $C(a_1 - m\Delta_{11}, a_2, \ldots, a_n) > C(a_1 - (m-1)\Delta_{11}, a_2, \ldots, a_n)$, in which case $a_1 - m\Delta_{11} < a_1^* < a_1 - (m-2)\Delta_{11}$.

Ignoring boundary constraints, we find the result of the initial search over A_1 is an interval of width $2\Delta_{11}$, the center of which, a_1°, is the best estimate of a_1^* thus far. At this point the analyst may choose to continue the search over A_1, keeping the remaining decision variables fixed at their previously established values. To accomplish this, the analyst chooses a new increment for A_1, Δ_{12}, which is less than the initial increment. The starting point for this search is the center point of the interval about a_1^* which was obtained in the initial search, a_1°. The procedure described for the initial search of A_1 is then repeated until a new value of a_1° is derived. The entire process is repeated over and over again until a_1° is bracketed by a sufficiently small interval. When the search over A_1 terminates, the search over A_2 begins, fixing A_1 at the last value of a_1° derived and holding $A_3, \ldots, A_n$ at their initial values, $a_3, \ldots, a_n$. The procedure for the search over A_2 is identical to that for A_1. After all n variables have been searched over once, the search returns to A_1 and starts the whole process over again. The search terminates when for any i

$$C(a_1^{\,0}, a_2^{\,0}, \ldots, a_i^{\,0} + \Delta_{im}, \ldots, a_n^{\,0}) > C(a_1^{\,0}, a_2^{\,0}, \ldots, a_i^{\,0}, \ldots, a_n^{\,0}) \quad (11.10)$$

When the initial search over A_1 terminates, the analyst may choose to search over the remaining variables before refining the search over A_1. If this is the case, A_1 is fixed at the initial value of a_1°, and the search over A_2 is conducted in increments Δ_{21}. This process is repeated for all n variables. Here the search returns to A_1, again searching in increments Δ_{11}. The search increment for any variable is not reduced until a point $(a_1^\circ, a_2^\circ, \ldots, a_n^\circ)$ is found such that for any i

$$C(a_1^{\,0}, a_2^{\,0}, \ldots, a_i^{\,0} + \Delta_{i1}, \ldots, a_n^{\,0}) > C(a_1^{\,0}, a_2^{\,0}, \ldots, a_i^{\,0}, \ldots, a_n^{\,0}) \quad (11.11)$$

When this condition is achieved, the increments on all variables are reduced to Δ_{i2}, $i = 1, 2, \ldots, n$, and the search over all decision variables is repeated until the termination criterion given in (11.10) is satisfied.

The method of sectioning is illustrated in the following examples.

Example 11.4

Using the mathematical model given in equation (4.94) and the method of sectioning, we find the optimal inventory operating policy for the problem described in example 4.11. Let

$$A_1 = r$$
$$A_2 = Q$$
$$\Delta_{11} = \Delta_{21} = 10$$
$$\Delta_{12} = \Delta_{22} = 2$$
$$\Delta_{13} = \Delta_{23} = 1$$

Both variables are to be searched in increments of 10 before refining the search on either. When the condition specified by (11.11) is satisfied for $\Delta_{11} = \Delta_{21} = 10$, the increment for both variables is reduced to two and finally to one. The starting values for r and Q are

TABLE 11.5
Optimization of the Problem Given in Example 4.11 through the Method of Sectioning and Equation 4.94

Iteration	i	Δ_{1j}	Δ_{2j}	A_1	A_2	a_1^o	a_2^o	$C(A_1, A_2)$
1. . . .1	10	10	15	80				$1,075.28
2. . . .1	10	10	25	80				1,275.00
3. . . .1	10	10	5	80				936.77
4. . . .1	10	10	−5	80	5			boundary violated
4. . . .1	10	10	5	90	5			1,016.02
5. . . .1	10	10	5	70	5			863.45
6. . . .1	10	10	5	60	5			799.02
7. . . .1	10	10	5	50	5			748.83
8. . . .1	10	10	5	40	5			723.54
9. . . .1	10	10	5	30	5	40		748.05
10. . . .1	10	10	15	40	5	40		800.56
11. . . .2	2	2	7	40				704.45
12. . . .2	2	2	9	40	7			707.29
13. . . .2	2	2	7	42	7			709.48
14. . . .2	2	2	7	38	7			701.00
15. . . .2	2	2	7	36	7			699.39
16. . . .2	2	2	7	34	7	36		699.94
17. . . .2	2	2	9	36		34		698.10
18. . . .2	2	2	11	36	9	34		718.06
19. . . .2	2	2	9	38	9			701.88
20. . . .2	2	2	9	34	9			696.22
21. . . .2	2	2	9	32	9	34		696.61
22. . . .2	2	2	11	34	9	34		715.01
23. . . .3	1	1	10	34				703.34
24. . . .3	1	1	8	34				694.82
25. . . .3	1	1	7	34	8			699.94
26. . . .3	1	1	8	35	8			694.97
27. . . .3	1	1	8	33	8	34		695.27

to be 15 and 80, respectively. The values of r and Q are to be restricted to positive values. If at any iteration in the search a boundary condition is violated, that iteration is to be deleted and we discontinue our search in that direction, setting a_i^o equal to the last value of A_i, $i = 1,2$.

The sectioning search for this problem is described in detail in Table 11.5 and is shown graphically in Figures 11.2A through 11.2C. It

FIGURE 11.2A

Optimization of the Problem Given in Example 4.11 through the
Method of Sectioning and Equation (4.94)

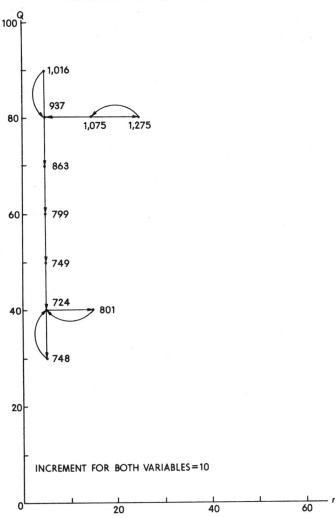

should be noted that the value of a_i^o is destroyed whenever A_i is changed. A new value of a_i^o is specified only when variation of A_i ceases. As shown in iteration number 10, it is possible to destroy and reestablish the value of a_i^o in the same iteration.

The search carried out in this problem indicates that the optimal values of r and Q are 8 and 34, respectively. A comparison of this result with that given in example 4.11 shows that the method of sectioning has produced the optimal solution.

FIGURE 11.2B
Optimization of the Problem Given in Example 4.11 through the
Method of Sectioning and Equation (4.94)

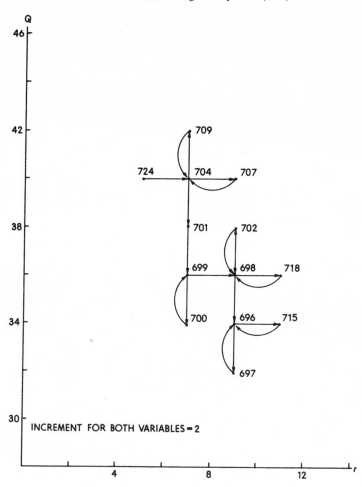

FIGURE 11.2C
Optimization of the Problem Given in Example 4.11 through the
Method of Sectioning and Equation (4.94)

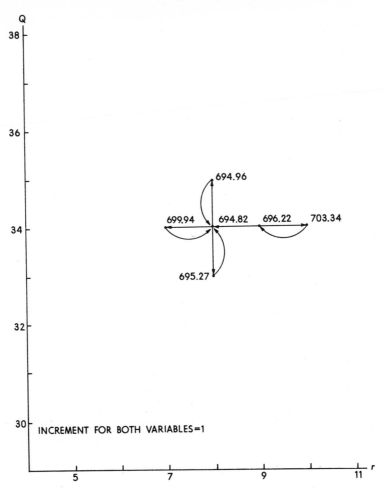

Example 11.5

Solve the problem given in example 11.4 when the annual cost of each operating policy examined is evaluated through simulation instead of the mathematical model given in equation (4.94). Each policy investigated should be evaluated on the basis of 10 years' simulation.

The only thing which has changed from the previous example is the tool used to evaluate **the mea**sure of system effectiveness. The

FIGURE 11.3A
Optimization of the Problem Given in Example 4.11 through the
Method of Sectioning and Simulation

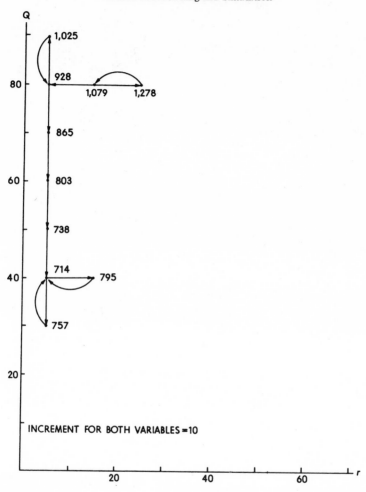

INCREMENT FOR BOTH VARIABLES =10

search using the method of sectioning and simulation is shown in Figures 11.3A through 11.3C. The reader will notice that the search patterns here and in the preceding example are identical when the increments for r and Q are 10. However, the patterns differ markedly from that point on. The solution suggested as optimal by Figure 11.3C calls for a reorder point of nine and an order quantity of 40. The estimated cost of maintaining this policy is $699.42. The actual expected annual cost of maintaining this policy is $707.29, by equation (4.94). Therefore, the error induced by simulation would

FIGURE 11.3B
Optimization of the Problem Given in Example 4.11 through the
Method of Sectioning and Simulation

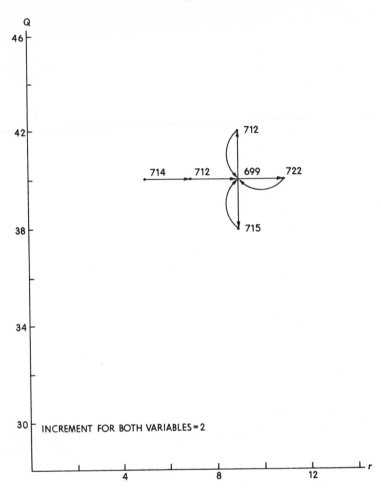

hardly be considered critical, since the difference in annual cost between the optimal solution proposed here and the true optimal solution is only $12.37.

The similarity between Figures 11.2A and 11.3A and the dissimilarity between Figures 11.2B and 11.3B and 11.2C and 11.3C is explained by analyzing the effect of random variation in the three cases. Let m_1 and m_2 be the expected costs of operation for any two adjacent search points and let $\bar{x}_1$ and $\bar{x}_2$ be the estimates of m_1 and

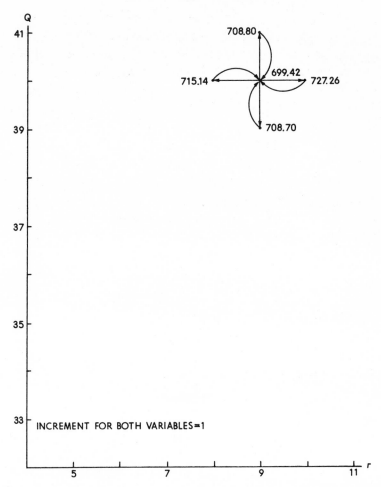

FIGURE 11.3C

Optimization of the Problem Given in Example 4.11 through the
Method of Sectioning and Simulation

m_2 obtained by simulation of each for a period of 10 years. $\bar{x}_1$ and $\bar{x}_2$ can be expressed by

$$\bar{x}_1 = m_1 + \varepsilon_1 \qquad (11.12)$$

$$\bar{x}_2 = m_2 + \varepsilon_2 \qquad (11.13)$$

where ε_1 and ε_2 represent the random variation in $\bar{x}_1$ and $\bar{x}_2$, respectively, and for our purposes can be assumed to be normally distributed with a mean of zero and variances of $\sigma_{\bar{x}_1}^2$ and $\sigma_{\bar{x}_2}^2$. In searching for an optimum, we look at the difference between $\bar{x}_1$ and $\bar{x}_2$.

$$\bar{x}_1 - \bar{x}_2 = (m_1 - m_2) + (\varepsilon_1 - \varepsilon_2) \tag{11.14}$$

Although $\sigma_{\bar{x}_i}$ may vary with m_i, a unit change in m_i is likely to produce a much smaller change in $\sigma_{\bar{x}_i}$, if any, particularly as the number of years of simulation is increased. Therefore the range of variation of $(\varepsilon_1 - \varepsilon_2)$ is likely to remain relatively unchanged as the differences $(m_1 - m_2)$ is varied.

Let us assume that we have two adjacent search points for which $(m_1 - m_2)$ is much greater than

$$\sqrt{\sigma_{\bar{x}_1}{}^2 + \sigma_{\bar{x}_2}{}^2}$$

the standard deviation of $(\varepsilon_1 - \varepsilon_2)$. Although the observed difference between $\bar{x}_1$ and $\bar{x}_2$ is made up of both components, most of the difference would be expected to be due to the difference between m_1 and m_2. Conversely, when $(\bar{x}_1 - \bar{x}_2)$ is large relative to

$$\sqrt{\sigma_{\bar{x}_1}{}^2 + \sigma_{\bar{x}_2}{}^2}$$

the difference between $\bar{x}_1$ and $\bar{x}_2$ can be taken as a reflection of the difference between m_1 and m_2. As the search increment is reduced, a general reduction in the difference between m_1 and m_2 can be expected, while a proportionate reduction in

$$\sqrt{\sigma_{\bar{x}_1}{}^2 + \sigma_{\bar{x}_2}{}^2}$$

is not likely. Therefore, as $(m_1 - m_2)$ decreases, the contribution of $(\varepsilon_1 - \varepsilon_2)$ to the difference between $\bar{x}_1$ and $\bar{x}_2$ becomes more significant. Finally, a point is reached at which one cannot tell whether the difference $(\bar{x}_1 - \bar{x}_2)$ is due to a similar difference $(m_1 - m_2)$ or to the random variation $(\varepsilon_1 - \varepsilon_2)$.

In Figure 11.3A the difference between the actual costs of operation $(m_1 - m_2)$ for any two adjacent search points is so large, relative to the inherent random variation $(\varepsilon_1 - \varepsilon_2)$, that the effect of this difference could not be mistaken and is largely reflected in the difference between the simulated costs $(\bar{x}_1 - \bar{x}_2)$. However, in Figures 11.3B and 11.3C, the reduction in the search increment significantly reduced the difference in true operating costs for adjacent points. It now becomes difficult to determine whether a difference in simulated costs is due to a difference in actual costs of to random variation.

The masking effect of random variation is a constant problem in simulation analyses. To reduce this effect, the techniques already discussed regarding parameter estimation may be employed.

The results of example 11.4 are not intended to imply that the method of sectioning will always generate the optimal solution when applied to a mathematical model, even when an assumption of convexity is justified. This point is illustrated in the following example.

Example 11.6

By sectioning, find the optimal quality control plan for the problem given in example 5.9 using the model given by equation (5.59). Let

$$A_1 = N$$
$$A_2 = c$$
$$\Delta_{11} = \Delta_{21} = 10$$
$$\Delta_{12} = \Delta_{22} = 2$$
$$\Delta_{13} = \Delta_{23} = 1$$

All increments are to be changed when the conditions given by (11.11) are satisfied. The starting point for the search is $A_1 = 20$ and $A_2 = 15$.

In this problem there are natural limits on the values of A_1 (N) and A_2 (c). First, neither may be negative. Second, $A_1 \geqslant A_2$. Again any iteration which violates the above constraints is to be deleted.

The sectioning search for the optimal sampling plan is shown graphically in Figures 11.4A through 11.4C. The search is terminated at $N = 66$, $c = 5$, with an associated cost of \$10,710.73. The optimal solution given in example 5.9 calls for a sample size of 149 and an acceptance number of 12, yielding a cost per lot of \$10,592.58. Therefore the method of sectioning has failed to seek the true optimal. However, although there is a significant difference in the two sampling plans, the associated difference in costs is less than 2 percent. Here we have an example of a search which reaches the region of the optimal solution without obtaining it.

Example 11.6 illustrates a potentially serious flaw in the section-

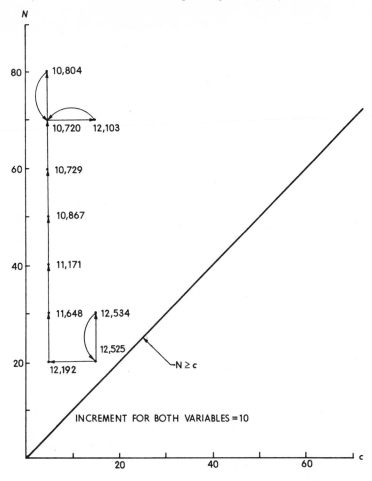

FIGURE 11.4A
Optimization of the Problem Given in Example 5.9 through the
Method of Sectioning and Equation (5.59)

ing search. The unidimensional character of the search prohibits simultaneous variation of the decision variables and therefore limits the horizon which may be searched. Ignoring all other considerations, such as time consumed in the search, we would prefer a technique which allowed the search to proceed in one of a multitude of directions at any point in the search. It is not surprising, then, that

FIGURE 11.4B
Optimization of the Problem Given in Example 5.9 through the
Method of Sectioning and Equation (5.59)

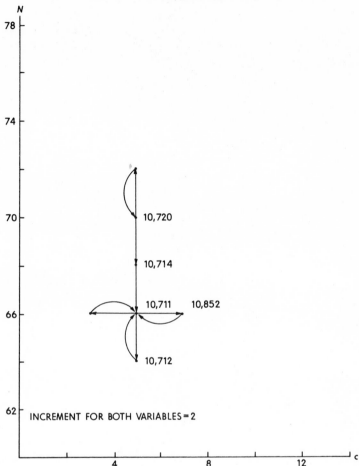

INCREMENT FOR BOTH VARIABLES = 2

sectioning may stop short of optimality and in some cases may even
fail to approach the region of the optimal. It follows that if
sectioning fails to reach the region of the optimum when used in
conjunction with a mathematical model, it can be expected to
perform even less successfully when used with the corresponding
simulator.

FIGURE 11.4C
Optimization of the Problem Given in Example 5.9 through the
Method of Sectioning and Equation (5.59)

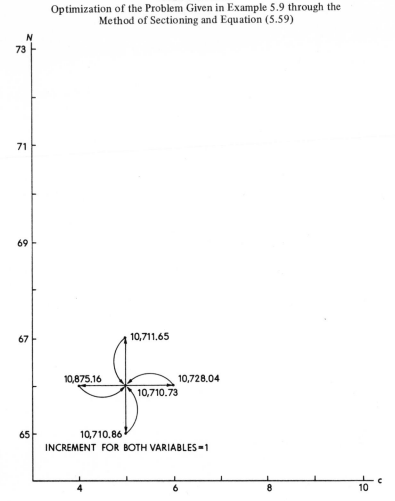

INCREMENT FOR BOTH VARIABLES = 1

Search by Regression

Regression analysis provides the systems analyst with a powerful and versatile optimum-seeking tool. The success of this technique rests on the assumption that the objective function, $C(A_1, A_2, \ldots, A_n)$, can be reasonably approximated through the method of least squares by another function, $H(A_1, A_2, \ldots, A_n)$—the reliability of the approximation increasing as the region of the optimum is approached. The search is initiated by selecting m points in the solution space to be searched. Let $(a_{1j}, a_{2j}, \ldots, a_{nj})$ be the jth point, $j = 1, 2, \ldots, m$. The objective function is then evaluated at each of these points. Let $(a'_1, a'_2, \ldots, a'_n)$ be the least optimal of the m points included in the analysis. Through the method of least squares, the best-fitting equation of the form $H(A_1, A_2, \ldots, A_n)$ is derived. $H(A_1, A_2, \ldots, A_n)$ is optimized through the classical methods of calculus. If $H(A_1, A_2, \ldots, A_n)$ reliably approximates $C(A_1, A_2, \ldots, A_n)$, the optimal point for $H(A_1, A_2, \ldots, A_n)$ should be at or near the optimal for $C(A_1, A_2, \ldots, A_n)$. Let $(a^\circ_1, a^\circ_2, \ldots, a^\circ_n)$ be the optimal point for $H(A_1, A_2, \ldots, A_n)$. The objective function is now evaluated at $(a^\circ_1, a^\circ_2, \ldots, a^\circ_n)$, the point $(a'_1, a'_2, \ldots, a'_n)$ is replaced by the point $(a^\circ_1, a^\circ_2, \ldots, a^\circ_n)$ in the set of m points, and the new least optimal point, $(a'_1, a'_2, \ldots, a'_n)$, is located. Again the function $H(A_1, A_2, \ldots, A_n)$ is fit to the new set of m points, and the procedure is repeated until the optimal solution is obtained. A graphical representation of the procedure for a function of a single decision variable is shown in Figure 11.5.

FIGURE 11.5
Illustration of One Iteration of the Search by Regression

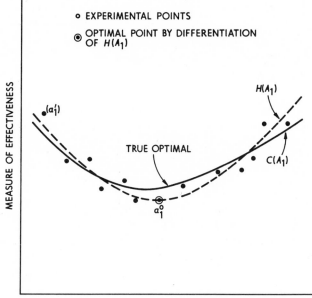

Eliminating the least optimal point at each step in the search will eventually narrow the area of the search to a small set of points near the optimum, provided the objective function is convex. Further, the time taken to fit $H(A_1, A_2, \ldots, A_n)$ to the experimental points is a function of the number of points. Therefore, if the number of points included in the analysis is held constant, the time consumed in performing points included in the analysis is held constant, the time consumed in performing the least squares fit of $H(A_1, A_2, \ldots, A_n)$ to these points will remain relatively constant.

Two properties of the search by regression are noteworthy. First, the search increment is not restricted to a predetermined value. The magnitude of the search increment at any iteration is the distance from the least optimal point, $(a_1', a_2', \ldots, a_n')$, to the indicated optimal point, $(a_1^o, a_2^o, \ldots, a_n^o)$. Second, the direction to the next point evaluated in the search is unlimited.

Polynomials probably represent the most widely used functional form for $H(A_1, A_2, \ldots, A_n)$, second degree polynomials being the most popular within this class. In all examples in this chapter $H(A_1, A_2, \ldots, A_n)$ will be defined as

$$H(A_1, A_2, \ldots, A_n) = b_0 + \sum_{i=1}^{n} b_i A_i + \sum_{i=1}^{n} b_{i+n} A_i^2 \qquad (11.15)$$

According to this definition of $H(A_1, A_2, \ldots, A_n)$, any interaction between the decision variables is ignored. If the analyst feels that significant interaction exists, the appropriate terms, such as $A_i A_j$, A_i/A_j, etc., may be added to those given in equation (11.15).

The least squares fit of $H(A_1, A_2, \ldots, A_n)$ to the m data points at each iteration of the search consists of deriving the values of b_0, b_{1i}, and b_{2i} for $i = 1, 2, \ldots, n$. Since the number of parameters estimated is $2n + 1$, the number of data points required at any point in the search, m, must satisfy the condition

$$m \geq 2n + 1 \qquad (11.16)$$

Optimization of $H(A_1, A_2, \ldots, A_n)$ at each iteration in the search is accomplished by taking first partial derivatives of $H(A_1, A_2, \ldots, A_n)$ with respect to each of the decision variables, setting each derivative equal to zero, and solving for the optimal value of each decision variable. For example, optimization of $H(A_1, A_2 \ldots, A)$ as defined by (11.15) is carried out as follows:

$$\frac{\partial H(A_1, A_2, \ldots, A_n)}{\partial A_i} = b_i + 2b_{i+n} A_i, \qquad i = 1, 2, \ldots, n \qquad (11.17)$$

Solving for the optimal value of A_i, a_i^o, we get

$$b_i + 2b_{i+n} A_i = 0, \qquad i = 1, 2, \ldots, n \qquad (11.18)$$

and

$$a_i^o = -b_i/2b_{i+n}, \qquad i = 1, 2, \ldots, n \qquad (11.19)$$

The discussion thus far would imply that the decision variables must be of a continuous nature. However, the search by regression can be carried out when one or more decision variables are discrete. Each time a new value of a decision variable is calculated in the course of the search, the value of that variable can be rounded off to the nearest integer value or can be truncated, dropping the decimal portion of the value.

As we have already indicated, the search described here is initiated by generating m points in the solution space. The method of generating these points can be left to the discretion of the analyst. However, not more than $m - 2n - 1$ points may be coincident. The authors have found it convenient to generate these points at random. To accomplish this, upper and lower limits must be established for each of the decision variables. This may be necessary in any case due to natural limits on the variables and/or constraints imposed upon the system. For example, in the quality control systems discussed in Chapter 5 the lower limit on both N and c would be zero. The upper limit for c is N, and the maximum possible sample size is the lot size, L. However, the analyst may wish to limit the range of variation of some or all of the decision variables more severely than required by the natural limits of the variables or by constraints imposed upon the system so that the search is limited to an area in which he believes the optimal is located.

Let l_i and u_i be the lower and upper limits on the ith decision variable and let r be a random number. The first m values of A_i, a_i, are generated as follows:

$$a_i = (u_i - l_i)r + l_i \qquad (11.20)$$

After the initial m points $(a_1, a_2, \ldots, a_n)$ are generated, the limits l_i and u_i may be relaxed or may remain in effect. However, if the limits are relaxed, they should not be relaxed beyond the natural limits of the variables or beyond the constraints imposed upon the system If at any iteration during the search $a_i^{\circ} < l_i$ or $a_i^{\circ} > u_i$, a_i° is set equal to the limit violated, $i = 1, 2, \ldots, n$.

The reader will notice that the procedure described thus far does not include a termination criterion. Therefore the analyst will have to specify his own rule for terminating the search. The simplest rule is to break off the search after a specified number of iterations. Another rule is to terminate the search whenever the region of the search has been reduced to a sufficiently small area. To illustrate, let $(a_{1j}, a_{2j}, \ldots, a_{nj})$ be the jth point in the search at a given iteration. An interval d_i is chosen for the variable A_i such that whenever

$$\max_j a_{ij} - \min_j a_{ij} < d_i \qquad (11.21)$$

for all i, the search is terminated. A third criterion is to terminate the search whenever the same point is optimal for a given number of consecutive iterations.

The search by regression is illustrated in the following example.

Example 11.7

Find the optimal inventory policy for the problem given in example 4.12 using a search by regression and simulation. Each policy investigated is to be simulated for a period of 10 years.

The decision variables in example 4.12 are the review period, T_R, and the point to which inventory level is raised at each order, R. The following relationship will be used to approximate the cost of operation, $C(R, T_R)$:

$$H(R, T_R) = b_0 + b_1 R + b_2 T_R + b_3 R^2 + b_4 T_R^2 \qquad (11.22)$$

At each iteration of the search the relationship given by equation (11.22) will be fit to eight experimental points ($m = 8$). The initial eight points will be generated at random. The limits on T_R and R are as follows:

$$0 < R < 200$$
$$0 < T_R < 1$$

The search will be terminated at any iteration for which the difference between the maximum and minimum values of R is 15 or less and when the difference between the maximum and minimum values of T_R is 0.10 or less. Note that for the search to terminate, both conditions must hold at the same time.

The initial eight points generated and the associated costs are given below, where a_{1j} and a_{2j} are values of R and T_R, respectively.

TABLE 11.6

j	(a_{1j}, a_{2j})	Simulated Cost
1.	(116, 0.405)	$2,168
2.	(44, 0.735)	3,467
3.	(143, 0.744)	1,851
4.	(197, 0.134)	5,594
5.	(12, 0.355)	3,646
6.	(163, 0.953)	2,124
7.	(95, 0.186)	2,923
8.	(163, 0.594)	2,555

The search for this problem is summarized in Table 11.8 and shown graphically in Figure 11.6. Table 11.8 does not include a summary for every iteration. However, the table does include each iteration for which the optimal changed, and several prior to and following that iteration. For each iteration given, the point brought into the analysis at that iteration, $(a_1^{\circ}\ a_2^{\circ})$, is given. In addition, the least optimal point at each iteration, (a_1', a_2'), is also given and is calculated *after* $(a_1^{\circ}, a_2^{\circ})$ is brought into the search. Therefore, if $(a_1^{\circ}, a_2^{\circ})$ enters the search at the kth iteration, it replaces $(a_1'\ a_2')$ in the $(k-1)$st iteration. Finally, the optimal point at each stage of the search is recorded. The cost associated with each of these three points, calculated through 10 years of simulation, is also shown.

In our discussion of the regression search we indicated that the point $(a_1^{\circ}a_2^{\circ}, \ldots, a_n^{\circ})$ was the best estimate of the optimum at each iteration. The degree to which $(a_1^{\circ}, a_2^{\circ}, \ldots, a_n^{\circ})$ approximates true optimal conditions is dependent upon how well $H(A_1, A_2, \ldots, A_n)$ approximates $C(A_1, A_2, \ldots, A_n)$, which in turn depends upon the variance of the estimate of $C(A_1, A_2, \ldots, A_n)$ when simulation is used to evaluate the measure of effectiveness. To illustrate this point, look at the ninth iteration in Table 11.8. The point (108, 0.797) replaces the point (155, 0.661), which was the least optimal point in the eighth iteration. However, upon evaluating $C(108, 0.797)$, we see that the entering point is not, in fact, optimal. Now look at the 40th iteration. We see that the entering point, (97, 0.580), actually becomes the least optimal point in the region searched at that iteration. The iterations at which the entering point became the optimal point are the 10th, 12th, 26th, 41st, and 46th. When the search terminated at the 73d iteration, the following points were included in the region searched:

TABLE 11.7

j	(a_{1j}, a_{2j})	Simulated Cost
1. . .	(97, 0.515)	$1,560
2. . .	(100, 0.550)	1,579
3. . .	(97, 0.511)	1,563
4. . .	(98, 0.513)	1,570
5. . .	(100, 0.501)	1,583
6. . .	(101, 0.583)	1,576
7. . .	(95, 0.525)	1,583
8. . .	(88, 0.529)	1,658

TABLE 11.8
Optimization of the Problem in Example 4.12 by Regression Analysis and Simulation

Iteration	Least Optimal Point (a_1', a_2')	Cost $C(a_1', a_2')$	Entering Point (a_1^o, a_2^o)	Cost $C(a_1^o, a_2^o)$	Optimal Point	Minimum Cost
0	(197, 0.134)	$5,594			(143, 0.744)	$1,851
1	(12, 0.355)	3,646	(103, 0.822)	$2,033	(143, 0.744)	1,851
2	(44, 0.735)	3,467	(140, 0.971)	2,212	(143, 0.744)	1,851
3	(95, 0.186)	2,923	(124, 0.803)	1,988	(143, 0.744)	1,851
⋮	⋮	⋮	⋮	⋮	⋮	⋮
8	(155, 0.661)	2,145	(131, 0.749)	1,879	(143, 0.744)	1,851
9	(163, 0.958)	2,124	(108, 0.797)	2,099	(143, 0.744)	1,851
10	(123, 0.846)	2,118	(99, 0.667)	1,838	(99, 0.667)	1,838
11	(108, 0.797)	2,099	(89, 0.305)	1,970	(99, 0.667)	1,838
12	(103, 0.822)	2,033	(89, 0.532)	1,615	(89, 0.532)	1,615
13	(124, 0.803)	1,988	(118, 0.565)	1,715	(89, 0.532)	1,615
⋮	⋮	⋮	⋮	⋮	⋮	⋮
25	(71, 0.559)	1,955	(71, 0.559)	1,955	(89, 0.532)	1,615
26	(116, 0.555)	1,716	(100, 0.550)	1,579	(100, 0.550)	1,579
27	(93, 0.573)	1,730	(93, 0.573)	1,730	(100, 0.550)	1,579
⋮	⋮	⋮	⋮	⋮	⋮	⋮
39	(109, 0.628)	1,658	(109, 0.530)	1,656	(100, 0.550)	1,579
40	(97, 0.580)	1,707	(97, 0.580)	1,707	(100, 0.550)	1,579
41	(109, 0.530)	1,656	(97, 0.511)	1,563	(97, 0.511)	1,563
42	(96, 0.358)	1,954	(96, 0.358)	1,954	(97, 0.511)	1,563
⋮	⋮	⋮	⋮	⋮	⋮	⋮
45	(106, 0.532)	1,639	(106, 0.532)	1,639	(97, 0.511)	1,563
46	(97, 0.473)	1,621	(97, 0.515)	1,560	(97, 0.515)	1,560
⋮	⋮	⋮	⋮	⋮	⋮	⋮
73	(88, 0.529)	1,658	(88, 0.529)	1,658	(97, 0.515)	1,560

Based upon the analysis conducted here we would conclude that the optimum is

$$R = 97$$

$$T_R = 0.515$$

From example 4.12, the optimal values of R and T_R are 92 and 0.449 years, respectively, with an associated annual cost of operation of $1,510. Applying equation (4.107), the actual mean annual cost of maintaining the operating policy derived in this example is $1,593. Therefore, accepting the policy derived through the search by regression would cost $83 more than the optimal policy.

FIGURE 11.6
Search Pattern for Example 11.7. (The Number in Parentheses Is the Iteration at Which the Point Became Optimal)

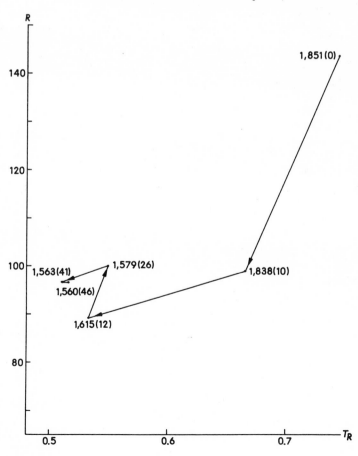

Example 11.8

Determine the optimal solution to the quality control problem given in example 5.9 by applying the search by regression first to the model given in equation (5.59) and then by simulating the system. The number of lots simulated at each iteration of the search is to be 100.

The approximating equation to be used in both cases is to be of the form

$$H(N, c) = b_0 + b_1 N + b_2 c + b_3 N^2 + b_4 c^2 \qquad (11.23)$$

The upper and lower limits for N and c are

$$1 \le N \le 200$$
$$0 \le c \le N$$

FIGURE 11.7
Search by Regression for Example 11.8 Using the Mathematical
Model Given in Equation (5.59) (The number in Parentheses Is the
Iteration at Which the Point Became Optimal.)

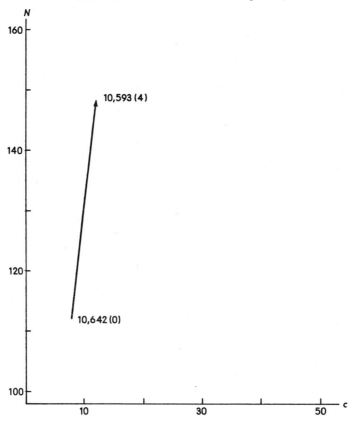

The termination criterion is to break off the search whenever the same point remains optimal for 15 consecutive iterations of the search. The search patterns for these two problems are shown in Figures 11.7 and 11.8.

When the model given in equation (5.59) was used to evaluate the cost of the quality control systems searched, the true optimal system resulted. Even when simulation was used to evaluate this cost, the search proved successful, although the indicated optimum, $N = 145$ and $c = 13$ is not the true optimum. The success of the search by regression in both cases indicates that the relationship defined in

FIGURE 11.8
Search by Regression for Example 11.8 Using Simulation (The Number in Parentheses Is the Iteration at Which the Point Became Optimal.)

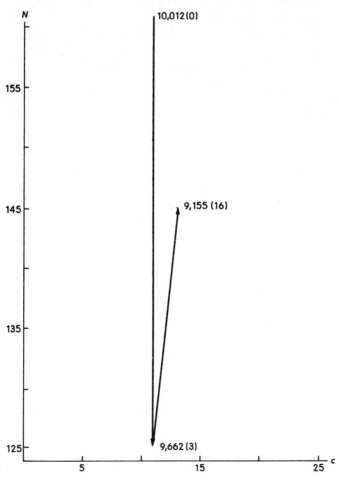

equation (11.23) approximates the true cost equation rather well, at least in the vicinity of the optimum.

In discussing optimum-seeking techniques we have assumed that the functions analyzed are convex. However, in most practical problems the analyst does not know whether the objective function is convex or not. If the function considered actually has several minima (or maxima), the search technique used may terminate at or near the wrong minima (maxima). To check this possibility the analyst may wish to run the search several times, choosing a different starting point each time. If the search terminates in the same region, the analyst would probably be justified in assuming that the region of the true optimum has been found.

Most of the termination criteria discussed above are somewhat arbitrary and are not specifically related to the objectives of the search. To illustrate, consider Figure 11.6, which shows the search for example 11.7. At the 26th iteration the optimal inventory policy was (100, 0.550) with an associated annual cost of $1,579. Over the remainder of the search, 47 iterations, the total annual cost was reduced by $19. The question to be raised here is, was the $19 saved worth the expenditure in computer time required to save it? This question leads us to another termination criterion. The analyst might adopt the philosophy that the search should be continued only as long as the savings resulting from the search outweigh the cost of executing the search. With reference to example 11.7, we could have calculated the computer time required per iteration and from this determined the cost of an iteration. In Figure 11.6, the optimum was improved at the 26th iteration and at the 41st iteration. The savings between the 26th and 41st iterations was $16 per year. If the cost of 15 iterations is less than $16, we would continue the search. Otherwise we would consider terminating the search at the 41st iteration. This decision rule would be appropriate if the inventory policy implemented as a result of the search is to remain in effect for one year. If the policy is to be used for a period of two years, the cost of 15 iterations should be compared with $32.

The discussion of optimum-seeking techniques presented here is by no means exhaustive. Many other techniques are available, and the interested reader should consult the references at the end of this chapter. For example, the authors have found the sequential simplex proposed by Spendley, Hext, and Himsworth (1962) useful in many simulation experiments, although its discussion is beyond the scope of this book. The analyst should bear two criteria in mind in evaluating any optimum-seeking method. First, it should be fast.

That is, the amount of computer time required per iteration should be small. Second, the technique should provide reasonable assurance that it will terminate in the region of the true optimum. Unfortunately the analyst will frequently find that no single technique will satisfy both of these objectives. For this reason, it is not uncommon to find that two or more techniques are used simultaneously in the same problem by switching at various points in the search from one technique to another.

REGRESSION ANALYSIS

In the preceding two sections of this chapter we have presented methods for determining the most desirable course of action when several alternatives are available. However, a simulation may be used to achieve other objectives. Simulation can be useful in determining the interrelationship among several variables. In fact, this is precisely what we did in the preceding section of this chapter. Our attempt there was to develop a regression equation which described the system under study as a function of the decision variables. The analyst might adopt a similar approach in describing the system as a function of other variables as well. For example, suppose an optimal inventory operating policy has been determined through simulation and an appropriate search technique. The optimal policy is based upon assumptions regarding demand and lead time. Since parameters such as mean annual demand and mean lead time are usually estimated, the analyst might wish to know how variations in these estimates from the true parameters will affect the annual cost of maintaining the proposed inventory policy. That is, if his estimates are, in fact, in error by a given amount, how will the cost of maintaining the system be affected? Since he does not know how much his estimates are in error, the analyst would need a relationship which would estimate annual cost for any given values of mean demand and mean lead time. The relationship is usually derived for a range of values of the parameters which is likely to bracket the true values of the parameters.

Regression analysis can be useful in developing the type of relationship just described. The analyst first specifies an equation which he believes will explain the relationship between the dependent variable (annual cost in the above example) and the independent variables (mean demand and mean lead time in the above example). Through regression analysis he can determine, with sufficient data, whether the specified equation does explain the observed variation of the dependent variable. To make this determination, the system studied is simulated for various combinations of the independent variables, and the analyst calculates the measure of effectiveness for each combination. Through least squares, the best-fitting equation of the type initially specified is determined by calculating the values of the coefficients in the equation, based upon the values of the dependent and independent variables obtained during the simulation. A complete regression analysis should include at least the following information:

1. The values of the constants in the hypothesized equation.
2. A test to determine whether a significant amount of variation in the dependent variable, other than random variation, is left unexplained by the hypothesized equation. This test is often referred to as a test for lack of fit.
3. A measure of the proportion of the variation in the dependent variable which is explained by the hypothesized equation. The index of correlation is one such measure.

Through item 1 the analyst is able to completely specify the relationship of the form hypothesized which best fits the data resulting from the simulation. For example, suppose the hypothesized relationship for the demand–lead time example discussed above is

$$y = b_0 + b_1 \lambda + b_2 \mu + b_3 \lambda\mu + \varepsilon \qquad (11.24)$$

where λ is mean annual demand, μ is mean lead time, ε represents random variation, and y is annual cost. The information provided by item 1 consists of estimating the numerical values of b_0, b_1, b_2, b_3.

As we mentioned earlier in this chapter, an estimate of cost, y, (or any other measure of effectiveness) obtained through simulation is composed of two components: the true cost and random error. If an equation of the type given in (11.24) is reliable, it will explain at least a large part of the variation in true cost. For example, if m is the true cost and equation (11.24) is accurate, then

$$m = b_0 + b_1 \lambda + b_2 \mu + b_3 \lambda\mu \qquad (11.25)$$

In other words, if equation (11.24) is reliable, any difference between y and m is due to random variation. The test mentioned in item 2 provides the analyst with a tool for determining whether the proposed relationship may be considered reliable.

Once a reliable equation has been developed, the analyst may wish to know what portion of the variation in the dependent variable is due to variation in the parameter estimated (m) and what portion is due to random variation (ε). The index of correlation, R^2, is probably the most frequently used statistic for this determination.

In general, regression analysis is a useful tool for developing empirical relationships among variables and parameters, whether these quantities are under the control of the decision maker or not. In the search by regression the independent variables were the decision variables. In the demand—lead time example the independent variables were parameters which were presumed to be uncontrollable. The same approach might be taken in studying the effect of changes in cost parameters. Finally, a complete mathematical model of the type derived in Chapter 4 might be developed through regression analysis and simulation by considering all of these variables and parameters in the same equation. However, it should be recognized that as the number of variables and parameters increases, the prospects for successful application of regression analysis decreases, due to the complex interactions which may exist among these quantities.

For a detailed discussion of the theory of regression analysis the reader is referred to Graybill (1961). More elementary discussions of regression analysis and its applications are presented in Draper and Smith (1966), Ezekiel and Fox (1963), and Ostle (1963). An application of regression analysis to simulation experiments is presented in Walsh (1963).

ANALYSIS OF VARIANCE

Selection of the variables to be considered in a simulation experiment is one of the first tasks the experimenter must face. In general any variable which significantly affects the measure of system performance should be included. The conservative analyst will tend to include any quantity which has a remote chance of affecting the measure of effectiveness of the system. The frequent result of this philosophy is that so many variables are included in the simulation that it becomes infeasible to carry out the simulation due to the amount of time it would require. This is particularly true when many of the variables are random variables. On the other hand, if significant variables are omitted, the simulation will probably fail to reproduce reality. The problem, then, is to determine what quantities should be included in the simulation and what quantities should not.

The analysis of variance is a statistical technique which allows the user to determine which variables and interactions among these variables significantly affect the measure of system effectiveness. The analysis of variance would usually be applied to a short pilot run of the simulator in which all variables initially considered are included. In this pilot study, all of the variables should be allowed to vary over a range of values which represents the full range to be expected. Applying the analysis of variance to the results of the pilot study will allow the analyst to assess the significance of each variable and all interactions among the variables. Any variable which proves insignificant when taken by itself and when taken in combination with the other variables may be dropped from further consideration.

It should be pointed out that the analysis of variance does not directly measure the extent of the significance of a given variable. That is, it does not tell the analyst whether one variable is more significant than another, nor does it tell the analyst how a significant variable affects the measure of effectiveness. The outcome of an analysis of variance is a judgment that a variable is or is not significant with respect to its affect on system performance.

Graybill (1961) and Scheffé (1959) present excellent advanced treatments of the analysis of variance. More applied treatments of this subject are contained in Brownlee (1960), Bennett and Franklin (1954) and Ostle (1963). The power of single and two factor analysis of variance experiments is discussed at length in Bowker and Lieberman (1959). Applications of the analysis of variance to simulation experiments are presented in Burdick and Naylor (1966), Jacoby and Harrison (1962), and Naylor, Burdick, and Sasser (1967).

PROBLEMS

1. Consider the problem described in example 4.13. Suppose that lead time is not, in fact, constant but is normally distributed with a mean of 0.0083 years and standard deviation of 0.0020 years. Assuming the optimal operating policy given in example 4.13 ($r = 4$, $Q = 61$), estimate the total cost of operating the system by simulation using a 95 percent confidence interval having a width of not more than $\pm \$15$. To obtain an estimate of σ^2, run the simulator given in Chapter 9 for 10 years and record the standard deviation of mean annual cost, $\sigma_{\bar{x}}$. Noting that $\sigma = \sqrt{n}\, \sigma_{\bar{x}}$, where n is the number of years simulated, find the value of n which will yield the specified confidence interval. Run the simulator for n years and determine whether the desired confidence interval is obtained.

2. Solve problem 1 by building a routine into the simulator which will compute a 95 percent confidence interval about mean annual cost internally. The simulator is to run until the confidence interval specified in problem 1 is obtained.

3. A periodic review inventory system with lost sales is to be simulated for various demand conditions. Lead time is zero and units are demanded one at a time. Each review costs $60 and each order placed costs $100. A lost sale costs $10 and the inventory carrying charge is $20 per unit-year. The period between successive reviews is 0.5 years, and the number of units on each order is that quantity sufficient to bring inventory position to 42 units. The demand conditions to be simulated are as follows:

a) The time between successive demands is 0.005 years and constant.

b) The time between successive demands is exponentially distributed with $\lambda = 200$.

c) The time between successive demands is gamma distributed with $\lambda = 1000$, $n = 5$.

d) The time between successive demands is gamma distributed with $\lambda = 5000$, $n = 25$.

Each condition is to be simulated until a 90 percent confidence interval about mean annual cost is within $\pm\,\$20$.

4. After solving problem 3 for each of the four conditions, derive a 95 percent confidence interval for σ, where n is the number of years simulated in that problem. Would you consider the estimate of σ reliable?

5. The optimal solution to the problem given in example 4.11 called for a reorder point of eight and an order quantity of 34. Lead time was assumed to be constant at 0.08 years. After further study it was found that lead time is actually gamma distributed with $\lambda = 125$ and $n = 10$. This development has led the analyst to believe that the ordering policy should be changed. He has decided to simulate the following operating policies as well as the current policy to determine whether any is an improvement over that already proposed, under gamma lead time:

$$r = 7, Q = 32$$
$$r = 7, Q = 34$$
$$r = 7, Q = 36$$
$$r = 8, Q = 32$$
$$r = 8, Q = 36$$
$$r = 9, Q = 32$$
$$r = 9, Q = 34$$
$$r = 9, Q = 36$$

Compute intervals after every 50 years of simulation, eliminating alternatives where possible. The analysis is to be terminated wherever

$$\max_i U_i - \min_i L_i < \$10$$

or when only one alternative remains. Can the policy originally proposed still be considered optimal?

6. A building contains 1,000 light bulbs. The frequency distribution of time until failure, in days, is given below.

Time until Failure (Days)	Frequency of Time until Failure
0.00– 2.00	43
2.01– 4.00	84
4.01– 6.00	135
6.01– 8.00	102
8.01–10.00	88
10.01–12.00	61
12.01–14.00	33
14.01–16.00	18
16.01–18.00	9
18.01–20.00	4
20.01–22.01	1
22.01–24.00	0

The building manager wishes to determine the best policy for replacing burned-out bulbs. One such policy is to replace them as they burn out which will cost $1 per replacement. Another possibility is to replace all bulbs every ith week in addition to replacing any which fail during the weeks between bulk replacement. The cost of replacing all bulbs at one time is $0.20 per bulb. By simulation, determine the optimal replacement policy out of the five listed below.

a) Replacement upon failure only.

b) Replacement upon failure in addition to quantity replacement every week.

c) Replacement upon failure in addition to quantity replacement every two weeks.

d) Replacement upon failure in addition to quantity replacement every three weeks.

e) Replacement upon failure in addition to quantity replacement every four weeks.

Terminate the simulation when only one replacement policy remains or when

$$\max_i U_i - \min_i L_i < \$40/\text{year}$$

7. An electronic detection device is composed of three components, 1, 2, and 3, such that if any single component fails, the device fails. The mean and standard deviation of component life are given in the accompanying table. The

Component	Mean Life (m_i)	Standard Deviation of Life (σ)
1	1.2 years	0.10 years
2	1.4 years	0.15 years
3	1.1 years	0.10 years

distribution of time until failure for each component is normal with means and standard deviations as given in the table. This detection device is to function for one year. The probability that it will survive for this period is the probability that each of the three components lasts for at least one year or

$$P(\text{Survival for one year}) = \prod_{i=1}^{3} \int_{1}^{\infty} \frac{1}{\sigma\sqrt{2\pi}} \exp\left\{-\left[\frac{(x_i - m_i)^2}{2\sigma^2}\right]\right\} dx_i$$

$$= (0.9772)(0.9961)(0.8413)$$

$$= 0.8189$$

A reliability of 0.8189 is not considered high enough. To increase the reliability of the device, stand-by components can be added which will take over upon failure of the original component, thereby extending the life of the equipment. The life distribution of each stand-by component is exponential with mean given in the following table. Any number of stand-by units can be added but at the

Component	Mean Life of Stand-by	Cost/Stand-by Unit Added
1	0.05 years	$0.20
2	0.07 years	0.30
3	0.04 years	0.20

additional cost indicated in the table. For example, the mean life of the third component can be increased 0.08 years by adding two stand-by units which would cost $0.40 over the present cost. By simulation, determine the number and arrangement of stand-by components which will bring the system reliability to 0.98 at the minimum cost.

8. The distribution of demand for parking space in a particular downtown area has been found to be Poisson with mean 200 per eight-hour day. A parking lot is to be located in this area. The cost of operating and maintaining the lot is estimated to be $9.000 per year per 100 parking spaces provided. The price of a parking space on the lot is to be $0.25 no matter how long the space is occupied. The distribution of the time a car spends on the lot is exponential with a mean of two hours. The parking lot is to remain open eight hours each day, 365 days per year. By simulation, determine the optimal number of parking spaces provided.

9. Simulate the following reorder point inventory system in which stock-outs result in lost sales, lead time is constant, and units are demanded one at a time.
  Demand—Poisson with mean demand of 30,000 units per year.
  Lead Time = 0.008 years.
  $C_I = \$20$
  $C_o = \$300$
  $C_L = \$70$
Determine the optimal ordering policy. Simulate each alternative investigated for a period of one year.

10. Simulate the system described in problem 9 with the following change. The mean annual demand is 30,000 units but the demand rate during the first half of the year is higher than that for the second. Demand during the first half of the year is Poisson distributed with mean 20,000 units and that during the second half of the year is Poisson distributed with mean 10,000 units. Find the optimal ordering policy and compare it with that found when the demand rate was constant throughout the year.

11. Find the optimal quality control system for the problem given in example 5.14.

12. A computer center operates 24 hours per day requiring one computer operator per eight-hour shift. Each operator is paid at a rate of $4 per hour. If an operator cannot work his sift, he must either be replaced on that shift or the machine he operates is shut down for that shift at a cost of $300 per hour. To provide insurance against the possibility of loss of machine time, it has been proposed that several of the operators be put "on call" during those shifts on which they are not working. The proposal calls for paying operators "on call" at a rate of $0.50 per hour for remaining available. Each operator is paid time and one half for all work over eight hours per day. The probability that an operator can work his shift is 0.95. The probability that an operator "on call" can be reached when needed is 0.90. By simulation determine the optimal number of "on call" operators.

13. A company manufactures electric blenders at a rate of 100,000 per year. Each blender is guaranteed for a period of four years. The cost of manufacturing a blender which has a mean life of m years, C_m is

$$C_m = a + bm + cm^2$$

where $a = \$5.00, b = \$4.00, c = \$0.20$.

Time until failure for each blender is exponentially distributed with a mean of m. Each failure which occurs during the guarantee period costs the manufacturer an average of $6.67. By simulation determine the optimal value of m. At each iteration of the required search, simulate the life of 200 blenders.

14. Solve problem 13 when the cost of a failure, T, during the guarantee period is a random variable with density function

$$f_T(t) = 0.005(20 - t), \qquad 0 < t < 20$$

15. In problem 13 the unit production cost, C_m is expected to increase at an average rate of 7 percent per year for the next five years and the cost of failures by 10 percent per year during the same period. Find the optimal value of m for each year. Start the search for each year using the previous year's optimal.

16. Find the optimal crew size for the problem given in example 5.3 by simulation if service time is normally distributed with a mean of $0.001/n$ year and standard deviation of $0.0001/n$ years.

17. For the problem described in example 4.11, suppose that available storage space was limited to 36 units. Any time the inventory level exceeds 36 units a cost of $5 is incurred for each unit placed in storage in excess of 36. By simulation determine the optimal inventory policy.

18. Simulate the system given in problem 17 when each unit in inventory in excess of 36 is stored at a cost of $40 per unit year plus a handling cost of $2 per unit. Note that unit years of inventory must now be calculated for units stored at $20 per unit year and for units stored at $40 per unit year. Determine the optimal ordering policy by the method of sectioning.

19. In problem 17 assume that an inventory of more than 36 units cannot be handled. If an order is received which raises the inventory level above 30 units, those units in excess of 30 are returned to the supplier at a cost of $2 per unit returned. By simulation and the method of sectioning, determine the optimal policy for maintaining inventory.

20. In example 5.7 assume that there is an additional cost for parts replacement and unit replacement. If the entire unit must be replaced it costs $300. The probability that a failing unit will have to be replaced by a new unit is 0.20. The cost of parts for failing units which do not have to be replaced, V, is a random variable with density function given by

$$f_V(v) = \frac{1}{50}, \qquad 0 < v < 50$$

By simulation, determine the optimal values of n and T.

21. In example 5.7 assume that the entire crew may not be available when required due to other responsibilities. In particular, the probability that x of n crewmen are available during any maintenance period is given by

$$p_X(x) = \binom{n}{x} p^x (1 - p)^{n-x}, \qquad x = 0, 1, \ldots, n$$

where $p = .92$. If a maintenance period is scheduled to begin but no crewmen are available, that maintenance period is skipped. Assume that the crew size does not change during the maintenance period. Find the optimal values of n and T through simulation and an appropriate search technique. At each iteration of the search simulate two years of operation.

22. Solve the problem given in example 5.9 when the proportion defective, P, is normally distributed with a mean of 0.05 and standard deviation of 0.004.

23. Solve the problem given in example 5.9 if the lot size, L is considered a decision variable. Total annual production is three million units, and L may assume any value up to three million. Use the search by regression to find values of N,c, and L which minimize the annual cost of quality control. At each iteration of the search, simulate at least one year of operation and the inspection of at least 50 lots.

24. Using the search by regression and simulation, find the optimal quality control system for the problem in example 5.11 when annual production is 500,000 units and the lot size, L, is a decision variable. At each iteration of the search simulate at least one year of operation and the inspection of at least 50 lots. The optimal system is that for which the annual cost of quality control is a minimum.

25. By simulation and the search by regression, find the optimal sample sizes and acceptance numbers for the problem described in example 5.14. Simulate the inspection of 100 lots at each iteration of the search.

26. Simulate the problem described in example 4.11 with the following modification. Instead of reviewing the status of inventory at each demand, inventory is reveiwed every T_r years. If at a review inventory position is at or below r, an order is placed for Q units. The cost of a review may be considered to be $5. Using an appropriate search technique, determine the optimal values of T_r, r, and Q. Each policy investigated should be simulated for five years.

27. A directive from top management has been issued which indicates that the company's annual investment in inventory for a particular product should be kept below $1,000. For this product a reorder point inventory system has been proposed. Each stock-out results in a lost sale at a cost of $70. The inventory carrying charge is $60 per unit-year and orders are placed at a cost of $300. Demand is Poisson distributed with a mean rate of 300 units per year. Units are demanded one at a time. Lead time is exponentially distributed with a mean of 0.004 years. Determine the optimal inventory operating policy. How well does the optimal policy meet management's directive?

28. The inventory system described in problem 9 is to be simulated with the following modification. When an order is received, it is subjected to an incoming inspection by the quality control department. If the lot is rejected upon this inspection, it is returned to the supplier and another order is placed with the supplier for a quantity equal to that rejected. If the order is accepted, it is placed in inventory. The inspection procedure consists of selecting five units from the receipt lot and accepting the lot if no defective units are found. If one or more defective units are detected the lot are rejected. The density function of proportion defective, P, is given by

$$f_P(p) = 21(1 - p)^{20}, \qquad 0 < p < 1$$

Develop a subroutine which will carry out the inspection procedure, place a new order when necessary, and update all necessary counters. Ignore all quality control costs. Assume inspection is nondestructive. Find the optimal inventory operating policy for this system.

29. Simulate the system described in problem 28 when the cost of quality control is considered. The cost of inspecting one unit is $4. The cost of rejecting a lot is the cost of placing a new order. Each accepted defective unit costs $2. The simulator should calculate and distinguish between the annual cost of

operating the inventory system and the annual cost of quality control. Find the optimal values of the sample size, N; the acceptance number, c; the reorder point, r; and the order quantity, Q. Simulate each alternative investigated for a period of six months. Use the search by regression to determine the optimal solution. Let

$$H(N, c, r, Q)$$
$$= b_0 + b_1 N + b_2 c + b_3 r + b_4 Q + b_5 N^2 + b_6 c^2 + b_7 r^2 + b_8 Q^2$$

30. A service station has n gasoline pumps. Cars arrive at the service station in a Poisson fashion with a mean rate of 250 per day. If a car arrives and no pump is available, it leaves the service station without waiting for service. The number of gallons of gasoline sold per car is normally distributed with a mean of 12 gallons and standard deviation of 3 gallons. Service time per car is exponentially distributed with a mean of five minutes. The service station makes $0.02 profit per gallon sold. The service station maintains one attendent for each two pumps in service. Each attendent is paid $5,000 per year. By simulation and the method of sectioning, find the most profitable number of pumps.

31. Solve problem 30 if the probability that a car will wait for service is $1/(m + 1)$ where m is the total number of cars waiting for service but not in service.

32. A trucking firm has a contract with eight different companies under which it agrees to deliver their products within a small urban area. Truck drivers are paid $6,000 per year. The annual cost of a truck is $10,000 and includes the costs of operation, maintenance, and the initial investment distributed over the life of the truck. The firm charges $20 per hour per truck (including the driver). The number of hours of service demanded per day by each of the eight companies is binomially distributed with the following parameters:

Company	n	p
I	8	0.125
II	8	0.875
III.	8	0.375
IV.	8	0.500
V	8	0.250
VI.	8	0.375
VII	8	0.750
VIII. . . .	8	0.250

The trucking firm operates eight hours per day and does not begin delivery for any customer unless the delivery can be completed on the same day it started. If delivery cannot be accomplished on the same day requested by the customer, the rental cost for that customer is reduced by $2 per hour per day late. On any given day the trucking firm attempts to complete back ordered service first. The next highest priority is given to those companies requesting the largest blocks of time on that day. The trucking firm operates 300 days per year. By simulation, find the number of trucks which will maximize annual profit.

33. Solve problem 32 with the following modification. The probability that a truck is operable when needed is 0.95. The time in hours required to repair a truck when it is down, T, is exponentially distributed with a mean of six hours. Does this modification change the optimal number of trucks found in the previous problem?

34. The ABC Company manufactures one of its products in a single operation which consists of converting one unit of raw material into one unit of final product. Demand for the final product is Poisson distributed with a mean rate of 1,000 units per year. Each demand consists of a request for 10 units. Unfilled demand results in a lost sale at a cost of $2. The final product inventory carrying cost is $1.50 per unit-year. The carrying cost for raw materials in $0.50 per unit-year. The production rate is 30,000 units per year, and each setup costs

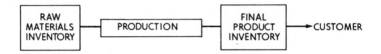

$500. The cost of placing an order for raw materials is $35. An order for replenishment of the final product inventory results in a set up of the production line. The order size is Q, and orders are placed whenever inventory position falls to r. If the raw materials inventory level is such that only a portion, p, of the order for Q units can be produced, that part, pQ, is produced and the remainder is back ordered. The unfilled portion of the order is filled when the raw materials inventory is replenished. If this occurs while the production line is in operation, the production period is extended to produce a total of Q units. If the order for raw materials arrives after production of pQ units has ceased, the line is set up to produce the remaining $(1 - p)Q$ units.

Reorder point systems are to be used for both inventories. Find the optimal operating policies. Assume that order lead time for raw materials is 0.01 years and constant.

35. In problem 34 assume that each raw material order is inspected before it is placed in inventory. If the order is rejected, it is returned to the supplier and a new order is placed. If the order is accepted, it is placed in inventory but each defective unit included in the order is eventually detected and discarded on the production line at a cost of $1.38 per defective item. The density function of proportion defective has been found to be given by

$$f_P(p) = 800(0.05 - p), \qquad 0 < p < 0.05$$

It costs $2 to inspect one unit of raw material, and inspection is nondestructive. Find the optimal quality control system and the optimal inventory operating policies.

36. Solve problem 34 when the production line may fail during operation. The time between successive failures is normally distributed with a mean of 0.10 years and standard deviation of 0.02 years. The time between successive failures is measured in operating time and does not include downtime or idle time. The distribution of downtime per failure is exponentially distributed with a mean of 0.005 years.

37. After packaging, finished products are transferred in lots of 1,000 to finished goods inventory by conveyor. Packing cartons are placed on the conveyor automatically, seven feet apart from center to center. Cartons are unloaded by hand and are removed from the conveyor within a distance of seven feet of the unloader. That is, the unloader cannot reach a carton which is more than three and a half feet from him. Any carton which is not removed by the unloader is automatically dumped from the conveyor and must be retrieved at a later time. The time taken to unload a carton is normally distributed with a mean of 15 seconds and standard deviation of 3 seconds. The distance from the loading point to the unloading point measured along the conveyor is 100 feet. The conveyor can be run at any speed desired. Let x be the number of cartons removed per hour and y the number of cartons missed by the unloader per hour. By simulation and an appropriate search technique, find the conveyor speed which will maximize $x - y$.

38. Solve problem 37 when the distance between successive cartons is exponentially distributed with a mean of eight feet.

39. A company has two plants, A and B, which are located within the same urban area. The company runs a bus service between the two plants between 9 a.m. and 5 p.m. The bus starts each day at plant A. At each plant the bus waits until N persons have boarded the bus before leaving for the other plant. Transit time between the two plants is normally distributed with a mean of 31 minutes and a standard deviation of 5 minutes. Passengers arrive at the terminal at plant A in a Poisson fashion at an average rate of nine per hour, and at the terminal at plant B in a Poisson fashion with a mean rate of five per hour. What should the value of N be to minimize the mean waiting time per person? Waiting time does not include time spent on the bus.

40. Find the optimal inventory policies for the system described in problem 26 of Chapter 9 using the cost information given in problem 28.

41. The ABC Company manufactures toothpaste tubes. The tubes are formed from lead slugs which are purchased from an outside source. After the tubes are formed, they are capped with plastic closures. The caps are manufactured internally, but the plastic from which the caps are molded is purchased externally. The manufacturing operation from the receipt of lead slugs and plastic to packing and shipping is summarized in the figure below.

Whenever the inventory of lead slugs falls to r_s pounds, an order is placed for 100,000 pounds of slugs (one million slugs). Lead time on slugs is exponentially distributed with a mean of one week. When lead slugs are received, they are placed in inventory until they are needed for production. The inventory carrying cost is $0.009 per slug per year.

The ABC Company produces tubes continuously on three lines at a rate of 20,000 per line per day, five days per week. Slugs are fed to each line from a hopper which holds 2,000 slugs. After a tube is formed, it is capped. The capping operation is automated, and if a cap is cracked or broken, jamming occurs—resulting in a shutdown of the line until the trouble is relieved. The time

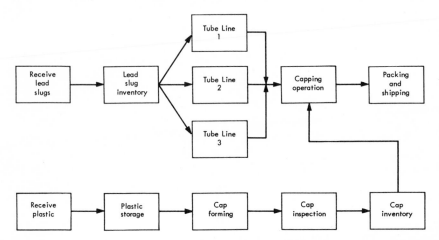

to repair such line failures is exponentially distributed with a mean of four minutes, and the cost of resulting lost production is $0.60 per minute of downtime.

When the inventory of plastic falls to r_p, an order is placed for 100,000 units of plastic with a local firm. (1 unit of plastic = 1 cap). The lead time on orders for plastic is one day (constant). Orders for plastic are placed in inventory upon receipt and held there at a cost of $0.0001 per unit per year. Plastic is fed directly from inventory to the molding operation which forms the caps. Caps can be produced at a rate of 120,000 per day. However, caps are not produced continuously throughout the year. Cap production may be scheduled in whatever manner the production department feels is appropriate. However, each setup for cap production costs $86.

Subsequent to production, caps are inspected in lots of 100,000. Broken or cracked caps are considered defective. The sample size and acceptance number have not been determined, but rejection of a lot results in its scrapping at a cost of $0.004 per cap. The unit cost of inspection is $0.06. The distribution lot proportion defective for broken or cracked caps is defined by

$$f_P(p) = 1000(1 - p)^{999}, \qquad 0 < p < 1$$

If a lot is accepted, it is placed in inventory and stored until it is used. The storage cost is $0.0004 per unit per year. Caps are fed to the capping operation from a hopper which holds 6,000 caps. Caps are taken from inventory as necessary.

If a stock-out of either caps or lead slugs occurs, the line requiring the out-of-stock item is shut down until the supply is replenished, at a cost of $1,200 per line per day of downtime. In the case of a stock-out of either item, an emergency order is placed. Each unit of plastic purchased on such a basis costs $0.0001 more than would normally be the case, and lead time is exponentially distributed with a mean of two hours. Each lead slug purchased on an emergency basis costs $0.0015 more than normal. Lead time on emergency orders of lead slugs is normally distributed with a mean of two days and standard deviation of 0.4 days. The order quantities in both cases are the same as those specified for orders placed under normal conditions.

1. Develop a simulator for the production of toothpaste tubes.
2. Determine the optimal values of r_s and r_p.
3. Determine the optimal sampling plan for the inspection of caps.
4. How should the production of caps be scheduled?

42. Consider the intersection illustrated below. Main street is a one way, west to east, two-lane street. Left turns are permitted from Main street to First street, provided the turning vehicle is in the left lane of Main street. Similarly, right turns are permitted on to First street from the right lane of Main street. First street is two-lane, one lane north, one lane south. Right turns are permitted from First street to Main street for traffic moving north. However, no turns are permitted to traffic moving south on First street at the intersection.

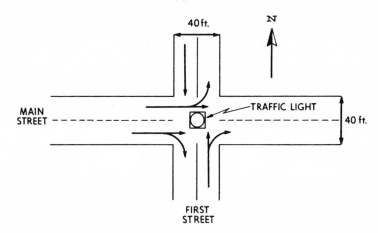

The time between successive arrivals at the intersection on Main street is exponentially distributed with a mean of 20 seconds. The time between successive southbound arrivals on First street is exponentially distributed with a mean of 40 seconds. The interarrival time for northbound traffic is exponentially distributed with a mean of 60 seconds.

Let
P(left turn off of Main street) = 0.05
P(right turn off of Main street) = 0.03
P(right turn from First street) = 0.18

When the traffic light turns green, those vehicles queued because of the preceding red phase start to move through the intersection. The first car in the line starts through the intersection four seconds after the light turns green, the second car starts three seconds after the first, the third two and one half seconds after the second, the fourth two seconds after the third. The delay for the fifth, sixth, etc., vehicles is two seconds. Once a vehicle starts, it accelerates at a rate of five feet/sec^2 up to a maximum velocity of 30 m.p.h.

Assume a vehicle length of 18 feet. The amber phase of the traffic light lasts four seconds. If a vehicle arrives at the intersection during the amber phase, it stops and waits for the next green phase.

Simulate the delay of vehicles at the intersection on both Main and First streets. In particular, the simulator should record the mean delay per vehicle and the mean delay per delayed vehicle at the intersection for a given length of red and green phases. Determine the red-green phasing which minimizes mean delay time per vehicle and that which minimizes mean delay per vehicle per delayed vehicle.

43. The Quality Control Department of your company has just released new quality standards which will go into effect in 60 days if serious objections are not raised in the near future. The product of concern to you is a 120-volt floodlamp with a rated life of four hours. Your department produces these lamps in large quantities each week. The proposed plan for your department is as follows:

1. A sample of lamps from each week's production will be selected. Each lamp will be tested for four consecutive hours. Any lamp which fails in this time period will be considered defective.
2. The acceptable quality level is 1 percent defective items.
3. The sample size and acceptance numbers for inspection are to be selected from MIL–STD–105D, Sampling Procedures and Tables for Inspection by attributes. These sampling plans are summarized below.

Weekly Production	Sample Size	Acceptance Number
501–1,200 80		2
1,201–3,200 125		3
3,201–10,000. 200		5
10,001–35,000. 315		7
35,001–150,000 500		10
150,000–500,000 800		14

4. If the number of lamps which fail during the four-hour test period exceeds the acceptance number, the entire week's production will be returned to the production department and scrapped.   Floodlamps are produced on four production lines which operate 24 hours per day. Weekly production records for 1966 and 1967 are available and are given on page 571. Quality control records are also available for this period and are as given on pp. 572-573. Floodlamps are sold for $0.90 each. The production cost per

1966 INSPECTION SUMMARY			1967 INSPECTION SUMMARY		
WEEK	SAMPLE	DEFECTIVES	WEEK	SAMPLE	DEFECTIVES
1	100	0	1	100	0
2	100	2	2	100	0
3	100	3	3	100	3
4	100	0	4	100	12
5	100	0	5	100	4
6	100	0	6	100	1
7	100	7	7	100	0
8	100	2	8	100	16
9	100	10	9	100	2
10	100	11	10	100	0
11	100	24	11	100	6
12	100	7	12	100	0
13	100	0	13	100	6
14	100	11	14	100	15
15	100	7	15	100	4
16	100	1	16	100	0
17	100	1	17	100	3
18	100	0	18	100	5
19	100	5	19	100	6
20	100	0	20	100	1
21	100	11	21	100	10
22	100	8	22	100	3
23	100	5	23	100	5
24	100	3	24	100	0
25	100	12	25	100	1
26	100	2	26	100	5
27	100	4	27	100	5
28	100	4	28	100	25
29	100	9	29	100	8
30	100	3	30	100	0
31	100	2	31	100	10
32	100	0	32	100	0
33	100	0	33	100	10
34	100	3	34	100	2
35	100	3	35	100	19
36	100	0	36	100	9
37	100	6	37	100	9
38	100	6	38	100	2
39	100	1	39	100	1
40	100	4	40	100	1
41	100	2	41	100	3
42	100	4	42	100	3
43	100	13	43	100	8
44	100	2	44	100	3
45	100	1	45	100	8
46	100	0	46	100	6
47	100	2	47	100	4
48	100	6	48	100	11
49	100	7	49	100	2
50	100	11	50	100	1
51	100	2	51	100	2
52	100	12	52	100	2

1966 PRODUCTION SUMMARY

WEEK	LINE 1			LINE 2			LINE 3			LINE 4		
	PROD.	SCRAP	NET PROD.	PROD.	SCRAP	NET PR	PROD.	SCRAP	NET PROD.	PROD.	SCRAP	NET PROD.
1	220	2	218	331	3	328	403	0	403	328	2	326
2	440	2	438	381	3	378	352	0	352	299	1	298
3	283	2	281	263	1	262	314	1	313	373	0	373
4	368	1	367	216	0	216	329	1	328	306	1	305
5	309	0	309	366	1	365	405	0	405	334	2	332
6	329	2	327	274	2	272	337	1	336	257	1	256
7	422	3	359	390	0	390	395	1	394	346	0	346
8	262	3	359	443	1	442	410	4	406	342	2	340
9	375	1	374	385	0	385	368	2	366	378	1	377
10	342	2	340	389	1	388	380	2	378	287	0	287
11	346	2	344	384	2	382	341	1	340	325	0	325
12	399	2	397	439	2	437	371	3	368	303	1	302
13	202	1	301	309	0	309	392	1	391	369	0	369
14	321	1	320	346	2	344	317	3	314	316	1	315
15	206	1	305	271	3	268	206	3	203	310	1	309
16	351	2	319	320	0	320	405	3	402	283	1	282
17	263	2	261	236	1	235	394	1	393	307	1	306
18	417	0	378	343	1	342	393	3	390	327	0	327
19	281	3	378	402	0	402	388	3	385	338	2	337
20	230	3	327	356	2	354	322	3	319	333	2	331
21	350	2	348	385	1	384	281	0	281	263	2	261
22	235	0	335	413	0	413	342	1	341	290	3	287
23	256	2	296	349	2	347	355	4	351	330	2	328
24	241	1	240	388	0	388	337	1	336	374	4	358
25	364	2	362	380	1	379	402	0	402	360	0	328
26	254	3	391	398	2	396	325	0	325	331	3	367
27	265	3	362	331	4	327	335	2	333	301	1	300
28	277	1	376	316	0	316	328	1	327	249	1	249
29	226	1	298	375	2	373	331	1	330	388	2	387
30	226	1	324	294	2	292	378	2	376	317	1	316
31	281	0	381	412	3	409	391	2	389	328	2	326
32	250	3	347	366	1	365	399	3	396	296	2	294
33	252	3	349	278	1	277	368	0	368	283	0	283
34	221	0	345	342	2	340	301	0	301	303	3	300
35	412	5	255	370	1	369	376	1	375	318	1	317
36	200	1	316	413	2	411	327	1	326	350	3	347
37	2CC	1	302	387	2	385	378	0	378	406	2	404
38	284	3	281	328	3	325	310	0	310	374	3	371
39	225	0	322	327	0	327	337	4	333	340	5	340
40	423	0	422	331	2	329	405	5	402	340	5	335
41	2C3	0	303	339	0	339	343	2	341	384	3	381
42	375	3	373	298	3	295	367	4	363	327	2	325
43	2C8	0	308	360	0	358	361	1	360	389	3	386
44	2C6	0	304	371	0	371	302	3	299	304	2	302
45	229	1	329	294	0	294	364	1	363	325	1	324
46	2E8	0	285	283	0	283	333	1	332	345	0	347
47	355	3	354	321	1	320	336	2	334	385	0	387
48	2E2	1	379	400	0	400	358	0	356	385	0	343
49	226	4	324	365	0	365	415	0	415	338	3	336
50	248	0	348	304	3	301	343	0	340	271	0	271
51	220	2	318	322	3	319	322	0	322	452	0	452
52	318	0	318	307	0	307	292	2	290	314	3	311

ALL PRODUCTION LISTED IN GROSS

WEEK	LINE 1 PROD.	SCRAP	NET PROD.	LINE 2 PROD.	SCRAP	NET PR	LINE 3 PROD.	SCRAP	NET PROD.	LINE 4 PROD.	SCRAP	NET PROD.
1	356	0	356	316	1	315	405	3	402	359	0	359
2	258	1	297	323	0	323	287	1	286	341	4	337
3	353	3	350	361	1	360	305	3	302	259	1	258
4	402	3	309	334	1	333	340	3	337	352	0	352
5	306	3	305	408	3	405	231	2	229	343	1	342
6	327	2	325	300	2	298	367	0	367	431	2	429
7	385	0	385	323	2	321	332	2	330	320	1	319
8	305	2	307	336	2	334	394	1	393	343	2	341
9	306	0	308	263	3	260	367	1	366	409	2	397
10	232	0	332	321	1	320	362	2	360	440	1	439
11	375	4	371	351	0	351	354	2	352	372	1	371
12	347	0	323	361	2	359	316	0	316	318	2	316
13	222	0	387	383	1	382	290	1	289	320	3	317
14	357	0	325	280	2	278	365	2	363	400	0	400
15	227	2	325	252	1	351	391	0	391	303	0	393
16	240	0	340	366	1	365	324	2	322	371	1	371
17	233	0	233	378	2	376	353	1	352	243	1	242
18	222	0	322	378	2	376	351	3	348	430	0	429
19	413	3	410	366	2	364	367	1	366	306	5	391
20	318	2	316	352	3	349	316	3	313	449	1	447
21	266	2	354	307	3	304	311	2	309	408	0	407
22	417	2	415	324	1	323	442	1	441	352	1	352
23	438	1	427	319	1	318	445	0	445	351	0	350
24	383	0	383	363	1	362	344	1	343	350	1	350
25	271	1	270	470	2	468	395	0	395	398	0	397
26	295	0	395	372	0	372	265	0	263	400	0	400
27	324	1	323	423	3	420	247	2	245	320	3	317
28	306	1	305	358	4	354	390	2	388	372	1	371
29	215	0	215	350	1	349	359	3	356	228	3	225
30	243	0	343	359	0	359	359	3	356	293	2	291
31	265	0	267	308	3	305	355	2	353	376	0	376
32	232	2	330	340	2	338	356	2	354	439	0	439
33	356	0	356	389	1	388	383	2	381	350	3	347
34	316	1	315	357	1	356	410	0	410	349	1	347
35	345	2	347	350	0	350	361	4	357	365	1	364
36	264	2	262	350	0	350	347	2	345	310	0	330
37	288	2	286	338	4	334	248	2	246	308	4	304
38	270	2	268	268	1	267	321	2	319	297	0	297
39	229	3	326	329	4	325	370	0	370	279	2	277
40	253	0	353	354	1	351	317	3	314	351	0	351
41	211	0	211	354	4	350	289	0	289	355	0	355
42	210	2	308	310	0	310	342	2	340	292	2	290
43	242	2	340	342	1	342	367	1	366	317	0	317
44	226	4	322	394	0	393	255	2	253	422	2	420
45	286	2	284	346	3	346	350	0	350	391	0	391
46	235	1	334	445	3	442	314	0	314	347	2	344
47	246	0	246	300	4	296	391	2	389	358	3	367
48	268	2	266	292	3	289	355	1	354	343	1	343
49	239	1	338	381	4	377	358	0	358	406	0	405
50	281	1	380	249	2	247	363	1	362	317	2	315
51	343	3	340	385	3	382	395	1	394	420	1	419
52	336	0	336	252	3	249	324	0	324	395	1	394

ALL PRODUCTION LISTED IN GROSS

lamp is $0.60 per unit. The cost of inspecting one lamp is $1.04 and the scrap cost is $0.52, $0.09 of the value of the product being recoverable.

One method which has been suggested to improve the life of the lamp is replacement of the filament. The present filament costs $0.04. A new filament is available which will increase the life of the lamp by 15 percent. The price of the new filament is $0.09. As members of the systems analysis group within the production department you have been asked to determine whether this sampling plan can be accepted by your department as a standard for future operation. What are your recommendations?

REFERENCES

Bennett, C. A. and Franklin, N. L.   *Statistical Analysis.* New York: John Wiley & Sons, Inc., 1954.

Bowker, A. H. and Lieberman, G. J.   *Engineering Statistics.* Englewood Cliffs, N. J.: Prentice-Hall., 1959.

Brownlee, K. A.   *Statistical Theory and Methodology in Science and Engineering.* New York: John Wiley & Sons, Inc., 1960.

Burdick, Donald S. and Naylor, Thomas H.   "Design of Computer Simulation Experiments for Industrial Systems," *Business Applications,* Vol. 9, No. 5. (May 1966), pp. 329–39.

Conway, R. W. "Some Tactical Problems in Simulation Method," No. RM–32244–PR, The RAND Corporation, Santa Monica, California, October 1962.

Draper, N. and Smith, H.   *Applied Regression Analysis.* New York: John Wiley & Sons, Inc., 1966.

Ehrenfield, S. and Ben–Tuvia, S.   "The Efficiency of Statistical Simulation Procedures," *Technometrics,* Vol. 4, No. 2 (May 1962), pp. 257–75.

Ezekiel, M. and Fox, K. A.   *Methods of Correlation and Regression Analysis.* New York: John Wiley & Sons, Inc., 1963.

Fishman, George S. "Problems in the Statistical Analysis of Simulation Experiments: The Comparison of Means and the Length of Sample Records," No. RM–4880–Pr, The RAND Corporation, Santa Monica, California, February 1966.

Fishman, George S. and Kiviat, Philip J.   "Spectral Analysis of Time Series Generated by Simulation Models," No. RM–4393–PR, The RAND Corporation, Santa Monica, California, February 1965.

Friedman, M. and Savage, L. S.   *Selected Techniques of Statistical Analysis.* New York: McGraw-Hill Book Co., Inc., 1947.

Gafarian, A. V. and Ancker, C. J., Jr.   "Mean Value Estimation from Computer Simulation," *Operations Research,* Vol. 14, No. 1 (January–February 1966) pp. 25–44.

Graybill, F. A. *An Introduction to Linear Statistical Models.* New York: McGraw-Hill Book Co., Inc., 1961.

Jacoby, J. E. and Harrison, S.   "Multi-Variable Experimentation and Simulation Models," *Naval Research Logistics Quarterly,* Vol. 9, (1962), pp. 121–36.

McMillan, C. and Gonzalez, R. F.   *Systems Analysis.* Rev. ed. Homewood, Ill: Richard D. Irwin, Inc., 1968.

Naylor, T. H., Balintfy, J. L., Burdick, D. S., and Chu, K.   *Computer Simulation Techniques.* New York: John Wiley & Sons, Inc., 1966.

Naylor, T. H., Burdick, D. S., and Sasser, W. E.   "Computer Simulation Experiments with Economic Systems: The Problem of Experimental Design," *Journal of the American Statistical Association,* Vol. LXII (1967), pp. 1315–37.

Nemhauser, G. L.   *Introduction to Dynamic Programming.* New York: John Wiley & Sons, Inc., 1966.

Ostle, B.   *Statistics in Research.* Ames, Iowa: The Iowa State University Press, 1963.

Scheffé, H.   *The Analysis of Variance.* New York: John Wiley & Sons, Inc., 1959.

Spendley, W., Hext, G. R., and Himsworth, F. R.   "Sequential Application of Simplex Design in Optimization and Evolutionary Operation," *Technometrics,* Vol. 4, No. 4 (November 1962), pp. 441–61.

Walsh, J. E.   "Use of Linearized Nonlinear Regression for Simulations Involving Monte Carlo," *Operations Research,* Vol. 11, (1963) pp. 228–35.

Wilde, D. J.   *Optimum Seeking Methods.* Englewood Cliffs, N.J.: Prentice-Hall, Inc., 1964.

Wilde, D. J. and Beightler, C. S.   *Foundations of Optimization.* Englewood Cliffs, N.J.: Prentice-Hall, Inc., 1967.

SECTION FOUR

Simulation Languages

CHAPTER
12

SIMULATION LANGUAGES

The purpose of this chapter is to present, in brief, three special purpose simulation languages. These languages are the General Purpose Simulation System (GPSS/360), SIMSCRIPT I, and SIMSCRIPT II. GPSS in its various versions was initially developed by G. Gordon at the International Business Machine Corp.; it is probably the most widely used simulation language. SIMSCRIPT was developed by the RAND Corporation and has been in use since 1963; it is probably the second most widely used special purpose language. SIMSCRIPT II was announced in 1968.

The purpose of higher order simulation languages is to provide the user with a means for communicating the problem to the machine in a relatively simple fashion. All of the models discussed heretofore have been programmed in the FORTRAN IV computer language. The choice of FORTRAN was based upon the universality of the language, and for this reason FORTRAN must remain at the top of any list.

However, to construct a computer simulation model of a real world system in any general purpose, problem-oriented language such as FORTRAN requires a great deal of effort. The programmer is totally responsible for all detail in the model. We have seen that this can become an arduous task. Special purpose languages were developed to eliminate the major portion of this programming effort by providing a simulation-oriented framework about which models could be constructed.

In the next sections we shall describe the major features of GPSS/360, SIMSCRIPT I, and SIMSCRIPT II. We hope to provide insight into the basic features of each language. The final section of the chapter will then discuss some the bases for evaluating and comparing these simulation languages.

GENERAL PURPOSE SIMULATION SYSTEM (GPSS/360)

GPSS is basically a transaction-flow simulation language. Models are constructed in this language through the use of a flow chart. The flow chart traces the movement of transactions (or units of traffic) through blocks which represent the logic of the real system. The simulated time is advanced and the logical decisions are made as these transactions pass through the various blocks. From the flow chart the programmer constructs the simulation program. This is easily accomplished because the modeling blocks are also the basic programming statements. This particular feature makes GPSS easy to learn. It does not require any prior programming knowledge.

In GPSS each system is described in terms of elements called "entities." The language is built about a set of four types of entities: dynamic, statistical, equipment, and operational. There are GPSS statements or blocks which pertain to each of the entities listed above. Other program features of GPSS are "standard numerical attributes" (hereafter referred to as SNA). These are numerical quantities which represent properties or states of the simulated system and may be accessed or modified by the program in execution.

Let us go back to the simple single channel queueing system that was presented previously to further illustrate the aspects of GPSS. Figure 12.1 illustrates that system again.

FIGURE 12.1
Single Channel Queueing System

UNITS ARRIVING   QUEUE   SERVICE FACILITY

In this system units arrive in a random fashion and proceed to enter the queue, where they wait until they can receive service on a first-come first-serve basis. In GPSS terms these units of traffic are called "transactions"; they are the dynamic entities in GPSS. When the FORTRAN model of this system was constructed in Chapter 8, we created a "unit vector" for each unit entering the system in which we stored pertinent information about that unit. GPSS provides similar features called "transaction parameters," which may be used at the programmer's discretion for storage of pertinent information about the transaction. These transaction parameters represent one type of the SNA's of a given transaction. The other important SNA's associated with transactions are:

1. Transit time – The accumulated time a transaction has been in the system.
2. Priority – The priority of the transaction relative to all other transactions in the system.

All SNA's are referred to by a mnemonic designator and can be accessed and modified by various block types. For example, M1 when used properly will be interpreted by GPSS to mean the transit time of a particular transaction.

Upon entry to the system the transaction proceeds to a queue. In GPSS a queue represents one type of statistical entity. The other statistical entity is called a TABLE and will be discussed later. The queue also possesses several SNA's. There are listed below. The mnemonic reference used is shown in parentheses beside the item.

1. Current contents or length (Qj)[1].
2. Average contents (QAj).
3. Maximum contents (QMj).
4. Total number of entries (QCj).
5. Number of zero entries. This is the number of times the queue reaches an empty condition (QZj).
6. Average time transactions spend in queue (including zero entries) (QTj).
7. Average time transactions spend in queue (excluding zero entries) (QXj).

The last stage in this queueing system is seen as the unit enters the service facility and is held for service. The service facility itself represents one of the equipment entities. This entity is called a FACILITY and is characterized by the fact that only one transaction can occupy it at any time. The equipment entity used to represent parallel or multi transaction processing capability is called a STORAGE. The SNA's associated with a FACILITY are listed below:

---

[1]Here the j refers to the particular number given to any queue. This shall be discussed later.

1. Status indicator – Used essentially to indicate whether or not the facility is presently being used.
2. Utilization of the facility.
3. Number of transactions which have entered the facility.
4. Average time each transaction used the facility.

At this point it is expedient to discuss the GPSS block types that we would use to build a model of our simple queueing system. This will entail the presentation of some more SNA's.

The SNA's and entities of GPSS discussed so far are assumed to exist and are available for the analyst's use. The actions performed on them constitutes the difference between any two models; the user must define this interaction of transactions and the other entities.

Each GPSS block in the flow chart must be coded into a convenient format for computer input. The flow chart for the queueing system under discussion is shown in Figure 12.3. It represents the analyst's model in GPSS terms. The task is now to code this onto cards. The types of cards necessary to specify the model are:

BLOCK definition cards
ENTITY definition cards
GPSS/360 control cards
GPSS/360 system control cards

The format for GPSS cards is shown in Figure 12.2.

FIGURE 12.2
GPSS/360 Card Format

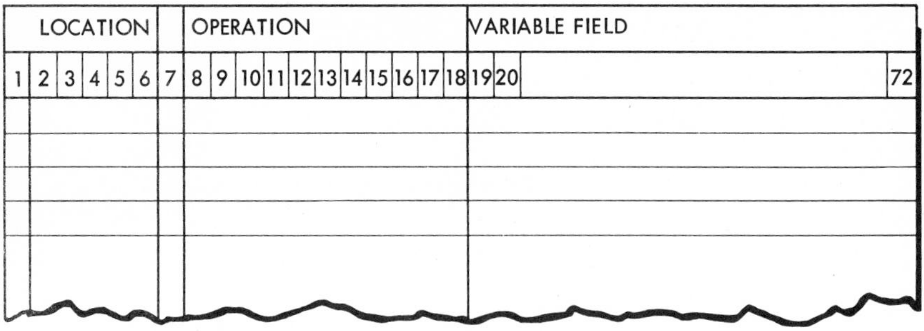

LOCATION		OPERATION		VARIABLE FIELD	
1 2 3 4 5 6	7	8 9 10 11 12 13 14 15 16 17 18	19 20		72

The "location field" is used to identify the block in a manner similar to statement numbers is FORTRAN. One difference is that GPSS blocks may be given names. The "operation field" is used to record the block type; this must be one of the standard block types, which will be discussed later. The "variable field" is used to specify the arguments for a particular block. There may be up to five arguments for a particular block type. Some blocks require only one; others may use from two to five arguments. The arguments are named "A" through "E", representing up to five consecutive fields on the card. Fields are separated by commas.

ENTITY definition cards have the same basic format as BLOCK definition cards. They are used to establish various entities in the model, such as capacities of storages, etc. The GPSS/360 control cards are used to relay control information to the system about such items as length of run and certain output options. The GPSS/360 System Control Cards provide information to the operating system about the entire job.

FIGURE 12.3
GPSS Flow Chart for Simple Queueing Systems

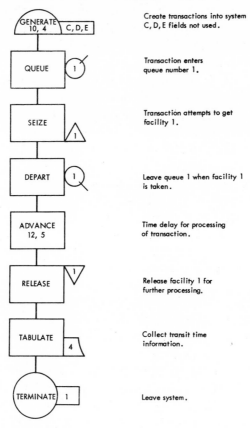

Create transactions into system
C, D, E fields not used.

Transaction enters
queue number 1.

Transaction attempts to get
facility 1.

Leave queue 1 when facility 1
is taken.

Time delay for processing
of transaction.

Release facility 1 for
further processing.

Collect transit time
information.

Leave system.

Transactions are introduced into a system model with the GENERATE block. The transactions are created into the system based upon the "interarrival time" concept; *i.e.*, the GENERATE block essentially generates interarrival times. The GENERATE block contains arguments which allow the user to specify the characteristics of the interarrival time distribution. For our purposes the most important arguments are the "mean" and the "modifier." These are the first two arguments in the variable field. Field A, the mean, is interpreted as the average time between arrivals (this is shown as 10 time units in Figure 12.3). Field B, the modifier, used in its basic form, specifies a spread about the mean; *i.e.*, interarrival time values are computed from the rectangular distribution over the limits mean ± modifier. In this case it is 10 ± 4 time units.

Upon entry to the system the transaction proceeds to the QUEUE block. Each entity is given a separate number or name. This queue has been given the number one. The choice of numbers or names is up to the programmer. Obviously each queue must be given a different name or number. The programmer uses this number as the identifier for the mnemonic of the SNA he may with to refer to. For example, when Q1 appears, its value will be taken as the current length of queue number one.

Once in the queue the transaction attempts to SEIZE the facility. This is accomplished when the facility becomes available and the transaction in question is first in line. Again the facility is given a unique number. After the transaction successfully SEIZES the facility, it then DEPARTS the queue. At this point the transaction is conceptually being processed in the service facility.

The amount of time the transaction is delayed in the service facility is simulated by the ADVANCE block. This block, as shown, causes a time value to be generated in much the same manner as was performed for the GENERATE block. This value, however, represents the amount of time the transaction will be delayed at that block. In this particular case that will be in the range of 12 ± 5 time units.

After the time delay in the ADVANCE block has passed, the transaction RELEASES facility 1, making it available for further service. The transaction then proceeds to the TABULATE block. This block causes certain information to be collected. Along with this card the user must supply a TABLE card which indicates what particular information is to be collected and how it is to be collected. The TABLE card would, in this case, be labeled with a 4 in the location field. Finally the transaction is TERMINATED and conceptually leaves the system. All of these blocks constitute types of operational entities.

FIGURE 12.4

Listing of Simple GPSS/360 Program for Single Channel Queueing System

BLOCK NUMBER	*LOC	OPERATION A,B,C,D,E,F,G	COMMENTS	CARD NUMBER
	*	SIMULATE		1
	*	GPSS/360 MODEL OF A SINGLE CHANNEL QUEUEING SYSTEM		2
				3
1		GENERATE 10,4	ARRIVALS ENTER SYSTEM	4
2		QUEUE 1	UNITS ENTER QUEUE NO. ONE	5
3		SEIZE 1	ATTEMPT TO GET FACILITY NO. ONE	6
4		DEPART 1	LEAVE QUEUE AFTER FACILITY IS TAKEN	7
5		ADVANCE 12,5	TIME DELAY FOR SERVICING	8
6		RELEASE 1	SERVICE COMPLETE FACILITY RELEASED	9
7		TABULATE 4	COLLECT TOTAL TIME IN TABLE NO. FOUR	10
8		TERMINATE	UNIT LEAVES SYSTEM	11
	*			12
	*	TABLE DEFINITION CARDS		13
	*			14
		4 TABLE M1,0,15,20		15
		7 QTABLE 1,0,15,20		16
	*			17
	*	GPSS/360 CONTROL CARD		18
	*			19
		START 200		20
		END		21

Let us now turn our attention to Figure 12.4, which shows a complete listing of the GPSS/360 program that we described above. Comment cards have been included to further describe the program. Note that the source listing of the GPSS program contains comments on the block definition cards. This is permissible in GPSS and provides a convenient documentation facility.

The TABLE card shown in the program is used to describe both that entity to be printed out and the method of tabulation. The A field is used to define the quantity to be tabulated, which in this case is the transit time M1. Field B defines the upper limit of the first class interval; field C defines the class width; and field D defines the number of frequency classes to be generated. Hence, as each transaction passes through the TABULATE block, its transit time is recorded in TABLE 4. Several options which will not be discussed here, exist regarding the use of the TABLE card.

Immediately below the TABLE card is shown a QTABLE card. This card is included in the program and does not require a corresponding TABULATE card. This is due to the fact that a queue is defined as a statistical entity. Field A of the QTABLE card contains the number of the queue being referred to. The remaining fields are the same as the TABLE card. The QTABLE is used to tabulate information regarding the waiting time aspects of the queue.

The START card represents one of the GPSS/360 control cards. It specifies the termination criterion. In this case the START card specifies that the simulator keeps running until 200 transactions have been terminated.

Standard Output

Assuming the program executes properly, the following output information is generated automatically by GPSS/360:

1. Symbolic listing – This is a listing of the model exactly as the programmer has constructed it.
2. GPSS/360 input listing – All symbolic references used by the programmer are changed to a standard GPSS numbering system and blocks are labeled.
3. Clock time – Actual value of simulator clock at the end of simulation run.
4. Block counts – The entry and wait counts of all blocks in the program are printed.

5. Facility statistics — For each facility defined in the program GPSS prints utilization, total number of entries, average time a unit is held at the facility, and the number of the transaction holding the facility at the end of the run.
6. Queue statistics — For each queue defined in the system, GPSS provides the following information: maximum contents, average contents, total number of entries, total number of transactions which entered the queue but were delayed, average time each transaction spent in queue, average time spent in the queue for those transactions which were delayed, and the number of the table referring to the queue defined by a QTABLE card.
7. TABLES   A listing of the tables defined by the user.

There are output options which will not be discussed here. These include a TRACE block, which provides the facility to follow the flow of transactions through selected blocks; a PRINT block, which allows desired output to be printed chronologically; and a facility for printing titles and graphing histograms.

The remainder of the output from the GPSS run of the simple program is shown in Figures 12.5 through 12.7.

Additional Features

Several additional features exist within GPSS/360. It is not within the scope of this chapter to detail all of these features; however, some of the major features are discussed below.

Other Block Types

ASSIGN — Provides the facility for entering information into transaction parameters.

GATE — The normal flow of a transaction may be blocked or altered by this block. This is a block which acts upon a logic condition. It may be used conveniently to interrogate the status of equipment entities.

TEST — This block is used to make an algebraic comparison between two arguments. Based upon the results of the comparison, a transaction can either be blocked or diverted.

FIGURE 12.5

GPSS/360 MODEL OF A SINGLE CHANNEL QUEUEING SYSTEM

```
*
*
1   GENERATE    10   4
2   QUEUE       1
3   SEIZE       1
4   DEPART      1
5   ADVANCE     12   5
6   RELEASE     1
7   TABULATE    4
8   TERMINATE   1
*
*   TABLE DEFINITION CARDS
*
*
4   TABLE       M1   0   15   20
7   QTABLE      1    0   15   20
*
*   GPSS/360 CONTROL CARD
*
*   START       200
```

RELATIVE CLOCK 2500 ABSOLUTE CLOCK

BLOCK COUNTS

BLOCK	CURRENT	TOTAL	BLOCK	CURRENT	TOTAL	BLOCK	CURRENT	TOTAL	BLOCK	CURRENT	TOTAL
1	0	247									
2	47	247									
3	0	200									
4	0	200									
5	0	200									
6	0	200									
7	0	200									
8	0	200									

FACILITY	AVERAGE UTILIZATION	NUMBER ENTRIES	AVERAGE TIME/TRAN	SEIZING TRANS. NO.	PREEMPTING TRANS. NO.
1	.997	200	12.464		

FIGURE 12.6

QUEUE	MAXIMUM CONTENTS	AVERAGE CONTENTS	TOTAL ENTRIES	ZERO ENTRIES	PERCENT ZEROS	AVERAGE TIME/TRANS	$AVERAGE TIME/TRANS	TABLE NUMBER	CURRENT CONTENTS
1	47	23.847	247	2	.8	241.372	243.342	7	47

$AVERAGE TIME/TRANS = AVERAGE TIME/TRANS EXCLUDING ZERO ENTRIES

TABLE 4

ENTRIES IN TABLE	MEAN ARGUMENT	STANDARD DEVIATION	SUM OF ARGUMENTS	NON-WEIGHTED
200	254.094	145.312	50819.000	

UPPER LIMIT	OBSERVED FREQUENCY	PER CENT OF TOTAL	CUMULATIVE PERCENTAGE	CUMULATIVE REMAINDER	MULTIPLE OF MEAN	DEVIATION FROM MEAN
0	0	.00	.0	100.0	-.000	-1.748
15	5	2.49	2.4	97.5	.059	-1.645
30	8	3.99	6.4	93.5	.118	-1.542
45	6	2.99	9.4	90.5	.177	-1.438
60	5	2.49	11.9	88.0	.236	-1.335
75	2	.99	12.9	87.0	.295	-1.232
90	8	3.99	16.9	83.0	.354	-1.129
105	10	4.99	21.9	78.0	.413	-1.026
120	6	2.99	24.9	75.0	.472	-.922
135	4	1.99	26.9	73.0	.531	-.819
150	5	2.49	29.4	70.5	.590	-.716
165	9	4.49	33.9	66.0	.649	-.613
180	1	.49	34.4	65.5	.708	-.509
195	6	2.99	37.4	62.5	.767	-.406
210	11	5.49	42.9	57.0	.826	-.303
225	4	1.99	44.9	55.0	.885	-.200
240	4	1.99	46.9	53.0	.944	-.096
255	2	.99	47.9	52.0	1.003	.006
270	8	3.99	51.9	48.0	1.062	.109
OVERFLOW	96	47.99	100.0	.0		

AVERAGE VALUE OF OVERFLOW 385.96

FIGURE 12.7

TABLE 7 ENTRIES IN TABLE 200	MEAN ARGUMENT 241.629	STANDARD DEVIATION 145.375	SUM OF ARGUMENTS 48326.000	NON-WEIGHTED

UPPER LIMIT	OBSERVED FREQUENCY	PER CENT OF TOTAL	CUMULATIVE PERCENTAGE	CUMULATIVE REMAINDER	MULTIPLE OF MEAN	DEVIATION FROM MEAN
0	2	.99	.9	99.0	-.000	-1.662
15	10	4.99	5.9	94.0	.062	-1.558
30	7	3.49	9.4	90.5	.124	-1.455
45	4	1.99	11.4	88.5	.186	-1.352
60	3	1.49	12.9	87.0	.248	-1.249
75	7	3.49	16.4	83.5	.310	-1.146
90	9	4.49	20.9	79.0	.372	-1.043
105	8	3.99	24.9	75.0	.434	-.939
120	4	1.99	26.9	73.0	.496	-.836
135	5	2.49	29.4	70.5	.558	-.733
150	8	3.99	33.4	66.5	.620	-.630
165	2	.99	34.4	65.5	.682	-.527
180	6	2.99	37.4	62.5	.744	-.423
195	8	3.99	41.4	58.5	.807	-.320
210	7	3.49	44.9	55.0	.869	-.217
225	5	1.99	46.9	53.0	.931	-.114
240	2	.99	47.9	52.0	.993	-.011
255	8	3.99	51.9	48.0	1.055	.091
270	4	1.99	53.9	46.0	1.117	.195
OVERFLOW	92	45.99	100.0	.0		

AVERAGE VALUE OF OVERFLOW

TRANSFER — This block is generally used to direct a transaction to a nonsequential block. This transfer may be effected in several ways: logically, statistically, conditionally, or unconditionally.

PREEMPT-RETURN — These blocks provide the capability for a transaction to "interrupt" a facility in process and cause it to begin operation on a higher priority transaction. When the higher priority transaction is finished, it "RETURNS" the facility to normal processing.

ENTER-LEAVE — These blocks perform an analogous operation on storages to the SEIZE-RELEASE on facilities. They cause transactions to be entered into storages and to leave storages.

LINK-UNLINK — These provide the user with the machinery necessary to model desired queueing disciplines. Transactions may be placed on a "user chain" and then removed in an order reflecting characteristics of the transactions.

TRANSACTION-ORIENTED BLOCK TYPES — Blocks exist which permit simulation of situations in which transactions are "broken up" and the various parts are sent to different places in the model. For example, consider a maintenance shop which repairs electric motors. The first operation is to disassemble the motor and send the component parts to different repair stations. This can be handled using the SPLIT block. Components can be reassembled using the ASSEMBLE block. Transactions may be synchronized in the model using MATCH and GATHER blocks. These delay one transaction at one point in the model until another transaction has reached another point in the model.

Computational and Reference Entities

The previous example of the simple single channel queueing system is not representative of the complex systems we are often asked to analyze. GPSS provides tools for the analyst to describe complex mathematical relationships which may exist. Further, GPSS provides a facility whereby the analyst may conveniently describe various distributions pertinent to his model, for example, the distribution of interarrival times.

The user of GPSS may describe a probability distribution in a very simple manner. From this, distribution values may be generated in a Monte Carlo fashion using a uniform random number generator. Several types of functions are permitted in GPSS, including both discrete and continuous valued functions. To construct a function in GPSS the user is required to use the FUNCTION card plus FUNCTION follower cards. The FUNCTION card is defined by a number in the location field, the word FUNCTION in the operation field, the independent variable in field A (which is a random number for most Monte Carlo determinations), and the type of function (discrete or continuous) and the number of points included in the B field. For example, 1 FUNCTION RN1, C24 indicates that FUNCTION 1 is continuous with 24 points being included in its description. Random number generator number one will be used for the independent variable. The mnemonic RN1 is the reference for the random number generator. Within GPSS/360 there are eight separate random number generators. These are one type of the system SNA's. Function follower cards must immediately follow the FUNCTION definition card. On these cards are punched the pairs of $x - y$ coordinates used to specify a point. In the above example there would be 24 such pairs placed in the following format $x_1, y_1, x_2, y_2 \ldots x_{24}, y_{24}$. A maximum of six pairs may be placed on one card. Hence four follower cards would be required. The user would then be able to refer to this function, and values would be produced from it. The method of reference would be to use the words "FN1." Thus the function represents one type of computational SNA.

Functions defined in this manner may be used to modify the mean of either a GENERATE or an ADVANCE block. When functions are employed as modifiers, a value is generated from the function and is then multiplied by the mean to arrive at a result.

The user may also define mathematical or logical expressions by use of the VARIABLE statement. The VARIABLE statement is used to define an arithmetic relationship between SNA's. The VARIABLE statement may include the following arithmetic operators:

+ Algebraic addition.
− Algebraic subtraction.
* Algebraic multiplication.
/ Algebraic division.

@ Modulo division in which the quotient is discarded and the remainder is the result.

The VARIABLE block may be used in integer, floating point, or Boolean mode.

The system provides a method for retaining certain pieces of data which can be used in computations throughout the simulation. This facility is effected through use of the SAVEVALUE block. Single values or arrays of information may be saved with the use of the SAVEVALUE. In that it has replacement, addition, and subtraction modes, the SAVEVALUE block provides a convenient method for accumulating information, replacing information, and deleting information.

GPSS also provides for SYSTEM ATTRIBUTES which are not directly altered by the block diagram. Among these are the various random number generators which were discussed previously. Also included as system attributes are:

Constant designators – Kj is an indication that the integer j is a constant. For example, K529 indicates that the number 529 is a constant.

Simulator clock – The master clock for the simulator may be referenced by the mnemonic C1.

Debugging Aids

GPSS/360 provides an extensive set of diagnostic messages at three different phases of operation. The error messages are provided at the assembly program phase pertaining to the GPSS symbolic listing; they are also provided at the input phase as the symbolic deck is converted to the GPSS internal format. They are also provided during execution of the model. The model can be validated at the programmer's discretion using the PRINT and TRACE blocks.

Method of Operation

It is helpful to know how GPSS performs simulations. The reader should have a better idea of why GPSS is termed a transaction flow language by now and it is relatively simple to describe GPSS/360 in terms of transactions. Interestingly, GPSS/360 operates to effect simulations in a manner very similar to that discussed in Chapter 8.

During the simulation a scan routine is initiated to determine the next most imminent event. This aspect is very similar to the method of Chapter 8. However, GPSS makes some sophisticated modifications to that basic mechanism. If a transaction is blocked, *e.g.*, waiting to seize a facility, GPSS places this transaction on what is called a DELAY CHAIN. Transactions which are free to move at a given clock time are on the CURRENT EVENTS CHAIN in order of priority. Those which are not scheduled to move until a later time are placed on the FUTURE EVENTS CHAIN. The scan proceeds to move any transactions on the CURRENT EVENTS CHAIN.

Transactions on the CURRENT EVENTS CHAIN are moved in the model until they are blocked. Then they are placed on the DELAY CHAIN. After all transactions on the CURRENT EVENTS CHAIN are dealt with, GPSS moves the clock up to the next most imminent event represented on the FUTURE EVENTS CHAIN. The FUTURE EVENTS CHAIN is ordered in ascending order of time. Each transaction carries its own event time; so GPSS updates the master clock to that event time and proceeds to move all transactions on the FUTURE EVENTS CHAIN with that event time to the CURRENT EVENTS CHAIN. In moving transactions on the CURRENT EVENTS CHAIN, GPSS determines whether the status of equipment has changed. If so, it will attempt to move any affected transactions from the delay chain to the CURRENT EVENTS CHAIN.

The terminology is different and the mechanics are somewhat different, but GPSS essentially operates in the same fashion as our queueing simulator of Chapter 8. The power of GPSS comes from the fact that it provides the framework when the proper number of transactions have passed through a TERMINATE block. The final phase of GPSS is to make summary calculations and write output.

Summary on GPSS

GPSS is a widely used and well-known simulation language. It is a transaction-flow type of language, and models may easily be constructed of systems which involve the movement of units through various phases of operation. The language itself is easily understood and requires little or no prior knowledge of computer programming.

Systems are described in GPSS in terms of entities and attributes of entities. The programmer generally has ready access to all of these attributes for mathematical and logical operations within the model.

The output produced by GPSS is of a fixed format. The programmer has relatively little flexibility in that area. However, all in all GPSS must stand as a powerful simulation tool.

BASIC PRINCIPLES OF SIMSCRIPT[2]

SIMSCRIPT has three features that enable it to reduce the programming time required for simulation. These are its world view of the model to be simulated; its method of communicating to the computer the world to be simulated; and its universal features, which are useful for programming in general and for simulation programming in particular[3]. We will concentrate on the first two principals — the SIMSCRIPT world view and its basic approach to simulation programming.

SIMSCRIPT's World View

SIMSCRIPT requires that the world to be simulated be structured in terms of the concepts listed in Figure 12.8. As of any moment, the simulated world has a status characterized in terms of how many and which type of *entities* exist, what the current values of their *attributes* are, what *sets* the various entities belong to and who are the members of the sets which they own. For the sake of programming efficiency, we make a distinction between temporary and permanent entities. The former can be created and destroyed (can appear and disappear) in the course of a simulation run. The latter,

FIGURE 12.8
Concepts Used in SIMSCRIPT to View World

Status
- Entities
  - Temporary
  - Permanent
- Attributes
- Sets

Events
- Exogenous
- Endogenous

---

[2] Reproduced from M. A. Geisler and H. M. Markowitz, "A Brief Review of SIMSCRIPT as a Simulating Technique," The RAND Corp., RM – 3778 – PR, August 1963. By permission of the authors and publishers.

[3] A number of those who have used SIMSCRIPT have commented that, because of the way it structures the problem, it would be worth formulating simulation models in SIMSCRIPT terms even if there were no program to translate from SIMSCRIPT language into machine language.

however, are with a run from start to finish (are always part of the run).

We can illustrate the meanings of the foregoing, as used in SIMSCRIPT, by defining them in terms of a simple job shop example. Within a shop, for instance, permanent entities would be the things in the environment – the types of machines and the types of personnel to operate them. A temporary entity woule be a job that comes through for processing. Respective attributes of these would be the number of each type of machine, the number of each type of personnel, and the receipt time of the job. A set would be the collection of jobs waiting for processing.

Part of the SIMSCRIPT world view is an *event* – a point in time when status changes. *Exogenous* events are caused from outside of the simulation process. To continue the job shop example, an exogenous event might be the addition of a new machine. *Endogenous* events are caused by prior occurrences inside the simulation, perhaps a rescheduling of jobs in a queue. Thus, as illustrated in Figure 12.9, during the course of the simulation, the exogenous events (vertical arrows) occur at preset times, perhaps causing one or more subsequent endogenous events, which in turn cause still other endogenous events.

Using this concept of an event, SIMSCRIPT automatically orders all events in time sequence so that the most imminent event always occurs next. As a result, simulated time in the model is advanced from event to event rather than at fixed intervals of time.

We will not formally define the basic concepts of entity, attribute, set, and event, but will rely mainly on their meaning in common English usage. The precise meaning of these terms, as far as SIMSCRIPT is concerned, is determined by the way they are used. Hence, we cannot understand what we call the SIMSCRIPT viewpoint until we see how a world to be simulated, conceived in these terms, is communicated to the computer.

FIGURE 12.9
Schematic Representation of Exogenous and Endogenous Events
through Time

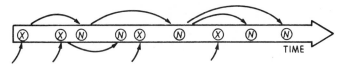

Ⓧ EXOGENOUS EVENT
Ⓝ ENDOGENOUS EVENT

Let us suppose, then, that an analyst familiar with the precise way we use our basic concepts can in fact conceive of a world to be simulated as containing entities of various kinds with their attributes and sets. He further conceives of this world as changing when certain types of events occur. How does he "tell it to SIMSCRIPT?"

SIMSCRIPT's Method of Communication

In order to describe *status*, the analyst must fill out a definition form as illustrated in Figure 12.10. (We will get a closer look at the various panels of this form in subsequent figures.) On this form he must list, by name, each type of entity, each attribute, and each type of set distinguished in his simulated world. In addition, because the computer must be directed in its use of the limited memory capacity, the user of SIMSCRIPT must provide a small amount of additional information, such as the number of words of computer storage needed to store the values of the attributes of any temporary entity and also, where in the entity record the user would like each of the attributes to be stored.

The first panel of the definition form (Figure 12.11) informs SIMSCRIPT of the temporary entities and their attributes. According to the example presented in Figure 12.11, this particular simulation contains a type of temporary attribute called a JOB. A four-word record is used to store the current values of its attributes. Thus, if the programmer writes an event routine that says "CREATE JOB," four consecutive words of memory, not otherwise occupied, will be found and subsequently used to store the attributes of the particular job just created. The form also indicates that a temporary attribute called RECT (receipt time) is to be stored in the third word of a JOB record, in the second half of the word (which is another computer direction).

The second panel of the definition form (Figure 12.12) is used to inform SIMSCRIPT about permanent entities and their attributes. Thus, according to the Figure 12.12 example, the system contains a permanent attribute called MG (short for machine group), there is an attribute called FREE (which represents the number of free machines in the machine group), and there is a random variable called FACTR associated with each machine group.

Figure 12.13 shows the third panel, which is used for sets. The example has a set called QUE; the "X" in column 58 indicates that it is a "ranked" set (rather than a first-in-first-out or last-in-last-out

FIGURE 12.10

SIMSCRIPT Definition Form (Reduced)

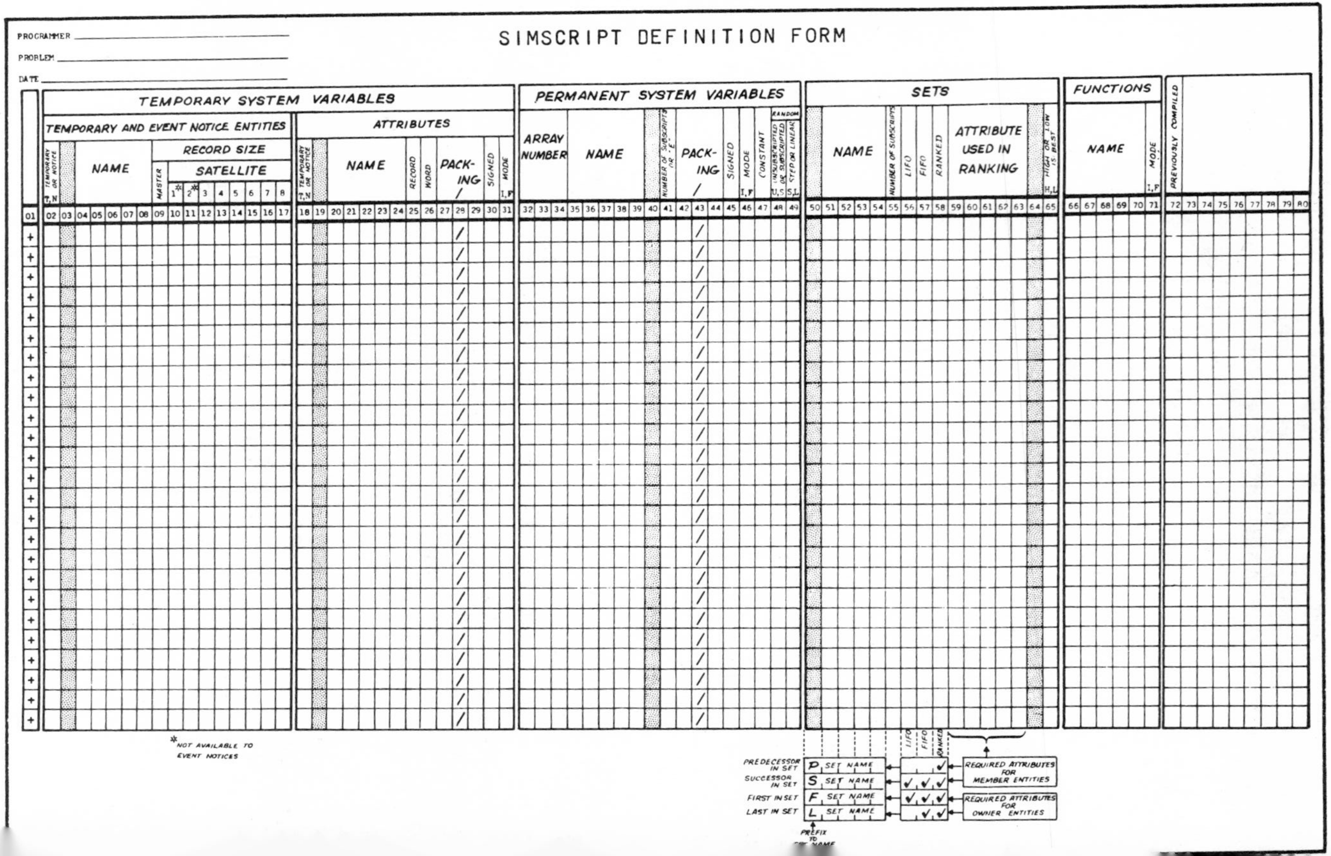

FIGURE 12.11
Example of Temporary Entities and Their Attributes
Using First Panel of SIMSCRIPT Definition Form

		TEMPORARY SYSTEM VARIABLES																											
	TEMPORARY AND EVENT NOTICE ENTITIES																ATTRIBUTES													
		NAME	RECORD SIZE												NAME		PACK-ING							
				SATELLITE										
				1	2*	3	4	5	6	7	8											
01	02	03	04	05	06	07	08	09	10	11	12	13	14	15	16	17	18	19	20	21	22	23	24	25	26	27	28	29	30	31
+	T		J	&	B			4									T		R	E	C	T			3	2	/	2		I
+																												/		
+																												/		
+																												/		
+																												/		
+																												/		
+																												/		
+																												/		

*NOT AVAILABLE TO
EVENT NOTICES

set). Columns 59 through 63 specify that the members of this set are
to be ranked according to the attribute RECT.

Thus the names of the various types of entities, attributes, and sets
to be distinguished in the specific simulation are indicated on the
definition form, together with information needed by SIMSCRIPT to
process these properly.

The various types of events occurring in a simulated world are
described to SIMSCRIPT by means of event routines written in the
SIMSCRIPT source language. Figure 12.14 presents an example of
such an event routine. This particular routine describes what occurs
at an End of Process (abbreviated EPROC) in a simple job simulator.

The SIMSCRIPT source program language is especially designed to
allow the programmer to specify those operations which must
typically be accomplished in event routines. These include the
operations enumerated in Figure 12.15, namely, changing current
status, causing (or canceling) future events, processing decision rules,
accumulating and summarizing information on how well the simulated system is doing, and displaying this information in a form
intelligible to the human being. Let us consider briefly how SIM-
SCRIPT specifies each such action.

Since status consists of entities, attributes, and sets, the only ways
it can change are if an entity is created or destroyed, a new value is read
or computed for some attribute, or some entity gains or loses
set membership. Actions of this sort are specified by the commands
of CREATE, DESTROY, READ, LET, FILE, REMOVE, (illustrated

FIGURE 12.12
Example of Permenent Entities
and Their Attributes Using Second
Panel of SIMSCRIPT Definition
Form

PERMANENT SYSTEM VARIABLES																
ARRAY NUMBER		NAME					NUMBER OF SUBSCRIPTS	PACK-ING /	SIGNED I,F	MODE	CONSTANT	UNDSUBSCRIPTED OR SUBSCRIPTED U,O,S,L	RANDOM STEP OR LINEAR SL			
32	33	34	35	36	37	38	39	40	41	42	43	44	45	46	47	48	49
		1	M	G						E		/				
		2	F	R	E	E				1		/	I			
		3	F	A	C	T	R					/				S	L
												/				
												/				
												/				
												/				
												/				

FIGURE 12.13
Example of Sets Using Third Panel
of SIMSCRIPT Definition Form

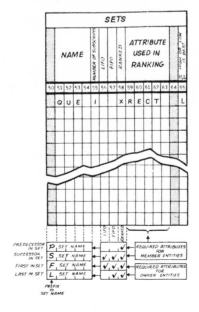

FIGURE 12.14
Endogenous Event Routine Describing the End Process for an Order at a Machine Group

1	STATEMENT NUMBER 2 5	Continuation 6	STATEMENT 7 72
			ENDOGENOUS EVENT EPROC
			STORE ORDRP(EPROC) IN ORDER
			STORE MGPRC(EPROC) IN MG
			DESTROY EPROC
C			– DISPOSITION OF THE ORDER –
			IF ROUT(ORDER) IS EMPTY, GO TO 10
			CALL ARRVL(ORDER)
			GO TO 20
	10		LET CUMCT = CUMCT + TIME – DATE(ORDER)
			LET NORDR = NORDR + 1.0
			DESTROY ORDER
C			– DISPOSITION OF THE MACHINE –
	20		IF QUE(MG) IS EMPTY, GO TO 30
			REMOVE FIRST ORDER FROM QUE(MG)
			CALL ALLOC(MG, ORDER)
			ACCUMULATE NINQ(MG) INTO CUMQ(MG) SINCE TMQ(MG),
		X	POST NINQ(MG) – 1.0
			RETURN
	30		LET NOAVL(MG) = NOAVL(MG) + 1
			RETURN
			END

FIGURE 12.15
Types of Operations Performed in Event Routines

a) Change Status
b) Cause (or Cancel) Future Events
c) Process Decision Rules
d) Accumulate and Summarize Information
e) Display Results

FIGURE 12.16
Examples of Commands that Change Status
CREATE JØB
DESTRØY JØB
LET RECT(JØB) = TIME
READ DUE(JØB)
FILE JØB IN QUE(MG)
REMØVE JØB FRØM QUE(MG)
REMØVE FIRST JØB FRØM QUE(MG)

FIGURE 12.17
Examples of the SIMSCRIPT Versions of Conventional
Types of Control Commands

GØ TØ (10, 20, 25), X(I)
IF (A(B(I))GR(5), GØ TØ 20
GØ TØ 55, FØR EACH JØB ØF QUE(MG), WITH
(RECT(JØB)) LS (TIME-LEAD)
IF QUE(I) IS EMPTY, RETURN

FIGURE 12.18
Example of FIND MIN Command
FIND MPRI = MIN ØF PRI(MG), FØR EACH MG OF
SRVD(LC), WITH(FREE(MG))GR(O), WITH (FQUE(MG))
GR(O), WHERE MMG, IF NØNE, GØ TO 50

FIGURE 12.19
Examples of Accumulate and Compute Statements

ACC FREE(MG) INTØ CFREE(MG) SINCE
TFREE(MG), ADD 1.0

COMPUTE MX, SX = MEAN, STD−DEV ØF
X(I), FØR I = (1)(N)

in Figure 12.16). Using these commands, the programmer tells SIMSCRIPT how status is to change when a particular kind of event occurs. Similarly, with the aid of the CAUSE and CANCEL statements, the programmer can specify how the occurrence of one event causes some subsequent event or cancels a previously scheduled event that has not yet occurred.

As we use it here, the phrase "decision rule" denotes any tests or calculations performed to determine how status will change or what events should be caused. To facilitate such decision calculations, SIMSCRIPT has a complement of arithmetic and control statements (some are illustrated in Figure 12.17) somewhat similar to those

FIGURE 12.20

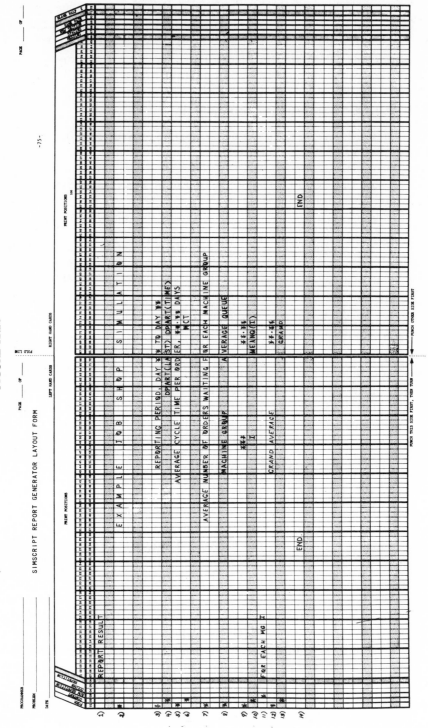

SIMSCRIPT REPORT GENERATOR LAYOUT FORM

-75-

contained in other recent programming languages. In addition, SIMSCRIPT has "FIND MIN," "FIND MAX," and "FIND FIRST" commands (illustrated in Figure 12.18) which are particularly suited to perform search operations frequently found in many simulations. The case illustrated, for example, instructs the computer by a single "FIND MIN" statement to do the following:

> To search over the set of machine groups (MG) served by a particular labor class (here SRVD is a set duly defined on the definition form, and LC is a labor class determined earlier in the routine). In this search, machine groups with no FREE machines are excluded, as are machine groups with no jobs in queue. Among all machine groups in the set with a free machine and something in queue, the one with lowest (best) priority is chosen. The variable MMG is set equal to the minimizing machine group; the variable MPRI is set equal to the minimum priority value. If, as can happen, there is no machine group that meets the conditions set forth in the FIND statement, the computer is instructed to go to Statement 50. Otherwise, it proceeds with the following command.

Similarly, many fairly complex decision rules can frequently be described with a single FIND MIN, FIND MAX, or FIND FIRST command.

Accumulating information over time and summarizing it as of a particular point in simulated time is made easier by the use of ACCUMULATE and COMPUTE STATEMENTS, shown in Figure 12.19. The accumulate statement is used for taking an integral under a curve drawn over time; the use of the COMPUTE statement should be apparent from the example.

Finally, the display of information is specified by means of the Report Generator. As Illustrated in Figure 12.20, the programmer specifies the form, content, and row or column repetition desired on a report generator layout sheet. The left-hand side of this sheet is keypunched first, and the right-hand side last. From the resulting deck, SIMSCRIPT produces a report routine which can be called as required by any event routine or other subroutine of the simulation program.

In sum, the analyst must first conceive of the world to be simulated as having a *status* consisting of *entities* of various types, with various attributes, set ownerships, and set memberships. Status changes when events take place. Once the world to be simulated is thus conceived, it is described to SIMSCRIPT by means of the definition form and event routines. On the definition form, the user notes the names of entities, attributes, and sets, plus a small amount of pertinent information concerning each. With the event routines and their subroutines and report routines, the user describes the effects his various events have on the system. The event routines and subroutines are written in the SIMSCRIPT source language, which is particularly suited to instructing the computer, *e.g.*, to change current status, cause or cancel future events, process decision rules, and accumulate or summarize information. Then the report generator specifies how information should be displayed.

SIMSCRIPT II

In 1968 the RAND Corporation announced the availability of a new special purpose simulation language, SIMSCRIPT II (Kiviat, Villanueva, and Markowitz). This language was designed primarily as a discrete event simulation language. It is, however, a language well-suited for general purpose programming problems.

The language is divided into essentially five different levels:

Level 1:   A very basic programming language designed for teaching programming concepts.

Level 2:   An extension of the basic programming language to a language roughly equivalent to FORTRAN.

Level 3:   A language roughly equivalent to ALGOL or PL/1. In this level is included the report generator capabilities of the language.

Level 4:   The SIMSCRIPT entity — attribute features are included in this level. At this level is also provided the list-processing capability.

Level 5:   This level introduces the simulation feature into SIMSCRIPT II Included at this level are time advance routines, event and activity processing, process generation, accumulation and analysis of statistical information.

To say that SIMSCRIPT II is an extension of SIMSCRIPT I would be a gross understatement. The first four levels of SIMSCRIPT II provide an extremely powerful and easy to use programming language. The fifth level provides the framework about which the discrete event simulation capability is introduced into the language. SIMSCRIPT II is an integrated language which permits the non-programmer to first learn a basic programming language and then to build upon that knowledge in a logical fashion. Although this language is new, we belive this is a major breakthrough for discrete event simulation.

POINTS FOR COMPARISON OF SIMULATION LANGUAGES

At this point it would be presumptious to compare in detail the aspects of GPSS/360 and SIMSCRIPT. The reader is not really acquainted with either to any great extent. In recent years, however, several excellent articles have appeared which compare many aspects of special purpose simulation languages. Included among these are articles by Krasnow and Merikallio (1964), Reitman (1967), Teichroew and Lubin (1966), Tocher (1965), and Young (1964). In this section we shall attempt to summarize, not the findings or conclusions of these authors, but rather the bases of comparison selected. This should provide further insight into the philosophy of special purpose simulation languages.

This discussion can begin with the question, "What does the user really need in a simulation language?" In this regard we shall list several of the major points about which a comparison may be made.

1. Capability of the language to describe the real world system. In other words, having the language do what you want it to is certainly important. The degrees of ease associated with this are also very important. It is possible to imagine that almost any real world system could be modeled with a FORTRAN computer model. The problem arises when the time to construct that model is considered.

2. The ability to validate the model once constructed represents another criterion. Chapter 10 was devoted to this aspect. Within the constructs of almost all special purpose computer languages there exists some basic set of diagnostic routines. For example, GPSS/360 provides for diagnostic messages both during compilation and execution.

3. An important feature is the flexibility for modifying the state of the system. Within this category are included the storage and retrieval of data, arithmetic operations and the use of subroutines, and logical testing and program control. Flexibility becomes more important as the models become more and more complex.

4. The ability to collect and output statistics is another important consideration. This aspect aids in validating the model as described in Chapter 10. It also provides the analyst with the information upon which decisions are made and conclusions are based. If a particular simulation language is weak in this respect, many of the other criteria become useless anyway.

5. The final criterion is in the area of operational ease, transferability, and efficiency. Among the specific points to be considered in this area are (a) the availability of the language, (b) the ability to easily learn the language, (c) the efficiency with which a program runs. These items are important from management's standpoint because they indicate to some extent the basic costs involved in selecting a particular simulation language.

The choice of a particular simulation language must ultimately be based upon a synthesis of the results of the above comparisons. Many computer installations use a particular language because it is available at no cost with the particular computer. Many other installations use a particular language because they lack sufficient funds to train personnel in a new language. Obviously many installations choose a particular language because it does, in fact, fit the needs of the installation.

One point is clear at this time. There is no single superior special purpose digital simulation language. The ultimate choice of a particular simulation language must be based upon the particular needs of the analysts who will be using the language.

WHAT ABOUT THE FUTURE?

To be sure simulation languages are presently in a state of change. In the future we shall, perhaps, not have to rely upon FORTRAN because of its universality. We hope a language will emerge which gains the acceptance of all computer vendors as well as users.

Kiviat (1966) suggests that simulation languages will advance in basically two directions: the way in which they are used, and the language features they offer. Among the language features which advanced simulation languages will offer are (a) hybrid features which incorporate the thinking of both the discrete and analog simulation schools, (b) data display capabilities and the use of CRT displays and plotters which will provide more and more graphic output, and (c) features that allow an analyst to interact with a program while it is being run on a time-sharing computer system. The use of simulation languages will change because the languages themselves will become more general. This will evolve because the languages will contain more features and will allow an analyst to write his model in terms of his own technical jargon.

REFERENCES

Geisler, M. A. and Markowitz, H. M. "A Brief Review of SIMSCRIPT as a Simulating Technique," The RAND Corporation, RM–3778–PR, (August 1963).

General Purpose Simulation System/360 Introductory User's Manual. Program Library, Reference H20–0304–1, International Business Machines Corporation.

Kiviat, Philip J. "Development of Discrete Digital Simulation Language," *SIMULATION* (February 1966).

Kiviat, Philip J. "Simulation Language Report Generators," The RAND Corporation, P–3349 (April 1966).

Kiviat, Philip J. "Development of New Digital Simulation Languages," *Journal of Industrial Engineering*, Vol. 17, No. 11 (November 1966), pp. 604–9.

Kiviat, Philip J., Villanueva, R., and Markowitz, H. M. *The SIMSCRIPT II Programming Language*, The RAND Corporation, R–460–PR (October 1968).

Krasnow, H. S. and Merikallio, R. A. "The Past, Present, and Future of General Simulation Languages," *Management Science*, Vol. 11, No. 2 (November 1964), pp. 236–67.

Markowitz, Harry M., Hansner, B., and Karr. H. *SIMSCRIPT – A Simulation Programming Language*. Prentice-Hall, Inc., 1963.

Reitman, Julian. "The User of Simulation Languages–the Forgotten Man," *Proceedings of the ACM 22nd National Conference*. Washington: Thompson Book Co., 1967.

Teichroew, Daniel and Lubin, John F. "Computer Simulation–Discussion of Technique and Comparison of Languages," *Communications of ACM*, Vol. 9, No. 10 (October 1966), pp. 723–41.

Tocher, K. D. "Review of Simulation Languages," *Operational Research Quarterly*, Vol. 16, No. 2 (June 1965).

Young, Karen. "A User's Experience with Three Simulation Languages (GPSS, SIMSCRIPT, AND SIMPAC)," System Development Corporation, T M–1755/000/00, February 1964.

APPENDIXES

APPENDIX
A

STATISTICAL TABLES

TABLE 1

$$F_Z(z) = \int_{-\infty}^{z} \frac{1}{\sqrt{2\pi}} e^{-x^2/2} \, dx$$

z	$F_Z(z)$	z	$F_Z(z)$	z	$F_Z(z)$
−3.990	0.0000	−3.690	0.0001	−3.390	0.0004
−3.980	0.0000	−3.680	0.0001	−3.380	0.0004
−3.970	0.0000	−3.670	0.0001	−3.370	0.0004
−3.960	0.0000	−3.660	0.0001	−3.360	0.0004
−3.950	0.0000	−3.650	0.0001	−3.350	0.0004
−3.940	0.0000	−3.640	0.0001	−3.340	0.0004
−3.930	0.0000	−3.630	0.0001	−3.330	0.0004
−3.920	0.0000	−3.620	0.0002	−3.320	0.0005
−3.910	0.0001	−3.610	0.0002	−3.310	0.0005
−3.900	0.0001	−3.600	0.0002	−3.300	0.0005
−3.890	0.0001	−3.590	0.0002	−3.290	0.0005
−3.880	0.0001	−3.580	0.0002	−3.280	0.0005
−3.870	0.0001	−3.570	0.0002	−3.270	0.0005
−3.860	0.0001	−3.560	0.0002	−3.260	0.0006
−3.850	0.0001	−3.550	0.0002	−3.250	0.0006
−3.840	0.0001	−3.540	0.0002	−3.240	0.0006
−3.830	0.0001	−3.530	0.0002	−3.230	0.0006
−3.820	0.0001	−3.520	0.0002	−3.220	0.0006
−3.810	0.0001	−3.510	0.0002	−3.210	0.0007
−3.800	0.0001	−3.500	0.0002	−3.200	0.0007
−3.790	0.0001	−3.490	0.0002	−3.190	0.0007
−3.780	0.0001	−3.480	0.0003	−3.180	0.0007
−3.770	0.0001	−3.470	0.0003	−3.170	0.0008
−3.760	0.0001	−3.460	0.0003	−3.160	0.0008
−3.750	0.0001	−3.450	0.0003	−3.150	0.0008
−3.740	0.0001	−3.440	0.0003	−3.140	0.0009
−3.730	0.0001	−3.430	0.0003	−3.130	0.0009
−3.720	0.0001	−3.420	0.0003	−3.120	0.0009
−3.710	0.0001	−3.410	0.0003	−3.110	0.0009
−3.700	0.0001	−3.400	0.0003	−3.100	0.0010

TABLE 1 *(continued)*

z	$F_Z(z)$	z	$F_Z(z)$	z	$F_Z(z)$
−3.090	0.0010	−2.560	0.0052	−2.030	0.0212
−3.080	0.0010	−2.550	0.0054	−2.020	0.0217
−3.070	0.0011	−2.540	0.0055	−2.010	0.0222
−3.060	0.0011	−2.530	0.0057	−2.000	0.0227
−3.050	0.0012	−2.520	0.0059	−1.990	0.0233
−3.040	0.0012	−2.510	0.0060	−1.980	0.0239
−3.030	0.0012	−2.500	0.0062	−1.970	0.0244
−3.020	0.0013	−2.490	0.0064	−1.960	0.0250
−3.010	0.0013	−2.480	0.0066	−1.950	0.0256
−3.000	0.0014	−2.470	0.0068	−1.940	0.0262
−2.990	0.0014	−2.460	0.0069	−1.930	0.0268
−2.980	0.0014	−2.450	0.0071	−1.920	0.0274
−2.970	0.0015	−2.440	0.0073	−1.910	0.0281
−2.960	0.0015	−2.430	0.0075	−1.900	0.0287
−2.950	0.0016	−2.420	0.0078	−1.890	0.0294
−2.940	0.0016	−2.410	0.0080	−1.880	0.0301
−2.930	0.0017	−2.400	0.0082	−1.870	0.0307
−2.920	0.0018	−2.390	0.0084	−1.860	0.0314
−2.910	0.0018	−2.380	0.0086	−1.850	0.0322
−2.900	0.0019	−2.370	0.0089	−1.840	0.0329
−2.890	0.0019	−2.360	0.0091	−1.830	0.0336
−2.880	0.0020	−2.350	0.0094	−1.820	0.0344
−2.870	0.0021	−2.340	0.0096	−1.810	0.0352
−2.860	0.0021	−2.330	0.0099	−1.800	0.0359
−2.850	0.0022	−2.320	0.0102	−1.790	0.0367
−2.840	0.0023	−2.310	0.0104	−1.780	0.0375
−2.830	0.0023	−2.300	0.0107	−1.770	0.0384
−2.820	0.0024	−2.290	0.0110	−1.760	0.0392
−2.810	0.0025	−2.280	0.0113	−1.750	0.0401
−2.800	0.0026	−2.270	0.0116	−1.740	0.0409
−2.790	0.0026	−2.260	0.0119	−1.730	0.0418
−2.780	0.0027	−2.250	0.0122	−1.720	0.0427
−2.770	0.0028	−2.240	0.0125	−1.710	0.0436
−2.760	0.0029	−2.230	0.0129	−1.700	0.0446
−2.750	0.0030	−2.220	0.0132	−1.690	0.0455
−2.740	0.0031	−2.210	0.0135	−1.680	0.0465
−2.730	0.0032	−2.200	0.0139	−1.670	0.0475
−2.720	0.0033	−2.190	0.0143	−1.660	0.0485
−2.710	0.0034	−2.180	0.0146	−1.650	0.0495
−2.700	0.0035	−2.170	0.0150	−1.640	0.0505
−2.690	0.0036	−2.160	0.0154	−1.630	0.0516
−2.680	0.0037	−2.150	0.0158	−1.620	0.0526
−2.670	0.0038	−2.140	0.0162	−1.610	0.0537
−2.660	0.0039	−2.130	0.0166	−1.600	0.0548
−2.650	0.0040	−2.120	0.0170	−1.590	0.0559
−2.640	0.0041	−2.110	0.0174	−1.580	0.0571
−2.630	0.0043	−2.100	0.0179	−1.570	0.0582
−2.620	0.0044	−2.090	0.0183	−1.560	0.0594
−2.610	0.0045	−2.080	0.0188	−1.550	0.0606
−2.600	0.0047	−2.070	0.0192	−1.540	0.0618
−2.590	0.0048	−2.060	0.0197	−1.530	0.0630
−2.580	0.0049	−2.050	0.0202	−1.520	0.0643
−2.570	0.0051	−2.040	0.0207	−1.510	0.0655

TABLE 1 *(continued)*

z	$F_Z(z)$	z	$F_Z(z)$	z	$F_Z(z)$
−1.500	0.0668	−0.970	0.1660	−0.440	0.3300
−1.490	0.0681	−0.960	0.1685	−0.430	0.3336
−1.480	0.0695	−0.950	0.1711	−0.420	0.3373
−1.470	0.0708	−0.940	0.1736	−0.410	0.3409
−1.460	0.0722	−0.930	0.1762	−0.400	0.3446
−1.450	0.0735	−0.920	0.1788	−0.390	0.3483
−1.440	0.0750	−0.910	0.1814	−0.380	0.3520
−1.430	0.0764	−0.900	0.1841	−0.370	0.3557
−1.420	0.0778	−0.890	0.1867	−0.360	0.3595
−1.410	0.0793	−0.880	0.1894	−0.350	0.3632
−1.400	0.0808	−0.870	0.1922	−0.340	0.3670
−1.390	0.0823	−0.860	0.1949	−0.330	0.3707
−1.380	0.0838	−0.850	0.1977	−0.320	0.3745
−1.370	0.0854	−0.840	0.2005	−0.310	0.3783
−1.360	0.0869	−0.830	0.2033	−0.300	0.3821
−1.350	0.0885	−0.820	0.2061	−0.290	0.3859
−1.340	0.0901	−0.810	0.2090	−0.280	0.3898
−1.330	0.0918	−0.800	0.2119	−0.270	0.3936
−1.320	0.0934	−0.790	0.2148	−0.260	0.3975
−1.310	0.0951	−0.780	0.2177	−0.250	0.4013
−1.300	0.0968	−0.770	0.2207	−0.240	0.4052
−1.290	0.0985	−0.760	0.2236	−0.230	0.4091
−1.280	0.1003	−0.750	0.2266	−0.220	0.4130
−1.270	0.1021	−0.740	0.2297	−0.210	0.4169
−1.260	0.1039	−0.730	0.2327	−0.200	0.4208
−1.250	0.1057	−0.720	0.2358	−0.190	0.4247
−1.240	0.1075	−0.710	0.2389	−0.180	0.4286
−1.230	0.1094	−0.700	0.2420	−0.170	0.4325
−1.220	0.1112	−0.690	0.2451	−0.160	0.4365
−1.210	0.1132	−0.680	0.2483	−0.150	0.4404
−1.200	0.1151	−0.670	0.2515	−0.140	0.4444
−1.190	0.1170	−0.660	0.2547	−0.130	0.4483
−1.180	0.1190	−0.650	0.2579	−0.120	0.4523
−1.170	0.1210	−0.640	0.2611	−0.110	0.4562
−1.160	0.1230	−0.630	0.2644	−0.100	0.4602
−1.150	0.1251	−0.620	0.2677	−0.090	0.4642
−1.140	0.1272	−0.610	0.2710	−0.080	0.4681
−1.130	0.1293	−0.600	0.2743	−0.070	0.4721
−1.120	0.1314	−0.590	0.2776	−0.060	0.4761
−1.110	0.1335	−0.580	0.2810	−0.050	0.4801
−1.100	0.1357	−0.570	0.2844	−0.040	0.4841
−1.090	0.1379	−0.560	0.2878	−0.030	0.4881
−1.080	0.1401	−0.550	0.2912	−0.020	0.4920
−1.070	0.1423	−0.540	0.2946	−0.010	0.4960
−1.060	0.1446	−0.530	0.2981	0.000	0.5000
−1.050	0.1469	−0.520	0.3016	0.010	0.5040
−1.040	0.1492	−0.510	0.3051	0.020	0.5080
−1.030	0.1515	−0.500	0.3086	0.030	0.5119
−1.020	0.1539	−0.490	0.3121	0.040	0.5159
−1.010	0.1563	−0.480	0.3156	0.050	0.5199
−1.000	0.1587	−0.470	0.3192	0.060	0.5239
−0.990	0.1611	−0.460	0.3228	0.070	0.5279
−0.980	0.1636	−0.450	0.3264	0.080	0.5319

TABLE 1 *(continued)*

z	$F_Z(z)$	z	$F_Z(z)$	z	$F_Z(z)$
0.090	0.5358	0.620	0.7323	1.150	0.8749
0.100	0.5398	0.630	0.7356	1.160	0.8770
0.110	0.5438	0.640	0.7389	1.170	0.8790
0.120	0.5477	0.650	0.7421	1.180	0.8810
0.130	0.5517	0.660	0.7453	1.190	0.8830
0.140	0.5556	0.670	0.7485	1.200	0.8849
0.150	0.5596	0.680	0.7517	1.210	0.8868
0.160	0.5635	0.690	0.7549	1.220	0.8888
0.170	0.5675	0.700	0.7580	1.230	0.8906
0.180	0.5714	0.710	0.7611	1.240	0.8925
0.190	0.5753	0.720	0.7642	1.250	0.8943
0.200	0.5792	0.730	0.7673	1.260	0.8961
0.210	0.5831	0.740	0.7703	1.270	0.8979
0.220	0.5870	0.750	0.7734	1.280	0.8997
0.230	0.5909	0.760	0.7764	1.290	0.9015
0.240	0.5948	0.770	0.7793	1.300	0.9032
0.250	0.5987	0.780	0.7823	1.310	0.9049
0.260	0.6025	0.790	0.7852	1.320	0.9066
0.270	0.6064	0.800	0.7881	1.330	0.9082
0.280	0.6102	0.810	0.7910	1.340	0.9099
0.290	0.6141	0.820	0.7939	1.350	0.9115
0.300	0.6179	0.830	0.7967	1.360	0.9131
0.310	0.6217	0.840	0.7995	1.370	0.9146
0.320	0.6255	0.850	0.8023	1.380	0.9162
0.330	0.6293	0.860	0.8051	1.390	0.9177
0.340	0.6330	0.870	0.8078	1.400	0.9192
0.350	0.6368	0.880	0.8106	1.410	0.9207
0.360	0.6405	0.890	0.8133	1.420	0.9222
0.370	0.6443	0.900	0.8159	1.430	0.9236
0.380	0.6480	0.910	0.8186	1.440	0.9250
0.390	0.6517	0.920	0.8212	1.450	0.9265
0.400	0.6554	0.930	0.8238	1.460	0.9278
0.410	0.6591	0.940	0.8264	1.470	0.9292
0.420	0.6627	0.950	0.8289	1.480	0.9305
0.430	0.6664	0.960	0.8315	1.490	0.9319
0.440	0.6700	0.970	0.8340	1.500	0.9332
0.450	0.6736	0.980	0.8364	1.510	0.9345
0.460	0.6772	0.990	0.8389	1.520	0.9357
0.470	0.6808	1.000	0.8413	1.530	0.9370
0.480	0.6844	1.010	0.8437	1.540	0.9382
0.490	0.6879	1.020	0.8461	1.550	0.9394
0.500	0.6914	1.030	0.8485	1.560	0.9406
0.510	0.6949	1.040	0.8508	1.570	0.9418
0.520	0.6984	1.050	0.8531	1.580	0.9429
0.530	0.7019	1.060	0.8554	1.590	0.9441
0.540	0.7054	1.070	0.8577	1.600	0.9452
0.550	0.7088	1.080	0.8599	1.610	0.9463
0.560	0.7122	1.090	0.8621	1.620	0.9474
0.570	0.7156	1.100	0.8643	1.630	0.9484
0.580	0.7190	1.110	0.8665	1.640	0.9495
0.590	0.7224	1.120	0.8686	1.650	0.9505
0.600	0.7257	1.130	0.8707	1.660	0.9515
0.610	0.7290	1.140	0.8728	1.670	0.9525

TABLE 1 *(continued)*

z	$F_Z(z)$	z	$F_Z(z)$	z	$F_Z(z)$
1.680	0.9535	2.210	0.9865	2.740	0.9969
1.690	0.9545	2.220	0.9868	2.750	0.9970
1.700	0.9554	2.230	0.9871	2.760	0.9971
1.710	0.9564	2.240	0.9875	2.770	0.9972
1.720	0.9573	2.250	0.9878	2.780	0.9973
1.730	0.9582	2.260	0.9881	2.790	0.9974
1.740	0.9591	2.270	0.9884	2.800	0.9974
1.750	0.9599	2.280	0.9887	2.810	0.9975
1.760	0.9608	2.290	0.9890	2.820	0.9976
1.770	0.9616	2.300	0.9893	2.830	0.9977
1.780	0.9625	2.310	0.9896	2.840	0.9977
1.790	0.9633	2.320	0.9898	2.850	0.9978
1.800	0.9641	2.330	0.9901	2.860	0.9979
1.810	0.9648	2.340	0.9904	2.870	0.9979
1.820	0.9656	2.350	0.9906	2.880	0.9980
1.830	0.9664	2.360	0.9909	2.890	0.9981
1.840	0.9671	2.370	0.9911	2.900	0.9981
1.850	0.9678	2.380	0.9914	2.910	0.9982
1.860	0.9686	2.390	0.9916	2.920	0.9982
1.870	0.9693	2.400	0.9918	2.930	0.9983
1.880	0.9699	2.410	0.9920	2.940	0.9984
1.890	0.9706	2.420	0.9922	2.950	0.9984
1.900	0.9713	2.430	0.9925	2.960	0.9985
1.910	0.9719	2.440	0.9927	2.970	0.9985
1.920	0.9726	2.450	0.9929	2.980	0.9986
1.930	0.9732	2.460	0.9931	2.990	0.9986
1.940	0.9738	2.470	0.9932	3.000	0.9986
1.950	0.9744	2.480	0.9934	3.010	0.9987
1.960	0.9750	2.490	0.9936	3.020	0.9987
1.970	0.9756	2.500	0.9938	3.030	0.9988
1.980	0.9761	2.510	0.9940	3.040	0.9988
1.990	0.9767	2.520	0.9941	3.050	0.9988
2.000	0.9773	2.530	0.9943	3.060	0.9989
2.010	0.9778	2.540	0.9945	3.070	0.9989
2.020	0.9783	2.550	0.9946	3.080	0.9990
2.030	0.9788	2.560	0.9948	3.090	0.9990
2.040	0.9793	2.570	0.9949	3.100	0.9990
2.050	0.9798	2.580	0.9951	3.110	0.9991
2.060	0.9803	2.590	0.9952	3.120	0.9991
2.070	0.9808	2.600	0.9953	3.130	0.9991
2.080	0.9812	2.610	0.9955	3.140	0.9991
2.090	0.9817	2.620	0.9956	3.150	0.9992
2.100	0.9821	2.630	0.9957	3.160	0.9992
2.110	0.9826	2.640	0.9959	3.170	0.9992
2.120	0.9830	2.650	0.9960	3.180	0.9993
2.130	0.9834	2.660	0.9961	3.190	0.9993
2.140	0.9838	2.670	0.9962	3.200	0.9993
2.150	0.9842	2.680	0.9963	3.210	0.9993
2.160	0.9846	2.690	0.9964	3.220	0.9994
2.170	0.9850	2.700	0.9965	3.230	0.9994
2.180	0.9854	2.710	0.9966	3.240	0.9994
2.190	0.9857	2.720	0.9967	3.250	0.9994
2.200	0.9861	2.730	0.9968	3.260	0.9994

TABLE 1 *(concluded)*

z	$F_Z(z)$	z	$F_Z(z)$	z	$F_Z(z)$
3.270	0.9995	3.520	0.9998	3.770	0.9999
3.280	0.9995	3.530	0.9998	3.780	0.9999
3.290	0.9995	3.540	0.9998	3.790	0.9999
3.300	0.9995	3.550	0.9998	3.800	0.9999
3.310	0.9995	3.560	0.9998	3.810	0.9999
3.320	0.9995	3.570	0.9998	3.820	0.9999
3.330	0.9996	3.580	0.9998	3.830	0.9999
3.340	0.9996	3.590	0.9998	3.840	0.9999
3.350	0.9996	3.600	0.9998	3.850	0.9999
3.360	0.9996	3.610	0.9998	3.860	0.9999
3.370	0.9996	3.620	0.9998	3.870	0.9999
3.380	0.9996	3.630	0.9999	3.880	0.9999
3.390	0.9996	3.640	0.9999	3.890	0.9999
3.400	0.9997	3.650	0.9999	3.900	0.9999
3.410	0.9997	3.660	0.9999	3.910	0.9999
3.420	0.9997	3.670	0.9999	3.920	1.0000
3.430	0.9997	3.680	0.9999	3.930	1.0000
3.440	0.9997	3.690	0.9999	3.940	1.0000
3.450	0.9997	3.700	0.9999	3.950	1.0000
3.460	0.9997	3.710	0.9999	3.960	1.0000
3.470	0.9997	3.720	0.9999	3.970	1.0000
3.480	0.9997	3.730	0.9999	3.980	1.0000
3.490	0.9998	3.740	0.9999	3.990	1.0000
3.500	0.9998	3.750	0.9999		
3.510	0.9998	3.760	0.9999		

TABLE 2
Percentage Points of the Chi-Square Distribution

ν \ Q	0.995	0.990	0.975	0.950	0.900	0.750	0.500
1	392704.10^{-10}	157088.10^{-9}	982069.10^{-9}	393214.10^{-8}	0.0157908	0.1015308	0.454937
2	0.0100251	0.0201007	0.0506356	0.102587	0.210720	0.575364	1.38629
3	0.0717212	0.114832	0.215795	0.351846	0.584375	1.212534	2.36597
4	0.206990	0.297110	0.484419	0.710721	1.063623	1.92255	3.35670
5	0.411740	0.554300	0.831211	1.145476	1.61031	2.67460	4.35146
6	0.675727	0.872085	1.237347	1.63539	2.20413	3.45460	5.34812
7	0.989265	1.239043	1.68987	2.16735	2.83311	4.25485	6.34581
8	1.344419	1.646482	2.17973	2.73264	3.48954	5.07064	7.34412
9	1.734926	2.087912	2.70039	3.32511	4.16816	5.89883	8.34283
10	2.15585	2.55821	3.24697	3.94030	4.86518	6.73720	9.34182
11	2.60321	3.05347	3.81575	4.57481	5.57779	7.58412	10.3410
12	3.07382	3.57056	4.40379	5.22603	6.30380	8.43842	11.3403
13	3.56503	4.10691	5.00874	5.89186	7.04150	9.29906	12.3398
14	4.07468	4.66043	5.62872	6.57063	7.78953	10.1653	13.3393
15	4.60094	5.22935	6.26214	7.26094	8.54675	11.0365	14.3389
16	5.14224	5.81221	6.90766	7.96164	9.31223	11.9122	15.3385
17	5.69724	6.40776	7.56418	8.67176	10.0852	12.7919	16.3381
18	6.26481	7.01491	8.23075	9.39046	10.8649	13.6753	17.3379
19	6.84398	7.63273	8.90655	10.1170	11.6509	14.5620	18.3376
20	7.43386	8.26040	9.59083	10.8508	12.4426	15.4518	19.3374
21	8.03366	8.89720	10.28293	11.5913	13.2396	16.3444	20.3372
22	8.64272	9.54249	10.9823	12.3380	14.0415	17.2396	21.3370
23	9.26042	10.19567	11.6885	13.0905	14.8479	18.1373	22.3369
24	9.88623	10.8564	12.4011	13.8484	15.6587	19.0372	23.3367
25	10.5197	11.5240	13.1197	14.6114	16.4734	19.9393	24.3366
26	11.1603	12.1981	13.8439	15.3791	17.2919	20.8434	25.3364
27	11.8076	12.8786	14.5733	16.1513	18.1138	21.7494	26.3363
28	12.4613	13.5648	15.3079	16.9279	18.9392	22.6572	27.3363
29	13.1211	14.2565	16.0471	17.7083	19.7677	23.5666	28.3362
30	13.7867	14.9535	16.7908	18.4926	20.5992	24.4776	29.3360
40	20.7065	22.1643	24.4331	26.5093	29.0505	33.6603	39.3354
50	27.9907	29.7067	32.3574	34.7642	37.6886	42.9421	49.3349
60	35.5346	37.4848	40.4817	43.1879	46.4589	52.2938	59.3347
70	43.2752	45.4418	48.7576	51.7393	55.3290	61.6983	69.3344
80	51.1720	53.5400	57.1532	60.3915	64.2778	71.1445	79.3343
90	59.1963	61.7541	65.6466	69.1260	73.2912	80.6247	89.3342
100	67.3276	70.0648	74.2219	77.9295	82.3581	90.1332	99.3341
X	-2.5758	-2.3263	-1.9600	-1.6449	-1.2816	-0.6745	-0.0000

$$Q = Q(\chi^2 | \nu) = 1 - P(\chi^2 | \nu) = 2 \ \ [\Gamma(\tfrac{1}{2}\nu)]^{-1} \int_{\chi^2}^{\infty} e^{-\frac{1}{2}x} x^{\frac{1}{2}\nu - 1} \ dx$$

TABLE 2 *(continued)*

Q / ν	0.250	0.100	0.050	0.025	0.010	0.005	0.001
1	1.32330	2.70554	3.84146	5.02389	6.63490	7.87944	10.828
2	2.77259	4.60517	5.99147	7.37776	9.21034	10.5966	13.816
3	4.10835	6.25139	7.81473	9.34840	11.3449	12.8381	16.266
4	5.38527	7.77944	9.48773	11.1433	13.2767	14.8602	18.467
5	6.62568	9.23635	11.0705	12.8325	15.0863	16.7496	20.515
6	7.84080	10.6446	12.5916	14.4494	16.8119	18.5476	22.458
7	9.03715	12.0170	14.0671	16.0128	18.4753	20.2777	24.322
8	10.2188	13.3616	15.5073	17.5346	20.0902	21.9550	26.125
9	11.3887	14.6837	16.9190	19.0228	21.6660	23.5893	27.877
10	12.5489	15.9871	18.3070	20.4831	23.2093	25.1882	29.588
11	13.7007	17.2750	19.6751	21.9200	24.7250	26.7569	31.264
12	14.8454	18.5494	21.0261	23.3367	26.2170	28.2995	32.909
13	15.9839	19.8119	22.3621	24.7356	27.6883	29.8194	34.528
14	17.1170	21.0642	23.6848	26.1190	29.1413	31.3193	36.123
15	18.2451	22.3072	24.9958	27.4884	30.5779	32.8013	37.697
16	19.3688	23.5418	26.2962	28.8454	31.9999	34.2672	39.252
17	20.4887	24.7690	27.5871	30.1910	33.4087	35.7185	40.790
18	21.6049	25.9894	28.8693	31.5264	34.8053	37.1564	42.312
19	22.7178	27.2036	30.1435	32.8523	36.1908	38.5822	43.820
20	23.8277	28.4120	31.4104	34.1696	37.5662	39.9968	45.315
21	24.9348	29.6151	32.6705	35.4789	38.9321	41.4010	46.797
22	26.0393	30.8133	33.9244	36.7807	40.2894	42.7956	48.268
23	27.1413	32.0069	35.1725	38.0757	41.6384	44.1813	49.728
24	28.2412	33.1963	36.4151	39.3641	42.9798	45.5585	51.179
25	29.3389	34.3816	37.6525	40.6465	44.3141	46.9278	52.620
26	30.4345	35.5631	38.8852	41.9232	45.6417	48.2899	54.052
27	31.5284	36.7412	40.1133	43.1944	46.9630	49.6449	55.476
28	32.6205	37.9159	41.3372	44.4607	48.2782	50.9933	56.892
29	33.7109	39.0875	42.5569	45.7222	49.5879	52.3356	58.302
30	34.7998	40.2560	43.7729	46.9792	50.8922	53.6720	59.703
40	45.6160	51.8050	55.7585	59.3417	63.6907	66.7659	73.402
50	56.3336	63.1671	67.5048	71.4202	76.1539	79.4900	86.661
60	66.9814	74.3970	79.0819	83.2976	88.3794	91.9517	99.607
70	77.5766	85.5271	90.5312	95.0231	100.425	104.215	112.317
80	88.1303	96.5782	101.879	106.629	112.329	116.321	124.839
90	98.6499	107.565	113.145	118.136	124.116	128.299	137.208
100	109.141	118.498	124.342	129.561	135.807	140.169	149.449
X	+0.6745	+1.2816	+1.6449	+1.9600	+2.3263	+2.5758	+3.0902

Note: For $\nu > 100$ take

$$\chi^2 = \nu \left(1 - \frac{2}{9\nu} + X \sqrt{\frac{2}{9\nu}} \right)^3 \text{ or } \chi^2 = \tfrac{1}{2}[X + \sqrt{(2\nu - 1)}]^2$$

according to the degree of accuracy required. X is the standardized normal deviate corresponding to $P = 1 - Q$, and is shown in the bottom line of the table.

Source: E. S. Pearson and H. G. Hartley, *Biometrika Tables for Statisticians*, Vol. I (2d ed., London: Biometrika, 1958). By permission of the editors and publishers.

TABLE 3
Percentage Points of the t-Distribution

ν	Q=0.4 2Q=0.8	0.25 0.5	0.1 0.2	0.05 0.1	0.025 0.05	0.01 0.02	0.005 0.01	0.0025 0.005	0.001 0.002	0.0005 0.001
1	0.325	1.000	3.078	6.314	12.706	31.821	63.657	127.32	318.31	636.62
2	.289	0.816	1.886	2.920	4.303	6.965	9.925	14.089	22.326	31.598
3	.277	.765	1.638	2.353	3.182	4.541	5.841	7.453	10.213	12.924
4	.271	.741	1.533	2.132	2.776	3.747	4.604	5.598	7.173	8.610
5	0.267	0.727	1.476	2.015	2.571	3.365	4.032	4.773	5.893	6.869
6	.265	.718	1.440	1.943	2.447	3.143	3.707	4.317	5.208	5.959
7	.263	.711	1.415	1.895	2.365	2.998	3.499	4.029	4.785	5.408
8	.262	.706	1.397	1.860	2.306	2.896	3.355	3.833	4.501	5.041
9	.261	.703	1.383	1.833	2.262	2.821	3.250	3.690	4.297	4.781
10	0.260	0.700	1.372	1.812	2.228	2.764	3.169	3.581	4.144	4.587
11	.260	.697	1.363	1.796	2.201	2.718	3.106	3.497	4.025	4.437
12	.259	.695	1.356	1.782	2.179	2.681	3.055	3.428	3.930	4.318
13	.259	.694	1.350	1.771	2.160	2.650	3.012	3.372	3.852	4.221
14	.258	.692	1.345	1.761	2.145	2.624	2.977	3.326	3.787	4.140
15	0.258	0.691	1.341	1.753	2.131	2.602	2.947	3.286	3.733	4.073
16	.258	.690	1.337	1.746	2.120	2.583	2.921	3.252	3.686	4.015
17	.257	.689	1.333	1.740	2.110	2.567	2.898	3.222	3.646	3.965
18	.257	.688	1.330	1.734	2.101	2.552	2.878	3.197	3.610	3.922
19	.257	.688	1.328	1.729	2.093	2.539	2.861	3.174	3.579	3.883
20	0.257	0.687	1.325	1.725	2.086	2.528	2.845	3.153	3.552	3.850
21	.257	.686	1.323	1.721	2.080	2.518	2.831	3.135	3.527	3.819
22	.256	.686	1.321	1.717	2.074	2.508	2.819	3.119	3.505	3.792
23	.256	.685	1.319	1.714	2.069	2.500	2.807	3.104	3.485	3.767
24	.256	.685	1.318	1.711	2.064	2.492	2.797	3.091	3.467	3.745
25	0.256	0.684	1.316	1.708	2.060	2.485	2.787	3.078	3.450	3.725
26	.256	.684	1.315	1.706	2.056	2.479	2.779	3.067	3.435	3.707
27	.256	.684	1.314	1.703	2.052	2.473	2.771	3.057	3.421	3.690
28	.256	.683	1.313	1.701	2.048	2.467	2.763	3.047	3.408	3.674
29	.256	.683	1.311	1.699	2.045	2.462	2.756	3.038	3.396	3.659
30	0.256	0.683	1.310	1.697	2.042	2.457	2.750	3.030	3.385	3.646
40	.255	.681	1.303	1.684	2.021	2.423	2.704	2.971	3.307	3.551
60	.254	.679	1.296	1.671	2.000	2.390	2.660	2.915	3.232	3.460
120	.254	.677	1.289	1.658	1.980	2.358	2.617	2.860	3.160	3.373
∞	.253	.674	1.282	1.645	1.960	2.326	2.576	2.807	3.090	3.291

$Q = 1 - P(t|v)$ is the upper-tail area of the distribution for v degrees of freedom, appropriate for use in a single-tail test. For a two-tail test, $2Q$ must be used.

Source: E. S. Pearson and H. G. Hartley, *Biometrika Tables for Statisticians,* Vol. I (2d ed., London: Biometrika, 1958). By permission of the editors and publishers.

TABLE 4

Critical Values, d (N), of the Maximum Absolute Difference between
Sample and Population Cumulative Distributions*

Sample size (N)	Level of significance (α)					Sample size (N)	Level of significance (α)				
	0.20	0.15	0.10	0.05	0.01		0.20	0.15	0.10	0.05	0.01
1	0.900	0.925	0.950	0.975	0.995	14	0.274	0.292	0.314	0.349	0.418
2	0.684	0.726	0.776	0.842	0.929	15	0.266	0.283	0.304	0.338	0.404
3	0.565	0.597	0.642	0.708	0.828						
4	0.494	0.525	0.564	0.624	0.733	16	0.258	0.274	0.295	0.328	0.392
5	0.446	0.474	0.510	0.565	0.669	17	0.250	0.266	0.286	0.318	0.381
						18	0.244	0.259	0.278	0.309	0.371
6	0.410	0.436	0.470	0.521	0.618	19	0.237	0.252	0.272	0.301	0.363
7	0.381	0.405	0.438	0.486	0.577	20	0.231	0.246	0.264	0.294	0.356
8	0.358	0.381	0.411	0.457	0.543						
9	0.339	0.360	0.388	0.432	0.514	25	0.21	0.22	0.24	0.27	0.32
10	0.322	0.342	0.368	0.410	0.490	30	0.19	0.20	0.22	0.24	0.29
						35	0.18	0.19	0.21	0.23	0.27
11	0.307	0.326	0.352	0.391	0.468	over 35	$\dfrac{1.07}{\sqrt{N}}$	$\dfrac{1.14}{\sqrt{N}}$	$\dfrac{1.22}{\sqrt{N}}$	$\dfrac{1.36}{\sqrt{N}}$	$\dfrac{1.63}{\sqrt{N}}$
12	0.295	0.313	0.338	0.375	0.450						
13	0.284	0.302	0.325	0.361	0.433						

*Values of d (N) such that $Pr[\max|S(x) - F_0(x)| > d(N)] = $, where $F_0(x)$ is the theoretical cumulative distribution and $S(x)$ is an observed cumulative distribution for a sample of N.

Source: F. J. Massey, Jr., "The Kolmogorov-Smirnov Test for Goodness of Fit", *The Journal of the American Statistical Association* (Vol. 46, 1951). By permission of the author and publishers.

TABLE 5

8481	5016	0080	4376	2579	8293	5950	1048	0650	4135
0744	3447	6173	3288	6378	6704	0966	9986	5202	1728
5558	7239	2976	4836	6134	5120	1541	6514	3581	2079
9371	1463	2164	2301	3142	3866	8707	9986	2011	5111
3033	1660	6365	9054	1155	8844	4085	9589	2924	1725
1053	7320	6532	7234	8972	6466	1217	0100	1458	9416
4389	3504	4086	9434	0136	5695	6876	7937	5476	3396
2158	8854	9534	1196	4941	2697	7497	1149	1952	3482
6749	3676	4943	1406	8614	2060	6433	1660	8875	3194
2878	3447	4804	6761	5309	0636	0522	2004	3207	4684
0591	6549	2206	6185	6188	2649	2389	9483	0924	1389
1025	3438	0546	2545	1089	1280	6701	9742	3453	5573
4244	9217	1628	4524	0163	9895	9586	2083	8459	0644
4331	9032	1388	5661	0472	7128	1902	0343	7724	6528
8853	3490	2589	8744	1221	4667	8396	4779	9937	7206
5059	4192	6331	5485	5922	0982	9390	8993	3621	2602
0821	4340	3194	0118	4773	8668	1891	7989	9190	2296
5262	1746	7108	6496	2570	4243	5029	8949	4989	5008
1210	1858	9365	6562	0269	9923	1796	6626	8591	1990
3642	6629	5775	3219	8801	4047	6861	0765	2379	3494
9598	5322	3747	0363	5995	5504	6804	7033	0957	9516
3894	3173	2853	9312	2498	8878	4956	8748	6247	0673
3603	3011	6762	0848	8316	3485	6388	8925	3799	0898
1121	2978	6313	5857	8457	1395	7240	8630	3895	6348
1930	4583	4227	4120	6893	7005	2264	6067	5627	7985
6309	9158	2830	3262	9809	4606	8669	1154	5841	7696
4460	3043	5383	0327	9668	1697	8335	0869	2188	1908
8371	5095	7273	1866	4193	4163	2035	2832	4996	7143
9397	5549	9298	9076	1299	6669	0088	2809	9631	3162
9304	1468	4013	7465	0861	6787	3581	7977	8409	4798
5606	2435	8546	3209	4802	6690	8527	2219	6706	1930
6693	8333	3082	7546	2910	8553	8725	1237	4423	1570
0556	7715	8994	4245	1540	8159	3889	5273	6977	2703
6973	9299	4959	7146	1426	7086	8743	6982	5547	3394
4920	1223	5208	6661	4907	1102	0501	3625	8513	3192
0132	0928	8241	0838	7627	4174	1170	3142	2455	4891
4051	3101	9854	4488	6931	3266	3147	2560	8011	8848
0267	5612	5604	9917	7928	8034	9989	4353	2075	9497
0609	9469	3149	4086	8911	8547	3518	9349	1836	0548
2593	1666	5750	5105	4287	4380	7860	7792	1625	7659
8812	9491	2602	4100	4962	1037	9778	1778	4223	3193
3540	5985	0019	7155	1471	1851	8682	9957	3772	4706
9535	5375	1239	1624	5378	6803	7177	7911	4660	5669
3174	7677	8282	6669	5879	7874	9931	6581	9784	2697
8864	4760	1129	6205	4949	4205	0222	7479	6470	8194
5245	7341	0593	5656	6799	3071	1751	4339	5630	9496
5468	6083	4511	1440	2135	5777	9903	1048	6726	8602
3951	7928	6818	4167	4840	1392	1323	5014	7538	9854
7319	4064	4024	5401	2834	7518	3978	3742	1005	4619
5892	8731	6269	5189	2071	4084	9789	3620	9819	4548

TABLE 5 *(continued)*

3242	6397	8426	3786	5191	1321	6727	5452	5388	9308
0416	4213	9406	2802	9432	4999	3475	8057	0002	8934
0246	3859	4668	9062	4197	9773	4550	3714	5148	8454
2814	1571	6627	6681	0303	8987	3028	0558	7877	6400
5920	1393	5980	0661	8776	0624	5207	1932	7321	4298
3906	4681	5598	9984	0375	1404	5171	6170	6383	6347
7258	6165	5833	0071	2984	6790	8609	8647	6415	0683
1214	0573	8274	9115	9157	2034	2445	5435	9744	4536
4828	3177	9897	9919	5869	9010	8837	0863	8423	3307
6287	9116	2215	5989	5981	8145	8240	1530	7458	9970
1598	6821	7075	5875	0245	0668	9151	8647	7429	4272
9778	8636	8762	1999	5880	0824	4373	9362	6260	2365
8952	5288	0466	9910	7144	0830	9275	1917	0610	9236
5778	0913	5272	6099	1354	7132	7069	0188	1909	4307
0932	2149	2525	2537	8298	6570	8800	2441	2156	5667
0580	5025	2881	0130	5057	4082	8972	9835	4749	7304
7110	6803	8772	7671	5783	6512	0099	3751	8842	7472
3516	8338	8002	8263	3090	1156	0401	4136	5073	4886
3024	5210	8913	6068	8147	5977	8064	9438	2902	9089
7500	1611	4775	1468	3388	6160	7037	4106	1394	0766
8409	7755	2108	6656	9543	9669	1410	3628	1328	1791
3394	2075	6482	8046	6463	1491	2935	7817	6514	2185
7972	6538	4763	3795	8692	8036	8700	4506	9138	6185
0284	5983	5167	8152	3790	6287	7871	0352	2690	5959
8983	6383	8001	3034	6166	7171	1078	8159	1291	2783
6533	0247	9197	8378	2253	7739	7705	6733	8874	9823
7224	0467	6877	5628	6840	5690	5418	3347	2711	9359
2865	3164	8483	4106	8907	4077	2381	1610	1832	2248
3120	8893	4125	9851	5582	1633	9387	1761	7331	2684
1996	7049	9318	1176	3296	6817	7665	6283	5268	6951
9370	3885	9041	5378	7754	3187	9338	1011	9064	7690
1981	2983	3759	2061	8316	6811	3253	3330	1970	1705
5285	1795	4801	5368	1418	7428	0359	6575	5736	8147
8176	0025	6882	8755	0234	6609	3010	9330	9191	2172
5319	1026	9431	3200	8002	9613	5323	9555	8236	9595
4157	6878	8673	1092	4805	1716	0648	6140	4379	1807
7980	8388	2456	4784	8265	3205	1770	5160	3478	0881
3510	3374	6263	0124	2307	4114	7085	8465	1161	4896
7737	7432	7034	0194	2630	9709	7814	0228	3034	3535
0374	8840	1522	2942	3944	2144	4522	2432	0373	8788
2863	2747	9402	2733	0921	1819	6624	0732	5925	4732
2764	8831	9680	5869	6628	3670	6271	2924	1963	0091
7703	5530	6379	4509	2588	8934	0937	3331	0980	4279
2140	1589	9380	2141	4093	5476	3328	2126	8490	8188
9726	6430	7230	8616	8192	8009	7062	9341	5513	6591
2278	7140	8758	0241	9399	7099	9974	2460	8360	4250
3374	5834	6316	2777	9176	7982	5396	9307	2661	8352
6938	6379	6525	9795	2704	1346	4287	3089	8354	7404
7582	9626	7744	9510	4027	4894	6450	2446	6804	1455
4148	1048	0891	2231	8907	8279	1146	4403	8329	1743

TABLE 5 *(continued)*

4885	7232	7085	0340	4336	0532	4270	4837	1973	8815
5428	3992	7382	7324	2608	3398	2815	4203	4767	7777
3315	2036	5697	1808	7575	1496	5039	6201	0415	0400
1297	7528	6985	5172	6837	8496	8266	8967	9986	2324
7475	0511	5681	3923	4940	7732	6884	5628	7167	8584
9347	9006	5403	2317	8733	0568	2532	1636	3516	1787
4290	2110	0046	6860	5198	0907	1439	5444	7350	7106
5735	5813	0727	4205	6857	5411	5580	7855	5489	1416
8968	1864	9224	4349	9202	8414	1571	7343	1898	7775
0666	2734	0415	6647	3781	3762	7338	8733	9876	0529
6694	6173	8755	8430	5826	9901	3164	6583	5119	2708
5538	0989	1366	1158	9415	9812	2739	6264	9057	7258
1569	7039	2403	5477	4197	9928	5527	5251	0712	7685
7284	8836	3133	1896	6051	7190	0897	0624	5625	3243
1763	0418	4246	8951	3465	5671	8135	2430	2109	4961
0366	8319	0670	7324	7852	7711	3341	9178	4381	0453
0364	3670	1590	7311	4063	9579	4668	1119	1866	6692
7347	2728	2446	8199	8540	1839	1380	9248	2300	9229
4338	9541	1645	7652	4326	5975	1131	4883	4383	1292
7398	3383	5282	3832	8808	3070	6320	7158	1702	6312
6939	2728	7365	0934	3375	2778	4444	7467	1948	1087
7035	7404	6552	6210	8718	0382	9554	6608	1163	5798
4938	4427	1574	3156	0419	3368	6244	4139	7129	1738
3279	8825	2041	6140	1686	4005	2485	0350	0165	3832
1564	7112	2466	2982	5765	4803	8972	4325	4479	9719
4056	5572	0322	4667	3924	6899	4063	1183	1834	6502
3485	9436	6314	5854	4408	4962	7424	2038	5972	8160
1638	5289	7974	4648	2488	3808	7994	9627	9162	6787
4907	9233	7934	1220	9550	7959	8774	9417	2158	4233
0683	7417	1426	8386	8022	4215	1935	4190	1716	9067
9671	4025	6059	0634	7474	0502	4248	5267	0264	8606
7583	3603	6263	5196	6813	1978	8659	1498	6940	8035
2790	9903	1617	2877	8955	3486	6331	1132	9749	1779
0576	3990	1908	3159	0353	5082	7988	0900	6831	5185
0892	8746	8162	2188	8363	2494	9828	1751	3734	3110
1657	1779	1915	2049	8042	9810	0209	4779	6464	4623
4964	4806	1901	0060	8579	4560	1547	7470	4533	2866
4392	1788	4692	5284	1924	9149	6322	7462	3976	8655
1820	9220	1720	5556	5729	0746	1803	6430	5384	5462
5238	8811	4516	9626	1046	9375	7800	2381	5964	4102
5344	3316	5727	9992	9790	7124	1084	2911	8386	8925
4273	9727	0933	6744	4556	5590	2256	0131	5106	7873
0224	4470	1958	2713	6692	3025	7807	4749	5625	5419
0302	1004	6426	9556	7162	6811	2202	0492	6548	8400
9331	1280	9862	0060	6299	1508	5990	0817	8613	9138
8957	2945	1036	8910	9540	2355	6245	2148	6490	4408
8240	9190	1906	5192	6797	8422	5612	9682	0143	2114
2542	3731	7303	3262	5741	0792	6813	2916	2038	6322
0726	4964	5380	5851	5836	4016	8130	4832	2474	4900
4849	5569	4492	2238	7872	4681	0470	6129	6203	5200

TABLE 5 *(concluded)*

0539	8496	7992	4920	9527	2997	9045	4747	7501	4986
1915	0352	5809	2544	5313	5647	9648	8684	3733	6289
0301	5708	8271	4045	9575	0051	4934	5608	5682	0784
9951	1701	8596	7462	7912	9092	2898	3680	8779	0211
5609	5552	0647	9712	0879	9184	4150	9309	0589	8840
2455	4523	6955	3377	6692	8974	0416	1472	9500	3068
9249	7210	9071	4290	1130	5030	9629	3164	2542	4247
9960	3141	8112	1821	5230	9628	1851	3519	9637	2183
5674	0820	1222	6979	9339	4943	4926	3450	4220	0609
9404	7985	8465	5645	3389	0894	7495	8323	0949	4241
7496	2813	8722	2631	3166	0827	3718	8114	7051	0044
7069	2073	1928	2539	8378	8342	5670	5512	8590	7510
9133	6576	0851	3487	9378	9183	9000	6537	2478	4459
7096	9568	3753	3495	3271	4817	6566	9666	2309	2288
3204	8597	5353	6016	4558	9183	9790	8969	0794	3218
7109	7279	0960	4399	0869	8689	8891	6751	2150	9326
3394	0442	6077	5931	7551	4217	0434	4604	4648	4475
7017	9064	6717	2292	9643	1217	2499	0517	1424	1745
2995	5058	7099	9742	5927	2994	5451	8606	4021	5574
1765	7486	7079	2308	6737	8675	6895	3186	6325	0219
5319	2058	6878	5678	3504	1144	6847	3681	2757	0927
2685	5805	8110	7167	4265	1945	0139	6676	3755	1353
2104	0567	1930	5732	1748	7363	1562	5607	7610	6336
8060	8677	4792	9741	6898	7026	2691	1270	4268	0465
9556	7349	7278	7265	4364	8450	6843	8904	3512	4372
9775	4868	0045	0837	0782	2490	1417	3243	0208	3952
7122	0875	3765	6884	0804	4450	4192	2243	8114	8705
9733	8654	2824	8987	4339	4041	7863	2145	9859	9935
0183	3196	2537	3344	5869	1429	5254	3676	5192	6353
9069	0725	2347	2726	9256	1085	8861	3301	6796	7445
9069	0544	8478	4274	6765	9569	9174	2368	4533	8255
0208	9853	8265	8064	7257	5828	2673	1528	3534	6296
9928	2518	6052	1043	0290	9007	0848	9286	6798	2308
9706	8658	3571	3824	7587	5360	0396	8410	1509	9143
2488	2717	7217	7883	5766	8203	3840	7306	0502	5080
9567	7495	1102	9055	6112	5830	8087	7832	6556	7592
0501	9689	0266	3976	4655	5650	5807	8118	9651	0534
4659	1490	8845	1817	5819	7942	6610	8637	4442	6922
5671	1191	2459	4269	7457	4878	7545	7203	1643	4227
2317	3840	7326	0257	7274	8337	2339	1057	8644	0464
1736	4968	7549	5535	8530	3409	3102	9145	9134	6452
0159	0684	4797	5886	8324	2633	4001	4905	6267	5477
8285	6108	5336	2454	5368	2240	5864	1955	1726	1042
1822	7513	2677	6808	6386	8294	1767	3780	6121	8517
1222	0604	5896	4625	3294	6281	4299	0832	9069	5569
9303	5278	5827	1891	2629	2241	0342	2763	3042	8856
0952	9759	4568	7300	0490	3189	8905	7782	1543	8885
2971	1264	8021	4308	8889	5943	1979	8292	7180	4864
8466	4567	4878	5901	9596	4200	1210	0315	0684	8630
5934	6056	5035	3285	1987	7032	0291	1916	0611	9026

APPENDIX
B

SAMPLE OUTPUT FROM GENERAL
INVENTORY SIMULATION PROGRAM

Sample Output: Periodic Review Model with Lost Sales
and Five-Year Simulation with Printout Each Year

```
AIR= 0.4100000E 02
AIQ= 0.9200000E 02
REVTIM= 0.5000000E 00
CI= 0.2000000E 02
CO= 0.1000000E 03
CB1= 0.5000000E 02
CB2= 0.1000000E 02
CP= 0.6000000E 02
TIMLIM= 0.5000000E 01
DEC= 0.1000000E 01
ALEVEL= 0.4200000E 02
DELT= 0.1000000E 01
LOST=    1
PERREV= 0.1000000E 01
ITER=    1
A= 0.1000000E 03
B= 0.1000000E 01
C= 0.0
D= 0.0
G= 0.0
H= 0.1000000E 01
```

```
PERIODIC REVIEW MODEL
LOST SALES
MEAN ANNUAL DEMAND =0.10000000E 03 UNITS
MEAN LEAD TIME =0.0             YEARS
```

```
III=    1 I1=    1  TIME=0.10000000E 01
```

	PER TIME PERIOD	EXPECTED PER YEAR
NUMBER OF REVIEWS	0.20000000E 01	0.20000000E 01
UNIT YRS OF INVENTORY	0.75034286E 02	0.75034286E 02
UNIT YRS OF STOCKOUTS	0.0	0.0
NUMBER OF STOCKOUTS	0.0	0.0
NUMBER OF ORDERS	0.10000000E 01	0.10000000E 01
INVENTORY CARRYING COST	0.15006855E 04	0.15006855E 04
STOCKOUT COST (TIME*QUANTITY)	0.0	0.0
STOCKOUT COST (QUANTITY)	0.0	0.0
ORDERING COST	0.10000000E 03	0.10000000E 03
REVIEW COST	0.12000000E 03	0.12000000E 03
TOTAL COST	0.17206855E 04	0.17206855E 04

```
NO OF DEMANDS RECEIVED = 0.11500000E 03
TOTAL UNITS DEMANDED = 0.11500000E 03
AVERAGE UNITS PER DEMAND = 0.10000000E 01
```

Periodic Review Model *(continued)*

III=   1 I1=   2 TIME=0.20000000E 01

	PER TIME PERIOD	EXPECTED PER YEAR
NUMBER OF REVIEWS	0.20000000E 01	0.20000000E 01
UNIT YRS OF INVENTORY	0.16871719E 02	0.45953003E 02
UNIT YRS OF STOCKOUTS	0.0	0.0
NUMBER OF STOCKOUTS	0.19000000E 02	0.95000000E 01
NUMBER OF ORDERS	0.20000000E 01	0.15000000E 01
INVENTORY CARRYING COST	0.33743433E 03	0.91906006E 03
STOCKOUT COST (TIME*QUANTITY)	0.0	0.0
STOCKOUT COST (QUANTITY)	0.19000000E 03	0.95000000E 02
ORDERING COST	0.20000000E 03	0.15000000E 03
REVIEW COST	0.12000000E 03	0.12000000E 03
TOTAL COST	0.84743433E 03	0.12840601E 04

NO OF DEMANDS RECEIVED = 0.21800000E 03
TOTAL UNITS DEMANDED = 0.21800000E 03
AVERAGE UNITS PER DEMAND = 0.10000000E 01

III=   1 I1=   3 TIME=0.30000000E 01

	PER TIME PERIOD	EXPECTED PER YEAR
NUMBER OF REVIEWS	0.20000000E 01	0.20000000E 01
UNIT YRS OF INVENTORY	0.16019836E 02	0.35975281E 02
UNIT YRS OF STOCKOUTS	0.0	0.0
NUMBER OF STOCKOUTS	0.24000000E 02	0.14333333E 02
NUMBER OF ORDERS	0.20000000E 01	0.16666660E 01
INVENTORY CARRYING COST	0.32039673E 03	0.71950562E 03
STOCKOUT COST (TIME*QUANTITY)	0.0	0.0
STOCKOUT COST (QUANTITY)	0.24000000E 03	0.14333333E 03
ORDERING COST	0.20000000E 03	0.16666660E 03
REVIEW COST	0.12000000E 03	0.12000000E 03
TOTAL COST	0.88039673E 03	0.11495054E 04

NO OF DEMANDS RECEIVED = 0.32600000E 03
TOTAL UNITS DEMANDED = 0.32600000E 03
AVERAGE UNITS PER DEMAND = 0.10000000E 01

III=   1 I1=   4 TIME=0.40000000E 01

	PER TIME PERIOD	EXPECTED PER YEAR
NUMBER OF REVIEWS	0.20000000E 01	0.20000000E 01
UNIT YRS OF INVENTORY	0.21887344E 02	0.32453293E 02
UNIT YRS OF STOCKOUTS	0.0	0.0
NUMBER OF STOCKOUTS	0.20000153E 01	0.11250000E 02
NUMBER OF ORDERS	0.20000019E 01	0.17500000E 01
INVENTORY CARRYING COST	0.43774683E 03	0.64906567E 03
STOCKOUT COST (TIME*QUANTITY)	0.0	0.0
STOCKOUT COST (QUANTITY)	0.20000153E 02	0.11250000E 03
ORDERING COST	0.20000018E 03	0.17500000E 03
REVIEW COST	0.12000000E 03	0.12000000E 03
TOTAL COST	0.77774683E 03	0.10565657E 04

NO OF DEMANDS RECEIVED = 0.40800000E 03
TOTAL UNITS DEMANDED = 0.40800000E 03
AVERAGE UNITS PER DEMAND = 0.10000000E 01

Periodic Review Model *(concluded)*

III=   1 I1=   5 TIME=0.50000000E 01

	PER TIME PERIOD	EXPECTED PER YEAR
NUMBER OF REVIEWS	0.20000000E 01	0.20000000E 01
UNIT YRS OF INVENTORY	0.19233231E 02	0.29809280E 02
UNIT YRS OF STOCKOUTS	0.0	0.0
NUMBER OF STOCKOUTS	0.18000000E 02	0.12599999E 02
NUMBER OF ORDERS	0.20000000E 01	0.17999992E 01
INVENTORY CARRYING COST	0.38466455E 03	0.59618555E 03
STOCKOUT COST (TIME*QUANTITY)	0.0	0.0
STOCKOUT COST (QUANTITY)	0.18000000E 03	0.12599998E 03
ORDERING COST	0.20000000E 03	0.17999992E 03
REVIEW COST	0.12000000E 03	0.12000000E 03
TOTAL COST	0.88466455E 03	0.10221851E 04

NO OF DEMANDS RECEIVED = 0.51000000E 03
TOTAL UNITS DEMANDED = 0.51000000E 03
AVERAGE UNITS PER DEMAND = 0.10000000E 01

UNIT YRS INVENTORY	MEAN=0.29809280E 02	STD DEV=0.11352158E 02
UNIT YRS STOCKOUTS	MEAN=0.0	STD DEV=0.0
NUMBER OF STOCKOUTS	MEAN=0.12600002E 02	STD DEV=0.48538637E 01
NUMBER OF ORDERS	MEAN=0.18000002E 01	STD DEV=0.20000035E 00
NUMBER OF REVIEWS	MEAN=0.20000000E 01	STD DEV=0.0
TOTAL COST	MEAN=0.10221851E 04	STD DEV=0.17567157E 03

Sample Output: Reorder Point Model with Lost Sales
and Five-Year Simulation with Printout Each Year

AIR= 0.4000000E 01
AIQ= 0.3100000E 02
REVTIM= 0.0
CI= 0.5000000E 02
CO= 0.3000000E 03
CB1= 0.0
CB2= 0.7000000E 02
CP= 0.0
TIMLIM= 0.5000000E 01
DEC= 0.0
ALEVEL= 0.0
DELT= 0.1000000E 01
LOST=   1
PERREV= 0.0
ITER=   1
A= 0.3000000E 03
B= 0.1000000E 01
C= 0.8299999E-02
D= 0.0
G= 0.0
H= 0.1000000E 01

REORDER POINT MODEL
LOST SALES
MEAN ANNUAL DEMAND =0.30000000E 03 UNITS
MEAN LEAD TIME =0.82999989E-02 YEARS

Reorder Point Model *(continued)*

III=   1 I1=   1 TIME=0.10000000E 01

	PER TIME PERIOD	EXPECTED PER YEAR
NUMBER OF REVIEWS	0.32600000E 03	0.32600000E 03
UNIT YRS OF INVENTORY	0.17220200E 02	0.17220200E 02
UNIT YRS OF STOCKOUTS	0.0	0.0
NUMBER OF STOCKOUTS	0.0	0.0
NUMBER OF ORDERS	0.10000000E 02	0.10000000E 02
INVENTORY CARRYING COST	0.86100977E 03	0.86100977E 03
STOCKOUT COST (TIME*QUANTITY)	0.0	0.0
STOCKOUT COST (QUANTITY)	0.0	0.0
ORDERING COST	0.30000000E 04	0.30000000E 04
REVIEW COST	0.0	0.0
TOTAL COST	0.38610098E 04	0.38610098E 04

NO OF DEMANDS RECEIVED = 0.32600000E 03
TOTAL UNITS DEMANDED = 0.32600000E 03
AVERAGE UNITS PER DEMAND = 0.10000000E 01

III=   1 I1=   2 TIME=0.20000000E 01

	PER TIME PERIOD	EXPECTED PER YEAR
NUMBER OF REVIEWS	0.26700000E 03	0.29650000E 03
UNIT YRS OF INVENTORY	0.17660965E 02	0.17440582E 02
UNIT YRS OF STOCKOUTS	0.0	0.0
NUMBER OF STOCKOUTS	0.40000000E 01	0.20000000E 01
NUMBER OF ORDERS	0.90000000E 01	0.95000000E 01
INVENTORY CARRYING COST	0.88304810E 03	0.87202905E 03
STOCKOUT COST (TIME*QUANTITY)	0.0	0.0
STOCKOUT COST (QUANTITY)	0.28000000E 03	0.14000000E 03
ORDERING COST	0.27000000E 04	0.28500000E 04
REVIEW COST	0.0	0.0
TOTAL COST	0.38630481E 04	0.38620291E 04

NO OF DEMANDS RECEIVED = 0.59300000E 03
TOTAL UNITS DEMANDED = 0.59300000E 03
AVERAGE UNITS PER DEMAND = 0.10000000E 01

III=   1 I1=   3 TIME=0.30000000E 01

	PER TIME PERIOD	EXPECTED PER YEAR
NUMBER OF REVIEWS	0.32000000E 03	0.30433325E 03
UNIT YRS OF INVENTORY	0.17479645E 02	0.17453598E 02
UNIT YRS OF STOCKOUTS	0.0	0.0
NUMBER OF STOCKOUTS	0.10000000E 01	0.16666660E 01
NUMBER OF ORDERS	0.10000000E 02	0.96666660E 01
INVENTORY CARRYING COST	0.87398218E 03	0.87267969E 03
STOCKOUT COST (TIME*QUANTITY)	0.0	0.0
STOCKOUT COST (QUANTITY)	0.70000000E 02	0.11666661E 03
ORDERING COST	0.30000000E 04	0.28999998E 04
REVIEW COST	0.0	0.0
TOTAL COST	0.39439822E 04	0.38893459E 04

NO OF DEMANDS RECEIVED = 0.91300000E 03
TOTAL UNITS DEMANDED = 0.91300000E 03
AVERAGE UNITS PER DEMAND = 0.10000000E 01

Reorder Point Model *(concluded)*

III=   1 I1=   4 TIME=0.40000000E 01

	PER TIME PERIOD	EXPECTED PER YEAR
NUMBER OF REVIEWS	0.29400024E 03	0.30175000E 03
UNIT YRS OF INVENTORY	0.17778778E 02	0.17534882E 02
UNIT YRS OF STOCKOUTS	0.0	0.0
NUMBER OF STOCKOUTS	0.19073486E-05	0.12500000E 01
NUMBER OF ORDERS	0.90000153E 01	0.95000000E 01
INVENTORY CARRYING COST	0.88893872E 03	0.87674390E 03
STOCKOUT COST (TIME*QUANTITY)	0.0	0.0
STOCKOUT COST (QUANTITY)	0.13351440E-03	0.87500000E 02
ORDERING COST	0.27000044E 04	0.28500000E 04
REVIEW COST	0.0	0.0
TOTAL COST	0.35889431E 04	0.38142439E 04

NO OF DEMANDS RECEIVED = 0.12070000E 04
TOTAL UNITS DEMANDED = 0.12070000E 04
AVERAGE UNITS PER DEMAND = 0.10000000E 01

III=   1 I1=   5 TIME=0.50000000E 01

	PER TIME PERIOD	EXPECTED PER YEAR
NUMBER OF REVIEWS	0.26600000E 03	0.29459985E 03
UNIT YRS OF INVENTORY	0.19369644E 02	0.17901825E 02
UNIT YRS OF STOCKOUTS	0.0	0.0
NUMBER OF STOCKOUTS	0.0	0.10000000E 01
NUMBER OF ORDERS	0.90000000E 01	0.93999996E 01
INVENTORY CARRYING COST	0.96848218E 03	0.89509106E 03
STOCKOUT COST (TIME*QUANTITY)	0.0	0.0
STOCKOUT COST (QUANTITY)	0.0	0.70000000E 02
ORDERING COST	0.27000000E 04	0.28199998E 04
REVIEW COST	0.0	0.0
TOTAL COST	0.36684822E 04	0.37850908E 04

NO OF DEMANDS RECEIVED = 0.14740000E 04
TOTAL UNITS DEMANDED = 0.14740000E 04
AVERAGE UNITS PER DEMAND = 0.10000000E 01

UNIT YRS INVENTORY	MEAN=0.17901840E 02	STD DEV=0.37890214E 00
UNIT YRS STOCKOUTS	MEAN=0.0	STD DEV=0.0
NUMBER OF STOCKOUTS	MEAN=0.10000000E 01	STD DEV=0.77459663E 00
NUMBER OF ORDERS	MEAN=0.94000025E 01	STD DEV=0.24496889E 00
NUMBER OF REVIEWS	MEAN=0.29459985E 03	STD DEV=0.12672436E 02
TOTAL COST	MEAN=0.37850913E 04	STD DEV=0.66789185E 02

APPENDIX
C

SEARCH PROGRAMS

COMPUTER PROGRAM FOR SEARCH AND SECTIONING

The program given in Figure C.1 drives the sectioning search, calculating the next point searched at each iteration and determining the point at which the search should be terminated. The search increment is changed at the same time for all variables. The measure of effectiveness for each point searched is evaluated in SUBROUTINE SUBSYS(IND,YY) where IND is an indicator and YY is the value of the measure of effectiveness computed in SUBSYS. Information pertinent to the search is read in by the main program. This information includes the following:

MX = The number of decision variables.

NSTEP = The number of increments for each of the decision variables.

RF(I) = The initial value of the Ith decision variable (this variable is also the value of the Ith decision variable at subsequent iterations in the search).

XMIN(I) = Lower limit on the Ith decision variable.

XMAX(I) = Upper limit on the Ith decision variable.

XSTEP(I,J) = Jth search increment for the Ith decision variable.

All information pertinent to the calculation of the measure of effectiveness is read in SUBROUTINE SUBSYS(IND,YY) with the exception of the values of the decision variables which are calculated in the main program. If values of the decision variables are read in by SUBSYS, they will be ignored.

IND is an indicator which tells SUBSYS what function it should

630

perform. If IND is zero when SUBSYS is called, SUBSYS reads in all information necessary for computing the measure of effectiveness and immediately returns to the main program. If IND is greater than zero when SUBSYS is called, the read statements in SUBSYS are bypassed, and the value of the measure of effectiveness is computed for the values of RF(I), I = 1,2, . . . ,MX, calculated in the main program. The values of RF(I) are passed to SUBSYS by a common statement. Therefore the statements DIMENSION RF(20) and COMMON/BLOKL/RF must be included in SUBSYS.

The search begins by setting IND to zero and calling SUBSYS. Since IND is zero at this point, SUBSYS reads in all information necessary for computation of the measure of effectiveness and returns to the main program. Here IND is set to unity, and all information pertinent to the sectioning search is read. The upper and lower limits of each decision variable read in at this point remain in effect throughout the search. If at any iteration in the search these boundaries are violated, that iteration is deleted.

The following variables are used in the search in addition to those already defined:

ADVAN(I) = Indicates whether the Ith decision variable is to be changed at the next iteration and, if so, the direction of the change.
= 1, Ith variable is increased.
= 0, Ith variable is not changed.
= −1, Ith variable is decreased.

YMIN = Minimum value of the objective function at any given point in the search.

J = Counts the number of increments used in the search, J = 1,2, . . . ,NSTEP.

COUNT = Counts the number of consecutive iterations for which the objective function has not been reduced for a given value of J.

SAVE(I) = Optimal value of the Ith decision variable at a given point in the search.

For each value of J, ADVAN(I) is set first to +1 and then to −1. For all K ≠ I, ADVAN(K) = 0. The value of ADVAN(I) changes from +1 to −1 when continued increase in RF(I) fails to further reduce the value of the objective function, and changes from −1 to 0 when continued decrease in RF(I) fails to further reduce this value. When ADVAN(I) changes from −1 to 0, ADVAN(I+1) = 1, unless I = MX, in which case ADVAN(1) = 1.

If YY is less than or equal to YMIN at RF(I), I = 1,2, . . . ,MX, YMIN is set equal to YY, COUNT is set equal to zero, and SAVE(I) is set equal to RF(I), I = 1,2 , . . ,MX. If YY is greater than YMIN at RF(I), I = 1,2, . . . ,MX, ADVAN(I) is changed from +1 to −1 or −1 to zero and COUNT is increased by one. If YMIN remains unchanged for 2*MX iterations (COUNT = 2*MX), the search increment is changed by increasing the value of J by one. The search is terminated when all NSTEP increments have been used in the search.

COMPUTER PROGRAM FOR SEARCH BY REGRESSION

The program presented for the search by regression is divided into two parts. The main program reads information pertinent to the search, calculates the next search point, and terminates the search. SUBROUTINE SEARCH performs the required least-squares fit and can provide a complete regression table where desired.

The indicator IND is used in a fashion identical to that described in the program for sectioning. The following variables are read by the main program:

IX = The initial random number.
KK = The number of points included at each point in the search.
MX = The number of decision variables.
NN = A dummy variable which is always unity in this search.
RMIN(I) = Lower limit for the Ith decision variable.
RMAX(I) = Upper limit for the Ith decision variable.
DELTA(I) = Termination criterion for the Ith decision variable.

The first KK values of each decision variable are generated at random. The function used to approximate the objective function is of the form

$$y = b_1 + \sum_{i=2}^{n+1} (b_i x_i + b_{i+n} x_i^2) \qquad (C.1)$$

where n = MX. The corresponding program variables are:

COEF(K) = b_k.
X(1,J) = 1 (coefficient of b_1).

$$X(I,J) = \begin{cases} \text{Jth value of (I - 1)st decision variable, I = 2,3,} \\ \text{. . . ,MX + 1.} \\ \text{Jth value of (I − MX − 1)st decision variable squared,} \\ \text{I = MX + 2, MX + 3, . . .2*MX + 1.} \end{cases}$$

Y(J,NN) = Value of the objective function for the Jth values of the decision variables.

Therefore, for each value X(I,J) either generated initially or calculated in the course of the search for I > 1, X(MX2,J) = X(I,J)**2 where MX2 = I + MX. The value of the Ith decision variable passed to SUBROUTINE SUBSYS(IND,YY) (the subprogram used to compute the value of the objective function is defined by RF(JJ), which is stored in common. That is, RF(IJ) = X(I,J) where JJ = I − 1 and I = 2,3,..., MX + 1.

JMAX = Point in the search at which the objective function is a maximum.

Therefore X(I,JMAX) is the value of the Ith decision variable which is replaced at the next iteration, I = 2,3, . . . ,MX + 1.
That is,

$$X(I,JMAX) = -COEF(I)/(2.*COEF(MX2)) \qquad (C\ 2.)$$

where MX2 = I + MX.

The sequence of operations at each iteration of the search consists first of locating the value of the Ith decision variable to be replaced (that for which the objective function is a maximum). This is accomplished in the statements 26 through 12 in which the value of JMAX is defined. The next step is to call SEARCH to calculate the values of COEF(L), L = 1,2, . . . ,2*MX + 1 for the points currently in the search. The next point searched is defined by the vector of points −COEF(I)/(2.*COEF(MX2)), I = 2,3, . . . ,MX + 1 and replaces the vector X(I,JMAX), I = 2,3, . . . ,MX + 1, as shown in equation (C.2). If the new value of X(I,JMAX) violates the boundaries specified for the Ith decision variable, X(I,JMAX) is set equal to the boundary violated. The new value of X(I,JMAX) is calculated in the DO loop ending with statement 103[RF(I - 1) = X(I,JMA)]. To evaluate the point just defined, SUBROUTINE SUBSYS(IND,YY) is called where YY is the value of the objective function returned to the main program.

The final step at each iteration is to determine whether the search should be terminated or not.

XMIN(I) = Minimum value of X(I,J) taken over all J.
XMAX(I) = Maximum value of X(I,J) taken over all J.

If DELTA(I) > XMAX(I) − XMIN(I) for all I, the search is terminated. Otherwise the search is continued by returning to statement 26. The main program is shown in Figure C.2.

In SUBROUTINE SEARCH, the coefficients COEF(L) are evaluated through the Doolittle method. This is accomplished in the first part of the subroutine (down to statement 1021). The statement following statement 1021 is a control statement which will transfer of control back to the main program since NN has been defined as unity. If this statement is removed, SUBROUTINE SEARCH will carry out a complete regression analysis, printing out the values of COEF(L) and a regression table. SUBROUTINE SEARCH is shown in Figure C.3.

FIGURE C.1
Program for the Search by Sectioning

```
  DIMENSION RF(20),XMIN(20),XMAX(20),XSTEP(20,20),SAVE(20),ADVAN(20)
  COMMON/BLOKL/RF
  IND=0
  CALL SUBSYS(IND,YY)
  READ 1,MX,NSTEP
  XM=MX
  IND=1
1 FORMAT(1X2I5)
  DO 2 I=1,MX
  READ 3,RF(I),XMIN(I),XMAX(I)
  DO 4 J=1,NSTEP
4 READ 3,XSTEP(I,J)
2 ADVAN(I)=0
3 FORMAT(1X3F10.2)
  ADVAN(1)=1
  YMIN=10.**30
  J=1
  COUNT=0
7 CALL SUBSYS(IND,YY)
  IF(YY.GT.YMIN) GO TO 8
  COUNT=0
  YMIN=YY
  DO 6 I=1,MX
  SAVE(I)=RF(I)
  PRINT 3,SAVE(I),YMIN
6 RF(I)=SAVE(I)+ADVAN(I)*XSTEP(I,J)
  GO TO 71
8 COUNT=COUNT+1.
  IF(COUNT.GE.2.*XM) GO TO 20
21 DO 9 I=1,MX
  IF(ADVAN(I).EQ.0.) GO TO 9
  IF(ADVAN(I).LT.0.) GO TO 10
  ADVAN(I)=-1.*ADVAN(I)
  GO TO 12
10 ADVAN(I)=0
  IF(I.EQ.MX) GO TO 11
  K=I+1
  ADVAN(K)=1
  GO TO 12
11 ADVAN(1)=1
  GO TO 12
9 CONTINUE
12 DO 13 I=1,MX
13 RF(I)=SAVE(I)+ADVAN(I)*XSTEP(I,J)
  GO TO 71
20 IF(J.EQ.NSTEP) GO TO 30
  COUNT=0
  J=J+1
  DO 14 I=2,MX
  ADVAN(I)=0
14 RF(I)=SAVE(I)
  ADVAN(1)=1
  RF(1)=SAVE(1)+ADVAN(1)*XSTEP(1,J)
71 DO 80 I=1,MX
  IF(RF(I).LT.XMIN(I).OR.RF(I).GT.XMAX(I)) GO TO 21
80 CONTINUE
  GO TO 7

30 STOP
  END
```

FIGURE C.2
Main Program for the Search by Regression

```
      DIMENSION COEF(10),RF(20),XMIN(20),XMAX(20),RMIN(20),RMAX(20)
      DIMENSION DELTA(20),X(10,100),Y(1100,10)
      COMMON/BLOKL/RF
      COMMON/BLOKM/NN,MM,KK,X,Y,COEF
      READ(5,1)IX,KK,MX,NN
      IND=0
      CALL SUBSYS(IND,YY)
      IND=1
   1  FORMAT(1X415)
      MX1=MX+1.
      DO 100 I=2,MX1
 100  READ(5,101)RMIN(I),RMAX(I),DELTA(I)
 101  FORMAT(1X3F10.4)
      MM=2*MX+1
      DO 200 J=1,KK
      DO 200 I=2,MX1
 200  READ(5,101)X(I,J)
      DO 2 J=1,KK
      DO 102 I=2,MX1
      MX2=I+MX
      X(MX2,J)=X(I,J)**2
      JJ=I-1
 102  RF(JJ)=X(I,J)
      X(1,J)=1.
      CALL SUBSYS(IND,YY)
   2  Y(J,NN)=YY
  26  YMAX=Y(1,NN)
      JMAX=1
      DO 12 I=2,KK
      WRITE(6,31)Y(I,NN)
  31  FORMAT(1XE14.7)
      IF(YMAX.GE.Y(I,NN)) GO TO 12
   3  YMAX=Y(I,NN)
      JMAX=I
  12  CONTINUE
      CALL SEARCH
      DO 103 I=2,MX1
      MX2=I+MX
      X(I,JMAX)=-COEF(I)/(2.*COEF(MX2))
      IF(X(I,JMAX).GE.RMIN(I)) GO TO 4
      X(I,JMAX)=RMIN(I)
      GO TO 5
   4  IF(X(I,JMAX).LE.RMAX(I)) GO TO 5
      X(I,JMAX)=RMAX(I)
   5  X(MX2,JMAX)=X(I,JMAX)**2
 103  RF(I-1)=X(I,JMAX)
      CALL SUBSYS(IND,YY)
      Y(JMAX,NN)=YY
      DO 104 I=2,MX1
      XMIN(I)=RMAX(I)+1.
 104  XMAX(I)=RMIN(I)-1.
      DO 13 J=1,KK
      WRITE(6,14)Y(J,NN),(X(I,J),I=2,MX1)
  14  FORMAT(1X8E14.7)
      DO 13 I=2,MX1
      IF(X(I,J).GT.XMIN(I)) GO TO 105
      XMIN(I)=X(I,J)
 105  IF(X(I,J).LT.XMAX(I)) GO TO 13
      XMAX(I)=X(I,J)
  13  CONTINUE
      DO 106 I=2,MX1
      DIF=XMAX(I)-XMIN(I)
      IF(DIF.GT.DELTA(I)) GO TO 26
 106  CONTINUE
      STOP
      END
```

FIGURE C.3
Subroutine Search

```
      SUBROUTINE SEARCH
      DIMENSION X(10,100),Y(1100,10),G(10),A(10,10),COEF(10),SS(10)
      DIMENSION B(10,10),C(10),AMEAN(10)
      COMMON/BLOKM/NN,MM,KK,X,Y,COEF
      DO 1 L=1,MM
      G(L)=0
      DO 1 LL=L,MM
    1 A(L,LL)=0
      VAR=0
      DFEE=0
      DO 2 L=1,MM
      DO 2 J=1,KK
      AN=NN
      AMEAN(J)=0
      DO 2 K=1,NN
      G(L)=G(L)+Y(J,K)*X(L,J)
      DO 2 LL=L,MM
    2 A(L,LL)=A(L,LL)+X(L,J)*X(LL,J)
      DFLF=KK-MM
      DO 1015 K=1,MM
      DO 1013 L=K,MM
      IF(K-1)1108,1108,1109
 1109 K1=K-1
      DO 1014 I1=1,K1
 1014 A(K,L)=A(K,L)-A(I1,K)*B(I1,L)
 1108 B(K,L)=A(K,L)/A(K,K)
 1013 CONTINUE
      IF(K-1)1111,1111,1112
 1112 K1=K-1
      DO 1016 I1=1,K1
 1016 G(K)=G(K)-A(I1,K)*C(I1)
 1111 C(K)=G(K)/A(K,K)
 1015 SS(K)=C(K)*G(K)
      DO 1021 K=1,MM
      M2=MM-K+2
      M1=MM-K+1
      COEF(M1)=C(M1)
      IF(K-1)1021,1021,1110
 1110 DO 1020 I1=M2,MM
 1020 COEF(M1)=COEF(M1)-COEF(I1)*B(M1,I1)
 1021 CONTINUE
      IF(NN.LT.10) RETURN
      DO 3 L=1,MM
      LL=L-1
    3 WRITE(6,4)LL,COEF(L)
    4 FORMAT(1X,'B(',I4,')=',E14.7////)
      SSLF=0
      TSS=0
      DO 5 J=1,KK
      SQ=0
      SUM=0
      DO 6 K=1,NN
      SUM=SUM+Y(J,K)
    6 SQ=SQ+Y(J,K)**2
      VAR=SQ-((SUM**2)/AN)+VAR
      DFEE=DFEE+AN-1.
      AMEAN(J)=SUM/AN
      SLF=AMEAN(J)-COEF(1)
```

FIGURE C *(continued)*

```
      DO 7 K=2,MM
    7 SLF=SLF-COEF(K)*X(K,J)
    5 SSLF=SSLF+AN*(SLF**2)
      AMLF=SSLF/DFLF
      WRITE(6,8)
    8 FORMAT(1X,'SOURCE OF VARIATION',3X,'D OF F',3X,'SUM OF SQUARES',3X
     1,'MEAN SQUARE',//)
      DO 9 L=1,MM
      LL=L-1
      WRITE(6,10)LL,SS(L),SS(L)
   10 FORMAT(1X,'B(',I3,')',19X,'1.0',3XE14.7,3XE14.7)
    9 TSS=TSS+SS(L)
      WRITE(6,11)DFLF,SSLF,AMLF
   11 FORMAT(1X,'LACK OF FIT',11XF6.1,3XE14.7,3XE14.7)
      IF(DFEE)12,12,13
   12 R=(TSS-SS(1))/(TSS+SSLF-SS(1))
      GO TO 15
   13 AMEE=VAR/DFEE
      R=(TSS-SS(1))/(TSS+SSLF+VAR-SS(1))
      WRITE(6,14)DFEE,VAR,AMEE
   14 FORMAT(1X,'EXPERIMENTAL ERROR',4XF6.1,3XE14.7,3XE14.7///)
   15 WRITE(6,16)R
   16 FORMAT(1X,'INDEX OF CORRELATION = ',F9.5)
      RETURN
      END
```

INDEX

This book has been set in 11 and 10 point Press Roman, leaded 2 points. Section and chapter numbers are in 14 point Univers Medium No. 689, and section and chapter titles are in 18 point Univers Bold No. 693. The size of the type page is 27 x 46 picas.